INTRODUCTION TO CIRCUITS

LEE W. CHURCHMAN, Allan Hancock College

INTRODUCTION TO CIRCUITS

HOLT, RINEHART AND WINSTON
NEW YORK

Cover photo: A timing logic thick-film hybrid microcircuit. Courtesy of Applied Technology, division of Itek Corporation, Sunnyvale, California.

Library of Congress Cataloging in Publication Data

Churchman, Lee W
   Introduction to circuits.

   Includes index.
   1. Electric circuits. I. Title.
TK454.C58   621.319′2   74-22333
ISBN 0-03-091198-2

PRINTED IN THE UNITED STATES OF AMERICA
6 7 8 9   032   9 8 7 6 5 4 3 2 1

This book is dedicated

to

my wife, Patricia

CONTENTS

vii

Considering the large number of circuits books now on the market, some special justification seems necessary before a new one is brought out. In fact, there are two such justifications:

1. Level of presentation.
2. Content, length, and format.

LEVEL OF PRESENTATION.   The level of presentation is appropriate for the typical first-year student of electronics in a community college. Though the total content is quite sufficient for a first circuits course in an engineering technology curriculum, the explanations, examples, and the majority of the problems may be mastered by the *average* student with a *reasonable* amount of study. No mathematical knowledge beyond the ability to count is assumed at first, and though the level of mathematical competence required increases as the student progresses through the text, nowhere is a competence assumed that could not reasonably be previously attained in nearly any parallel "math for electronics" course.

CONTENT, LENGTH, AND FORMAT.   The content is limited to that which is usually taught in a first circuits course. Material which is usually skipped has been deleted. This permits a more adequate presentation of the essential core material which is the heart of any circuits course. For instance, more time than usual is spent on networks, because students normally have difficulty with them. In accord with the present direction of the development of the technology, in explanations and examples as well as in student problems attention is given to selected nonsinusoidal waveforms and to the "black-box" definitions of components. Both the traditional discrete components and the products of modern thin-film technology receive their share of attention.

The length of the book is appropriate for a one-semester or two-quarter course. The organization and format allow students with no previous background to master the material, though it is desirable that this text be preceded by either a survey course or previous experience on the part of the student.

Wherever appropriate, the format of the material is:

1. The concept to be understood is first fully explained in a non-mathematical conceptual fashion.
2. The mathematical formulation of the concept is either stated or derived, and the result is analyzed.
3. Problems are solved using this mathematical formulation.
4. Problems for student solution are presented. Student problems are to be given at the end of each section, as well as at the end of each chapter.

PREREQUISITES. This text is designed for the first of a series of courses leading to technical competence in electronics. The coverage is limited to what the average student can—with work—learn in one semester or two quarters. Nothing is included which has not been shown by experience to be part of the essential foundation of knowledge of the skilled technician.

No previous knowledge of electronics is assumed, though it is of course desirable. Either previous experience with electronics or a survey course will prove helpful, but it is possible to master this book without any such background. If you study, you will be rewarded with a sound knowledge of basic electronics theory.

The ability to apply mathematics to the solution of problems in electronics will be necessary before you can complete this course. This does *not* mean that you must have knowledge of algebra, trigonometry, and logarithms to begin this course. If you do not now possess this ability, you may acquire it while taking this course. This text is designed with the knowledge that most students do not begin their study of electronics with a working knowledge of mathematics. Most institutions offering this course offer a concurrent course in mathematics. Taking both courses at the same time will give you mathematical competency as it is needed for electrical applications in this course.

USE OF THE TEXT. Each section of this text explains a single concept or a few closely related concepts. The preliminary explanation of the concepts included in each section is nonmathematical. This explanation is followed by as much mathematical formulation as is necessary to permit the practical application of the concept. If you study and understand the preliminary explanation, and if you develop the necessary mathematical competency, the practical quantitative problem solving will offer little difficulty.

This is the real key to learning. If you solve the problems given, you will almost inevitably learn. If you do not attempt to solve the problems you are not at all likely to learn. It is true that some students learn more readily and with less necessity for the practical applications of problem solving than others. It is also true that the kind of overconfidence which leads the student to say to himself, "I know this stuff; I'll wait till it gets harder before I work a few problems," is the most common cause of failure to complete the course.

* * *

I would like to thank everyone who has assisted me in this project. My particular thanks must go to Walter Conrad, President of Allan Hancock College, the Board of Trustees, and the Sabbatical Leave Committee, who provided the time which made this book possible. I owe a great deal to my fellow electronics instructors, Philip Wahl and Robert Rauch, who helped in more ways than I can count. The staff at Rinehart Press were more than diligent; particular thanks must go to Julia Edinger, not only for her concern for quality, but for her moral support during a difficult time.   L.W.C.

INTRODUCTION
TO
CIRCUITS

PART 1
RESISTIVE CIRCUITS

ONE

INTRODUCTION TO ELECTRICITY

ELEMENTARY PARTICLES.   The shattering of a giant tree by a bolt of lightning and the silent speed and accuracy of a pocket calculator are both examples of the results of the flow of electrons. The tree shatters because of the uncontrolled flow of billions upon billions of electrons, while the sums and products of the calculator are achieved by the most precise and delicate control of the movement of relatively few electrons. Electricity at work consists of the movement of electrons. It is our ability to control the flow of electrons that has made electrical and electronic technology possible.

Atoms are the fundamental building blocks of all matter. Matter is anything that has weight and takes up space. Therefore, all substances, including this book, your hands that hold it, and your eyes that read it, are made of atoms. All atoms are made up of electrons, protons, and—except for atoms of hydrogen—neutrons.

Atoms are unbelievably small. If we could place copper atoms

1-1
Nature of Matter

taken from a wire in your TV set in a neat row, it would take over 100,000,000 of them to stretch one inch. Small as these atoms are, electrons are much smaller. It would take over 40,000 electrons to span the diameter of one single copper atom!

Electrons and protons possess a property which we call *charge*. We do not know why these two types of particles possess this property. We do not even know what charge is. We know only what charge does, but even this limited knowledge has been enough to lead to the development of modern electronics.

All electrons have the same kind of charge. We say that each electron possesses a single negative charge—never more, never less. Similarly, each proton has a single positive charge. Neutrons are neutral (have no charge) and play no role in electronics.

ATOMIC STRUCTURE. Every atom consists of a central *nucleus* (plural, *nuclei*), around which orbit one or more electrons. The simplest atom is the hydrogen atom. The nucleus consists of a single proton, with its single positive charge. A single electron, with its single negative charge, orbits the nucleus. Figure 1-1 is a diagram of the hydrogen atom.

Note that the negative charge of the electron is exactly balanced by the positive charge of the proton. If we add the charges with regard to sign, the sum is zero.

$$+1 \quad \text{(nuclear charge)}$$
$$-1 \quad \text{(electron charge)}$$
$$\overline{0 \quad \text{(net charge)}}$$

The complete atom, then, exhibits no external effect due to the charge on the particles of which it consists. This is true for all complete atoms, except, as we shall see later, for some comparatively minor magnetic effects.

The number of protons in the nucleus, and the number of electrons in orbit around the nucleus, must always be a whole number. Scientists have never been able to find in nature nor create in the laboratory a fractional part of either an electron or a proton. After hydrogen, therefore, the next simplest atom possible is one containing two protons and two electrons. In fact, an atom of the element helium does contain two protons and two electrons, as shown in Figure 1-2.

The nucleus of the helium atom contains two protons with a total positive charge of $+2$, but the nucleus also contains two neutrons. The neutrons are uncharged particles and so do not affect the total nuclear charge. Physicists think that the neutrons provide the nucleus with the stability required to keep its protons confined in the very small space of the nucleus.

Electron in orbit

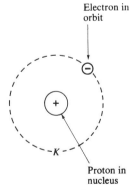

Proton in nucleus

Figure 1-1 A hydrogen atom showing the single electron revolving around a central nucleus consisting of a single proton.

Balancing the nuclear charge of $+2$ is the charge of -2 due to the two electrons contained in the helium atom. Again, the net charge of the complete atom is zero and there is no external electrical effect due to the charges within the atom.

According to modern atomic theory, electrons move around the nucleus in very erratic fashion. We cannot predict the motions of electrons through the space around the nucleus. But we can say that the electrons move largely through regions that have definite shapes. These regions are called *atomic orbitals*. Two electrons can occupy each orbital, and groups of orbitals form larger regions called *shells*.

In the shell closest to the nucleus, the K shell, there can be only one orbital and, therefore, only two electrons. If there are three protons in the nucleus of an atom, there must be three electrons in orbit around the nucleus to balance the positive nuclear charge. But the K shell is filled (completed) when it contains two electrons, so a second shell, the L shell, begins to form. An atom of the element lithium contains three protons in its nucleus and three electrons in orbit around the nucleus, as shown in Figure 1-3.

The L shell can contain four orbitals, or eight electrons (4 orbitals $\times$ 2 electrons per orbital). Thus, the L shell is filled in an atom of the element neon, which has ten protons in its nucleus and ten electrons in orbit around the nucleus, as shown in Figure 1-4.

In the sodium atom, the M shell is begun. As you can see in Figure 1-5, the sodium atom has 11 protons in its nucleus, 2 electrons in the K shell, 8 electrons in the L shell, and 1 electron in the M shell.

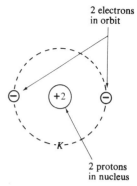

2 electrons
in orbit

2 protons
in nucleus

Figure 1-2 A helium atom showing 2 protons in the nucleus and 2 electrons orbiting the nucleus. The nucleus also contains 2 neutrons, which are not shown since they contribute only mass, not charge.

Figure 1-3 A lithium atom—2 electrons fill the K shell, and the third electron necessary to balance the 3 proton charges on the nucleus is in the L shell.

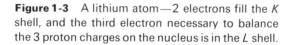
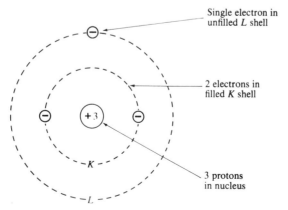

Single electron in
unfilled L shell

2 electrons in
filled K shell

3 protons
in nucleus

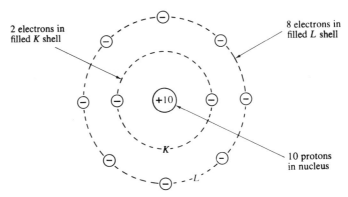

Figure 1-4   A neon atom, containing 10 protons in its nucleus and 10 electrons in orbit around the nucleus. Both the *K* and *L* shells are filled.

Figure 1-6 shows the schematic structure of a copper atom. The 29 positive charges contained by the 29 protons in the nucleus are balanced by the 29 negative charges of the 29 electrons that orbit the nucleus. All of the shells are filled except the outermost which, like that of lithium, contains only one electron.

If a piece of copper wire is pure, it contains only atoms like the one shown in Figure 1-6. Pure copper is a soft, ductile, reddish material. In the solid

Figure 1-5   A sodium atom has 11 protons in its nucleus and 11 electrons orbiting the nucleus. The outermost electron is in the *M* shell.

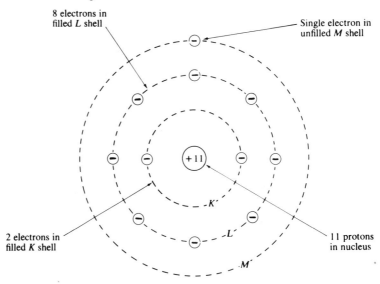

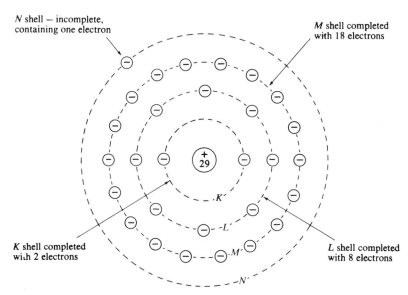

N shell — incomplete, containing one electron

M shell completed with 18 electrons

K shell completed with 2 electrons

L shell completed with 8 electrons

Figure 1-6   A copper atom—the inner shells are filled, and the valence shell, which is by definition the outermost, contains 1 electron.

metal, the positions of the atoms are fixed relative to each other, so that the shape of the piece of metal is constant unless force is exerted against it. The single electron in the outer shell (called the *valence* shell) can move easily from one atom to the next in solid copper, making copper highly useful in electricity and electronics.

Figure 1-7 shows the still more complex atom of germanium. This atom contains 32 protons in the nucleus and 32 electrons in orbit around it. The valence shell contains four electrons. This larger number of electrons in the outermost shell causes germanium to act both chemically and electronically in a very different fashion than does copper. The number and arrangement of electrons around the nucleus give each atom its characteristic physical and chemical properties.

The atomic structures shown in Figures 1-1 through 1-7 should not be taken too literally. Atoms are three-dimensional structures, and the drawings, of course, are not. The shells of atoms are broken up into subshells, and within each shell some of the electrons follow circular orbits while others follow elliptical orbits. The structure of the nucleus is quite complex. All nuclei except the lightest, hydrogen, contain neutrons and other particles. We do not discuss these particles because they play no direct part in electricity or electronics.

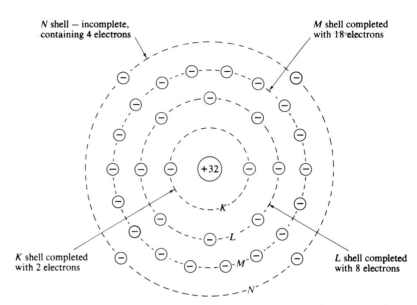

Figure 1-7 A germanium atom—the valence shell contains 4 electrons. These additional electrons give germanium a set of physical and chemical properties different from those of copper.

ATOMS AND MOLECULES. Substances composed of atoms which are all alike are called elements. Everything on and in the earth is made up of arrangements of about 90 elements. In fact, nearly all familiar substances are made up from no more than 20 of these elements. Also, most substances are not made of a single kind of atom but of combinations of different atoms. If the atoms are arranged in definite combinations, in which one or more atoms of one kind are linked to one or more atoms of another kind, the substance is a *compound*. This combination of atoms forms another building block, the *molecule*. Water is a substance made up of molecules. Water is composed of atoms of oxygen and hydrogen, either of which by itself is a gas, not a liquid, at ordinary temperatures. But if we mix these two elements in the proper proportions and ignite the mixture, a considerable amount of energy is given off, and the two elements combine so that each atom of oxygen is attached to two atoms of hydrogen, thus forming the new substance water. See Figure 1-8.

**1-2
Electric Forces**

CHARGE. The forces that unite atoms to form new substances are the same forces that enable us to harness the movement of electrons to create electrical and electronic technology. They are the forces of *attraction* and *repulsion* between charges.

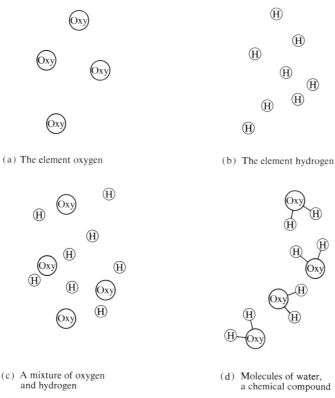

(a) The element oxygen

(b) The element hydrogen

(c) A mixture of oxygen
and hydrogen

(d) Molecules of water,
a chemical compound

Figure 1-8   Oxygen and hydrogen are both gases, as is the mixture of the two at ordinary temperatures. Two hydrogen atoms linked by chemical bonds to one oxygen atom produce a molecule of the liquid water.

There are two types of charge: the positive charge of the proton and the negative charge of the electron. The proton is part of the atomic nucleus, and the energy "locked up" in the proton becomes available only when the nucleus of the atom is shattered. It takes such enormous energy to shatter an atomic nucleus that the proton is not a useful particle in electricity. Electrons, on the other hand, are not part of the nucleus, and in many substances the outermost electrons are easily detached. Practically all of electrical and electronics technology is therefore based on the movement of these negative particles of charge.

If two electrons or two protons are placed near each other, a force occurs that tends to push the two particles away from each other. We say that *like charges repel.* If an electron and a proton are placed near each other, an equal force will be felt, but this force tends to pull the two particles toward each other. *Unlike charges attract.* See Figure 1-9.

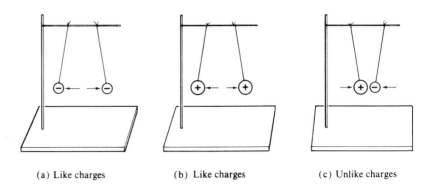

(a) Like charges (b) Like charges (c) Unlike charges

Figure 1-9 Like charges repel; unlike attract.

INVERSE SQUARE LAW. A similar force of attraction exists between any two objects—that force known to us as gravity. Gravity and the electrical forces of attraction and repulsion are similar in some respects but different in others. Electrical force may either attract or repel depending on whether the force is between unlike or like charges. Gravitational force is only attractive, and so far as we know there is only one kind of matter.

Both forces are described by what is known as an inverse square law. Stated mathematically for gravitational forces, it is

$$F = \frac{m_1 \, m_2}{d^2}(G) \tag{1}$$

Translated from the mathematical language of the formula, this says that the force of attraction between masses m_1 and m_2 is equal to the product of the masses, divided by the square of the distance between them, and multiplied by a proportionality constant (G).

The mathematical description of the force between charges is identical in form.

$$F = \frac{q_1 \, q_2}{d^2}(k) \tag{2}$$

This equation says that the force of attraction between charges q_1 and q_2 is equal to the product of the charges, divided by the square of the distance between them, and multiplied by a proportionality constant (k).

The two proportionality constants are quite different from each other. As a consequence of this difference, the forces acting between charged particles are far greater than gravitational forces. The ratio between the two is an incredibly large number. Due to their charge, the force of repulsion between two electrons is 1,000,000,000,000,000,000,000,000,000,000,000,000,000,000 times as great as the gravitational attraction between them due to their mass. Expressed in powers of ten, this ratio is $10^{39}:1$.* Since the ratio between these two forces is so great, gravitational forces are almost never a factor in determining what will happen to the position or velocity of charged particles, and are neglected in our calculations.

Since these forces of attraction or repulsion between two charged particles depend only on their charge and the distance between them, and not at all on any velocity they may have, they are known as *electrostatic forces*. Since the mathematical formulation describing the amount of force [Equation (2)] was first described by Charles A. Coulomb (1785), it is often known as Coulomb's law, and the forces the law describes are called Coulomb forces.

COULOMB. Just as still water in a pond cannot turn a waterwheel, so electrons at rest can do no work. Only a stream of water can turn a waterwheel, and only a stream of moving electrons can provide the nearly instantaneous transfer of information and energy that is the basis of our modern technological civilization.

1-3 Electron Flow

The charge transferred by a single moving electron is too small to be a convenient unit of measure. Instead, the total charge of a large number of electrons is used as the basic unit. Though originally defined in terms of electrochemical action, the coulomb (C) is now defined as the net charge on 6.25×10^{18} charged particles, all having the same charge. The symbol for electric charge is Q or q, meaning quantity. Thus, the charge on 6.25×10^{18} particles is $Q = 1$ C. The magnitude of electron and proton charges is the same, so 1 Q of electrons possesses 1 C of negative charge, while 1 Q of protons possesses 1 C of positive charge.

Just as the gallon is a unit quantity of water, so the coulomb is a unit quantity of charge. In the case of a waterwheel using the energy of a moving stream of water to grind corn, the determining factor is not the amount of water wetting the wheel, but the intensity of flow of water past the wheel. This is usually measured in gallons per minute. Similarly, the ability of a moving stream of electrons to do work is determined, in part, by its intensity of flow. The intensity of flow of a stream of electrons is measured in coulombs per second (C/sec).

AMPERE.   The term "coulombs per second" is cumbersome, so we use the word *ampere* (A) instead. 6.25×10^{18} electrons per second moving past a given point equal a rate of movement of charge of 1 C/sec, or 1 A. Twice that rate of flow, 12.5×10^{18} electrons per second, is a current flow of 2 A.

---

* Scientific notation—the use of the powers of ten—is discussed in Section 1-4.

CONDUCTORS.   In copper, as we have seen in Section 1-1, valence electrons are free to move from one atom to another. In this way electrons can move through the solid substance of a copper wire in much the same way water moves through pipes. See Figure 1-10.

Substances containing large numbers of electrons that can move from atom to atom (free electrons) are called *conductors*, since they can be used to conduct a stream of electrons from one point to another. At ordinary temperatures silver is the best conductor, but it is too expensive for most uses. Copper is nearly as good a conductor as silver and far less expensive. Aluminum is sometimes used as a conductor, too. Aluminum is not as good a conductor as copper, but it is both less expensive and lighter in weight.

No material used at ordinary temperatures is a perfect conductor. There is always some opposition to the flow of electrons. This opposition, much like friction in a mechanical system, results in the loss of energy from the moving stream of electrons. This lost energy appears in the form of heat, which warms the conductor. If too much energy is lost, the rise in temperature may melt or vaporize the conductor.

INSULATORS.   In many substances—including glass, most plastics, rubber, and wood—the outer, or valence, electrons are linked by chemical bonds to the corresponding electrons of adjacent atoms. In these substances the

Figure 1-10   Electrons can move from one atom to another in solid copper. Each atom always has 1 valence electron, but it is not always the same one. Illustration shows a net movement of charge from left to right.

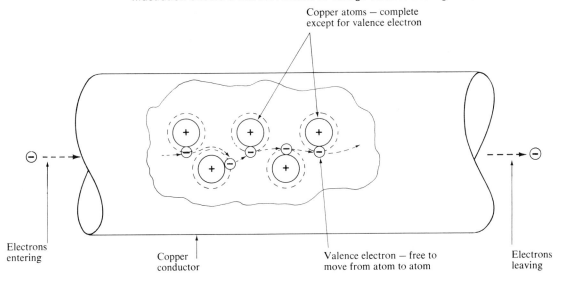

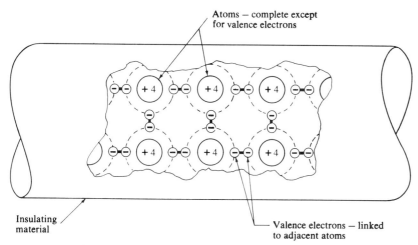

Atoms — complete except
for valence electrons

Insulating
material

Valence electrons — linked
to adjacent atoms

Figure 1-11   In an insulator valence electrons are linked to adjacent atoms and are not free to move from atom to atom. Many different structures are possible in insulating materials.

electrons are not free to move. Since electrons cannot move from atom to atom within these materials, they cannot conduct a flow of electrons. They are therefore nonconductors, or *insulators*. See Figure 1-11.

SCIENTIFIC NOTATION—POWERS OF TEN.   We have already, in the first few pages of this text, expressed some numbers in scientific notation. The quantity 1,000,000,000,000,000,000,000,000,000,000,000,000,000 was expressed as 10^{39}, which is obviously a much simpler and more compact way of expressing this very large number. If you count the zeros in the original number, you will find 39 of them. The fact that we rewrote this number as 10^{39}, read "ten to the thirty-ninth power," is no accident.

1-4
Notation and Units

Using scientific notation we also expressed the number of electrons in a coulomb as 6.25×10^{18} electrons. This is much less cumbersome than expressing this quantity as 6,250,000,000,000,000,000 electrons. Either form is, of course, correct since they are only different ways of expressing the same quantity.

In electronics we often have occasion to deal with very small quantities. The charge on a single electron is approximately 1.6×10^{-19} coulombs. This same quantity, expressed as an ordinary decimal number, would be written 0.000 000 000 000 000 000 16, which is obviously not as easy to work with as the corresponding scientific notation.

Reading, writing, thinking about, talking about, or calculating with very large or very small quantities is far more easily done by using scientific notation. Most small electronic calculators do not have the capacity to use or display more than 8 or 10 digits, and cannot therefore be used directly where calculations involve these very large or small quantities. If calculations are done by hand or with a slide rule, the position of the decimal in the final result is a very common source of error. If scientific notation is used, the calculations are made much more readily, whether by hand, with a slide rule, or with an electronic calculator, and the risk of misplacing the decimal point in the final result is reduced to a minimum.

Consider the information shown in Table 1-1.

TABLE 1-1　Scientific Notation

Number	Power of 10		Meaning	To Be Read As
			$\cdots$	
$1{,}000{,}000 = 10^6$	$= 1/10^{-6}$	$= 10 \times 10 \times 10 \times 10 \times 10 \times 10$		10 to the sixth power
$100{,}000 = 10^5$	$= 1/10^{-5}$	$= 10 \times 10 \times 10 \times 10 \times 10$		10 to the fifth power
$10{,}000 = 10^4$	$= 1/10^{-4}$	$= 10 \times 10 \times 10 \times 10$		10 to the fourth power
$1{,}000 = 10^3$	$= 1/10^{-3}$	$= 10 \times 10 \times 10$		10 to the third power
$100 = 10^2$	$= 1/10^{-2}$	$= 10 \times 10$		10 to the second power
$10 = 10^1$	$= 1/10^{-1}$	$= 10$		10 to the first power
$1 = 10^0$	$= 1/10^0$	$= 1/1$		10 to the zero power
$0.1 = 10^{-1}$	$= 1/10^1$	$= 1/10$		10 to the -1 power
$0.01 = 10^{-2}$	$= 1/10^2$	$= 1/(10 \times 10)$		10 to the -2 power
$0.001 = 10^{-3}$	$= 1/10^3$	$= 1/(10 \times 10 \times 10)$		10 to the -3 power
$0.000\,1 = 10^{-4}$	$= 1/10^4$	$= 1/(10 \times 10 \times 10 \times 10)$		10 to the -4 power
$0.000\,01 = 10^{-5}$	$= 1/10^5$	$= 1/(10 \times 10 \times 10 \times 10 \times 10)$		10 to the -5 power
$0.000\,001 = 10^{-6}$	$= 1/10^6$	$= 1/(10 \times 10 \times 10 \times 10 \times 10 \times 10)$		10 to the -6 power
			$\cdots$	

The dots beginning and ending the table indicate that the tabulation is not complete, but can be extended both ways indefinitely. Note that each quantity in the number column is one-tenth of the quantity above it. Also note that the exponent for each power of 10 in the second column is one less than the exponent for the power of ten above it. This symmetry may make the fact that $10^0 = 1$ seem more reasonable.

Consider the problem of writing a randomly chosen quantity, such as 370,000, in a more convenient form.

$$370{,}000 = 3.7 \times 100{,}000$$

This may be easily checked by multiplication.

In Table 1-1 we see that $100,000 = 10^5$. Therefore, by substitution,

$$370,000 = 3.7 \times 10^5$$

Observe the difference in the position of the decimal point between the original 370,000 and 3.7×10^5. In the original number the decimal, though not indicated, is located just to the right of the final zero. If we were to move it to the left, to its new position between the 3 and the 7, we would move it 5 places. This is the same as the power to which 10 is raised when the original number is written in scientific notation.

RULE   *To express a large number as a smaller number times some power of 10, move the decimal point to the left to the desired new location. The number of places the decimal is moved gives the proper positive power of 10.*

$$250 = 2.5 \times 10^2$$
$$197,000 = 1.97 \times 10^5$$
$$53,000 = 5.3 \times 10^4$$
$$250 = 0.25 \times 10^3$$
$$197,000 = 19.7 \times 10^4$$

EXAMPLES

In the first three examples the original number was expressed as a number between 1 and 10 multiplied by some power of 10. In the last two examples a slight variation was introduced. It is often desirable to express the original quantity as some number either greater than 10 or less than 1 multiplied by the appropriate power of 10. Inspection will reveal that the rule still applies— in each case the number of places the decimal is moved is the same as the exponent for the power of 10.

Suppose the original quantity to be expressed as a number between 1 and 10 multiplied by some power of 10 is less than 1. Consider the quantity 0.002 5, which may be written as

$$0.002\ 5 = 2.5 \times 0.001$$

This is easily checked by multiplication.

By Table 1-1, $0.001 = 10^{-3}$. Therefore

$$0.002\ 5 = 2.5 \times 10^{-3}$$

RULE   *To express a small number as a larger number times some power of 10, move the decimal point to the right to the desired new location. The number of places the decimal is moved gives the proper negative power of 10.*

EXAMPLES

$$0.05 = 5 \times 10^{-2}$$
$$0.000\ 007\ 3 = 7.3 \times 10^{-6}$$
$$0.000\ 000\ 000\ 000\ 296 = 2.96 \times 10^{-13}$$
$$0.008\ 2 = 0.82 \times 10^{-2}$$
$$0.004\ 6 = 46 \times 10^{-4}$$

In the last two examples we rewrote the original quantity as a number less than 1 or greater than 10 multiplied by some power of 10. In each example the rule still applies—the number of places the decimal is moved from its original location is the same as the exponent for the power of 10.

A calculation often gives a result expressed in powers of 10 but not reduced to the desired form. As an example we might have as the result of a multiplication the quantity 54×10^3. This can be easily changed to the desired form by first writing it in the intermediate form $(5.4 \times 10^1) \times 10^3$, where the quantity in parentheses represents the original 54. Then the powers of 10 may be combined by adding their exponents with regard to sign, according to the rules for exponents.

$$54 \times 10^3 = 5.4 \times 10^1 \times 10^3 = 5.4 \times 10^{1+3} = 5.4 \times 10^4$$

This may be proved by writing each of the forms in which this number is given in scientific notation in the more ordinary decimal form.

$$54 \times 10^3 = 54 \times 1000 = 54,000$$

$$5.4 \times 10^1 \times 10^3 = 5.4 \times 10 \times 1000 = 54,000$$

$$5.4 \times 10^4 = 5.4 \times 10,000 = 54,000$$

The exponents are added algebraically, according to sign. Where the exponents are all positive, this gives little difficulty. If one or both of the exponents are negative, the chances of error are considerably increased, particularly if the intermediate step is performed mentally. This operation produces perhaps the largest number of careless errors of any operation in mathematics. Therefore, it is wise to take the necessary two or three seconds to put the intermediate step on paper where at least it can be checked.

EXAMPLES

Original Quantity	Intermediate Step	Final Result
290×10^4	$(2.9 \times 10^2) \times 10^4$	2.9×10^6
0.029×10^4	$(2.9 \times 10^{-2}) \times 10^4$	2.9×10^2
0.029×10^{-4}	$(2.9 \times 10^{-2}) \times 10^{-4}$	2.9×10^{-6}
729×10^{-2}	$7.29 \times 10^2 \times 10^{-2}$	7.29
729×10^{-2}	$72.9 \times 10^1 \times 10^{-2}$	72.9×10^{-1}

In the last two examples the parentheses were omitted because they serve no mathematical function and were introduced only to make the method clear. In addition, the last example is different in that the final result is a number between 10 and 100 multiplied by the appropriate power of 10. The method is the same, regardless of what final result is most convenient.

Express the following numbers as numbers between 1 and 10 multiplied by   **Problems**
the proper power of 10.

1.	395,000	**11.**	0.002 3
2.	85.3	**12.**	0.000 002
3.	8,260	**13.**	0.010 1
4.	0.946	**14.**	29.3×10^{-2}
5.	0.030 6	**15.**	29.3×10^{-1}
6.	94,600	**16.**	0.005×10^{-3}
7.	738	**17.**	$1,003,000 \times 10^{-2}$
8.	703,000,000	**18.**	239×10^{4}
9.	5,970,000	**19.**	172×10^{-6}
10.	10.1	**20.**	210×10^{-2}

POWERS OF 10—ADDITION AND SUBTRACTION.   All the ordinary operations of arithmetic may be carried out using the scientific notation of powers of 10, and in all cases these operations will be more easily accomplished, with less chance of error, than if the quantities had been left in their original form. Only a few cautions are necessary.

Suppose the problem is to add 237 and 5120. Using ordinary notation, the problem is set up like this:

$$
\begin{array}{r}
5120 \\
+\ \ 237 \\
\hline
5357 = 5.357 \times 10^3
\end{array}
$$

Now suppose we convert both numbers to scientific notation in the usual way.

$$
\begin{array}{r}
5.12 \times 10^3 \\
+2.37 \times 10^2 \\
\hline
\end{array}
$$

And the result is nonsense!

If you add the two numbers excluding the powers of ten, you get 7.49, which, as you can see, has nothing to do with the correct sum of 5357 for the original problem. But what do you do with the powers of 10? If you add them, you get 10^5, which is nowhere near correct.

Now let's do it again, and do it right! Remember, you add a column of numbers only when the decimal points are properly aligned. When those numbers are expressed in terms of powers of 10, their decimal points include the power of 10. To ensure a correct sum, we must do two things. We must make sure the numbers to be added are written in a column with the decimal points aligned, and we must be sure they are expressed to the *same* power of 10. Heeding this warning, our problem becomes

$$
\begin{array}{ccc}
5.12 \times 10^3 & & 51.2 \times 10^2 \\
+0.237 \times 10^3 & \text{or} & +\ 2.37 \times 10^2 \\
\hline
5.357 \times 10^3 & & 53.57 \times 10^2
\end{array}
$$

The two results are, of course, the same value, though expressed differently. Either way is perfectly satisfactory. Both, when written in the ordinary fashion, equal 5357.

Problems   *Carry out the indicated addition or subtraction. Write the result as a number between 1 and 10 multiplied by the appropriate power of 10.*

1. $2 \times 10^2 + 3 \times 10^2$
2. $2 \times 10^2 + 3 \times 10^3$
3. $2.7 \times 10^3 + 3.3 \times 10^3$
4. $3.3 \times 10^6 - 2.7 \times 10^6$
5. $3.3 \times 10^{-6} + 2.7 \times 10^{-6}$

6. $4.7 \times 10^5 - 3.9 \times 10^4$
7. $1.8 \times 10^{-1} - 1.2 \times 10^{-1}$
8. $1.8 \times 10^{-1} - 1.2 \times 10^{-2}$
9. $5 \times 10^{-6} + 4 \times 10^{-4}$
10. $5 \times 10^{-5} - 4 \times 10^{-4}$

POWERS OF 10—MULTIPLICATION. The law of exponents in multiplication can be summed up in the following general form:

$$(a^m)(a^n) = a^{m+n} \qquad \text{(where } a \neq 0\text{)}$$

Using 10 instead of a, still in the general form:

$$(10^m)(10^n) = 10^{m+n}$$

EXAMPLES

$$(10^5)(10^3) = 10^{5+3} = 10^8$$
$$(10^5)(10^{-3}) = 10^{5+(-3)} = 10^2$$
$$(10^{-5})(10^3) = 10^{-5+3} = 10^{-2}$$
$$(10^{-5})(10^{-3}) = 10^{-5+(-3)} = 10^{-8}$$
$$(2 \times 10^3)(3 \times 10^4) = (2)(3) \times (10^3)(10^4) = 6 \times 10^7$$
$$(2.3 \times 10^{-3})(7.2 \times 10^5) = (2.3)(7.2) \times (10^{-3})(10^5) = 16.56 \times 10^2$$
$$= 1.656 \times 10^3$$

Note: Inspection of the last two examples in particular shows the sequence of mental operations. Multiply the numbers and *add* the exponents. If a slide rule is used, it is easy to keep track of the position of the decimal point in the multiplication of the numbers, since they will be numbers between 1 and 10. In the last example we could mentally round off the multiplication to $2 \times 7 = 14$, remembering that both numbers had been reduced in the rounding off, and consequently the result ought to be somewhat more than 14. The actual result of 16.56 is sufficiently close to the estimate so that no error in placement of the decimal is likely to occur.

Carry out the indicated multiplication. Write the result as a number between 1 and 10 multiplied by the appropriate power of 10.   **Problems**

1. $(2 \times 10^2)(3 \times 10^2)$

2. $(2 \times 10^2)(3 \times 10^3)$

3. $(2.7 \times 10^2)(3.3 \times 10^3)$

4. $(5 \times 10^6)(2 \times 10^{-5})$

5. $(1.8 \times 10^{-1})(6 \times 10^1)$

6. $(4.7 \times 10^5)(2.2 \times 10^4)$

7. $(1.8 \times 10^{-6})(5.6 \times 10^{-4})$

8. $(23.8 \times 10^{-12})(640 \times 10^{-7})$

9. $(2 \times 10^{-3})(5 \times 10^3)(3 \times 10^4)$

10. $2\pi(5 \times 10^5)(3 \times 10^{-8})$

POWERS OF 10—DIVISION. The law of exponents in division can be summed up in the following general form:

$$\frac{a^m}{a^n} = a^{m-n} \qquad \text{(where } a \neq 0\text{)}$$

We saw in Table 1-1 that $10^0 = 1$, and took it on faith at the time. The law of exponents in division provides us with a mathematical tool that can demonstrate the truth of the statement. Consider the following:

$$\frac{a^m}{a^m} = a^{m-m} = a^0$$

but

$$\frac{a^m}{a^m} = 1$$

since both numerator and denominator are the same. Therefore,

$$a^0 = 1$$

But what is true for a must be true for any number. Therefore,

$$10^0 = 1$$

Consider again the general form of the law of exponents in division, and substitute 10 for a.

$$\frac{10^m}{10^n} = 10^{m-n}$$

EXAMPLES

$$\frac{10^5}{10^3} = 10^{5-3} = 10^2$$

$$\frac{10^5}{10^{-3}} = 10^{5-(-3)} = 10^8$$

$$\frac{10^{-5}}{10^3} = 10^{-5-(3)} = 10^{-8}$$

$$\frac{10^{-5}}{10^{-3}} = 10^{-5-(-3)} = 10^{-2}$$

$$\frac{3 \times 10^4}{2 \times 10^3} = \frac{3}{2} \times 10^{4-3} = 1.5 \times 10^1 = 15$$

$$\frac{2.3 \times 10^{-3}}{7.2 \times 10^5} = \frac{23 \times 10^{-4}}{7.2 \times 10^5} = \frac{23}{7.2} \times 10^{-4-(5)} = 3.194 \times 10^{-9}$$

Note that the last example is rewritten so that the result of the numerical division is a number between 1 and 10. This technique, while not essential, reduces the chances of error in placing the decimal point, especially when using the slide rule.

Problems   *Carry out the indicated division. Write the result as a number between 1 and 10 multiplied by the appropriate power of 10.*

1. $\dfrac{10^3}{10^2}$

2. $\dfrac{10^2}{10^3}$

3. $\dfrac{10^{-3}}{10^{-2}}$

4. $\dfrac{10^{-2}}{10^{-3}}$

5. $\dfrac{4 \times 10^3}{2 \times 10^2}$

6. $\dfrac{6 \times 10^2}{2 \times 10^3}$

7. $\dfrac{6 \times 10^{-3}}{3 \times 10^{-2}}$

8. $\dfrac{8 \times 10^{-2}}{2 \times 10^{-3}}$

9. $\dfrac{2.2 \times 10^4}{4.7 \times 10^{-3}}$

10. $\dfrac{3.9 \times 10^{-4}}{5.6 \times 10^{-5}}$

POWERS OF 10—POWERS AND ROOTS. It is often necessary to raise a quantity expressed in scientific notation to some power, or to extract the square or cube root of such a quantity. Both operations are simple and straightforward.

In finding the power of a power, the exponents are multiplied. That is, in general.

$$(a^m)^n = a^{mn} \qquad \text{(where } a \neq 0)$$

$(10^3)^2 = 10^{(3)(2)} = 10^6$ EXAMPLES
$(10^{-4})^3 = 10^{(-4)(3)} = 10^{-12}$

Where the problem is to raise to a given power some number times 10 to a given power, the number is raised to the desired power, and the exponent of the power of 10 is multiplied by that power.

$(2 \times 10^3)^2 = 2^2 \times (10^3)^2 = 4 \times 10^6$ EXAMPLES
$(3 \times 10^5)^3 = 3^3 \times (10^5)^3 = 27 \times 10^{15} = 2.7 \times 10^{16}$

The process of extraction of roots is essentially the inverse. Instead of multiplying the exponent by the power to which the quantity is to be raised, the exponent is divided by the number representing the root which is to be extracted. In general,

$$\sqrt[n]{a^m} = a^{m/n} \qquad \text{(where } a \neq 0)$$

$\sqrt[2]{10^6} = 10^{6/2} = 10^3$ EXAMPLES
$\sqrt[3]{10^{12}} = 10^{12/3} = 10^4$

Note that if the fractional power shown in the intermediate step in the examples above is to be reduced, the power of 10 must be evenly divisible by the appropriate root. In practice the problem can always be written so that it will be evenly divisible.

$\sqrt[2]{4 \times 10^6} = \sqrt[2]{4} \times 10^{6/2} = 2 \times 10^3$ EXAMPLES
$\sqrt[2]{4.9 \times 10^3} = \sqrt[2]{49 \times 10^2} = \sqrt[2]{49} \times 10^{2/2} = 7 \times 10^1 = 70$
$\sqrt[3]{2.7 \times 10^{-11}} = \sqrt[3]{27 \times 10^{-12}} = \sqrt[3]{27} \times 10^{-12/3} = 3 \times 10^{-4}$

Note in the second example above that the number 2 is omitted from the front of the square root sign, or *radical* as it is more properly called. If no number precedes the radical, always assume that the required operation is the extraction of a square root. For any other root the numerical value of the root must be shown.

The examples also show that the operation of extraction of a root can be, and often is, represented by the use of a fractional exponent. In the law of exponents for powers and roots, above, it may be seen that if $m = 1$, the statement becomes

$$\sqrt[n]{a} = a^{1/n} \qquad \text{(where } a \neq 0\text{)}$$

Problems *Carry out the indicated operations. Write the result as a number between 1 and 10 multiplied by the appropriate power of 10.*

1. $\sqrt{4 \times 10^6}$

2. $(2 \times 10^2)^3$

3. $\sqrt{0.4 \times 10^5}$

4. $\sqrt{160 \times 10^{-3}}$

5. $(1.3 \times 10^{-2})^2$

6. $(1.69 \times 10^3)^{1/2}$

7. $(1.69 \times 10^3)^{-1/2}$

8. $(8 \times 10^6)^{1/3}$

9. $(1.1 \times 10^{-2})^3$

10. $(10 \times 10^3)^{1/2}$

POWERS OF 10—MIXED OPERATIONS. Combined operations of multiplication and division are easily performed using scientific notation.

EXAMPLE

$$\frac{(3 \times 10^3)(2 \times 10^4)}{4 \times 10^2} = \frac{(2)(3)}{4} \times \frac{(10^3)(10^4)}{10^2} = 1.5 \times 10^{3+4-2} = 1.5 \times 10^5$$

Note that the arithmetic operations involving the numerical quantities are performed separately from the combination of powers of 10. This is especially helpful where a slide rule is used, since it makes estimation of the expected result quite simple.

If addition or subtraction is a part of the calculation, care must be taken that the quantities to be added or subtracted are expressed to the same power of 10.

EXAMPLE

$$\frac{(3.9 \times 10^3)(2.2 \times 10^2)}{(3.9 \times 10^3) + (2.2 \times 10^2)} = \frac{(3.9)(2.2) \times 10^5}{(3.9 \times 10^3) + (0.22 \times 10^3)}$$

$$= \frac{8.58 \times 10^5}{4.12 \times 10^3} = 2.08 \times 10^2$$

In the second step of the example the two quantities in the denominator to be added are rewritten as numbers times 10 raised to the same power before the addition is performed.

Carry out the indicated operations. Write the result as a number between 1 and 10 multiplied by the appropriate power of 10. **Problems**

1. $\dfrac{(10^3)(10^{-2})}{(10^4)(10^2)(10^{-5})}$

4. $\dfrac{1}{(10^{-4})(10^{-2})}$

2. $\dfrac{(2\times 10^{-6})(3\times 10^2)}{4\times 10^5}$

5. $\dfrac{(2.2\times 10^6)(1.8\times 10^5)}{(2.2\times 10^6)+(1.8\times 10^5)}$

3. $\dfrac{1}{(10^4)(10^2)}$

6. $\dfrac{1}{2\pi[(4\times 10^{-4})(1.5\times 10^{-9})]^{1/2}}$

UNITS. It is not convenient to measure the length of a piece of lumber in miles, or to measure distances between cities in inches. Thus, we use not only miles and inches but also feet, yards, and several other units of length. In the same way, many of the basic units we use in electricity and electronics are inconveniently large or small. For example, the ampere (A) is too large. Most of our measurements are more conveniently made in terms of thousandths or millionths of an ampere. The size of the basic unit is modified by the use of a prefix. The prefix *milli-* (m) means thousandths, so 5 milliamperes is the same as 5 thousandths of an ampere, or 0.005 ampere. Using symbols, this is written 5 mA = 0.005 A.

Similarly, the prefix *micro-* (μ) means millionths. Thus, 3 microamperes is the same as 0.000 003 ampere. Using symbols, this is written 3μ A = 0.000 003 A.

Other prefixes that serve to identify the decimal value of a unit are shown in Table 1-2.

TABLE 1-2 Prefixes for Powers of 10

Prefix	Meaning	Power of 10	Symbol
Tera-	= Million million	$= 10^{12}$	T
Giga-	= Thousand million	$= 10^9$	G
Mega-	= Million	$= 10^6$	M
Kilo-	= Thousand	$= 10^3$	k
Centi-	= Hundredth	$= 10^{-2}$	c
Milli-	= Thousandth	$= 10^{-3}$	m
Micro-	= Millionth	$= 10^{-6}$	μ
Nano-	= Thousandth millionth	$= 10^{-9}$	n
Pico-	= Millionth millionth	$= 10^{-12}$	p

Thus, 1 km = 1000 m, 1 mA = 0.001 A, 1 μin. = 0.000 001 in., and 1 nsec = 0.000 000 001 sec.

Problems   *In solving the problems use the following data where applicable.*

Coulomb force constant (k) $= 9 \times 10^9$ newton-meter^2/coulomb^2
Gravitational constant (G) $= 6.7 \times 10^{-11}$ nt-m^2/coul^2
Electron charge (e) $= 1.6 \times 10^{-19}$ coul
Electron rest mass (m_e) $= 9 \times 10^{-31}$ kg
Proton rest mass (m_p) $= 1.7 \times 10^{-27}$ kg

1. If the mass of an electron is considered to be insignificant, and the mass of a proton and a neutron are each considered to be one unit, how many protons and how many neutrons are in the nucleus of an atom whose normal complement of electrons is six, and whose mass is twelve units?

2. If the atom of Problem 1 loses two electrons, what is its net charge?

3. What is the coulomb force of repulsion between two electrons spaced 10^{-14} meters apart?

4. What is the gravitational force of attraction between the two electrons in Problem 3?

5. What is the ratio between the gravitational and electrostatic forces of attraction between an electron and a proton spaced 10^{-10} meters apart?

6. To gain some idea of the real magnitude of the figure 10^{39}, representing the approximate ratio between electrostatic and gravitational forces, try the following calculation. Suppose someone gave you 10^{39} pennies. If you changed this sum to $10,000 bills, and stacked the bills in stacks 10 feet high, each stack containing 10,000 bills per foot of height, and arranged the stacks so that you had 10 stacks per square foot of floor space, what size room would be needed to contain them?

Key Words   **ampere (A)**   the intensity of flow of a stream of electrons in coulombs per second (C/sec)

atom   the basic building block of matter, consisting of a nucleus containing protons and neutrons, plus an outer shell or shells of orbiting electrons

compound   a substance built up of two or more different kinds of atoms grouped into definite combinations called molecules

coulomb (C)   the net charge on 6.25×10^{18} charged particles

electron   a negatively charged particle. Practically all of electricity and electronics is based on the movement of electrons.

element   a substance composed of like atoms

insulator   a substance in which valence electrons cannot move from atom to atom

molecule the building block of chemical compounds, composed of two or more atoms joined together

neutron a particle contained in the nucleus of every atom but those of hydrogen and possessing no charge

nucleus the center of an atom, containing protons and, except in atoms of hydrogen, neutrons

proton a positively charged particle contained in the nucleus of atoms

Summary of Concepts

1. Electricity at work consists of the movement of electrons through matter and through space.

2. All atoms consist of a central, positively charged nucleus, around which one or more electrons orbit.

3. The number of electrons orbiting around the nucleus of a neutral atom always equals the number of protons in the nucleus.

4. All nuclei except those of hydrogen contain neutrons.

5. The forces acting between charged particles are far stronger than corresponding gravitational forces.

6. Loss of energy from a moving stream of electrons appears in the form of heat.

7. Calculating with very large or very small quantities is done far more easily and with less chance of error by using scientific notation.

8. To express a large number as a smaller number times a power of ten, move the decimal to the left. The number of spaces the decimal is moved represents the positive power.

9. To express a small number as a larger number times a power of ten, move the decimal to the right. The number of spaces the decimal is moved represents the negative power.

To Help You Review

On a separate sheet of paper, fill in the blanks or answer the questions below. The number in parentheses following each question refers to the section in the chapter where the correct answer can be found.

1. Electricity consists of the movement of _____ through matter or space. (1-1)

2. If an atom contains five protons, how many electrons does it contain?
    (1-1)

3. Examine Figure 1-6. How many electrons are in the valence shell? How
    many protons are in the nucleus? (1-1)

4. Substances made up of different atoms arranged in definite combina-
    tions are _____. (1-1)

5. When atoms of one kind are linked to atoms of another kind, the
    building block formed is a _____. (1-1)

6. Neutrons have no charge, but their presence seems to make the atom
    _____. (1-1)

7. What gives each atom its physical and chemical properties? (1-1)

8. What is meant by the term "inverse square law"? (1-2)

9. In what ways are electrostatic and gravitational forces alike? In what
    ways are they different? (1-2)

10. What do we call substances in which electrons are free to move from
    atom to atom? (1-3)

11. To express a larger number as a smaller number times some power of
    ten, move the decimal to the _____. The number of spaces you move
    the decimal represents the _____. (1-4)

12. What does the presence of heat in an electrical conductor mean? (1-3)

13. Match the number of the prefix on the right with the letter of the correct
    meaning. (1-4)
    (a) thousand   1. centi-
    (b) millionth   2. micro-
    (c) million million   3. milli-
    (d) hundredth   4. pico-
    (e) thousand million   5. tera-
    (f) thousandth   6. nano-
    (g) million   7. giga-
    (h) millionth millionth   8. kilo-
    (i) thousandth millionth   9. mega-

TWO

RESISTIVE CIRCUIT ELEMENTS

CURRENT. As we have seen in the previous chapter, current is the rate of change of charge. The unit quantity of charge is the coulomb, which is the charge on 6.25×10^{18} electrons. A rate of change of charge of 1 C/sec is, by definition, 1 A. If 2.7 C move past a given point in 1 sec, then the intensity of current is 2.7 A. If this same amount of charge requires 3 sec to pass the point, then the intensity of current is $2.7/3 = 0.9$ A. In other words,

2-1
The Basic Law of Electricity

$$\text{amperes} = \frac{\text{coulombs}}{\text{seconds}}$$

Using symbols, this equation is

$$I = \frac{Q}{t} \tag{1}$$

where I is the current in amperes, Q the *change* in charge in coulombs, and t the time in seconds during which the change in charge occurred.

27

VOLTAGE.   In the first chapter we compared the work of moving water in turning a waterwheel to the ability of a moving stream of electrons to do work. The water cannot move the waterwheel to provide power to grind corn unless it can flow from a high level to a lower level. Similarly, electrons will not flow in a stream through a conductor and do useful work unless they, too, can, in a sense, flow downhill.

Water flows through our waterwheel because of a difference in height between inlet and outlet levels. This difference in height gives the water the potential of doing work in flowing through the wheel, and can be referred to as a potential difference.

In electricity and electronics the term *potential difference* is used. Potential difference is measured in units called volts (V). The term potential difference is usually applied to batteries, generators, and other sources of the moving stream of electrons we call the *current*. This current can do work. The amount of work that can be done depends on two things: the amount of charge transported by the stream and the work that can be done by each charge. The amount of charge is measured in coulombs, and the work per unit charge in volts.

RESISTANCE.   The stream of electrons moving from atom to atom within the body of the conductor always loses some energy by collisions with the atoms of the conductor itself. This imparts motion to the atoms of the material, causing them to vibrate around their fixed positions. The energy of motion thus imparted to them is what we perceive as heat. The greater the energy of vibratory motion of atoms about their positions, the higher the temperature of the material. This increase in temperature represents energy gained by the conductor, and this can only be energy lost by the moving stream of electrons.

The opposition to flow that causes the transfer of energy from the current to the material through which it flows is *resistance*. The unit of resistance is the *ohm*, (Ω, the Greek letter omega). In an equation the letter R means resistance in ohms.

Consider again our waterwheel. If the stream of water is flowing from a higher level to a lower level and if the wheel is spinning freely and doing no work, the water can flow through rapidly (an intense stream). But if the wheel is turning a massive stone to grind corn, the flow of water will be impeded.

The same holds true for our stream of electrons. Given a potential difference measured in volts, the current flow will be great if the opposition is slight (a few ohms of resistance). But if the opposition is increased to many ohms of resistance, the number of amperes in the current flow will be less.

CONDUCTANCE.   *Conductance* is the reciprocal of resistance. In an equation the letter G is used to denote conductance. That is,

$$G = \frac{1}{R} \tag{2}$$

and

$$R = \frac{1}{G} \tag{3}$$

The unit of conductance is the mho (ohm spelled backwards), and the symbol ℧ is used to represent conductance. This symbol is, of course, the symbol for resistance inverted.

Resistance and conductance are simply two ways of describing a single thing—how easily or with what difficulty a stream of electrons can move between two points. Wherever R appears, $1/G$ may be substituted for it, and vice versa.

OHM'S LAW.   The basic relationship of electricity is that of voltage, current, and resistance. We have already defined the ampere as a rate of change of charge of one coulomb per second. We may define the volt as that potential difference through which the movement of 1 coulomb of charge will do 1 unit (to be defined) of work. Now we may define the size of our resistance unit in terms of the other two.

One ohm is that resistance through which a potential difference of 1 volt will cause a current of 1 ampere to flow. Mathematically,

$$R = \frac{E}{I} \tag{4}$$

and, since conductance (G) is the reciprocal of resistance,

$$G = \frac{I}{E} \tag{5}$$

Suppose a circuit element has a current of 2.5 A flowing through it when a   EXAMPLE
potential difference of 1.8 V is applied across it. What is the resistance of the
circuit element?

Solution.   Using relationship (4) above,

$$R = \frac{E}{I} = \frac{1.8}{2.5} = 0.72\,\Omega$$

Currents as high as 2.5 A are unusual in electronics. Most frequently, currents   EXAMPLE
are measured in milliamperes (thousandths of an ampere). Resistances, on

the other hand, are usually larger than that given in the first example. If, in using Ohm's law, the current is given in milliamperes (mA), and the voltage in volts, the resistance will automatically come out in thousands of ohms (kΩ). Suppose the current supplied to a circuit is measured as 5.2 mA, while the potential difference between its terminals is measured as 13.3 V. The effective resistance between the two terminals of the circuit may be calculated as follows:

$$R = \frac{E}{I} = \frac{13.3\,\text{V}}{5.2\,\text{mA}} = 2.558\ \text{k}\Omega = 2.558 \times 10^3\,\Omega = 2558\,\Omega$$

The result is exactly the same as though the current had been expressed in amperes, as in the following:

$$R = \frac{E}{I} = \frac{13.3\,\text{V}}{0.0052\,\text{A}} = \frac{13.3}{5.2 \times 10^{-3}} = \frac{13.3}{5.2} \times 10^3 = 2.558 \times 10^3 = 2558\,\Omega$$

Either method may be used since both give the same result. It should be noted that the degree of precision to which the current was measured in the original problem was to only two figures. Since the process of calculation does not generate precision, we are not entitled to express our answer to any greater number of figures than are contained in the least precise of the original data. Therefore, the result of the preceding calculations is properly given as 2.6 kΩ or 2600 Ω.

In the first example the calculation could have been made for conductance rather than resistance. The following is a repeat of that example, calculated for conductance. In this, as in all examples to follow in this text, the results have been rounded off to the same number of significant figures as in the least precise of the original data.

EXAMPLE

$$G = \frac{I}{E} = \frac{2.5\,\text{A}}{1.8\,\text{V}} = 1.4\ \mho$$

This is the same as the first result, since

$$G = \frac{1}{R} = \frac{1}{0.72} = 1.4\ \mho$$

The basic relationship called Ohm's law has been stated in one form in Equation (4). Multiplying both sides of (4) by I, the equation becomes

$$E = IR \tag{6}$$

and dividing both sides of (6) by R, the result is

$$I = \frac{E}{R} \tag{7}$$

Equation (5) may be similarly treated, with the following results:

$$I = EG \tag{8}$$

$$E = \frac{I}{G} \tag{9}$$

Find the unknown values in the following problems to two significant figures.   **Problems**

1. Given $R = 100\,\Omega$ and $I = 1\,\text{A}$, find E and G.

2. Given $I = 2\,\text{A}$ and $E = 3\,\text{V}$, find R and G.

3. Given $E = 10\,\text{V}$ and $R = 5\,\Omega$, find I and G.

4. Given $G = 5\,\mho$ and $I = 2\,\text{A}$, find E and R.

5. Given $R = 4.7\,\text{k}\Omega$ and $E = 18\,\text{V}$, find I and G.

6. Given $I = 23\,\text{mA}$ and $R = 6.8\,\text{k}\Omega$, find E and G.

7. Given $E = 12\,\text{V}$ and $I = 80\,\text{A}$, find R and G.

8. Given $G = 83\,\mu\text{mho}$ and $E = 450\,\text{V}$, find I and R.

9. Given $I = 6.2\,\text{mA}$ and $G = 42\,\mu\text{mho}$, find E and R.

10. Given $E = 120\,\text{V}$ and $G = 60\,\mu\text{mho}$, find I and R.

11. A resistor is to be inserted in a circuit in place of a conductor through which a current of 25 mA is flowing. If the presence of the resistor does not significantly affect the value of the current, how many ohms of resistance should be used so that the voltage developed by the current flowing through the resistor is 8 V?

12. A circuit element of unknown characteristics is connected to a 4.7 kΩ resistor in such a way that the current flowing through the resistor and the current flowing through the unknown circuit element are the same. If the voltage is observed to be 34 V across the resistor and simultaneously 51 V across the unknown circuit element, what is the apparent resistance of the unknown circuit element?

ENERGY.   *Energy* is the ability to do work. A coiled spring contains energy. So does a charged battery. Water behind a dam can do work in moving from a high level to a lower level.   **2-2**
     Energy, Work, and Power

     Energy is often divided into two categories, potential and kinetic energy.

Potential energy is energy of position. For example, the water behind the dam can do work because of its elevation above the turbine through which it will flow. In a coiled spring the energy is stored in the displacement of atoms or molecules from their resting positions. Again, this is energy of position. In a battery the energy is stored in the form of a chemical reaction that results in the separation of charges. This is again the potential energy of position.

Kinetic energy is the energy of motion. A moving car contains stored energy, which will be dissipated with disruptive effects should it contact a brick wall while still moving. If the brakes are used to avoid this sudden stop, the stored energy of motion of the car must be dissipated in the form of heat in the braking system.

Potential energy can be transformed into kinetic energy. The potential energy stored in gasoline in the form of chemical compounds can be transformed into the kinetic energy of motion of a car. The potential energy of position of a weight elevated above its surroundings can be transformed into the kinetic energy of motion as the weight is allowed to fall. See Figure 2-1.

WORK.   *Work* is the product of force times distance. Suppose a sack of sand is lying on the floor. If you are to raise it to a table, you must exert a force

Figure 2-1   Potential and kinetic energy: (a) The weight has potential energy due to its height above the reference zero level. (b) In falling, the weight gains velocity as it loses height. The total energy remains constant, though potential energy is converted into kinetic energy. (c) At the instant of impact, the potential energy is zero, and all the kinetic energy is transformed into heat.

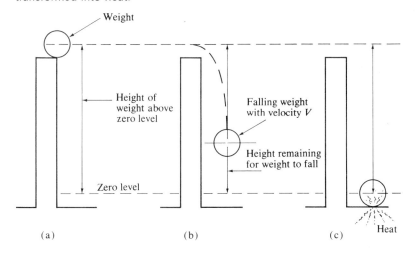

to raise it against its own weight, and you must exert that force for the distance you wish to raise the sand. If the distance is measured in feet and the force in pounds, the work done is the product of the two, and the unit of work is the foot-pound.

We are accustomed to distances measured in feet and forces in pounds. Many engineering and most scientific calculations in this country, and all calculations in nearly all other countries, are based on a different system. This system is called the MKS system, from the initials of the basic units of the system, the Meter, Kilogram, and Second. The meter is, of course, the unit of distance, the kilogram the unit of mass, and the second the unit of time.

There is a difference between mass and weight. *Mass* is a property of matter, but weight is the force exerted on that mass by a particular gravitational field. Thus, although your mass would be the same on the moon as it is on Earth, you would weigh only one-sixth as much on the moon. On Jupiter you would weigh more than two-and-a-half times what you weigh on Earth, but your mass would be the same. For this reason, the unit of force is defined independently of weight as the force required to give a mass of one kilogram an acceleration of one meter per second per second. This unit is called the *newton* (N).

The meter is fairly close in length to a more familiar unit, the yard. A meter is 39.37 inches.

The newton is equal to the downward force Earth's gravity exerts on a weight of 3.5776 ounces, which is just a little less than a quarter of a pound of force. One pound of force is almost exactly 4.5 N (4.4723).

Since work is the product of force times distance, and force is measured in newtons while distance is measured in meters, the work is measured in newton-meters (N-m). This hyphenated word is cumbersome, so it is often replaced by the word *joule* (J), which means the same thing. Thus, if a force of 1 N is exerted over a distance of 1 m, 1 J of work has been done. One joule equals 0.7367 foot-pound.

We have already seen that the volt is the work per unit charge. The volt is usually defined in MKS units. If we move a unit charge of 1 C from one point to another, and thereby do 1 J of work, the difference in potential between the two points was 1 V.

Distance does not enter into this definition, because the electric fields through which we move our coulomb unit charge vary, and the unit of potential, the volt, takes into account both the distance the charge must move and the force exerted on it during that movement. Ordinarily, we think of the volt as a measure of the force causing the electrons to move. As we have seen, this is only partially correct, since the volt is a work unit, and both force and distance are components of work. It is, in most situations, satisfactory to think of the volt as a measure of the force being exerted on charges. It provides an easy means of visualizing the action of a circuit in most cases. It is, however, sometimes necessary to remember that the volt is really a unit of work, not a unit of force. You will see why this is necessary in the next section.

POWER.   *Power* is the rate at which work is done. If work is measured in joules, then power is the number of joules of work accomplished per unit time. If the unit of time is the MKS unit, the second, then the unit of power is the joule per second, or *watt* (W). If 3 J of work are done in one second, power is expended at the rate of 3 W. If the same 3 J of work are accomplished in one-half second, the rate of expenditure of power is 6 W, though the total amount of work accomplished is the same as before.

In electrical measurements the *volt* is defined as the number of joules per coulomb of work required to transport charge. The current in *amperes* is defined as the number of coulombs per second transported. The product of the two, volts times amperes, can therefore be written

$$\frac{\text{joules}}{\text{coulomb}} \times \frac{\text{coulombs}}{\text{second}} = \frac{\text{joule-coulomb}}{\text{coulomb-second}}$$

Since coulombs appear in both the numerator and denominator of the product, they cancel, and the result is

$$\frac{\text{joules}}{\text{coulomb}} \times \frac{\text{coulombs}}{\text{second}} = \frac{\text{joules}}{\text{second}}$$

But this result has the dimension of watts. Therefore, expressed in equivalent terminology,

volts × amperes = watts

And in symbols we have

$$EI = P \tag{10}$$

where E is in volts, I in amperes, and P in watts. This fundamental relationship is nearly as important as Ohm's law.

The watt is a small unit of power. It is equal to 1/746 horsepower. Thus, if a car engine is rated at 100 horsepower, that same rating could be expressed as 74,600 watts.

Just as is the case with Ohm's law, Equation (10) can be solved for either E or I. The three forms in which it may appear are

$$P = EI \qquad E = \frac{P}{I} \qquad I = \frac{P}{E}$$

From Ohm's law (6),

$$E = IR$$

but from the above, it is also true that

$$E = \frac{P}{I}$$

Since E must equal itself, it is clear that

$$IR = \frac{P}{I}$$

This may be solved for P, giving

$$P = I^2 R \qquad\qquad\qquad\qquad\qquad\qquad\qquad \textbf{(11)}$$

Similarly, Ohm's law may be solved for I, as in Equation (7), and the result may be combined with the power equation ($P = EI$). If this is solved for P, as above, the resulting equation is

$$P = \frac{E^2}{R} \qquad\qquad\qquad\qquad\qquad\qquad\qquad \textbf{(12)}$$

Ohm's law and the power equation relate four quantities: power, voltage, current, and resistance or conductance. These four quantities are not all independent. Indeed, they are so related that if any two are known, the other two may be found. The only qualification is that the four quantities all refer to the same circuit element at the same time.

Given Ohm's law (6), the power equation (10), and Equations (11) and (12) resulting from the substitution of values from Ohm's law in the power equation, algebraic manipulation can solve each of them for any of the three variables contained in them. The result is twelve equations. If G is substituted for its reciprocal R, the result is nine new forms of the original equations, for a total of twenty-one forms of expression of the two original equations, Ohm's law and the power equation.

This is too many equations to memorize. If you remember Ohm's law and the power equation, you can derive the others as needed. It is highly desirable that you also remember the two substitution equations (11) and (12), since you will use them frequently, but they may be derived or the solution to a problem may be achieved by the use of both the fundamental equations.

Suppose 10 V is applied across a $50\,\Omega$ resistor. How many watts of power are   EXAMPLE
dissipated in the resistor?

Solution.   Since E and R are known and P is the unknown, Equation (12) may be used directly:

$$P = \frac{E^2}{R} = \frac{10^2}{50} = \frac{100}{50} = 2\,\text{W}$$

The same result may be achieved by first using Ohm's law to find the current (I), and then using this calculated value in the fundamental power equation.

$$I = \frac{E}{R} = \frac{10}{50} = 0.2 \, A$$

Substituting this result in the power equation gives

$$P = EI = (10)(0.2) = 2 \, W$$

The results are, of course, identical in both cases.

Problems   *Each horizontal line in the following table gives two values for E, I, R, or G, and P for some circuit element. Calculate the values for the quantities not given.*

Problem	E	I	R	G	P
1	10 V	1 A			
2	100 V		1000 Ω		
3	200 V			1000 μmho	
4	10 V				0.5 W
5		10 mA	4.7 kΩ		
6		150 mA		1200 μmho	
7		20 mA			1 W
8			100 kΩ		2 W
9				1 mho	$\frac{1}{4}$ W
10	20 kV	1 μA			

2-3
Resistance

BLACK-BOX RESISTORS.   If a potential difference exists between two points, and if current flows between the two points in response to that potential difference, then whatever pathway for current flow exists between those points is said to have resistance. If the value of the potential in volts and the value of the current in amperes are both known, then the value of the resistance in ohms can be calculated by Ohm's law (6).

This is not sufficient in itself to define the circuit component known as a resistor. It is quite possible that a change in potential difference applied will result in a new current between the two points which will not be different from the original current in the same ratio as the new voltage differs from the original. If this is true, then the resistance calculated from the new values will be different from the original resistance.

If a pathway for current flow obeys Ohm's law—that is, if the ratio between current and voltage is constant—then it is said to be an ohmic resistance. Not all materials or configurations of materials are ohmic resistances, but only those that are will be considered in this chapter.

The two points between which a difference in potential exists, and between which a current flows, are called *terminals*. A *resistor* is a two-terminal device. If we disregard the materials of which a resistor is made, and consider only the electrical effect of the component itself, then we can define a resistor as a two-terminal device in which the ratio between the voltage across and the current between the two terminals is a constant. The resistor thus defined can be called a *black-box* resistor, since we can consider it to be a closed container which we can experiment on only by applying voltage and current between the two terminals and observing the relationship between them. The black-box concept is useful when considering other types of components, too, and will be particularly useful when considering integrated circuits, which will soon be the most frequently encountered electronic circuit units.

VOLT–AMPERE CHARACTERISTICS.   If we graph the relationship between the voltage applied between the terminals of an ohmic resistive circuit element, and the corresponding current flow between the terminals, the graph will be a straight line, as in Figure 2-2.

The converse of this statement is also true. If the graph of the relationship between voltage and current for a circuit element is a straight line, then that circuit element is an ohmic resistance.

TEMPERATURE EFFECTS.   Two effects occur simultaneously when the temperature of a resistive circuit element is increased. (1) In many materials the number of free electrons increases when the temperature increases. Since the number of electrons available to be transported through the material is thus increased, the resistance of the material decreases with an increase in temperature. (2) In other materials, particularly those which already contain many free electrons, another factor predominates. An increase in the temperature of the material is an increase in the vibratory motion of the atoms of which the material is made about their fixed positions. This increase in motion increases the chance of collisions or other interactions between the moving electrons of the stream of current through the material and the atoms of which the material is made. This effect results in an increase in resistance with an increase in temperature.

Both effects are present at the same time in all materials. The nature of the material determines which effect will predominate. In general, the metals used as conductors have positive temperature coefficients of resistance, which

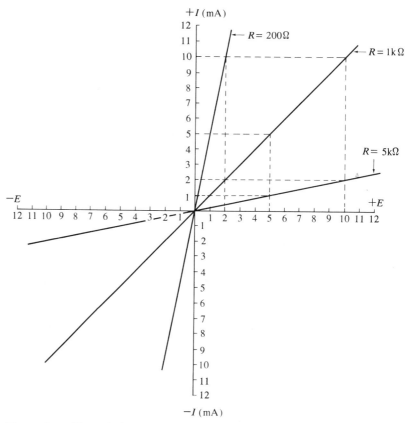

Figure 2-2 The relationship between voltage and current in a resistive circuit element. Three resistors are shown, with values of 200 Ω, 1 kΩ, and 5 kΩ. In each case the graph of the resistor is a straight line. Each point on the line representing a single resistor has a ratio E/I equal to that at any other point on that line, and equal to the value of the resistance in ohms.

means that their resistance increases with an increase in temperature. Carbon is an example of a material with a negative temperature coefficient of resistance. Its resistance decreases as the temperature increases.

In most instances the temperature coefficient of resistance (α) is small, and in most applications the change in temperature is also small. Therefore, the effect of α is usually neglected. If the effect cannot be neglected, then the circuit element cannot be considered an ohmic resistance, since an increase in current flow will cause an increase in temperature, which will change the resistance.

Temperature coefficients of resistance for some common resistive materials are given for 20 degrees Celsius (°C) in Table 2-1.

TABLE 2-1   Temperature Coefficients of Resistance (α)

Material	α (per °C)
Aluminum	0.003 9
Carbon	−0.000 3 (varies)
Constantan	0.000 008
Iron	0.005
Manganin	0.000 006
Nichrome	0.000 4
Silver	0.003 8
Steel	0.003
Tungsten	0.005

For a given conductor or circuit element of a purely resistive nature, the resistance at temperatures other than the reference temperature of 20°C can be calculated by using the following relationship:

$$R_t = R_0 + R_0(\alpha \Delta t) \tag{13}$$

where R_0 is the resistance at the standard temperature of 20°C, R_t is the resistance at the final temperature, Δt is the difference between 20°C and the final temperature, and α is the numerical value of the temperature coefficient from Table 2-1.

Suppose a tungsten wire having a resistance of 25 Ω at 20°C has its temperature increased to 320°C. Calculate the value of the resistance at the higher temperature.   EXAMPLE

Solution.   From the table, α for tungsten is 0.005. The change in temperature, Δt, is $320° - 20° = 300°C$. Substituting in Equation (13), we have

$$\begin{aligned}
R_t &= R_0 + R_0(\alpha \Delta t) \\
&= 25 + 25(0.005 \times 300) \\
&= 25 + 25(1.5) \\
&= 25 + 37.5 \\
&= 62.5\,\Omega
\end{aligned}$$

Suppose a resistive circuit element made of carbon has a measured resistance of 93.5 Ω at 20°C. If its temperature is raised to 35°C, what will be the value of its resistance?   EXAMPLE

Solution.   From Table 2-1, the value of α for carbon is −0.0003 (note that this is a negative value). Temperature change Δt is $35° - 20° = 15°C$. Substituting in Equation (13),

$$R_t = R_0 + R_0(\alpha\Delta t)^{\cdot}$$
$$= 93.5 + 93.5(-0.0003 \times 15)$$
$$= 93.5 + 93.5(-0.0045)$$
$$= 93.5 - 0.42$$
$$= 93.1\,\Omega$$

Note: We are not justified in giving an answer to more than three-figure accuracy, since the original value of the resistance was known to only three figures. This also assumes that α and the final temperature are known to this degree of precision.

POWER DISSIPATION.   As we have seen, the product of voltage and current is power in watts. The power expended in a resistor due to this product appears in the form of heat. This heat power is also measured in watts.

The actual temperature a given resistor will reach depends on the rate at which power is expended in it due to the product of the voltage across it and the current through it, and the rate at which the resistor can lose that heat. Heat may be lost by conduction, convection, and radiation. Heat loss by *conduction* occurs when excess heat power is carried away from the resistor by some material with which the resistor is in contact. Special component mountings, called *heat sinks*, are designed to help conduct heat away from resistors and other components.

Heat may also be lost by *convection*. The air immediately adjacent to the resistor is heated by it, and expands. This expansion reduces the density of the air, and the warmed and less dense air rises. This sets up air currents which continually move away the warmed air and permit cool air to flow in to maintain the temperature of the resistor at a safe level. In order for this cooling method to function, components must be mounted so that the warmed air can escape, and so that there is provision for the incoming air to be cooler and not already warmed by some other component. Forced air cooling is often used. A number of small fans are available for this purpose.

Radiation heat loss occurs in most electrical room heaters. The glowing ribbon of resistance wire that is the heating element radiates heat into the room, warming objects in the room more than the air itself is warmed. Heat transferred by radiation is very slight at temperatures of only a few tens of degrees Celsius above the temperature of the surroundings (ambient temperature), but this can become the most significant source of heat loss at high temperatures. At the temperatures at which most electronic components are normally operated radiant heat is not a significant factor. Heat conduction and convection are the major means of heat transfer.

RESISTOR SELECTION.   The power actually expended in a resistor depends on the voltage and current, but the maximum power that may be safely expended in a particular resistor depends on the materials of its construction, its physical size, and the conditions under which it will be used. A resistor mounted in a confined space cannot lose heat as efficiently as the same resistor mounted in the open, and consequently a given power dissipation results in a higher temperature of the component.

We need to know both the actual value of resistance in ohms for a desired resistor and the maximum power in watts it will be required to dissipate in a particular application before we can safely choose the proper component. A $10\,\Omega$, 1 W resistor would not be satisfactory in a circuit where the current flow through the resistor requires it to dissipate 1.5 W of electrical energy as heat. Since the next standard-size replacement resistor is 2 W, it would be necessary to use a $10\,\Omega$, 2 W resistor. Standard resistance power ratings include (but are not limited to) $\frac{1}{4}$, $\frac{1}{2}$, 1, 2, 5, 10, and 25 W. It is always safe to use a resistor of higher power-dissipating capability than is actually required, assuming its electrical characteristics are otherwise the same, though the higher wattage rating will be more expensive. A rule of thumb is to calculate the required power dissipation in the particular application and then to use or specify the next larger standard size.

A $4.7\,\text{k}\Omega$ resistor carries a current of 20 mA.   EXAMPLE
(a) What actual power is dissipated in the resistor?
(b) What standard wattage rating should be specified for this application?

Solution.   (a) $P = I^2\,R = (20 \times 10^{-3})^2\,(4.7 \times 10^3)$
$$= (400 \times 10^{-6})(4.7 \times 10^3)$$
$$= (4 \times 10^{-4})(4.7 \times 10^3)$$
$$= 18.8 \times 10^{-1}$$
$$= 1.9\,\text{W}$$

(b) 2 W, since it is the next larger standard size.

What is the maximum safe voltage that can be continuously applied across a   EXAMPLE
$20\,\text{k}\Omega$, 2 W resistor?

Solution.   Solving $P = \dfrac{E^2}{R}$ for E gives

$$E = \sqrt{PR} = \sqrt{(2)(20 \times 10^3)} = \sqrt{4 \times 10^4} = 2 \times 10^2 = 200\ \text{V}$$

Problems   **1.**   A nichrome resistance heating element has a resistance of $10\,\Omega$ at 20°C. If it is heated to 920°C, what is its resistance?

2.   What would have been the new value of resistance in Problem 1 if the heating element had been iron instead of nichrome?

3.   A material has a resistance of 100 Ω at 20°C and a resistance of 102 Ω at 220°C. What is the value of α for this material?

4.   Given $I = 10$ A, $E = 20$ V, find P and R.

5.   Given $I = 20$ mA, $R = 470$ kΩ, find P and E.

6.   Given $I = 150$ mA, $P = 2$ W, find E and R.

7.   Given $E = 9$ V, $R = 10$ kΩ, find P and I.

8.   Given $E = 200$ V, $P = \frac{1}{2}$ W, find R and I.

9.   Given $R = 100$ kΩ, $P = 10$ W, find E and I.

10. Given $I = 10\,\mu$A, $G = 10^3\,\mu$mho, find P and E.

2-4
Commercial
Resistors

CARBON RESISTORS.   For a good many years, the most frequently encountered component in electronic circuits has been the carbon resistor. The construction is shown in Figure 2-3. A carbon resistor consists of a pellet made of a mixture of carbon and an inert binder. At each end of the pellet, wire leads are attached. The pellet is then enclosed in a bakelite or plastic shell.

Figure 2-3   The actual resistance element of a carbon composition resistor is a pellet made of a mixture of carbon and a binder, usually kaolin. Varying the proportion of carbon to binder gives different values of resistance.

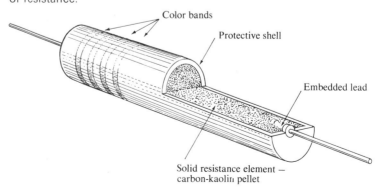

The actual amount of resistance depends on the physical dimensions of the pellet and on the relative proportions of carbon and binder of which it is made. The most commonly used binder is kaolin, or china clay. If the pellet is mostly pure carbon with very little kaolin binder, the resistance in ohms will be very low. If the pellet is mostly pure kaolin with very little carbon, the resistance will be quite high. Resistance values ranging from less than $10\,\Omega$ to more than $10\,M\Omega$ are commonly produced by using this manufacturing technique. If the resistor is small in size, its ability to dissipate heat will be slight, but if it is physically large, it will be able to dissipate considerable heat. Standard commercial carbon resistors are commonly produced in power ratings of $\frac{1}{8}$, $\frac{1}{4}$, $\frac{1}{2}$, 1, and 2 watts.

The temperature coefficient of carbon is a very small negative value (see Table 2-1); consequently, for small increases in temperature it is seldom significant. Carbon resistors are unable to withstand high temperatures without failure or change in value, and are not operated at temperatures where the temperature coefficient could make a significant difference to any but the most precise requirement.

When a carbon resistor is overheated, its resistance is often permanently increased. This is usually caused by the formation of cracks due to thermal expansion and contraction within the body of the pellet. Sometimes a crack will form all the way across the pellet, and the resistance of the component will become infinite. The resistor is said to have "opened up" when this occurs, and it must then be replaced. A slight increase in resistance is more common—and more difficult for the troubleshooter to locate.

WIRE-WOUND POWER RESISTORS.   Where more than 2 W of heat must be dissipated, wire-wound resistors are often used. The resistance element is a length of wire, usually constantan, manganin, or nichrome. The length and diameter of the wire are chosen to give the desired resistance. This wire is wound on a core, usually a hollow ceramic tube. Clamps at each end allow the necessary external electrical connections to be made. The entire resistor is usually dipped in a vitreous (glass-based) enamel, which is then baked on. See Figure 2-4.

All the materials of which wire-wound resistors are constructed are able to withstand high temperatures without damage. The vitreous enamel coating protects the wire element from the effects of oxidation, which would otherwise be pronounced at the relatively high operating temperatures used.

Wire-wound resistors are made in values ranging from a few ohms up to several tens of thousands of ohms, and in wattage ratings from 3 W to several thousand watts.

Wire-wound resistors are often used where precise control of the final

Figure 2-4 A wire-wound power resistor.

value is desired. Accuracy and stability of value, often essential in test instruments, may be achieved more readily than with carbon resistors, though the expense may be considerably higher.

DEPOSITED-FILM RESISTORS.   In this type of resistor a film of carbon or special metal alloy is deposited on a ceramic core. The core is usually cylindrical. The film as deposited has a lower resistance than is intended for the final resistor. To adjust the resistor to the final desired value, a spiral groove is cut through the film, thus increasing its resistance. The ends of the unit are then usually silvered, end caps pressed on, and leads connected to the end caps. The final step is a coating of glass, epoxy, ceramic, or other protective material, which makes the resistor impervious to moisture and provides insulation. See Figure 2-5.

A more stable deposited-film resistor may be made by depositing a thin film of tin oxide on the surface of glass at a red heat, so that it is fused into the glass. Using this technique, resistors of very high wattage ratings may be made. Though the cost is higher than for wire-wound resistors, they are more stable and reliable. See Figure 2-6.

Deposited-film construction is often used where the final value must be as accurate as possible. It is also well adapted to mass production using automatic machinery. The result is a resistor having less inherent noise than the carbon composition resistor, with more stability, but at a somewhat higher cost.

ADJUSTABLE RESISTORS.   Adjustable resistors are usually of the wire-wound type. In this construction a strip of the outer vitreous enamel is left off, and a metal collar is fitted over the wire element. The collar may be moved to

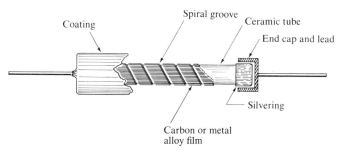

Figure 2-5 A deposited-film resistor. The value of the resistance depends on the nature and thickness of the carbon or metal alloy film, and on the width and length of the spiral groove.

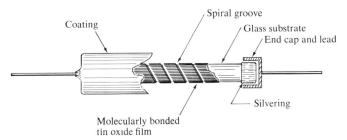

Coating
Spiral groove
Glass substrate
End cap and lead
Silvering
Molecularly bonded
tin oxide film

Figure 2-6 The construction of a tin oxide resistor is superficially similar to that of the deposited-film resistor, but the fusing of the tin oxide into the glass substrate increases its stability, its ability to dissipate heat, and its cost.

make contact at any point along the wire. This provides a means of adjusting the value of resistance between one end of the element and the point to which the collar is adjusted, which may be any value up to the maximum resistance of the element.

Adjustable resistors may also be used as voltage dividers. If a voltage is impressed across the two ends of the resistor, the voltage between one end and the adjustable collar will be divided proportionally to the position to which the collar is adjusted. See Figure 2-7.

Figure 2-7 Adjustable wire-wound resistors. (Courtesy Ohmite Manufacturing Co.)

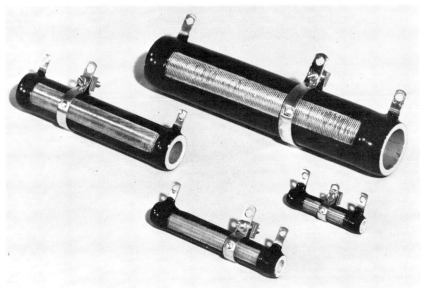

Figure 2-8 Potentiometers. If connections are made to only 1 end of the element and the wiper arm, this component functions as a rheostat. (Courtesy Allen-Bradley Co.)

RHEOSTATS AND POTENTIOMETERS. Rheostats and potentiometers are usually used where operator control of resistance is desired, as in the volume control of a radio or television receiver. The resistance element is a semi-circular ring which may be carbon composition or wire-wound. The two ends are connected to soldering lugs. A third soldering lug, usually positioned between the other two, is connected to a wiper arm. When the shaft connected to the wiper arm is turned, the arm rotates to contact the semicircular resistance element at any point between the two ends. See Figure 2-8.

The total resistance between the two ends of a potentiometer is constant, but the resistance between either end and the center terminal connected to the wiper arm may be varied by rotation of a knob connected to the shaft. Any value of resistance from zero up to the total resistance of the element may be obtained. Note that the sum of the resistance from one end to the center terminal plus the resistance from the center terminal to the other end is always constant and equals the total resistance of the element.

If connections are made to all three terminals, the two ends and the terminal connected to the wiper arm, the component is known as a *potentiometer*. If connections are made to only the wiper arm and one end, the component is a *rheostat*. Rheostats may be made with only two terminals, one connecting to the end of the element and the other to the wiper arm; or only two of the three available terminals of a component originally designed to be a potentiometer may be used.

RESISTOR COLOR CODE. Composition carbon resistors usually have their resistance value designated by a color code, since their small physical size makes it difficult to print the correct value directly on them. In this code, colors are used to designate values, as shown in Table 2-2.

TABLE 2-2   Resistance Color Code

Color	Value	Multiplier	Tolerance
Black	0	Unity	
Brown	1	10	
Red	2	100	2%
Orange	3	1000	
Yellow	4	10,000	
Green	5	100,000	
Blue	6	1,000,000	
Violet	7		
Grey	8		
White	9		
Silver		1/100	10%
Gold		1/10	5%

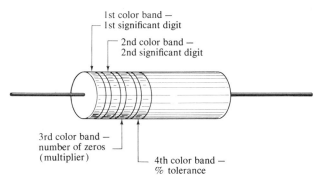

1st color band —
1st significant digit

2nd color band —
2nd significant digit

3rd color band —
number of zeros
(multiplier)

4th color band —
% tolerance

Figure 2-9   Nearly all small-wattage carbon resistors use this color code. The numerical values of the colors are shown in Table 2-2.

Color bands are painted around the body of the resistor. When the resistor is held properly, the bands are near the left end and are read from left to right. See Figure 2-9. Three bands are used to give the value of the resistor in ohms, to two significant figures. The first two bands give the two significant figures, according to the numerical value of the colors, as shown in Table 2-2. The third band is the multiplier, which gives the number of zeros that follow the two significant figures. Thus, a resistor color-coded yellow, violet, orange is a 47,000 Ω resistor.

If there are only three color-coded bands, the tolerance of the resistor is $\pm 20\%$ of its marked value. Some resistors are marked with a fourth band. If the fourth band is silver, the resistor's tolerance is $\pm 10\%$ of its marked value. If the fourth band is gold, the tolerance is $\pm 5\%$ of the marked value. A red fourth band indicates a $\pm 2\%$ tolerance.

If the *third* band of a resistor is gold or silver, then that color indicates a multiplier of $\frac{1}{10}$ or $\frac{1}{100}$ respectively. Thus, a resistor coded red, violet, gold, silver, would be a 2.7 Ω resistor, having a tolerance of $\pm 10\%$ of 2.7 Ω, or 0.27 Ω above or below the marked value.

Complete the table below by filling in the blank spaces.   **Problems**

	1st Band	2nd Band	3rd Band	4th Band	Value	Tolerance
1	Brown	Black	Brown	Gold		
2	Orange	Orange	Yellow	Silver		
3	Red	Red	Red	Red		
4	Brown	Black	Yellow	Gold		

Problems *(Continued)*

5	Brown	Black	Black	Silver		
6	Brown	Black	Silver	Gold		
7					2.2 MΩ	10%
8					10 kΩ	5%
9					560 Ω	2%
10					1 mΩ	20%
11					4.7 Ω	5%
12					68 Ω	10%

13.   What is the color code for a 1 Ω, 5% resistor?

2-5
Switches and
Switching Circuits

SWITCH TYPES.   A *switch* is a mechanical arrangement of conductors and insulators arranged so that the interconnection between two or more terminals may be changed at will by the operator, usually by means of some external control, such as a knob, toggle, or push button.

    Switches are usually categorized by the number of poles and the number of "throws." A single-pole, single-throw switch can make or break a single connection. That is, it can connect or disconnect two wires. A single-pole, double-throw switch can connect a single wire to either of two other wires. A double-pole, single-throw switch can connect or disconnect one pair of wires to another pair. A double-pole, double-throw switch can connect one pair of wires to either of two other pairs. Switches may have any number of poles and any number of throws. See Figure 2-10.

    Switches with fewer than three poles and three throws are usually slide or toggle switches. Microswitches are special cases, where the main design requirement is low force required for the mechanical operation of the switch. Switches are often combined with other components. For example, a potentiometer is used to control the volume of a radio or television receiver, and a switch is mechanically built into the potentiometer, though electrically separate from it, so that either extreme rotation of the control or pulling out the control knob will actuate the switch to turn the receiver on or off.

    Switches having more than three poles or three throws are commonly rotary disc switches or push-button switches. Rotary disc switches are constructed in decks, or layers. Such a switch may have an almost unlimited number of decks, and as many as twenty contacts may be made or broken on

Figure 2-10 A toggle switch. (Courtesy J-B-T Instruments)

each side of each deck as the switch is rotated to a new position. Range and function switches for instruments and band-change switches for receivers are common applications for rotary disc and push-button switches. See Figure 2-11.

SWITCHING CIRCUITS.   Switching circuits range from the very simple make-or-break on-off switches to the very complex switching circuits encountered in television studios. If we consider electronic switches as well as mechanical systems, then the modern general-purpose digital computer is perhaps the most complex example of a switching circuit.

Three major functions are performed by switching circuits. They may be used to (1) turn circuits on or off, (2) substitute components within an operating circuit or (3) change the configuration of an operating circuit. See Figure 2-12.

Interlock switches are often found on equipment in which hazardous high voltages are present. An interlock switch is usually connected so that when the cabinet containing the equipment is opened, the power to it is automatically disconnected. The power cord on most TV receivers is connected to the back panel of the set in such a way that the set is disconnected from its power when the back is removed. This is a form of interlock switch.

If an interlock switch is present, a hazard exists; otherwise the switch would not have been designed into the equipment. The hazard may be to the equipment or to the electronic technician who must service it. In either

Figure 2-11 A multiple deck rotary switch. (Courtesy J-B-T Instruments)

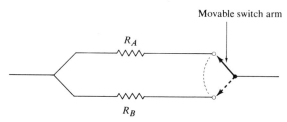

Figure 2-12 By changing the position of the movable switch arm, either of the two components, R_A or R_B, can be made a part of the operating circuit. This switch may be either a toggle switch or a rotary switch.

event, an interlock switch should never be bypassed except by those who *know what they are doing.* It should be clearly understood, as well, that the absence of an interlock switch does *not* mean that no hazard exists. It merely means that neither equipment nor personnel have automatic protection against danger.

2-6
Fuses and Lamps

FUSE TYPES. A *fuse* may be thought of as one form of current-operated switch. A fuse consists of a short section of small-diameter wire or flat ribbon conductor of a special alloy having a low melting temperature and a relatively high resistance. A fuse rated at 1 A, for example, will conduct a current of less than 1 A without difficulty. If the current through the fuse exceeds 1 A for more than a very short time, the power dissipated by this current flowing through the resistance of the fuse wire raises its temperature to the melting point. When the fuse wire melts, it breaks the circuit and interrupts the current flow.

Fuses have both current and voltage ratings. The current rating is the maximum current that the fuse can carry before the link melts. The voltage rating is the maximum voltage that the fuse can break without the danger of a sustained arc developing across the gap remaining as the link melts. Most fuses are rated to 250 V. If a fuse is to be used in a high-voltage circuit, types of fuses are available in which the link is surrounded by a material that produces a nonconducting gas which can quench the arc created when the link melts.

Nearly all fuses found on electronic devices are constructed the same way. They consist of a small glass tube with two metal end caps, and the fusible link is connected between the two end caps through the center of the tube. See Figure 2-13. Usually the current and voltage rating of the fuse are

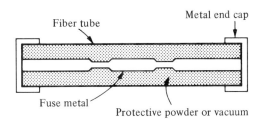

Figure 2-13   A cartridge fuse.

stamped on one end cap. There are variations in the diameter and length of the glass tube, the size of the end caps, and the method of attaching to a fuse holder, as well as variations in voltage rating and current-carrying capacity.

Some fuses are designated *slow-blow*. These fuses are designed to be used in circuits in which there is normally a high initial surge of current, followed by a diminished steady operating current flow. A fuse which would give adequate protection for the operating current would blow from the starting surge, while a standard fuse which would withstand the starting surge would be rated too high to provide adequate protection during operating conditions. A slow-blow fuse will not blow if the excess current flows for only a short time, as is the case with the starting surge, but will blow if excess current continues to flow for more than a fraction of a second. This permits the high starting surge while still providing protection to the circuit under normal operating conditions.

A fuse should never be replaced by one of higher current rating than specified for the equipment in which it is used. Fuses blow for four reasons.

1. The fuse itself may malfunction.
2. Incorrect voltage may be applied to the circuit.
3. An attempt may have been made to operate the device which the fuse protects beyond its design limitations.
4. The device which the fuse protects may have an internal malfunction. This is the most common cause of blown fuses.

Fuses sometimes blow for no apparent reason. Usually the cause is melting of the solder holding the link to the end cap, not melting of the link itself. Sometimes this occurs because of corrosion at the terminals of the fuse or fuse holder. This corrosion causes a poor contact, the resistance of which can produce enough heat to melt the solder. If a replacement fuse of the proper size blows, then the cause of the overload must be found and corrected. The fuse must *not* be replaced with one of higher current rating, or damage to the equipment will almost certainly result.

RESISTIVE LAMPS.   Resistive, or incandescent, lamps are only one of the several ways electrical energy can be converted into light. Others include light-emitting diodes (LED), electroluminescent strips and panels, and gas discharge lamps such as neon and fluorescent lamps, all of which may appear in many different configurations and designs. The only electrically operated light source that will be discussed in this section is the resistive lamp.

If a high current is passed through a wire of significant resistance, the wire will be heated. If the wire is heated to a sufficiently high temperature, it will give off light. This is the basis of resistive lamps. If the wire has too low a melting temperature, it will melt before it becomes hot enough to produce light. At low temperatures a red glow is all that would be produced. Extremely high temperatures are necessary to produce the yellow-white light we associate with incandescent lamps such as are found in the home.

If the lamp filament, the heated wire within the lamp, is to be able to attain these high temperatures without melting, it must obviously be made of a material with a high melting point. Tungsten has the necessary physical characteristics. It can be drawn into wire, it has sufficient resistance in small cross-sectional areas so that power is dissipated in the form of heat by current flow through it, and it does not melt at the necessary very high temperatures.

If a tungsten filament is energized in an atmosphere of air, which contains oxygen, the oxygen combines with the tungsten very rapidly, causing the filament to corrode in a matter of seconds. It is therefore necessary to enclose the filament in either a vacuum or an atmosphere of some inert gas. The filament is therefore enclosed in an oxygen-free glass envelope. The necessary electrical connections are brought out through the glass envelope, usually to terminals that serve both to make the necessary electrical connections and provide mechanical support to hold the lamp in place. See Figure 2-14.

Lamps differ in both electrical and mechanical characteristics. Usually both voltage and wattage ratings are given although the actual current depends on the applied voltage. The brightness and color of the light depend on the voltage. Voltages even slightly higher than the rated voltage make the light much brighter and considerably reduce the life of the lamp. Voltages below the rated voltage produce a yellow or reddish-yellow glow from the lamp and very significantly prolong its life. Lamps may be operated at slightly reduced voltages if the loss of light can be tolerated, but they should never be operated at voltages higher than the manufacturer's rating.

A resistive lamp is a nonlinear resistive circuit element. This is because of

Figure 2-14 An incandescent lamp.

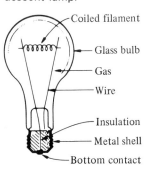

- Coiled filament
- Glass bulb
- Gas
- Wire
- Insulation
- Metal shell
- Bottom contact

the temperature effect of resistance. In Table 2-1, the α of tungsten is given as 0.005, a positive coefficient. The equation previously given relating change in resistance to change in temperature is good only to a rough first approximation at the very high temperature of the filament of an incandescent lamp. The correct relationship is much more complex and beyond the scope of this text.

If the voltage impressed across an incandescent lamp and the current flow through it are plotted as horizontal and vertical ordinates on a graph, the line of the graph representing corresponding voltages and currents will not be a straight line. For the ordinary resistors we have been considering the graph is linear, but since there is a significant change in resistance with change in temperature with an incandescent lamp, the volt–ampere characteristic curve is nonlinear. See Figure 2-15.

Use is sometimes made of this characteristic in circuit applications. Since an increase in voltage impressed across the lamp filament increases the dissipated power and thus the temperature of the filament, the resistance of the filament also increases. This increase in resistance means that the current does not increase in direct proportion to the increase in voltage. A circuit in which an incandescent lamp appears therefore will show less variation in current as voltage variations occur than would be the case if a linear resistive element had been used in place of the lamp.

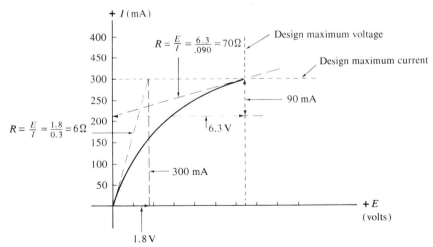

Figure 2-15   The volt–ampere characteristic curve for an incandescent lamp. As the current through the lamp increases, the temperature of the filament also increases. This increase in temperature is responsible for the increased resistance shown by the graph at operating voltages, compared with that at very low voltages and currents.

2-7
Conductors and
Insulators

CONDUCTOR TYPES. The ideal conductor would have zero resistance, zero weight, zero cost, and infinite corrosion resistance, and would be self-welding on contact to a desired terminal. No real conductor reaches any of these characteristics. The designer must balance the need for efficiency and low cost (which includes the cost of construction) against the requirements for any particular application.

Silver is the best conductor. It has adequate mechanical strength and high corrosion resistance, is easily drawn into wire of any desired size, and is easily soldered to make the necessary connections between components in a circuit. It is, however, quite expensive.

Copper is not as good a conductor as silver, but it is better than any other material. It has high corrosion resistance, although not as high as that of silver. It is easily fabricated into any desired shape and has sufficient mechanical strength. It is easily soldered. The cost of copper is very much less than the cost of silver. It is fairly heavy, but in most circuit applications this makes little difference. Copper is the material of choice for nearly all conductors used both in electronics and elsewhere.

Aluminum is the only other material widely used as a conductor in the form of wire. It can be easily drawn or extruded into the desired cross-sectional shapes. It has good resistance to corrosion, primarily because the corrosion products form a surface film that protects against further corrosion. Crimped or pressure connections are most often used.

The chief virtue of aluminum as a conductor lies in the fact that it is very light in weight. It is necessary to use conductors of larger diameter where aluminum is used instead of copper or silver, but the lightness of aluminum is such that the total weight is still less. Where weight is an important factor, aluminum is the material of choice. It is often used in power wiring, since the decrease in weight means that the supports may also be made lighter in weight, and therefore less expensively. The fact that aluminum is significantly less expensive than copper is also a factor.

Sometimes necessary fabrication techniques are more important than other considerations, even including conductivity, in determining what material should be used in a particular application. In the fabrication of integrated circuits, materials such as aluminum, gold, germanium, and silicon, often alloyed with other materials, are used as conductors.

Wire sizes are designated by gauge numbers. The most commonly used system of gauge numbers is the American Wire Gauge (AWG), formerly called the Brown and Sharpe Gauge (B & S). Each gauge number has a particular cross-sectional area. For the sake of simplicity, wire cross-sectional areas are measured in circular mils (cmil). The area in circular mils of a wire is the square of the number of thousandths of an inch in the diameter of the wire. For example, 18 gauge wire has a diameter of 0.0403 in. This is 40.3 mils, and this figure squared equals the area in circular mils, 1624. Table 2-3 gives a few of the wire sizes commonly encountered both in house wiring and in electronics.

TABLE 2-3   American Wire Gauge

Gauge Number	Diameter	Area (cmil)
8	0.1285	16,510
10	0.1019	10,380
12	0.080 81	6.530
14	0.604 08	4,107
16	0.050 82	2,583
18	0.040 30	1,624
20	0.031 96	1,022
22	0.025 35	642.4
24	0.020 10	404.0
26	0.015 94	254.1
28	0.012 64	159.8
30	0.010 03	100.5

Two wires of the same gauge number and, consequently, the same cross-sectional area in cmils, will have different resistances if they are made of different materials or are of different lengths. Consequently, another tabulation is necessary to give the specific resistivity (ρ, the Greek letter rho) for standardized conductors in ohms per cmil-ft (that is, 1 mil in cross-sectional area and one foot in length). These values are shown in Table 2-4.

TABLE 2-4   Specific Resistance (ρ) of Common Conductor Materials
(ohms per cmil-ft at 20°C)

Aluminum	17	Nichrome	675
Carbon	22,000	Platinum	60
Copper	10.4	Silver	9.56
Iron	61	Tungsten	34

The total resistance of a conductor depends on three factors: the length of the wire, its cross-sectional area, and the material of which it is made. The relationship between these three factors is given by

$$R = \frac{\rho l}{A} \tag{14}$$

where R is the resistance of the conductor in ohms, ρ is the specific resistivity for the conductor material, l is the length of the conductor in feet, and A is the cross-sectional area in cmils.

EXAMPLE Find the resistance of 50 ft of copper wire if the gauge size of the wire is 30.

Solution. For copper, ρ is 10.4, and the area for number 30 wire is 100.5 cmils. Substituting in Equation (14) gives

$$R = \frac{\rho l}{A} = \frac{(10.4)(50)}{(100.5)} = 5.17\,\Omega$$

POWER AND VOLTAGE LOSS. Current flowing through the resistance of a conductor dissipates power. According to Ohm's law and the power equation,

$$P = I^2 R$$

Current flowing through the resistance of the wire also causes a voltage to appear between the two ends of the wire. This voltage is usually called a *voltage drop* since it represents a decrease in the voltage that will appear at a load which is connected to some source of power by the wire. It is often called an *IR* drop since its magnitude is given by

$$E = IR$$

where E is the voltage drop in volts, I is the current flow through the wire, and R is the resistance of the wire.

EXAMPLE A coil contains 50 ft of 30 gauge copper wire. Its resistance has been calculated as 5.17 Ω. If this figure is rounded off to 5.2 Ω, how much power is expended by a current flow of 500 mA through the coil?

Solution. Since $I = 500$ mA $= 0.5$ A, and $R = 5.2$,

$$P = I^2 R = (0.5^2)(5.2) = 1.3\,\text{W}$$

EXAMPLE What *IR* drop will appear across the coil in the example above as a consequence of the current flow through it?

Solution. Given $I = 500$ mA $= 0.5$ A, and $R = 5.2\,\Omega$,

$$E = IR = (0.5)(5.2) = 2.6\,\text{V}$$

1. Calculate the resistance of 100 ft of 14 gauge copper wire.

2. Calculate the resistance of 100 ft of 14 gauge nichrome wire.

3. Calculate the resistance of 2 ft of 30 gauge silver wire.

4. How many watts of power will be dissipated by a current flow of 6 A through 100 ft of 14 gauge copper wire?

5. How many watts of power will be dissipated by a current flow of 2 A through 50 ft of 14 gauge nichrome wire?

6. How many watts of power will be dissipated by a current flow of 10 mA through 1 ft of 30 gauge silver wire?

7. What *IR* drop will appear across 100 ft of 14 gauge copper wire as a consequence of a current flow of 6 A through it?

8. What *IR* drop will appear across 50 ft of 14 gauge nichrome wire as a consequence of a current flow of 2 A through it?

9. What *IR* drop will appear across 2 ft of 30 gauge silver wire as a consequence of a current flow of 5 mA through it?

**2-8
Electrical Safety**

EQUIPMENT PROTECTION.   Most home electrical and electronic appliances are designed to be as nearly foolproof as possible. The user of a radio or television can do little damage to the receiver by simply twisting the controls, assuming they are not twisted off. This is not true of test equipment or of industrial and military electronic devices in general.

Damage to equipment may occur from any of several possible causes. The two most common are improper use, which includes failure to use properly such equipment protection devices as fuses, and exposure to hazardous environmental conditions. Both causes may ordinarily be avoided.

The first rule is simple—know what you are doing. Test equipment and industrial and military electronic devices have instruction manuals that describe their operation and maintenance. To be useful, the manual must be read and understood. It is hazardous to go beyond the instructions. Presumably, the author of the manual knew something of electronics in general and the specific equipment involved.

Hazardous environmental conditions for electronics equipment include heat, moisture, dust and dirt, and physical shock and vibration. Intense magnetic or electric fields can also cause either temporary malfunctions or permanent damage. All of these represent conditions to be avoided.

If the equipment has cooling vents or a blower to circulate cooling air, it must be permitted to operate as designed. If anything blocks entry or exit of cooling air, the internal temperature of the equipment may rise to the point where damage will occur.

PERSONAL PROTECTION.   Every year thousands are killed by electric shock. Many victims are electricians or electronic technicians, presumably with some knowledge of the characteristics of electricity. Nearly all these deaths are avoidable.

There are two ways by which an electric shock can directly cause death or serious damage. A shock may cause death or injury by tissue damage, usually to nerve or muscle tissue. Death may also occur because the shock has disrupted the synchronized action of the nervous impulses that cause the heart muscles to contract rhythmically and in the correct sequence. Indirectly, a shock which would otherwise be minor but which, for example, causes a person to fall off a ladder may be the cause of considerable damage.

Tissue damage is caused by the flow of current through the body from one point of contact to another. Usually, one point of contact is a hand, though any part of the body may be accidentally brought into contact with a source of current. A single contact will not produce a flow of current through the body, any more than a single wire to a light bulb will permit current flow through it to produce light. The second point of contact required to complete a path for current to flow through the body is usually the feet, through the soles of the shoes to "ground," which certainly includes concrete floors, and sometimes wood floors as well. Obviously, other second points of contact are possible, including contacts of hands or any other part of the body with anything that can serve as a conductor. Water and gas pipes are particularly good, and therefore particularly hazardous, grounds.

Theoretically, shock may be avoided by avoiding either contact—the contact with a source of current by one part of the body, or the simultaneous contact with another part of the circuit or a ground by another part of the body. Practically, the surest way to avoid shock is to attempt to avoid both contacts.

The amount of current flow through the body that may cause death is surprisingly small. Much depends on the state of health of the individual sustaining the shock and the path of the current through the body, but current flows as small as 10 mA are potentially lethal.

The potential difference that must exist between the two points of contact with the body to cause current flow in excess of this possibly lethal level depends on the body resistance between the points of contact. Most of that body resistance is in the skin. Changes in the amount of the invisible film of perspiration that covers the skin can produce significant changes in the body resistance from day to day, as can the presence of sores, metal slivers, or other breaks in the skin surface. Thus, the voltage that will be harmless and unfelt one day may prove deadly the next. Many farmers were killed with the old 32 V systems of the first stages of rural electrification.

The rules for survival are simple and easily obeyed.

1. *Know what you are doing.* If you aren't certain, don't do anything until you have made absolutely certain the step you are about to take is not hazardous.
2. *Don't be careless.* If it is necessary to work on a live circuit, exercise the same attentive care with which you would pick eggs out of a nest of rattlesnakes. Keep *all* your mind on what you are doing; don't day-dream or weaken your concentration by talking with a friend.
3. *Don't ground yourself.* Leather shoe soles on a concrete floor, an arm brushing against a pipe, or casual contact with a metal chassis all represent half a fatal accident. One error in judgment, one slip of the finger, or (even more deadly) one unsuspected equipment malfunction that puts a lethal voltage at a circuit point where it would not normally be—these are always waiting to be the other half of a fatal accident.
4. *Don't assume anything.* If your best friend and most respected co-worker tells you the power is off, check it yourself before going to work on the circuit.

Key Words

adjustable resistor   a wire-wound resistor with an adjustable metal collar replacing part of the outer vitreous enamel

carbon resistor   a pellet made of carbon and an inert binder (usually kaolin), with wire leads attached to each end

circular mil (cmil)   the unit of measurement for wire cross-sectional areas

conductance (G)   the reciprocal of resistance

deposited-film resistor   a ceramic core coated with a film of carbon or alloy and silvered on the ends

energy   the ability to do work

fuse   a form of current-operated switch consisting of a conductor with a low melting temperature and high resistance, and rated for both current and voltage

heat sink   a mounting that conducts heat away from a resistor

interlock switch   on hazardous equipment in which high voltages are present, prevents current from flowing through the circuit while the circuit components are exposed

joule (J)   the unit of measurement of work—the force of 1 newton exerted over a distance of 1 meter

kinetic energy   the energy of motion

mho   the unit of conductance (*ohm* spelled backwards)

newton (N)   the unit of force required to give a mass of 1 kilogram an acceleration of 1 meter per second per second

ohm (Ω)   the resistance through which a potential difference of 1 volt will cause a current of 1 ampere to flow

potential energy   stored energy—the energy of position

resistor   a two-terminal device in which the ratio between the voltage and the current is constant

"slow-blow" fuse   tolerates a high initial surge of current followed by diminished, steady current, and protects components in circuits where such a condition exists

specific resistivity (ρ)   the standard resistance of conductors 1 cmil in cross-sectional area and 1 foot in length

switch   a mechanical arrangement of conductors and insulators that enables the operator to change terminal connections externally

terminals   two points between which current flows

volt (V)   the potential difference through which the movement of 1 coulomb of charge will do one unit of work

voltage (IR) drop   the decrease in voltage that appears at a load connected to a source of power by a conductor

watt (W)   the unit of power (joules/second)

wire-wound power resistor   a length of wire wound around a core and clamped at either end, used when more than 2 W of heat must be dissipated

work   the product of force times distance

Summary of Concepts

1. Ohm's law gives the basic relationship between voltage V, current I, and resistance R: $V = IR$.

2. Any difference between charges provides the potential for doing work and is called potential difference.

3. The greater the energy of vibratory motion of atoms about their positions, the higher the temperature of the material.

4. The opposition to flow that causes the transfer of energy from the current to the material through which it flows is resistance.

5. Conductance is the reciprocal of resistance.

6. Power is the rate at which work is done.

7. Volts × amperes = watts, or $VA = W$.

8. If a potential difference exists between two points, causing current to flow between them, then the pathway of that flow has resistance.

9. A "black-box" resistor is one that can be studied only by applying voltage and current between the two terminals and observing the relationship that exists between them.

10. In many materials the number of free electrons increases when the temperature of the material increases.

11. There is a change in resistance with a corresponding change in temperature.

12. The temperature a resistor will reach depends on the rate of power expended in it and the rate at which the resistor can lose that heat.

13. Heat loss by conduction occurs when excess heat power is carried away from the resistor by some material with which the resistor is in contact.

14. Heat loss by convection occurs when the air around the resistor expands, rises, and sets up air currents that continually remove the warmed air.

15. Radiation heat loss occurs when heat warms objects more than the air around them.

16. The maximum power that may be safely expended in a resistor depends on the materials of which it is constructed, its size, and the conditions under which it is used.

17. When a carbon resistor is overheated, its resistance is often permanently increased. The resistance values of composition carbon resistors are usually designated by a color code.

18. Silver is the best electrical conductor and copper the next best and most widely used. Aluminum is the lightest and most economical conductor.

19. Wire sizes are designated by gauge numbers.

20. The total resistance of a wire conductor depends on the length of the wire, its cross-sectional area, and the material of which it is made.

21. Heat, moisture, dust and dirt, physical shock, and vibration are hazardous to all electronic equipment.

To Help You Review   *On a separate sheet of paper, fill in the blanks or answer the questions below. The number following each question refers to the section in the chapter where the correct answer can be found.*

1. What is the formula for computing amperes? (2-1)

2. The work done by an electric current is measured in _____. (2-1)

3. Electrons moving within a conductor collide with the atoms of the conductor, causing them to vibrate. This creates _____. (2-1)

4. What is the unit of resistance and what is its symbol? (2-1)

5. The formula $G = \dfrac{1}{R}$ explains what concept? (2-1)

6. What symbol represents conductance? (2-1)

7. Resistance and conductance are two ways of describing what single thing? (2-1)

8. Water behind a dam and a coiled spring are examples of what kind of energy? (2-2)

9. Kinetic energy is the energy of _____ ? (2-2)

10. Explain the initials of the MKS system of measurement. (2-2)

11. Work is the product of _____ times _____. (2-2)

12. The rate at which work is done is called _____. (2-2)

13. The unit of power is the _____. (2-2)

14. $EI = P$ explains what relationship? (2-2)

15. What four quantities are related by Ohm's law and the power equation? (2-2)

16. Explain what a "black-box" resistor is. (2-3)

17. Explain, graphically, when a circuit element is an ohmic resistance. (2-3)

18. What two things happen when the temperature of a resistive circuit is increased? (2-3)

19. Should an ideal conductor have a small or large positive temperature coefficient of resistance? Why? (2-3)

20. In what three ways can heat loss occur in a resistor? (2-3)

21. What do we need to know before we can select the right kind of resistor? (2-3) Name three kinds of resistors. (2-4)

22. What is the basic use of an electrical switch? Name three kinds of switches. (2-5)

23. Why does the conductor in a fuse need to have a low melting point? (2-6)

24. How does the resistive lamp give off light? (2-6)

25. What makes the most ideal conductor, and why? What is its only drawback? (2-7)

26. Explain the formula $R = \dfrac{\rho l}{A}$ (2-7)

27. In accidents involving electricity, it is not the single but the double contact that can prove fatal. Why? (2-8)

28. What does the safety advice "Don't ground yourself" mean? Explain. (2-8)

THREE

SERIES AND PARALLEL CIRCUITS

This chapter will help you understand

☐ how Kirchhoff's voltage and current laws apply to an electric circuit

☐ the essential similarities and differences between series and parallel circuits

☐ the computation of voltage and resistance in voltage and current dividers

3-1
Kirchhoff's Laws

THE ELECTRIC CIRCUIT. An electric circuit is a closed system. It consists of an energy source to provide the necessary energy to cause the electrons to move, conductors through which they move, and a load in which the energy provided by the source is expended.

With the proper device, almost any form of energy may be used as the source of the electromotive force which causes the electrons to move through the circuit. The two most commonly used are electrochemical energy sources, of which batteries are the most frequently encountered form; and moving magnetic fields, which are the energy sources in generators and transformers. Other sources include the special devices called transducers, which can convert heat, light, radio waves, mechanical stress, and other forms of energy into electromotive force.

Electrons move through conductors as though the conductors were hollow tubes, instead of solid matter. Except for such relatively unusual phenomena as spark or corona discharges, in which electrons are gained or lost to the air surrounding high-voltage conductors, the number of electrons within a conductor remains so very nearly constant that any difference is ignored.

The load will, at least at some instant, draw energy from the circuit. It may consist of a single simple resistor, or it may consist of some complex arrangement of a number of different kinds of components. Initially, only circuits in which the load consists of resistive circuit elements will be considered, though some relatively complex arrangements of resistors will be included.

KIRCHHOFF'S VOLTAGE LAW.   Consider a simple electric circuit consisting of a single battery as energy source, a single resistor as load, and the two conductors necessary to provide a complete path for the electrons from the energy source, through the load, and back again to the energy source. This is shown both pictorially and schematically in Figure 3-1.

The battery contains chemicals which react with each other in such a way as to cause an excess of electrons to appear at one terminal and a deficiency of electrons to occur at the other terminal. Since the electron is a negatively charged particle, that terminal with the excess of electrons is the negative terminal, while the terminal with the corresponding electron deficiency is the positive terminal.

Figure 3-1   A simple electric circuit. (a) The pictorial view shows the arrangement of components as they actually appear. (b) The schematic shows the same electrical arrangement using symbols to represent the components.

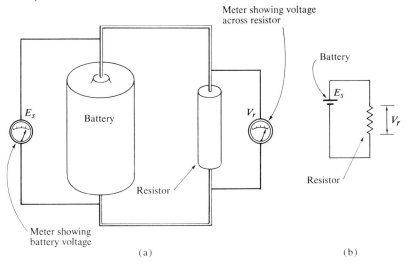

Energy is the ability to do work. The energy produced by the chemical reaction within the battery can cause electrons to do work by moving through some external load. As we have already said, the volt is a work unit. Therefore, the ability of the battery to do work in moving electrons through some external load is measured in volts. This is called a *potential,* since it does not depend on the work actually done. The amount of work actually done depends on both the potential and the nature of the load.

This potential, measured in volts, may also be called an *electromotive force* (emf), since it provides the force to drive the electrons through the load. It is thus correct to say the potential, or emf, of an ordinary flashlight battery is approximately 1.5 V.

This potential will cause current to flow through the load. The amount of current can be calculated by using Ohm's law. This current flowing through a resistance represents power expended in the load. The power expended in the load must be exactly equal to the power produced by the source, and since power is work per unit time, in any unit time the work produced by the source is equal to the work expended in the load.

In the physical reality of the circuit described, the actual movement of charge consists of a flow of negatively charged electrons moving from the negative terminal of the source of potential, through the load, and to the positive terminal of the source. Mathematically, it is not possible to distinguish between this situation and the situation where a hypothetical positive charge would move from the positive terminal of the source through the load to the negative terminal of the source.

Since the two possible mathematical descriptions of the circuit are indistinguishable, either may be used. The movement of negative charges from negative to positive, which corresponds to the physical reality, is called *electron flow*. The movement of positive charges from positive to negative, which is mathematically equivalent, is called *conventional current flow*. Calculations made using either system will have identical results. Conventional current flow was used long before the electron was discovered or before there was any knowledge of the actual physical reality of charge movement. Most engineering texts base all calculations on conventional current flow. We will use both systems.

Consider a hypothetical positive charge moving in the direction of conventional current flow through the circuit of Figure 3-1. Assume it starts at the negative terminal of the battery. Its path is through the battery, then through the conductor to the load, through the load, and back to the starting point. At the beginning it has no potential with respect to its original position, since the potential is a measure of the work that can be done in moving the charge from one position to another.

As the hypothetical positive charge moves through the battery, work is done on it, and as the charge arrives at the positive terminal, it has acquired a potential. For a standard flashlight battery, the potential is approximately 1.5 V. This potential represents the ability to do work and is a consequence of the chemical change that occurred within the battery as the positive charge moved through it.

The charge then moves through the conductor to the load. The charge does no work in moving through the conductor, since the conductor is presumed to have no resistance. The charge must, however, do work to move through the load resistance. The amount of work done must be equal to the amount of work put into the charge in its movement through the battery. This must be true since the positive charge may now move from the lower end of the load resistor to its original position at the negative terminal of the battery freely, with no work involved, since the conductor is presumed to be perfect (without resistance). At this point the positive charge can have no potential, or ability to do work, with respect to its original position, since it is now at its original position.

We may imagine a similar situation in which an elevator raises a weight which then rolls down a slope to its original level. The elevator must put work into the weight to raise it. This work then reappears, often in the form of heat, as the weight rolls down the slope. As the weight reaches its original level it has no more work potential with respect to that level, since the ability of the weight to do work depends on elevation. In the same way, our positive charge can do no more work with respect to its original position at the negative terminal of the battery once it has returned to the energy level of that original position.

An electron moves through a circuit in the same way as the positive charge. The initial position of the electron is at the positive terminal of the source. As it moves through the source, work is done on it, and as the electron reaches the negative terminal, it has a potential to do work, measured in volts. In the case of a flashlight battery, this potential is approximately 1.5 V and is expressed as minus 1.5 V with respect to the positive terminal of the battery.

As the electron moves through the conductor to the load, no work is done, since the conductor is assumed to have no resistance. In moving through the resistance of the load, work must be done. The work put into the electron by the battery now appears as heat in the resistive load. As the electron reaches the positive terminal of the load, all the work put into it by the battery has been transferred to the load. The electron may move through the conductor to the positive terminal of the battery without doing work, since we assume that the conductor offers no resistance. As the electron reaches its original position, it again can have no work potential with respect to that position, for this would, as we have seen, be a contradiction.

In either case—the hypothetical case of a positive charge moving in the direction of conventional current flow and the actual case of a negative charge moving in the direction of electron flow—the change in potential in moving the charge through the circuit from some starting point back to the original position is such as to bring the potential back to the starting value. Whatever potential is gained in such a circuit element as an emf source must be lost in one or more other circuit elements acting as load.

This is true for either a positive or a negative charge, and for a round trip through the circuit in either direction. It is also true where more than one path through the circuit and back to the starting point is possible. It is also true if the path does not go through a voltage source such as a battery, or if it goes through more than one such source. It remains true if more than one load circuit element is in the path, and it does not matter what the circuit element is.

The formal statement of this fact is Kirchhoff's voltage law: *The algebraic sum of the changes in potential encountered in moving through a complete loop in any circuit at any instant equals zero.*

Figure 3-2 A junction is a point in a circuit where two or more conductors are joined together. In any junction, the number of electrons leaving during any time interval must be the same as the number arriving during that same interval. (a) Pictorial view. (b) Schematic.

KIRCHHOFF'S CURRENT LAW. A circuit may have branches. It is a common situation to find two components connected to a common point, with that point connected to some voltage source. If this is the case, an electron coming from the source to that common point may go through one or the other of the components, but not both. This common point is called a *junction*, and is shown both pictorially and schematically in Figure 3-2.

The situation an electron encounters in entering a junction is a little like a car approaching a fork in the road. The car can go down one road or the other, but not both at the same time. On the other hand, if a stream of cars approaches the fork, then some can go down one road and some down the other. If no stopping is permitted on this road, then the number of cars entering the fork in the road at any given time is bound to be the same as the number of cars leaving by the two alternate pathways.

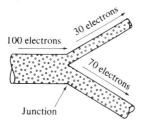

The same is true of electrons, and also of the hypothetical idea of positive charges used in conventional current flow. If, during a given time, one million electrons enter a junction, then during that same time exactly one million electrons must leave the junction. Some will follow one of the two or more paths leading from the junction, while others will follow one of the alternate routes, but the total number of electrons leaving the junction by all the paths available will be exactly equal to the total number entering the junction, even though they may be entering by several paths.

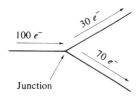

The *coulomb* is the unit quantity of charge, and since the electron is the unit negative charge, the coulomb may also be taken to refer to a specific number of electrons. If that number of electrons enters the junction in one second, then that same number of electrons must leave the junction during that second. That is the same as saying that one coulomb per second flowing into the junction means that there must be one coulomb per second flowing out of the junction, though either the inflow or outflow of electrons may be through more than one conductor.

The *ampere* is defined as the rate of flow of electrons in coulombs per second. Therefore, applying this definition to the previous paragraph, the rate of flow of current in amperes into the junction must be the same as the rate of flow of current in amperes out of the junction. The formal statement of this fact is Kirchhoff's current law: *The algebraic sum of the currents in amperes at any junction at any instant equals zero.*

Problems

1. A simple circuit, consisting of a single complete loop, has a source voltage of 10 V. If the voltage across R_1 is 6 V, what is the voltage across R_2?

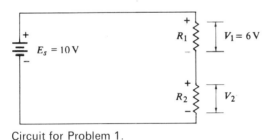

Circuit for Problem 1.

2. If the source voltage in a simple single-loop circuit is 12 V, the voltage across R_1 is 3 V, and the voltage across R_3 is 4 V, what is the voltage across R_2?

Circuit for Problem 2.

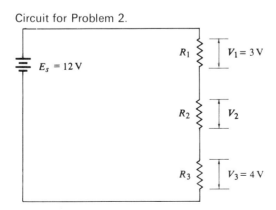

3. Consider the junction of three conductors. If a current of 2 A enters the junction as I_1, and a current of 0.75 A leaves the junction as I_2, what must be the value and direction of I_3?

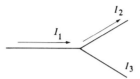

Junction for Problem 3.

4. Consider the junction of four conductors. I_1 is 4 mA, and I_2 is 7.2 mA, both entering the junction. I_3 is 15.6 mA, leaving the junction. What must be the value and direction of I_4?

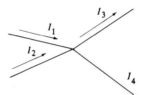

Junction for Problem 4.

5. Some of the values of current and voltage in the more complex circuit shown are noted in the following table. By applying Kirchhoff's voltage and current laws, fill in the remaining values.

Circuit for Problem 5.

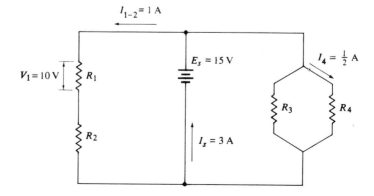

Component	Voltage Across	Current Through
E (voltage source)	15 V	3 A
R_1	10 V	1 A
R_2		
R_3		
R_4		$\frac{1}{2}$ A

3-2
Series Circuits

CURRENT.   A *series circuit* is one in which only one path is possible from any starting point, through the circuit, and back to the original starting point. It may consist of any number of circuit elements, but they must all be connected end to end to form a single complete loop. If the connection between any two circuit elements is considered to be a junction, then the current entering the junction from one circuit element must be exactly the same as the current leaving that junction to enter the next circuit element, by Kirchhoff's current law. Therefore, at that instant, the current flow through those two adjacent circuit elements must be the same.

This same reasoning can be applied to any two adjacent circuit elements, and therefore to all the circuit elements in the series circuit, including the energy source or sources. This leads to the following statement, deduced as a consequence of Kirchhoff's current law and characteristic of all series circuits: *In any series circuit, the current flow in all circuit elements at any instant is the same.*

VOLTAGE.   A series circuit provides only a single path, or loop. By Kirchhoff's voltage law the gains in potential provided by any and all sources in the loop must be exactly matched by losses in potential in all other circuit elements in the loop. Therefore, if we add the potentials in volts of all the sources in the circuit, that voltage will be the same as the sum of all the voltage drops in all the other circuit elements. This will be true regardless of the nature of the sources or their number, or of the nature of the other circuit elements or their number, with the necessary qualification that there must be at least one source and one other circuit element and that all the voltages must be measured at the same instant.

For the simple *resistive series circuit* this means that the sum of the voltage drops across the resistors will be exactly the same as the sum of the source voltages.

Voltage drops across resistive circuit elements are often referred to as

IR drops, since for a resistor or any other circuit element to which Ohm's law applies, $E = IR$.

The sum of the source voltages is an algebraic sum. The single source presents no problem. Two or more sources may, however, be present in more complex circuits. If this is the case, the *polarity* of their connections is important. Multiple sources may be so connected as to all exert a force tending to move charges through the circuit in the same direction, or they may be connected so that some exert a force on charges in one direction while others exert their force in the opposite direction. If the forces are opposing, the net force must be the difference between these opposing forces. A source of potential connected in such a way as to oppose the current flow caused by other sources in the same loop represents a loss of potential, just as does a resistive circuit element in the same loop.

In summary, we can use Kirchhoff's voltage law to state that *the algebraic sum of the voltages in any series circuit, at any instant, equals zero.*

RESISTANCE. Consider a series resistive circuit containing a single voltage source and any number of resistors. Using E to designate the source voltage, and V_1, V_2, and so on to designate the voltage drops across the resistances R_1, R_2, and so on, we have

$$E - V_1 - V_2 \ldots = 0$$

or

$$E = V_1 + V_2 \ldots \tag{1}$$

Suppose the series string of resistors is replaced by a single resistor of the proper resistance so that the current delivered by the source is exactly the same as was delivered to the original series string. So far as the source is concerned, it would be delivering to its load the same current at the same voltage. Therefore, the single resistor of appropriate value would be equivalent to the several resistors it replaced. This resistor may be called the *equivalent load resistor* (R_{eq}), or more frequently, the *total resistance* (R_t). Since the voltage to be applied to this resistor is the original source voltage E, then by Ohm's law

$$E = IR_t$$

where I is the same value as in the original circuit.

In the original circuit the voltage across any resistor is, again by Ohm's law,

$$V = IR$$

Therefore, replacing E in Equation (1) by its equivalent IR_t, and similarly replacing each V by its corresponding IR, we have

$$IR_t = IR_1 + IR_2 \ldots$$

continuing for as many resistors as are in the series string.

But by Kirchhoff's current law the current must be the same in each resistor in the original circuit, and by definition R_t was chosen so that the current through it would be the same as the current in the original circuit. Therefore, we may divide each term in the preceding equation by I, and the result is

$$R_t = R_1 + R_2 \ldots$$

Stated in words, rather than as an equation, this means that *the total resistance of any series circuit is the simple sum of the resistance values composing the circuit.*

It should be noted that the same logic can be applied to a part of a circuit. Any two or more resistors in series with each other may be replaced by a single resistor having a resistance value that is the simple sum of the values of the resistors it replaces. It is important to note that this applies *only* to resistors in series with each other. If the junction between the two resistors has any other circuit element connected to it, then this does not apply. It is, however, the first of the two basic ways by which complex circuits may be simplified for analysis.

POWER. Power has been shown to be the product of voltage and current in electric circuits. Since

$$E = V_1 + V_2 \ldots$$

we may multiply both sides of this equation by the same quantity, I, the current common to each element in the series circuit, including the source. Thus,

$$EI = V_1 I + V_2 I \ldots$$

Each term in the preceding equation represents power. EI is the power delivered to the circuit by the source. $V_1 I$ is the power dissipated in R_1, $V_2 I$ is the power dissipated in R_2, and so on for each resistor in the series circuit. Therefore,

$$P_s = P_1 + P_2 \ldots$$

Stated in words, this means that *the power delivered by the source is the sum of the powers consumed by the elements of the load.*

Problems

1. Given a simple series resistance circuit with $R_1 = 10\,\Omega$, $R_2 = 5\,\Omega$, and $E = 1.5$ V, what is the equivalent resistance? What current will flow through this equivalent resistance? What current will flow through R_1 in the original circuit? What current will flow through R_2 in the original circuit?

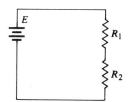

Circuit for Problems 1, 2, and 5.

2. Using the same circuit and values as given in Problem 1, what power in watts is dissipated in each of the resistors, and what is the power in watts delivered by the voltage source?

3. Given a series resistance circuit with $R_1 = 2.7$ kΩ, $R_2 = 10$ kΩ, $R_3 = 6.8$ kΩ, and $E = 25$ V, calculate the current through each resistor and the power in watts dissipated in each.

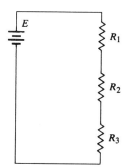

Circuit for Problems 3 and 6.

4. In the circuit shown, $E_1 = 5$ V, $E_2 = 12$ V, $R_1 = 20\,\Omega$, $R_2 = 40\,\Omega$, and $R_3 = 80\,\Omega$. Calculate the current through each resistor. Note the polarity of connection of the two batteries. Are they connected to be aiding or opposing?

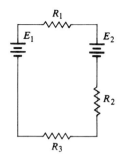

Circuit for Problems 4 and 7.

5. Using the circuit and the current values as calculated in Problem 1, what voltage must appear across each of the two resistors? Does the sum of these two voltages equal the source voltage, as required by Kirchhoff's voltage law?

6. Using the circuit and the values for components as given in Problem 3, calculate the voltage across each resistor, and compare it to the source voltage.

7. Using the circuit and the values for components as given in Problem 4, calculate the voltage across each resistor. Is there a violation of Kirchhoff's voltage law? Explain your answer.

3-3
Parallel Circuits

VOLTAGE.   A *parallel circuit* is one in which multiple paths exist from the source through the circuit and back again to the source. Such a circuit may consist of two or more circuit elements, but they must be connected so that the two terminals of each are connected, respectively, to two common junctions, to which the source is also connected (Figure 3-3). Any two circuit elements which are so connected are said to be in parallel with each other.

In such a circuit a path for the flow of charge carriers may be traced from the source through any single circuit element and back to the source. By Kirchhoff's voltage law the voltage drop across that single circuit element must be the same as the source voltage.

This same reasoning can be applied to any of the parallel connected circuit elements. If the voltage across each is the same as the source voltage, then it must also be true that the voltage across each circuit element must be the same.

RULE   *In a simple parallel circuit, the voltage across each circuit element at any instant is the same, and is the same as the source voltage.*

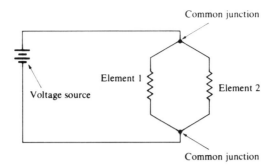

Figure 3-3 In a parallel circuit the current divides, part flowing through element 1 and part through element 2. The source voltage must appear across each element equally, since both are connected directly to the voltage source.

CURRENT. Current from the source flows into one junction, and current from the other junction flows into the opposite terminal of the source. At the first junction the current from the source must be equal to the sum of the currents flowing from the junction to the parallel connected circuit elements joined to it, by Kirchhoff's current law. At the other junction the currents from the parallel circuit elements join to flow into the source, and by Kirchhoff's current law their sum must be equal to the source current. Stated mathematically, this is

$$I_s = I_1 + I_2 \ldots$$

where I_s is the source current and I_1 and I_2 represent the currents through the parallel connected circuit elements. The dots following indicate, of course, that the summation is to be continued for as many circuit elements as are parallel connected.

RULE *The current supplied at any instant by the source to a parallel circuit is the sum of the currents through the individual circuit elements.*

PARALLEL RESISTANCE.

$$I_s = I_1 + I_2 + I_3 \ldots$$

and

$$I = \frac{E}{R}$$

By substitution, therefore,

$$\frac{E}{R_t} = \frac{E}{R_1} + \frac{E}{R_2} + \frac{E}{R_3} + \ldots$$

But as we have seen, E is the same for each parallel connected element and for the source voltage. Dividing each term of the above equation by E, the result is

$$\frac{1}{R_t} = \frac{1}{R_1} + \frac{1}{R_2} + \frac{1}{R_3} + \ldots$$

Since conductance is the reciprocal of resistance, this may be written as

$$G_t = G_1 + G_2 + G_3 + \ldots$$

The total conductance of a parallel circuit is therefore calculated in the same way as the total resistance of a series circuit.

The calculation for the total resistance of a parallel circuit is somewhat more complex. Suppose there are two resistors. Then

$$\frac{1}{R_t} = \frac{1}{R_1} + \frac{1}{R_2}$$

We may solve this equation for R_t, and the result is

$$R_t = \frac{R_1 R_2}{R_1 + R_2}$$

This is correct only for two resistors in parallel with each other. R_t is, as was the case with the series circuit, the total resistance, or the equivalent resistance which could replace resistors R_1 and R_2 without change to either the voltage or current in the rest of the circuit.

The total resistance of a series circuit is the simple sum of the individual resistance values and is, consequently, greater than any of the values of the individual resistors making up the series string.

The total resistance of a parallel bank of resistors is always *less* than the value of the least value of resistance in the bank. This may be verified mathematically, or it may be seen readily from the fact that each resistance added in parallel to another resistor provides an additional path for current flow. Therefore, the source current is increased with each additional resistor in the bank, and, consequently, the equivalent resistance of the bank as a whole is reduced.

POWER.   In a parallel bank of resistors, total current I_s is the simple sum of the individual branch currents. Thus,

$$I_s = I_1 + I_2 + I_3 \ldots$$

Voltage E is the same for each element in the parallel bank, and is equal to the source voltage. Therefore, each term in the above equation may be multiplied by E, and the result is

$$EI_s = EI_1 + EI_2 + EI_3 \ldots$$

But power is the product of voltage and current, $P = EI$. Substituting,

$$P_s = P_1 + P_2 + P_3 \ldots$$

This is exactly the result that was obtained for the series circuit. Again, the power delivered by the source is the simple sum of the powers consumed by the elements of the load.

This has been shown to be true for both simple series and simple parallel circuits. It is also true for any combination of circuit elements, in any configuration, though this is less easily demonstrated.

Problems   **1.**   Given a simple parallel resistance circuit with $E = 10$ V, $R_1 = 600\ \Omega$, and $R_2 = 300\ \Omega$, calculate the total (or equivalent) resistance of the parallel bank. What is the voltage across each resistor? What is the current flow through each resistor? What power is dissipated in each resistor?

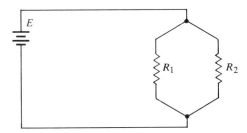

Circuit for Problems 1–3.

2.   Using the circuit of Problem 1 with $E = 25$ V, $R_1 = 4.7\ k\Omega$, and $R_2 = 6.8\ k\Omega$, calculate the total current drawn by the parallel bank and the total power delivered by the source. Compare this total power with the power dissipated in each resistor.

3.   Using the circuit of Problem 1 with $E = 10$ V, $R_1 = 600\ \Omega$, and $R_2 = 300\ \Omega$, what is the conductance in mhos of R_1? Of R_2? What is the total conductance of the parallel bank? Find the total resistance of the parallel bank by taking the reciprocal of the total conductance. How does this result compare with the result obtained by a different method in Problem 1?

4. Consider a circuit with a parallel resistance bank in which $R_1 = 6\ \Omega$, $R_2 = 3\ \Omega$, and $R_3 = 2\ \Omega$. Calculate the equivalent resistance for the parallel bank. *Hint:* Use the product divided by the sum equation for two resistors in parallel to first find the equivalent resistance for R_1 and R_2. Then, using this result, find the total resistance of this equivalent combined with R_3.

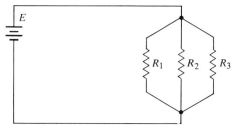

Circuit for Problems 4–6.

5. Using the circuit of Problem 4 with $R_1 = 6\ \Omega$, $R_2 = 3\ \Omega$, and $R_3 = 2\ \Omega$, calculate the equivalent resistance by converting these values to mhos of conductance, summing them, and converting the result to ohms by taking the reciprocal of the total conductance. How does this result compare to the result obtained by a different method in Problem 4?

6. Use the circuit of Problem 4 with $E = 150$ V, $R_1 = 10$ kΩ, $R_2 = 18$ kΩ, and $R_3 = 8.2$ kΩ. Calculate the current through each resistor, the total current drawn from the source, the power dissipated in each resistor, and the total power dissipated.

FIXED RESISTIVE VOLTAGE DIVIDERS.   *A fixed resistive voltage divider is a simple series circuit.* The voltage to be divided is applied to the opposite ends of the series string of two or more resistors. The applied voltage causes current to flow through the resistor string, and since the resistors are in series, the current will be the same in each. Since the voltage is the product of current times resistance, *IR*, the voltage developed across each resistor will depend on its resistance.

A large value of resistance will therefore have a large part of the applied voltage developed across it, and a resistor of smaller value will have a smaller fraction of the applied voltage appear across it. The fraction of the applied voltage that will appear across any resistor in the series string is the same as the fraction of the total resistance represented by the value of the resistor. This may be seen from

$$E_t = V_1 + V_2$$

3-4

Voltage and Current Dividers

where E_t is the applied voltage, and V_1 and V_2 are the voltages across each of the resistors in a two-resistor series string. But

$$V_2 = IR_2$$

and, substituting,

$$E_t = V_1 + IR_2$$

Since $I = V/R$ for any resistor,

$$E_t = V_1 + \frac{V_1}{R_1} R_2$$

Since $R_1/R_1 = 1$, it may be inserted in any term without changing the term's value. Therefore,

$$E_t = V_1 \frac{R_1}{R_1} + \frac{V_1}{R_1} R_2 = R_1 \frac{V_1}{R_1} + R_2 \frac{V_1}{R_1}$$

But V_1/R_1 is common to both terms, so

$$E_t = \frac{V_1}{R_1}(R_1 + R_2)$$

Since $R_1 + R_2 = R_t$, this becomes

$$E_t - \frac{V_1}{R_1} R_t$$

and, solving for V_1, this becomes

$$V_1 = \frac{R_1}{R_t} E_t \tag{2}$$

Thus, the voltage across any resistor in a series string is equal to the source voltage times a fraction which is the resistance of that resistor divided by the total resistance of the series circuit. This is true for two resistors, and it is also true for a series string composed of any number of resistors. In the development of Equation (2), R_2 could have been itself the total value of several resistors, since that total value is the equivalent resistance and would change neither voltage nor current in the rest of the circuit.

POTENTIOMETER VOLTAGE DIVIDERS. The physical construction of potentiometers is described in Section 2-4 and shown in Figure 2-8.

The total resistance is fixed. The resistance between the connection to the center arm and either end terminal depends on the position of the center arm. If the center arm, or wiper, is in the mid position, so that half the total resistance of the element is between the center terminal and the common terminal to which voltage is to be measured, then one-half of the applied voltage will be present between the center and the common terminals.

Similarly, any fraction from zero to the full value of the applied voltage may be present between the center terminal and the common terminal, depending only on the shaft position. Since the wiper arm position depends on a shaft which may be rotated at will, this provides a simple means of controlling precisely a desired voltage while the equipment is in operation. A volume control is a simple application of this device.

It needs to be noted that everything that has been said here applies *only* to unloaded voltage dividers. An *unloaded voltage divider* is one which does not deliver current to a load, but only presents a voltage to some point in a circuit. As soon as current is drawn by a load connected between the common terminal of a potentiometer or fixed voltage divider and the fraction of the resistance across which the voltage is to be divided, the circuit is no longer a simple series circuit, but becomes a combination of series and parallel configurations. This is because the load across the resistance provides an alternate current path, and with the resistance forms a parallel bank.

CURRENT DIVIDERS. *A current divider is a simple parallel circuit.* In a series circuit the voltage developed across each element is directly proportional to the resistance of that element compared to the resistance of the whole. In a parallel circuit the current through each element is directly proportional to the conductance of that branch compared to the conductance of the whole. Thus, by analogy,

$$I_1 = \frac{G_1}{G_t} I_t \tag{3}$$

where I_t is the total current, G_t is the conductance of the entire parallel bank, G_1 is the conductance of the branch through which the current is to be found, and I_1 is that current.

Frequently, the current divider to be considered has only two resistances in parallel. If that is the case, then it is often most convenient to work with resistance values rather than with conductance. The appropriate equation is

$$I_1 = \frac{R_2 I_t}{R_1 + R_2} \tag{4}$$

Note that the value of resistance appearing in the numerator is not the resistance through which flows the current to be solved for, but the other resistor in the parallel bank. Note also that this equation is valid *only* for a bank consisting of two resistors. If more than two resistors are in the bank, then either conductance must be used, or the circuit must be mathematically reduced by combining resistors to their equivalent values until the remaining circuit is a two-resistor bank.

CIRCUIT DUALITY. As we have just seen, the form of the equations describing resistive voltage dividers and resistive current dividers is the same, except that for the series voltage divider, voltage and resistance are used, while for the parallel current divider, current and conductance are used.

This is true, in general, for all series and parallel circuits. Given a statement about one, it may be converted into an equivalent statement about the other by simply interchanging the words *series* and *parallel, voltage* and *current, resistance* and *conductance*. See Table 3-1.

TABLE 3-1 Circuit Comparisons

	Series-Connected Components	Parallel-Connected Components
Duality applies	Current is the same through each component	Voltage is the same across each component
	Total voltage equals the sum of the IR drops $V_t = IR_1 + IR_2 \ldots$	Total current is the sum of the branch currents $I_t = \dfrac{E}{R_1} + \dfrac{E}{R_2} \cdots$
	Total resistance is the sum of the individual resistances $R_t = R_1 + R_2 \ldots$ R_t must be more than the value of the largest resistance, and consequently the total conductance must be less than the value of the smallest conductance	Total conductance is the sum of the individual conductances $G_t = G_1 + G_2 \ldots$ G_t must be more than the value of the largest conductance, and consequently the total resistance must be less than the value of the smallest resistance
	Open in one component prevents current through all components	Open in one component does not prevent current in other components
	Short across one component increases current through other components	Short across one component decreases or eliminates current through other components
Duality does not apply	Total power expended is the simple sum of the powers expended in each component, regardless of how they are connected	
	For all circuits, $P_t = P_1 + P_2 + P_3 \ldots$	

Suppose we are given the following statement: In a series circuit the sum of the voltages equals the supply voltage, and the voltage across a single circuit element is directly proportional to its resistance. This statement may be converted to a dual statement about parallel circuits by changing *series* to *parallel, voltage* to *current,* and *resistance* to *conductance*. Rewritten with these changes, the statement is as follows: In a parallel circuit, the sum of the currents equals the supply current, and the current through a single circuit element is directly proportional to its conductance.

This concept of *duality* of series and parallel circuits not only provides an aid in remembering the basic facts relating to the two types of circuits, but also supplies us with one of the most useful tools for the mathematical analysis of more complex circuits, as will be seen later.

Note that power does not enter into this duality relationship. Power is simply additive, regardless of the circuit configuration. The total power expended individually in the circuit elements adds directly to give the power provided by the source or sources. There can never be more power expended in the circuit than is produced by the source, nor will there ever be more power produced by the source than is expended.

1. In a simple voltage divider with $E_t = 10$ V, $R_1 = 12\ \Omega$, and $R_2 = 24\ \Omega$,   **Problems**
what is V_1 ?

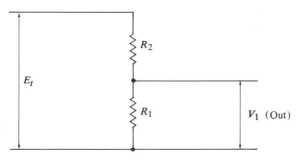

Voltage divider for Problems 1 and 2.

2. In the simple voltage divider of Problem 1, $E_t = 25$ V, $V_1 = 7$ V, and $R_1 + R_2 = 75\ \Omega$. Find the proper values for R_1 and R_2.

3. In the circuit shown, $E_t = 50$ V, $R_1 = 2.8$ kΩ, $R_2 = 4.7$ kΩ, and $R_3 = 10$ kΩ. Find V_1 and V_2.

Voltage divider for Problems 3 and 4.

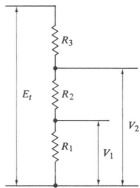

4. In the circuit of Problem 3 $E_t = 100$ V, $R_1 = 1$ kΩ, and $V_1 = 10$ V. If V_2 is to be three times V_1, find the proper values for R_2 and R_3.

5. In a circuit that includes a potentiometer as shown, $E_t = 10$ V. When the shaft of the potentiometer is rotated fully clockwise, wiper arm C is at terminal A of the potentiometer. When the shaft is rotated fully counterclockwise, the wiper arm is at terminal B. What is the output voltage V_{out} for full clockwise rotation? For full counterclockwise rotation? For $\frac{1}{10}$ clockwise rotation? For $\frac{1}{2}$ clockwise rotation? If the resistance of the potentiometer is doubled, what will happen to output voltage V_{out} at $\frac{1}{2}$ clockwise rotation? Why?

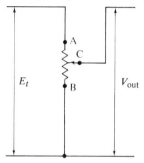

Circuit for Problem 5.

6. Consider a current divider driven by a constant current source. If I_t from the current source is 75 mA, and $R_1 = 100$ Ω, while $R_2 = 50$ Ω, find I_1 and I_2. Using your calculated values, do the currents at junction A sum to zero, as required by Kirchhoff's current law?

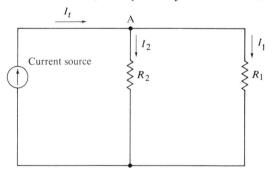

Circuit for Problem 6.

Key Words **battery** an electrochemical energy source that produces an excess of electrons at one terminal of the source

conventional current flow　the movement of positive charges from the positive terminal of a source through the load to the negative terminal of the source. This idea is opposed to the idea of electron flow.

current divider　a parallel circuit in which the current through each element is inversely proportional to the resistance of that element

electromotive force (emf)　potential, or the ability to do work. The force that drives electrons through a circuit

Electron flow　the movement of electrons from the negative terminal of a source through the load to the positive terminal of the source. The opposite of conventional current flow

equivalent load resistor　a single resistor equivalent to a resistor combination

IR **drops**　voltage drops across resistive circuit elements

parallel circuit　a circuit in which multiple paths exist from the source through the circuit and back again to the source

series circuit　a circuit in which there is only a single possible path of current flow

transducer　an energy source that converts heat, light, radio waves, mechanical stress, and other forms of energy into electromotive force

1. An electric circuit is a closed system consisting of an energy source, conductors, and a load.

   Summary of Concepts

2. Kirchhoff's voltage law states that the algebraic sum of the changes in potential encountered in moving through a complete loop in any circuit at any instant equals zero.

3. Kirchhoff's current law says that the algebraic sum of the currents in amperes in any junction at any instant equals zero.

4. Kirchhoff's voltage law states that the algebraic sum of the voltages in any series circuit at any instant equals zero.

5. The total resistance of any series circuit is the simple sum of the resistance values composing the circuit.

6. The power delivered by a source is the sum of the powers consumed by the elements of the load.

7. In a simple parallel circuit, the voltage across each circuit element at any instant is the same, and is the same as the source voltage.

8. The current supplied at any instant by a source to a parallel circuit is the sum of the currents through the individual circuit elements.

9. The total conductance of a parallel circuit is calculated in the same way as the total resistance of a series circuit.

10. The total resistance of a parallel bank of resistors is always *less* than the value of the least value of resistance in the bank.

11. In a parallel bank of resistors total current I_s is the simple sum of the individual branch currents.

12. A statement about a series circuit may be converted to a statement about a parallel circuit, or vice versa, by interchanging the words *series* and *parallel*, *voltage* and *current*, *resistance* and *conductance*. This is the concept of duality.

To Help You Review　　*On a separate sheet of paper, fill in the blanks or answer the questions below. The number following each question refers to the section in the chapter where the correct answer can be found.*

1. The two most common electrochemical energy sources are _____ and _____. (3-1)

2. The chemicals in a battery cause an excess of _____ to appear at its negative terminal. (3-1)

3. What is the difference between electron flow and conventional current flow? (3-1)

4. Describe the movement of an electron through a circuit, with respect to work. (3-1)

5. According to Kirchhoff's voltage law, what happens to potential? (3-1)

6. What happens to an electron when it encounters a junction that branches off a circuit in two different directions? (3-2)

7. During a given time, if exactly one million electrons enter a junction, then exactly _____ electrons will leave the junction. (3-2)

8. The preceding statement is an example of which of Kirchhoff's laws? (3-2)

9. If a number of circuit elements are connected end to end to form a single complete loop, what kind of circuit is formed? (3-2)

10. What is true of the current flow in the circuit elements of any series circuit? (3-2)

11. In a simple resistive series circuit, what statement can you make regarding voltage drops? (3-2)

12. According to Kirchhoff's voltage law, what statement can you make about any series circuit? (3-2)

13. What does the equation $E - V_1 - V_2 - V_3 \ldots = 0$ explain? (3-2)

14. Explain a parallel circuit in terms of terminal connections. (3-3)

15. Complete the following statement: The current supplied at any instant by the source to a parallel circuit is equal to the sum of _____. (3-3)

16. Compare the total resistance of a series circuit with that of a parallel circuit. (3-3)

17. A fixed resistive voltage divider is a simple _____ circuit. (3-4)

18. In a potentiometer the resistance between the connection to the center arm and either end terminal depends on _____. (3-4)

19. What is an unloaded voltage divider? (3-4)

20. In a series circuit the voltage developed across each element is directly proportional to _____. In a parallel circuit the voltage is directly proportional to _____. (3-4)

21. When can the equation $I_1 = \dfrac{R_2 I_t}{R_1 + R_2}$ be used? (3-4)

22. Explain the concept of duality. (3-4)

FOUR

SERIES–PARALLEL CIRCUITS

This chapter will help you understand

☐ how to solve a series–parallel circuit by circuit reduction

☐ special series–parallel circuits such as the balanced bridge circuit

☐ the analysis of defects in series–parallel resistive circuits, especially open circuits, short circuits, changes in value in components, and changes in the characteristics of supply voltages

4-1
Circuit Reduction

THE SERIES–PARALLEL CIRCUIT. A *series–parallel circuit* contains some circuit elements which are in parallel with others, and some which are in series with each other. The variety of configurations of series–parallel circuits is far greater than that of either simple series or simple parallel circuits.

In order to "solve" a series–parallel circuit, the circuit must usually first be reduced to a simpler configuration. If two components are in series with each other, they may be mathematically replaced by a single component having equivalent characteristics. Two resistors in series may be replaced by a single resistor having a resistance equal to the sum of the values of the individual resistors it replaces. Similarly, two resistors in parallel with each other may be replaced by a single resistor having a conductance equal to the sum of the values of conductance of the individual resistors it replaces.

Again, in the case of the parallel configuration, it may not be convenient to work with conductances. The equivalent relationship using resistance, and correct *only* for two resistances, is

$$R_t = \frac{R_1 R_2}{R_1 + R_2}$$

One of the major difficulties to be faced when series–parallel circuits of any degree of complexity are first encountered is the identification of those elements in series with each other, and those other elements which are in parallel with each other. As a first step, if there is a branch point between any two circuit elements, then those two elements are *not* in series with each other. A branch point is the junction or three or more conductors or terminals of circuit elements. Two circuit elements are in series with each other only if the same current flows through each. If there is some third circuit element connected between them, then the current flow through it must either add to or subtract from the current flow through one of the other circuit elements.

A circuit is said to be completely solved when the resistance, voltage, current, and power dissipation are known for each circuit element of the load, and the voltage, current, and power delivered are known for each source in the circuit, together with the proper polarities of voltage and directions of current flow. For a complex circuit this can obviously be a very time-consuming project, but it is seldom necessary in actual practice to completely solve a circuit. Usually, information is needed about only a single circuit element, or a part of the circuit. Sometimes, of course, the process of obtaining a single bit of needed information about a circuit element can involve a nearly complete solution to the entire circuit.

The simplest possible series–parallel configuration is that shown in Figure 4-1. It consists of a single voltage source, two resistors connected in parallel with each other, and a single resistor connected in series with the parallel bank.

None of the resistors has the full source voltage impressed across it. The current from the source to the parallel bank of resistors must also flow through the series resistor, and some of the source voltage will be dropped across this resistor. All of the source current will flow through the single series resistor. The actual voltage that will appear across the parallel bank of resistors will be the source voltage minus the voltage drop across the series resistor. The source current, which is the current through the series resistor, will divide and flow through the parallel resistors. Each of the parallel resistors will have a current flow through it that is inversely proportional to its resistance.

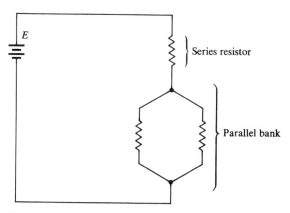

Figure 4-1   Two resistors form a parallel bank. This parallel bank is in series with the single series resistor. The total circuit current flows through the single series resistor, then divides so that part of the total circuit current flows through each of the two resistors in the parallel bank. Part of the source voltage appears across the series resistor, and the remainder of the source voltage appears across the parallel bank.

Figure 4-2 The two resistors forming the parallel bank in Figure 4-1 have been replaced with a single resistor. The value of the resistor replacing the parallel bank is chosen so that the same current as before will flow through the original series resistor, and the total circuit current will be the same as before.

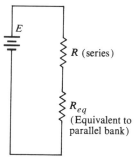

The solution proceeds by steps. The first step is to redraw the circuit as in Figure 4-2, replacing any combinations of two or more resistors, either in series with or parallel to each other, with a single resistor of equivalent value. In the simple configuration just discussed the only combination available for the first step is the two resistors in parallel with each other. The new drawing shows them replaced by a single resistor of appropriate value. This new drawing now shows two resistors in series with each other: the original series resistor and the single equivalent to the parallel bank of resistors.

Now another drawing may be made (Figure 4-3). This time, the two resistors in series with each other may be replaced by a single resistor of appropriate value. This is the final drawing—it now shows only a single source and a single resistor. In this simple circuit only two steps were required to reduce the circuit to a single source and a single resistor. In most circuits more steps will be required. You will save *no* time or effort by attempting shortcuts in this process, especially while you are learning the steps. Each drawing showing a stage of circuit simplification should be carefully made, and the components correctly labeled, since it is necessary to retrace the process from simplicity to complexity, in order to completely solve the circuit.

The final simplification of the circuit (Figure 4-3) shows a single source and a single resistor. Ohm's law gives the relationship between voltage, current, and resistance for a single resistor. If any two of these values are known, the third may be calculated. Usually, though not always, the source voltage is known, and the resistance of the individual resistors composing the original circuit is also known. If this is the case, then the single resistor in the final drawing will have a resistance value already calculated which represents the total resistance of the entire original circuit. From this and the source voltage, the total circuit current can be calculated.

Once this total circuit current is known, the information can be transferred to Figure 4-2, which shows the next-to-final stage of circuit simplification. In this case the drawing shows two resistors in series. One represents the series resistor in the original circuit, while the other is the equivalent resistance that replaced the parallel bank.

In this drawing it is evident that the source current must flow through both of the series resistors. The voltage drop across the original series resistor may now be determined by Ohm's law.

Since in this circuit it is evident from Kirchhoff's voltage law that the source voltage must be the sum of the voltage drops across the two resistors, it is equally evident that the voltage across the resistor equivalent to and substituting for the parallel bank must be the source potential minus the voltage drop across the series resistor.

Once the potential across the resistor equivalent to the parallel bank is known, this information may be substituted in the drawing of the original circuit, Figure 4-1. This is, of course, the potential across each of the two resistors in the original parallel bank, and from this potential the current through each can be calculated. This provides some check on the correctness of the calculations, since the sum of the currents through the resistors of the parallel bank should be equal to the source current, which is the same as the current through the series resistor.

At this point, both current and voltage are known for each resistor in the original circuit. With this information the power dissipated in each resistor may be calculated, and the sum of these powers should be equal to the power produced by the source. This provides a further check on the correctness of the calculations.

A final check of the calculations should be made to determine that the values of voltage and current are in agreement with Kirchhoff's voltage and current laws. Each junction ought to be checked, to see that the sum of the currents entering the junction is equal to the sum of the currents leaving the junction and that each possible loop from the source through the circuit and back to the opposite terminal of the source crosses voltage drops whose algebraic sum is equal to the source voltage.

Figure 4-3 All of the original resistors in the circuit of Figure 4-1 have been replaced by a single resistor. The value of this resistor is chosen so that the total circuit current is the same as in the original circuit.

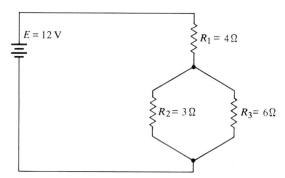

Figure 4-4

EXAMPLE   Given the circuit of Figure 4-4, with $E = 12$ V, $R_1 = 4$ Ω, $R_2 = 3$ Ω, and $R_3 = 6$ Ω, find the total circuit current, the current through each resistor, the voltage across each resistor, and the power expended in each resistor. Compare this power with the power delivered to the circuit by the source.

Solution.   First the original circuit is redrawn, as in Figure 4-5. This drawing shows the two resistors of the parallel bank, R_2 and R_3, replaced by their equivalent resistance, which is

$$R_{eq\ 2\text{-}3} = \frac{R_2 R_3}{R_2 + R_3}$$

$$= \frac{(6)(3)}{6 + 3}$$

$$= \frac{18}{9}$$

$$= 2\ \Omega$$

Now another drawing (Figure 4-6) may be made, with all three resistors of the original circuit combined into a single equivalent, $R_{eq\ 1\text{-}2\text{-}3}$, whose resistance is the simple sum of the two resistance values of Figure 4-5. That is,

$$R_{eq\ 1\text{-}2\text{-}3} = 4 + 2$$

$$= 6\ \Omega$$

By Ohm's law the total circuit current in Figure 4-6 may be easily calculated.

$$I_t = \frac{E}{R_{eq\ 1\text{-}2\text{-}3}}$$

$$= \frac{12}{6}$$

$$= 2\ A$$

Figure 4-5

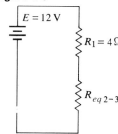

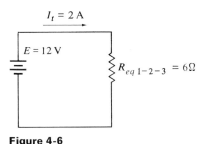

Figure 4-6

But this must be the current through R_1, as seen in Figure 4-7. Therefore, again by Ohm's law, the voltage across R_1 must be

$$V_1 = I_t R_1$$
$$= (2)(4)$$
$$= 8 \text{ V}$$

The voltage across $R_{eq\ 2\text{-}3}$ in Figure 4-7, which is the configuration of Figure 4-5, must be, by Kirchhoff's voltage law,

$$V_2 = E - V_1$$
$$= 12 - 8$$
$$= 4 \text{ V}$$

But voltage V_2 must be the voltage across each of the two resistors in the parallel bank in the original circuit. The original circuit has been redrawn in Figure 4-8 so that the values of voltage and current gained as the result of calculation can be indicated on it. (In a student solution, the circuit need not be redrawn. The values gained by calculation may be entered on the original circuit drawing.)

With the entries thus made, the currents through R_2 and R_3 may both be calculated, using Ohm's law.

Figure 4-7

$$I_2 = \frac{V_2}{R_2} \qquad \text{and} \qquad I_3 = \frac{V_3}{R_3}$$

$$= \frac{4}{3} \text{ A} \qquad\qquad\qquad = \frac{4}{6}$$

$$\qquad\qquad\qquad\qquad\qquad = \frac{2}{3} \text{ A}$$

Now all voltages and currents are known by calculation. By Kirchhoff's current law the sum of the currents at the junctions should be zero. This is the case, since the 2 A entering the upper junction equals the sum of the

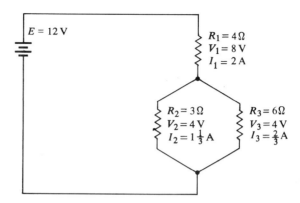

Figure 4-8

currents leaving, while the reverse arithmetic is true at the lower junction. It is also easily ascertained that the sum of the IR drops at any loop is equal to the source voltage.

The power expended in each resistor may be easily calculated by using the power equation, $P = EI$. For each resistor the power expended is

$$P_1 = V_1 I_1 \qquad P_2 = V_2 I_2 \qquad P_3 = V_3 I_3$$

$$= (8)(2) \qquad = (4)\,\frac{4}{3} \qquad = (4)\,\frac{2}{3}$$

$$= 16 \text{ W} \qquad = 5\frac{1}{3}\text{ W} \qquad = 2\frac{2}{3}\text{ W}$$

For the voltage source, the power delivered to the circuit is

$$P = EI_t$$

$$= (12)(2)$$

$$= 24 \text{ W}$$

This is the same as the sum of the power consumed by the resistors in the load, since

$$P_1 + P_2 + P_3 = 16 + 5\frac{1}{3} + 2\frac{2}{3}$$

$$= 24 \text{ W}$$

The solution is now complete, since all resistances, voltages, currents, and powers expended are known, and all are in agreement with the requirements of Ohm's law and Kirchhoff's laws, as well as the principle that energy expended must equal energy produced.

1. Consider a series–parallel circuit with $E = 25$ V, $R_1 = 1$ kΩ, $R_2 = $ **Problems**
1.8 kΩ, and $R_3 = 2.2$ kΩ. Calculate the voltage across each resistor, the
current through each resistor, and the power expended in each resistor.

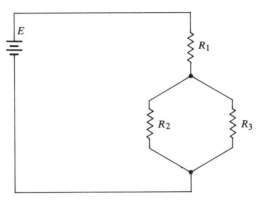

Circuit for Problems 1–4.

2. In the circuit of Problem 1, $E = 85$ V, $R_1 = 33$ kΩ, $R_2 = 47$ kΩ, and
$R_3 = 56$ kΩ. Calculate voltage, current, and power for each resistor.

3. In the circuit of Problem 1, $E = 23.8$ V, $R_1 = 39$ Ω, $R_2 = 47$ Ω, and
$R_3 = 10$ Ω. Calculate the power expended in R_3.

4. In the circuit of Problem 1, $E = 10$ V, $I_t = 1$ A, $R_2 = 30$ Ω, and $V_3 = 6$ V.
Calculate all the remaining voltages and currents, together with all
powers expended in the circuit. *Hint:* Kirchhoff's voltage law allows
some voltages to be deduced directly.

5. Using the circuit shown, with, $E = 18$ V, $R_1 = 10$ Ω, $R_2 = 50$ Ω, and
$R_3 = 30$ Ω, calculate all voltages, currents, and powers expended in the
circuit.

Circuit for Problem 5.

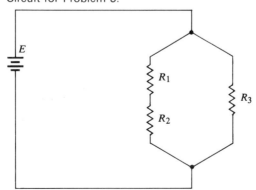

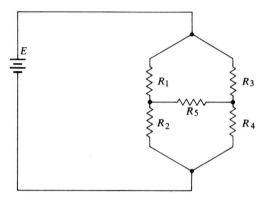

Figure 4-9 The basic bridge circuit cannot be solved by the method of progressive circuit reduction, since no two resistors are in parallel with each other, nor are any two resistors in series.

**4-2
Special Series–
Parallel Circuits**

BALANCED BRIDGES. The basic bridge circuit is shown in Figure 4-9. It is not susceptible to the kind of series–parallel analysis just discussed. Examination of the circuit will show that no two resistors are in series with each other since there are no two resistors which do not have a branch junction between them. In order that two resistors be in parallel with each other, it is necessary that the two terminals of each be connected respectively to two common junctions. Again, this is not the case in this circuit. Analysis of this circuit, while not difficult, cannot proceed by the method of series–parallel circuit reduction we have been using.

There is a special case of the bridge circuit, called the *balanced bridge,* which is of considerable interest because it forms the basic circuit for a number of test instruments. It is also, because of the way it is used, susceptible to our series–parallel analysis.

The simplest form of this circuit is called the *Wheatstone bridge.* In this circuit the center resistor is replaced by a meter capable of showing, with the appropriate polarity, current flow between the two center junctions (Figure 4-10).

In use, at least one of the four remaining resistors is to be adjusted in value until the current flow through the meter is not distinguishably different from zero. At this point the bridge is said to be balanced.

If, at this point, there is no distinguishable current flow between the two interior junctions of the bridge, we could cut the wire connecting the two junctions to the meter without any effect on the zero current through the meter, or on the current through any of the four remaining resistors.

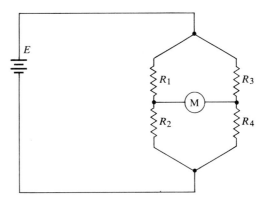

Figure 4-10   The Wheatstone bridge. If R_1 and R_2 divide the source voltage in the same ratio as do R_3 and R_4, then there can be no flow of current through the meter, since there is no difference of potential across it.

If this is done, even as a mathematical fiction, the remaining circuit consists of a simple parallel circuit bank of two branches, each branch of which consists of two resistors in series with each other.

The only condition under which there would be no current flow through the meter (before we cut the connecting wire, of course) would be when there is no potential difference between the two interior junctions of the bridge. This condition occurs if and only if the two branches of the parallel bank act as simple series voltage dividers, dividing the source voltage in the same ratio.

For there to be no potential difference between the two junctions, they must be at the same potential. The potential of either junction compared to a source terminal is given by the equation for a resistive voltage divider:

$$V = E_t \frac{R_1}{R_t}$$

This is true for both parallel branches. Thus, for the voltage dividers to have the same potential to a common point it is sufficient for the following relationship to be true:

$$\frac{R_x}{R_s} = \frac{R_1}{R_2}$$

where R_x and R_s are the two resistors in one series string of the two parallel voltage dividers, and R_1 and R_2 are the two resistors in the other branch of the circuit.

The Wheatstone bridge was originally designed to effect precise comparison measurements of unknown values of resistance by balancing an unknown resistance value R_x against a standard accurate resistor R_s. Then the relationship of interest is

$$R_x = R_s \frac{R_1}{R_2}$$

Obviously, the value of the unknown resistance is obtained by multiplying R_s by the ratio between R_1 and R_2, the two resistors which make up one branch of the original circuit. This series string of the original parallel branch is called the *ratio arm* of the bridge. Usually, in practical test instruments using this circuit, provisions are made for switching in or out of the circuit different values of these two resistors so that the final ratio can be multiplied or divided by powers of ten. This arrangement provides much greater range and flexibility in the use of the instrument.

LOADED VOLTAGE DIVIDERS.   A *loaded voltage divider* is one that delivers current to a load (Figure 4-11). The current through the two resistors that make up the divider is therefore not the same, and the circuit is not the simple divider considered before, but a series–parallel circuit.

Usually, the load current and voltage and the source voltage are known. This leaves the values of the two resistors—the resistor in parallel with the load and the resistor in series between this combination and the source—to be determined.

If the load voltage or current is not subject to variations under operating conditions, it is sufficient to use a single resistor between the source and

Figure 4-11   Unlike the voltage dividers previously considered, this one delivers current to a load. The current through divider resistors R_s and R_b is therefore not the same.

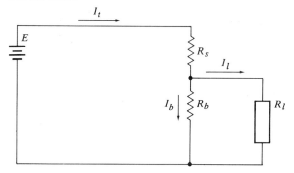

the load so that the load current flowing through that series dropping resistor reduces the source voltage by the desired amount.

However, the load current is often subject to variations in normal operating conditions. At the same time, the voltage to the load should ideally be held as nearly constant as possible. This is the main purpose of placing the resistor in parallel with the load: to maintain the load voltage as nearly constant as is reasonably feasible during normal variations in load current.

Suppose the load current is ordinarily 100 mA, but during the course of normal operation it may vary up or down by 20 mA, ranging from a low of 80 mA to a high of 120 mA. This represents a variation of $\pm 20\%$, and if there is only a single series dropping resistor between the load and the voltage source, then the current through that resistor will have to change by the full 20%. This, of course, means that the voltage dropped across the resistor will fluctuate up or down by the same 20%, being greatest when the load demand is greatest. This voltage, subtracted from the supply voltage, would leave the least voltage for the load when its current demand is greatest.

The purpose of the resistor in parallel with the load is to reduce the effect of this variation as much as is practical. This resistor is often called a *shunt* resistor. The word *shunt* is used in electricity and electronics to describe a circuit element that is used to provide an additional path for current, which is precisely the function of this resistor.

Suppose we choose to use a shunt resistor which will, at the voltage normally supplied to the load, draw a current equal to the load current. In the example just described, that is a current of 100 mA. This current must flow through the series dropping resistor along with the load current, so that the current through the series dropping resistor is 200 mA.

Now suppose the current demand of the load increases by 20%, to 120 mA. If the shunt current stays the same, the current through the series resistor is the sum of the two currents, or 220 mA, an increase of 10%. This 10% increase in voltage drop across the series dropping resistor, subtracted from the source voltage, gives a corresponding decrease in the voltage at the junction between the load and the shunt resistor. But this decreased voltage across the shunt reduces the shunt current, and therefore reduces the contribution this shunt current makes to the current in the series dropping resistor. This has the effect of diminishing the change in voltage across the series dropping resistor. Suppose we choose a situation in which the decrease in voltage at the junction is sufficient to drop the shunt current to 90 mA as the load current increases to 120 mA. The total current through the series resistor is now 210 mA, which is a change of only 5% compared to the 20% change expected without the use of a shunt resistor.

At this point the circuit designer is faced with the kind of conflict that is seemingly inherent in all design work. The design requirements are conflicting. The best regulation is achieved by increasing the shunt current, but this increases the total current through the series resistor and, consequently, the current that must be supplied by the source. This represents power—power that must be delivered by the source and excess power that appears as heat in both the series and shunt resistors. It also represents extra cost, both in the original construction of the circuit and in its operation. The extra cost in the original construction comes from the much higher price of high-power resistors and the costs of mounting them in a chassis, compared to lower-power components. The extra cost of operation comes from the increased demand for electricity and, perhaps more significantly, from the increased deterioration of associated circuit components caused by the excess heat produced by the series and shunt resistors. On the other hand, decreasing the current drawn by the shunt resistor decreases the effectiveness of the voltage regulation at the load and may permit variations in voltage that prevent the equipment from operating properly.

Safety is another reason for using a resistor in parallel with a load where a series dropping resistor is used between the voltage source and the load. In many circuits the component called the capacitor (discussed in detail in Chapter 12) can retain a lethal charge for some time after the equipment has been disconnected from a power source. The resistor in parallel with the load can remove this charge, or "bleed" it off, and is consequently called a bleeder resistor if it is used for this purpose. Most frequently, the resistor serves both purposes.

In the usual calculation the load current and the source voltage are both known. A bleeder or shunt current is assumed, usually 10 mA, though the figure depends on the total circuit current that may be drawn and the need for regulation. From this information the resistance value and power rating for the series dropping resistor and the shunt resistor may be calculated.

EXAMPLE   Consider the circuit of Figure 4-11, where $I_l = 30$ mA, and $V_l = 12$ V. If source voltage $E = 20$ V and bleeder current $R_b = 10$ mA, what values and power ratings should be used for the series and shunt resistors?

Solution. If the load current is 30 mA and the bleeder current is 10 mA, then the current through the series resistor must be the sum of the two, or 40 mA. Since the desired load voltage is 12 V and the source voltage is 20 V, the difference of 8 V must be dropped across the series resistor. Using Ohm's law, its resistance can be calculated as follows.

$$R = \frac{E}{I}$$

$$= \frac{8 \text{ V}}{40 \text{ mA}}$$

$$= 0.2 \text{ k}\Omega$$

$$= 200 \text{ }\Omega$$

The power dissipated in this resistor can be calculated by using the power relationship.

$$P = EI$$

$$= (8)(0.04)$$

$$= 0.32 \text{ W}$$

The nearest standard wattage rating higher than the design value is $\frac{1}{2}$ W, which is therefore the preferred size.

The current through the bleeder resistor was chosen to be 10 mA, and the voltage across it is 12 V. Its resistance is therefore

$$R = \frac{E}{I}$$

$$= \frac{12 \text{ V}}{10 \text{ mA}}$$

$$= 1.2 \text{ k}\Omega$$

$$= 1200 \text{ }\Omega$$

The power dissipated in the bleeder is

$$P = EI$$

$$= (12)(0.01)$$

$$= 0.12 \text{ W}$$

For this low wattage requirement, a $\frac{1}{4}$ watt resistor should be satisfactory.

Suppose the load current is given as 200 mA at a voltage of 140 V. If the source voltage is 300 V and the shunt current is to be 40 mA, what value and power ratings should be used for the series and shunt resistors?

If the load current is 200 mA and the shunt current is 40 mA, then the current through the series resistor is the sum of the two currents, or 240 mA. The voltage drop across the series resistor is the difference between the

300 V supply voltage and the 140 V needed at the load, a difference of 160 V. The resistance of the series resistor is therefore

$$R = \frac{E}{I}$$

$$= \frac{160 \text{ V}}{240 \text{ mA}}$$

$$\cong 667 \ \Omega$$

The power dissipated in this resistor is

$$P = EI$$

$$= (160)(0.24)$$

$$= 38.4 \text{ W}$$

The nearest standard resistance size still greater than the actual heat dissipation for this resistor is 50 W. The value of the resistance according to the calculations is not a standard size, however, and again offers a design problem. We might substitute the standard value closest to the calculated value, and accept the fact that this will give us a slightly different voltage at the load than we had planned on. Using less resistance increases the voltage at the load, while more resistance in the series resistor decreases it. In many cases this change in design load voltage is perfectably acceptable.

But if no variation in load voltage design value is acceptable, then the designer must make one of three possible choices. (1) He must specially order the resistor. (2) He must specify a resistor that can be adjusted to the desired value. (3) He must construct a resistance of the proper value by using two or more standard size resistance values in series or parallel.

If the third choice is made, as it may well be where only a single circuit of this design is to be constructed and mass production is not anticipated, then a new calculation will show that the voltage and power will both be divided between series resistors forming an equivalent, and current and power will be divided between parallel resistors forming an equivalent to the desired resistance.

Three 2 kΩ resistors will give the desired value if they are connected in parallel. If this is the case, then the full voltage of 160 V will appear across each resistor, but the current will divide evenly and each resistor will have a current flow of 80 mA through it. The necessary wattage rating for any one of the three is

$$P = EI$$

$$= (160)(0.080)$$

$$= 12.8 \text{ W}$$

Another possible solution is to use a 500 Ω resistor in series with a 180 Ω resistor, giving approximately the desired value. If this is done, the full design current of 240 mA will flow through each, and the power dissipation in each will be

$$P = I^2 R$$

$$= (0.24)^2 (500)$$

$$= (0.0576)(500)$$

$$= 28.8 \text{ W for the } 500 \text{ Ω resistor}$$

$$P = I^2 R$$

$$= (0.24)^2 (180)$$

$$= (0.0576)(180)$$

$$= 10.4 \text{ W for the } 180 \text{ Ω resistor}$$

This, too, is a possible solution. The solution of choice depends on a number of factors—the availability of resistors, the accuracy needed, the number of circuits to be built according to the design, the mounting space available for the resistors chosen, and so forth.

CIRCUIT GROUNDS AND POSITIVE AND NEGATIVE SUPPLIES. If the negative terminal of the voltage source is connected to the chasis and if all points in the circuit that are to be connected to the negative terminal are connected to the chassis, then the chassis serves as the conductor between these points and the negative supply voltage. If this is the case, the chassis is considered to be at "ground" potential, and all other potentials in the circuit are usually measured with respect to this ground. In this simple example nearly all other circuit potentials would be positive compared to ground.

Since electrons flow from the negative terminal of a voltage source through the external load or loads and back to the positive terminal of the source, the ground is actually the source of electrons to the circuit. Electron flow is from the chassis through the circuit to the positive terminal of the source. Through the voltage source these electrons are returned to ground.

In many circuits the positive terminal of the voltage source is connected to the chassis, and the electron flow is then from the negative terminal of the source, through the load or loads, to the chassis. The electrons then return through the chassis to the positive terminal of the source. In this case nearly all circuit potentials will be negative compared to the ground.

A voltage source is considered to be a positive source if its negative terminal is connected to the common ground. The source is considered to be negative if its positive terminal is connected to the common ground.

Some circuits require both positive and negative supply voltages for proper operation. A simple way of providing the necessary operating voltages from a single supply source is shown in Figure 4-12.

The supply voltage in this circuit is 20 V, and there are two loads. One requires 20 mA at +8 V for its proper operation, while the other requires 30 mA at −12 V. It is also desired that each load have a bleeder resistor drawing not less than 10 mA.

Since the sum of the voltages required, without regard to their polarity, is equal to the supply voltage, there is no need for a series dropping resistor. Instead, two parallel bleeder resistors, one from each terminal of the supply voltage, connected to a common ground, are sufficient.

The proper value of the two bleeder resistors can be determined by application of Kirchhoff's current law. As a preliminary step, assume the current in each bleeder will be 10 mA, the minimum acceptable value. If this assumption is made, then the positive supply terminal will deliver 30 mA, while the negative supply terminal current will be 40 mA. This is not possible, since the current into one side of the supply must be the same as the current out the other. The current from the negative side of the supply cannot be made less than 40 mA because this would make the bleeder current less than 10 mA, the agreed-on minimum. Therefore, the current to the positive terminal must be increased to equal the 40 mA negative terminal current.

Figure 4-12   Positive and negative supply voltages. Since the two grounds must be at the same potential, the voltage drop across R_{b1} must be the same as the voltage drop across the positive load, and the voltage drop across R_{b2} must be the same as the voltage drop across the negative load.

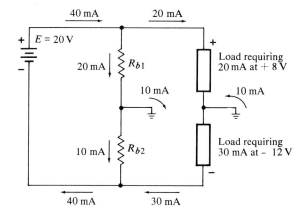

This puts the positive supply terminal current at 40 mA, and since its load current is 20 mA, its bleeder current must, by Kirchhoff's current law, be the other 20 mA.

If the junction of the two bleeder resistors is to be connected to the common ground and the junction of the two loads is also to be connected to the common ground, the two junctions must be at the same potential. That potential is the reference potential, against which all others are measured. The positive terminal of the supply is to be 8 V positive with respect to the ground, while the negative terminal is to be 12 V negative with respect to ground.

These same potentials must apply to the two bleeder resistors, since they are in parallel with their loads. If the current flow through the bleeder resistor between the positive supply voltage and ground is carrying 20 mA at a potential of 8 V, then its resistance and power dissipation must be

$$R = \frac{E}{I} \qquad\qquad P = EI$$

$$= \frac{8\text{ V}}{20\text{ mA}} \qquad\qquad = (8)(0.02)$$

$$= 400\ \Omega \qquad\qquad = 0.16\text{ W}$$

The resistor connected between the negative side of the supply and ground carries 10 mA at a potential of 12 V. Its resistance and power rating must be

$$R = \frac{E}{I} \qquad\qquad P = EI$$

$$= \frac{12\text{ V}}{10\text{ mA}} \qquad\qquad = (12)(0.01)$$

$$= 1200\ \Omega \qquad\qquad = 0.12\text{ W}$$

These values provide the desired result, with the proper polarity and supply voltage for each element of the load.

Problems

1. Consider a balanced bridge in which $R_1 = 1000\ \Omega$, $R_2 = 10\text{ k}\Omega$, and $R_3 = 3.72\text{ k}\Omega$. Find the value of R_4.

2. In the circuit of Problem 1, $R_1 = 1000\ \Omega$, $R_2 = 100\ \Omega$, and $R_3 = 2.91\text{ k}\Omega$. Find the value of R_4.

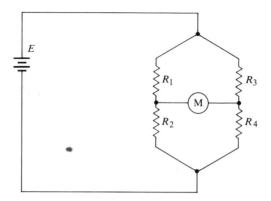

Circuit for Problems 1 and 2.

3.   Consider a loaded voltage divider in which the source voltage is 25 V. A bleeder current of 10 mA through R_2 is desired. If the load voltage is to be 20 V, and the load current 50 mA, find the proper resistance and wattage rating for both R_2, the bleeder resistor, and R_1, the series resistor.

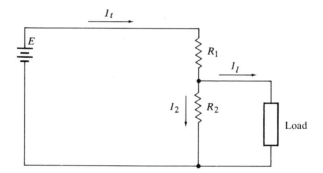

Circuit for Problems 3 and 4.

4.   The circuit of Problem 3 has a source voltage of 300 V. If the load voltage is to be 180 V and the load current 100 mA, find the proper resistance and wattage rating for both R_2 and R_1. Assume a bleeder current of 15 mA.

5.   Consider a circuit designed to provide a positive voltage to one load and, simultaneously, a negative voltage to another load. The source voltage is 100 V. The load to which the positive voltage is supplied requires 75 V at 40 mA. The load to which the negative voltage is supplied requires 25 V at 60 mA. Assume a 10 mA minimum bleeder current. What are the proper resistance and wattage values for R_1 and R_2?

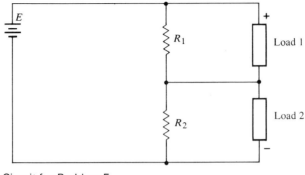

Circuit for Problem **5**.

VOLTAGE ANALYSIS. A limited number of types of defects can occur in series–parallel resistive circuits. Typical defects include open circuits, short circuits, changes in value of components, and changes in the characteristics of the supply potentials.

4-3
Series–Parallel
Analysis—Defective
Circuits

Open circuits are points within a circuit at which a break occurs, such as an open switch. An open circuit may occur within a component, as in the case of a resistor where overheating or a physical shock may cause a crack to interrupt the flow of electrons. Such a break may also occur in the connecting wires. In a printed circuit board, hairline cracks due to flexing of the board are particularly troublesome, since they are difficult to see.

Short circuits are unwanted connections between points in the circuit. Short circuits are unlikely with printed circuit wiring or with any modern solid state circuits, but may and do occur when point-to-point wiring (separate individual wires soldered between discrete components) is used. One of the most common causes of short circuits, aside from the easily observed screw or loose nut falling into a switch, is thermoplastic insulation in point-to-point wiring. If two wires are adjacent, and if there is some mechanical stress due to their positioning, then with time the insulation may actually flow away between them so that they make electrical contact with each other. This can be particularly annoying, since to a casual inspection the insulation separating the two wires may appear normal. Ordinary troubleshooting techniques will pinpoint the electrical location of the short, and careful inspection will show its physical location. Once found, it is easily corrected.

Changes in value of resistors are likely to show up only as an increase. Many things can go wrong with resistors, but they all tend to increase the value of the resistance. The only way an ordinary resistor will show significantly less than its marked resistance, making allowance for manufacturing tolerances, is if it has been mismarked at the factory. This occurs rarely, but it is not unknown.

In the case of some wire-wound resistors, adjacent turns of the resistance wire may come into contact with each other, thus providing an internal short circuit which bypasses part of the resistance. In the case of any of the standard brands of resistors, where the wire is wound on a ceramic tube and coated with a heat resistant material, this kind of defect is very rare.

Changes in the values of components do occur, but in the case of resistors are almost entirely confined to the type of construction where a carbon–kaolin pellet is encased in plastic. This is the most frequently encountered construction in resistors rated at 2 W or less. To repeat, changes in value will be increases, not decreases, and a component showing such change should be replaced, since it will almost always change further if it is not.

Changes in the characteristics of the supply voltage will in most cases cause corresponding changes in the operation of the circuit to which the supply voltage provides power. But this is a two-way street. Changes in the amount of power drawn by the circuit due to shorts, opens, or changes of value of components within the circuit will often cause changes in the supply voltage and current.

OPENS IN SERIES STRINGS. An open circuit occurring anywhere in a series string of resistors will stop all current flow through each element of the string. This means that for each resistor in the string the IR drop will be zero, and whatever potential exists at one terminal of the resistor with respect to the point of reference for voltage measurements (usually the chassis) will also exist at the other terminal.

Suppose a series string of four resistors has a break in the conductor between the two center resistors, as in Figure 4-13. If the negative side of the supply voltage is connected to the chassis as a common ground, then resistors R_1 and R_2, in series with the positive terminal, will show the full source voltage, measured to the chassis ground, at either of their terminals. Resistors R_3 and R_4 will be at ground potential for each of their terminals.

If the break is at the center of a conductor, then a voltmeter will measure the full supply potential between one end of the conductor and the other. This is a certain indication of a break in continuity, because if the conductor is intact, the voltage measured from one end of it to the

Figure 4-13 With an open circuit in a series string, no current can flow. Therefore, there can be no voltage drop across any of the resistors. With no voltage drops present, the full source voltage must appear across the break.

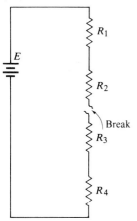

other will be very close to zero. Remember that because all conductors have some resistance, however slight, any conductor carrying current will show some potential drop, but it certainly should not be the full supply potential.

OPENS IN PARALLEL BANKS. Troubleshooting an open circuit condition in a bank of parallel connected resistors can be much more difficult than is the case with the series string. If one of several resistors in a parallel bank is open, there will ordinarily be no significant change in the potential measured across any of the resistors, provided that the bank is a simple parallel circuit and not connected to the source through a series dropping resistor.

If there is an open circuit in one resistor of such a parallel bank, the total equivalent resistance of the bank will go up, since one of the alternate paths for current flow has been removed. The current drawn by the bank as a whole will be reduced. If the current from the source to the parallel bank does not have a significant series resistance, there will be little change in the voltage across the parallel bank, though any change observed will be an increase. If there is significant series resistance between the voltage source and the parallel bank, then the current through that series resistance will be decreased, and the voltage measured across it will also be decreased. This means that the voltage across the parallel bank will increase.

The amount by which these changes in potential occur depends, of course, on the values of resistance in the circuit, the supply potential, and the amount by which a single open resistor changes the total resistance of the parallel bank. If the open resistor is of high value compared to the rest of the bank, the change will be slight. If the open resistor is the one with the least value in ohms, and therefore the one ordinarily carrying the greatest current, the change will be considerable and almost always detectable with a voltmeter.

Since an open circuit in one resistor of a parallel bank that is connected to a voltage source through series resistance has the effect of increasing the voltage across the bank, it will also increase the current through the remaining resistors of the bank. This increases the wattage dissipation actually occurring in these resistors, and may exceed their design limitations. The consequent overheating may damage them and cause them to become open also or to display increased resistance. Whether this occurs or not depends on how much the open condition in one resistor of the parallel bank has caused the current flow through the others to increase.

SHORTS IN SERIES STRINGS.   A short circuit may occur across a single component, in effect connecting its two terminals together, or it may occur from any point in a circuit to the circuit common ground. It may, though less commonly, occur between any two points in the circuit not at the same potential.

If a single resistor in a simple series string is "shorted out," it is, in effect, bypassed by the path of current flow. The total resistance of the series string is decreased since this one resistor has effectively been replaced by a conductor, and therefore the total current flow through the circuit increases. Since each of the other resistors in the circuit is carrying more current than before, the IR drop across each also increases. A voltmeter will show a higher than normal IR drop across each resistor in the string which is operating normally, and no voltage at all across the one short-circuited resistor. Again, the increased current flow caused by the one defective resistor may damage the other resistors. Whether or not damage will occur depends on whether or not the increased current exceeds the allowable wattage dissipation of the individual resistors.

A short to ground in a series circuit causes an increase in current in all the resistors in the string between the point at which the short occurs and the "hot" terminal of the supply source. The hot terminal is, of course, the one not connected to ground, and may be either the positive or negative terminal, depending on the configuration of the supply.

A short to ground causes an increase in the potential across and, consequently, the current through any such resistors. It also causes an increase in the current delivered by the power source.

A short to ground is the condition most likely to cause damage to other components, including the power source. If the power source is protected by a fuse, this malfunction in the circuit often causes the fuse to blow. If the fuse does not blow, or if the circuit is unfused, damage can be expected, particularly if the circuit has been operating for any length of time with the short existing.

At the point where the short occurs, and at both terminals of any resistors connected between that point and the common ground, there will be no current flow and no potential to ground. This condition is the same as with an open in a series string—all the resistors between the point of the defect and the common ground read zero voltage to ground. The distinguishing difference between the two situations is between the point of the defect and the hot side of the source voltage. With an open in a series string, the resistors on the hot side of the point of defect will all read full source potential to ground at both terminals, and the full source voltage will be read across the defect. With a short in a series string, all the resistors on the hot side of the point of defect will carry an inordinately high current, and therefore the voltage drop across each of them will be higher than normal.

SHORTS IN PARALLEL BANKS.   The change in voltages observed in short circuit in a parallel bank offers a clear indication of the nature of the difficulty. Either a short to ground at the hot end of the bank or a short from one common terminal of the parallel bank to the other will result in all the current flowing through the short, not through any of the resistors in the bank. The potential measured across the bank (from one terminal to the other) or from either terminal to ground will be zero.

If there is no series resistance between the point of defect and the source voltage, then the power source is effectively short-circuited, and the current demand on it will be excessive. Again, this will blow fuses or damage the components of the voltage source. If there is a series resistance, then the full source voltage will appear across it, and the current through it will be excessive. If the situation exists for any length of time, then it is possible the series resistor will be damaged. The resistor may show an increase in resistance, or the excessive sudden heat within it may crack the carbon–kaolin pellet so that the resistor "opens up," becoming an open circuit itself.

Troubleshooting technicians often believe that defects occur singly, that is, if the equipment quits working, there is a single cause. This is not always true. As we have seen, shorts may damage adjacent series components, while opens may damage adjacent parallel components. When an open or shorted condition is discovered in a circuit, it is necessary to consider whether the defect may have caused other damage in the circuit or whether the defect may have been caused by some prior malfunction.

CHANGED VALUE COMPONENTS.   If a resistor in a simple series string increases in value for any reason, the total resistance of the string will be increased, and consequently the current through each component in the string will decrease. The voltage across each component *except the defective one* will also decrease. The potential across the defective component may decrease, stay the same, or increase, depending on how much the resistance of the defective component increases. The larger the percentage increase in resistance, the greater the proportion of the source voltage that will appear as a voltage drop across the defective resistor. If the voltages are measured to ground as a reference, as they usually are, the actual potential across a resistor is the difference between the potential to ground of one terminal of the resistor and the potential to ground of the other terminal.

If a resistor in a simple parallel bank increases in value for any reason, the potential across it and across all other resistors in the same bank will be unchanged. The total resistance of the bank will increase, and the amount of current drawn by the bank from the source will be reduced.

If the parallel bank is connected to the source through a series resistance, then the current through the series resistance will decrease if the value of a resistor in the parallel bank increases. The amount of decrease may be slight, even with a considerable increase in the value of the resistance in the bank, since the other pathways in the same bank are unchanged. If the other pathways were carrying most of the current because of their lower design resistance, a change in the contribution to that current by a single higher-than-normal-value resistor may be within the voltage tolerance of the circuit anyway.

If the current through the individual circuit elements of the parallel bank can be measured, or if the resistance of the individual resistors can be determined, the defect can be easily isolated. This usually requires that at least one terminal of the suspected component be disconnected from the rest of the circuit.

Problems   1. In the series circuit shown, all resistors are 1000 Ω. Voltage measurements taken with respect to the negative terminal of the voltage source give readings of 10 V for points A, B, C, and D. Points E through H give readings of 0 V. What is the nature of the defect and what is its location?

Circuit for Problems 1 and 2.

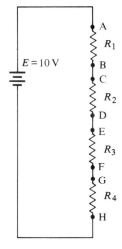

2. All resistors in the series circuit of Problem 1 are 1000 Ω. Voltage measurements taken with respect to the negative terminal of the voltage source give readings of 10 V for points A, B, and C. Points D through H give readings of 0 V. What is the nature of the defect and what is its location?

3. In a simple parallel bank containing three resistors $R_1 = 2$ kΩ, $R_2 = 3$ kΩ, and $R_3 = 6$ kΩ. The source voltage is 10 V. If the circuit is operating normally, what total current will be read by the milliam-meter? If R_1 is open, what will be the reading of the milliammeter? How will this open condition affect the voltage across each of the components? If R_2 is open and the other resistors normal, what will the reading on the milliammeter be? Suppose R_3 opens while the other resistors are unchanged. What is the new reading on the milliam-meter? What will happen to the voltage across the resistors if all three open up?

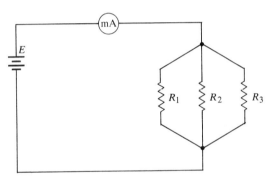

Circuit for Problem 3.

4. In a simple series string of three resistors, $E = 10$ V and $R_1 = R_2 = R_3 = 1$ kΩ. With the circuit operating normally, what voltage will be read from point B to the negative terminal of the voltage source? What is the expected voltage from point C to the negative source terminal? Actual measurements give the potential from B to the negative source terminal as 5 V, and the potential from C to the negative source terminal as 0 V. What circuit defect, if any, is indicated by these measurements, and where is it probably located?

Circuit for Problems 4 and 7.

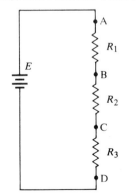

5. Consider a simple parallel bank of two resistors with $E = 12$ V, $R_1 = 3$ kΩ, and $R_2 = 6$ kΩ. The milliammeter is connected to read total circuit current. What reading can be expected on the milliammeter with the circuit operating normally? If the reading obtained is 2 mA, is a circuit defect indicated, and if so, what is the most likely cause?

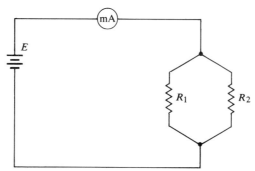

Circuit for Problems 5, 6, and 8.

6. In the circuit of Problem 5, what reading can be expected on the milliammeter if R_1 is short-circuited? Use the values of components as given in Problem 5. What will occur if R_2 is short-circuited? Could a shorted condition in one of the resistors cause damage to any other components in the circuit? If so, what precautions might be taken to prevent such damage?

7. In the circuit of Problem 4, $E = 10$ V, and $R_1 = R_2 = R_3 = 1$ kΩ. These are the values as shown on the schematic of the circuit, but measurements taken on the actual circuit show the voltage from A to D to be 10 V, the voltage from B to D to be 5 V, and the voltage from C to D to be 2.5 V. Do these readings indicate something wrong with the circuit? If so, what is the nature of the defect, and where is it most likely to be?

8. In the circuit of Problem 5, $E = 12$ V, $R_1 = 3$ kΩ, and $R_2 = 6$ kΩ. These are the values as shown on the schematic of the circuit. Current measurements taken with the milliammeter in the position shown indicate a total circuit current of 4 mA. Assuming only one faulty component in the circuit, what is the most likely defect? How can measurements be taken that would indicate without doubt the nature and location of the defect?

9. Consider a series–parallel circuit with $E = 12$ V, $R_1 = 2$ kΩ, $R_2 = 3$ kΩ, and $R_3 = 6$ kΩ. What voltage readings can be expected from point A to the negative terminal of the voltage source under the following conditions?

   a. Component values the same as the schematic values.

   b. R_1 open.

   c. R_2 open.

d. R_3 open.

e. R_1 doubled in value.

f. R_2 doubled in value.

g. R_3 doubled in value.

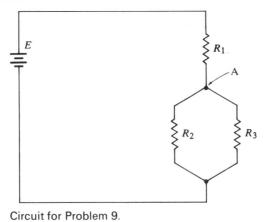

Circuit for Problem 9.

10. Consider a series–parallel circuit in which $E = 100$ V, $R_1 = 4.7$ kΩ, $R_2 = 2.2$ kΩ, $R_3 = 10$ kΩ, $R_4 = 820$ Ω, and $R_5 = 3.9$ kΩ. Using these values, calculate the voltages to be expected between points A, B, and C, and the negative terminal of the voltage source.

Circuit for Problems 10–16.

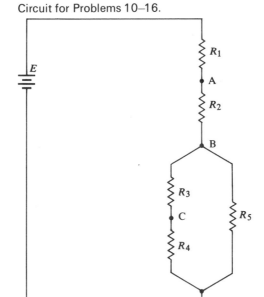

11. What would the voltage readings of Problem 10 be if R_1 is open-circuited? If R_2 is open? If R_3 is open? If R_4 is open? If R_5 is open?

12. What would be voltage readings of Problem 10 be if point A is shorted to ground (to the negative terminal of the voltage source)? If Point B is shorted to ground? If point C is shorted to ground?

13. What would the voltage readings of Problem 10 be if the value of R_2 increased to 15 kΩ?

14. If the value of R_3 in Problem 10 increased to 100 kΩ, which voltage values would increase? Which would decrease?

15. Is there a single circuit defect in the circuit of Problem 10 which would cause the voltage at point B to equal the source potential?

16. What could cause the voltage at point A in the circuit of Problem 10 to equal the source potential?

Key Words   **balanced bridge**   forms the basic circuit for a number of test instruments
bleeder resistor   a resistor in parallel with a load, which removes or "bleeds off" a charge that remains after the equipment has been disconnected from its power source
internal short circuit   may occur when adjacent turns of resistor wire in a wire-wound resistor come into contact with each other
loaded voltage divider   delivers current to a load
open circuit   a point within a circuit at which a break occurs, such as an open switch
series–parallel circuit   contains elements in series with each other and elements parallel to one another
short circuit   an unwanted connection between points in a circuit
shunt resistor   a resistor in parallel with the load, whose purpose is to reduce the effects of voltage variation
Wheatstone bridge   the simplest form of balanced bridge circuit, in which a meter replaces the center resistor and shows the current flow between the two center junctions

Summary of Concepts

1. A circuit is said to be completely solved when the resistance, voltage, power, and current dissipation are known for each circuit element of the load, and the voltage, current, and power delivered are known for each source in the circuit, together with polarities of voltage and directions of current flow.

2. A bridge is said to be balanced when a meter replacing the center resistor shows that the current flow is not distinguishably different from zero.

3. A voltage source is considered positive if its negative terminal is connected to the common ground. A voltage source is considered negative if its positive terminal is connected to the common ground.

4. Defects in series–parallel resistive circuits include (1) open circuits, (2) short circuits, (3) changes in value of components, and (4) changes in the characteristics of the supply potentials.

5. In a resistor a change in value is almost always positive.

6. Changes in the characteristics of the supply voltage cause corresponding changes in the operation of the circuit.

7. An open circuit in a series string of resistors stops all current flow.

8. If one of several resistors in a parallel bank is open, there is ordinarily no significant change in the potential across any of the resistors.

9. A short to one resistor in series decreases the total resistance of the series string.

10. A short to ground in a series circuit causes an increase in current.

11. A short in a parallel bank causes a change in voltage.

12. Voltage in a series string usually decreases across all the components except the defective one.

13. If a resistor in a simple parallel bank increases in value, the potential across it will be unchanged, the total resistance will increase, and the amount of current drawn from the source will be reduced.

On a separate sheet of paper, fill in the blanks or answer the questions below. The number following each question refers to the section in the chapter where the correct answer can be found.   **To Help You Review**

1. What do we need to know to be able to say that a circuit is completely solved? (4-1)

2. What is a series–parallel circuit? (4-1)

3. The simplest series–parallel configuration consists of (1) _____, (2) _____, and (3) _____. (4-1)

4. In order for two resistors to be parallel, the two _____ must be connected to two common _____ . (4-2)

5. What replaces the center resistor in a Wheatstone bridge? (4-2)

6. What word describes a circuit element that provides an additional path for current? (4-2)

7. What term is used to describe the process of removing a charge that remains after the source of power has been removed? (4-2)

8. Under what circumstance is a chassis considered to be at ground potential? (4-2)

9. List four defects that can occur in series–parallel resistive circuits. (4-3)

10. Name the defect caused by each of the following: (4-3)

    (a) a crack in a resistor

    (b) adjacent turns of resistance wire coming into contact

    (c) hairline cracks on a printed circuit board

    (d) a loose nut falling into a switch

    (e) thermoplastic insulation in point-to-point wiring

11. How does a change of value affect a resistor? (4-3)

12. What type of resistor is most likely to undergo a change of value? (4-3)

13. Match the lettered defects on the left with the numbered probable results on the right. (4-3)

    (a) Series resistor increases in value.

    1. All current flow through each element stops.

    (b) Open circuit occurs in a series string of resistors.

    2. No significant change in the potential across any of the resistors occurs.

    (c) A single resistor in series is shorted out.

    3. Total resistance is decreased.

    (d) One of several resistors in a parallel bank is open.

    4. Total resistance is increased and the amount of current drawn is reduced.

(e) A short to ground exists in a series circuit.

5. A current increase in all resistors between the trouble spot and the "hot" terminal occurs.

(f) A parallel resistor increases in value.

6. The voltage across each component—except the defective one—decreases.

FIVE
DC VOLTAGE SOURCES

This chapter will help you understand

- [ ] the characteristics of voltage sources
- [ ] voltage sources connected in series or parallel
- [ ] how chemical reactions in a cell provide electrical energy
- [ ] the chemistry of different types of primary and secondary cells

5-1 Black-Box Voltage Sources

VOLTAGE SOURCE CHARACTERISTICS. A theoretically perfect voltage source would be capable of delivering to any load a fixed voltage at any current drawn by the load, and for any length of time. No such voltage source exists, though in practical terms a local power utility can come quite close.

The power sold by electric utility companies is not dc, and is seldom directly usable by electronic circuits. Instead, the power as received must be converted to the desired dc voltage, usually within the equipment containing the electronic circuitry which is to be operated by the power. The circuit which makes this conversion is called the *power supply* and is what we have been referring to as the voltage source.

Voltage sources may be separated into two broad categories, though each category may be further subdivided. One category is that which receives its power from some external source on a continuing basis. The power supply of the preceding paragraph is an an example of this. So long as the external source is operating and connected to the power supply, the power supply can, in turn, continue to provide power to the electronic circuit of which it is a part.

The other category of power supply is the self-contained, in which the total energy is fixed. A flashlight battery is an example of this category. It contains just so much energy, and when this is expended, it cannot continue to operate the flashlight. Nearly all portable voltage sources are in this category.

Where a voltage source, such as a battery of any type, has such a limit to the total energy, that limit is an important characteristic of the source. Since $P = EI$, the power at a reasonably constant voltage is directly proportional to current I. Power is work per unit time. Total work is work per unit time, multiplied by time. Thus, the total work that can be done by a battery at a fixed voltage is the product of the length of time it can deliver some stated current, multiplied by the current in amperes. The time unit usually used is the hour, and the total energy available is given in ampere–hours.

INTERNAL RESISTANCE OF A SOURCE. Except for symbols in a book, or sketched on a blackboard, there is no such thing as a perfect voltage source. All practical voltage sources must contain internal conductors which cannot have zero resistance, and all must depend on the rate at which some chemical reaction can occur or on the conductivity of the circuit elements which enable it to perform its function.

This internal resistance may, in actuality, represent the total of some rather complex phenomena. Fortunately it can, at least to a close approximation, be lumped as a single circuit constant. The usual equivalent to a practical voltage source is a perfect voltage source with a series resistor connected internally between the perfect source and its external terminals (Figure 5-1). Whatever current flows from the external terminals of this equivalent source containing the internal series resistance must flow through this resistance. The potential of the perfect source is considered to be fixed regardless of the current drawn by the load. The load current, in flowing through the internal equivalent resistance of the source, will cause an IR drop across that resistance. This IR drop represents a value to be subtracted from the perfect voltage source potential to find the actual potential at the external terminals of the practical voltage source.

In most cases the value of this equivalent internal source resistance will be low. Values ranging from a few ohms in an aged penlite cell down to a very small fraction of an ohm in a lead–acid battery of the type used in automobiles are common.

This internal resistance can be difficult, if not impossible, to measure

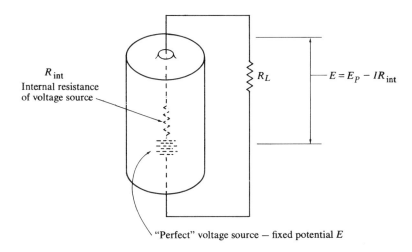

$E = E_P - IR_{int}$

Figure 5-1   The equivalent of a practical voltage source is a perfect voltage source with an internal series resistor connected between the external terminals.

directly. Indirectly, it may in most cases be measured easily. If an external resistor is placed across the voltage source terminals, it will be in series with the internal resistance of the source. Then whatever current flows through the external resistance must also be flowing through the internal resistance.

If the value of the external resistance is known, and the voltage across it measured, Ohm's law permits an accurate calculation of the current. This current is the current through the internal resistance of the source.

The open-circuit voltage of the source can be measured. This is the voltage at the terminals with no current being drawn by a load, and consequently no voltage drop across the internal resistance of the source. This, of course, is the potential of the equivalent perfect source. The difference between the open-circuit voltage of the practical source, and the potential actually present when the external resistor is connected and drawing current is the *IR* drop across the internal equivalent resistance.

Now the two necessary facts about the internal equivalent resistance are known: the current flow through it when the known load resistance is in place, and the potential across it under those same circumstances. Again, Ohm's law allows easy calculation of the resistance.

EXAMPLE   Suppose a battery has an open-circuit voltage of 1.52 V, and when a 10.4 Ω resistor is connected between its terminals, the voltage at the terminals falls to 1.38 V (Figure 5-2). What is the equivalent internal resistance?

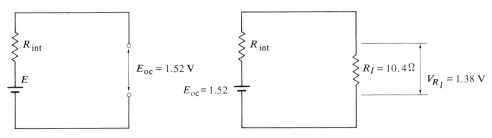

Open circuit voltage

Figure 5-2   Indirect measurement of internal resistance.

Solution.   The current through the external resistance is

$$I = \frac{E}{R}$$

$$= \frac{1.38}{10.4}$$

$$\cong 0.133 \text{ A}$$

This is also the current through the internal resistance of the source. The potential across that internal resistance is the difference between the open-circuit voltage and the terminal voltage with the load connected, which is

$$E_{oc} - V_{R_l} = 1.52 - 1.38$$

$$= 0.14 \text{ V}$$

The value of the internal resistance is

$$R = \frac{E}{I} = \frac{0.14}{0.133}$$

$$= 1.05 \text{ }\Omega$$

This is a somewhat higher figure than would be expected from a flashlight cell that had not deteriorated from age or use. The internal resistance of such a cell is inversely proportional to its remaining life expectancy, though the actual value for a new cell depends on its type and size. As the battery is used, the chemical reaction which produces the potential uses up the reacting materials. As the amount of reacting material decreases, the rate at which the reaction can occur decreases, and the equivalent resistance of the cell consequently increases.

Problems

1.   Consider a circuit in which the open-circuit voltage of the voltage source is 8 V. When 10 Ω load resistor R_l is connected across the terminals of the source, the voltage across the load is 4 V. What is the internal resistance of the source?

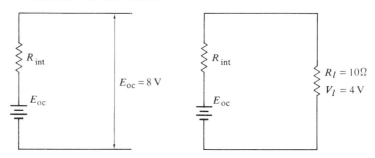

Circuit for Problem 1.

2. Consider a circuit in which the open-circuit voltage of the voltage source is 1.55 V. When 100 Ω load resistor R_l is connected across the terminals of the source, the voltage across the load is 1.50 V. What is the internal resistance of the source?

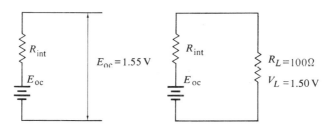

Circuit for Problems 2–4.

3. Using the circuit and the values of voltage given in Problem 2, together with the value of R_{int} calculated for that problem, what would be the value of V_l if R_l were 10 Ω?

4. Using the circuit of Problem 2 and the value of R_{int} calculated for that problem, what value of R_l would make $V_l = \frac{1}{2} E_{oc}$? What is the relationship between this R_l and R_{int}?

5-2
Sources in
Combination

VOLTAGE SOURCES IN SERIES. Two or more voltage sources may be connected in series with each other. If they are, Kirchhoff's laws still apply, so the current will be the same through each. The potentials are algebraically additive; that is, if the sources are connected *series-aiding*, the potential to the load will be the simple sum of the potentials of the individual sources [Figure 5-3(a)]; if they are connected *series-opposing*, the potential to

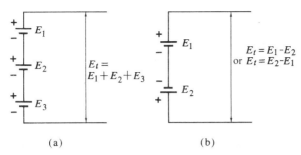

Figure 5-3   Voltage sources in series. (a) The sources are connected series-aiding, and the potential to the load is the simple sum of the potentials of the sources. (b) The sources are connected series-opposing and the potential to the load is the difference between the sum of the potentials in each polarity.

the load will be the difference between the sum of the potentials in each of the two polarities [Figure 5-3(b)].

Two sources are connected series-aiding if the positive terminal of one is connected to the negative terminal of the other. This leaves two free terminals, the negative terminal of the first, and the positive terminal of the second. These are the external terminals to which a load may be connected. The potential between these terminals, and the voltage across a load connected to them, is the sum of the individual source potentials.

What is commonly referred to as a flashlight "battery" is misnamed. It should properly be called a flashlight "cell." A *cell* is a single unit of structure in which a single chemical reaction is producing the terminal voltage. Most cells of the type familiar in consumer applications have a terminal voltage of approximately 1.5 V.

For many applications this is not sufficient. Transistor radios often use a battery composed of six such cells connected in series so their potentials sum. This gives a terminal potential of 9 V, and this physical arrangement of individual cells is properly termed a *battery*. Usually the cells of such a battery are connected together in the manufacturing process, and the resultant battery is encased in a protective metal or impregnated paper case.

Connecting cells together in series to form a battery increases the terminal voltage to be applied to a load, but it does not increase the amount of current that may be drawn by a load without exceeding the capabilities of the individual cells of the battery. The current flow within the battery is through the individual cells in series, and it can safely be no greater than each individual cell could deliver by itself.

Batteries in which the cells are connected in series-opposing are not manufactured. The situation in which voltage sources in general are in series-opposing with each other does, however, frequently occur in electronic circuits. If this is the case, the terminal potential of the combination is the algebraic sum of the individual potentials. A 1.5 V cell connected in series-opposing with a 9 V battery would have a terminal potential for the combination of 7.5 V. The polarity of the terminal potential of the combination will be the polarity of the source having the greatest absolute value of potential. In this case the polarity so far as the load was concerned would be that of the 9 V battery.

Advantage is sometimes taken of this fact by backpackers or others who wish to avoid the consequences of having a flashlight accidentally turned on during the day, which would almost certainly result in a complete exhaustion of the cells in a short while. If one of the cells of a two-cell flashlight is removed and reversed, so the two cells are in series-opposing, then the sum of their potentials is very close to zero, and if the switch is accidentally turned on, no significant current will flow through the load. The flashlight will not work this way, of course, but the cells cannot become accidentally exhausted. When needed, the cells can be reinserted correctly with some assurance that they will be in good condition.

VOLTAGE SOURCES IN PARALLEL.   If two voltage sources are connected in parallel, as in Figure 5-4, the combination can be seen to form a *series loop*, in which the two sources are in series-opposing and the internal resistances of the two sources are in a simple series configuration. The *net loop potential,* which will appear as *IR* drops across the two equivalent internal resistances, will be the difference in potential between the two perfect sources. If this

Figure 5-4   Two voltage sources connected in parallel form a series loop.

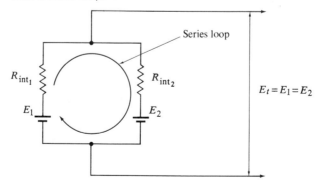

difference is zero, there will be no loop current. If the difference is not zero, there will be loop current. The magnitude of this current is, according to Ohm's law, the net loop potential divided by the sum of the equivalent internal resistance.

The loop current is a forward, or discharge, current for the source with the higher potential, and a reverse, or charge, current for the low-potential source. If the low-potential source is a cell or battery in which the chemical reaction is reversible, the reverse current flow can recharge the cell. This is the basis for the recharging system for the type of batteries found, for example, in automobiles.

If the two voltage sources connected in parallel can be represented as perfect sources with equivalent internal resistances in which the perfect source of each has the same potential, the net loop potential will be zero, and there will be no loop current. If this circuit is connected to an external load, then both sources will contribute current to the consequent flow through the load.

If the two equivalent internal resistances of the voltage sources are equal, the contributions of the two sources to the load current will also be equal. If the internal resistances are not equal, then the voltage source with the least internal resistance will make the greatest current contribution.

If we assume the ideal case, where differences are not significant in either the perfect source potential or equivalent internal resistance of any voltage sources connected in parallel, then the current contribution of each to the load will be the same. The potential across the load will be the potential of any of the sources in the parallel bank, assuming the IR drop across the internal resistances to be insignificant.

The practical case is never quite the ideal. Even two new cells will never have exactly the same internal resistance, nor will they have precisely the same open-circuit voltage. The internal resistance of any cell, however, increases, and the potential of its equivalent perfect source decreases as the cell is used. Since the greatest contribution to current flow in an external load is from that cell or battery in a parallel bank which has the least internal resistance, it will be depleted more rapidly, and its internal resistance will increase more rapidly than for other cells in the same bank. With use, then, the inequalities in parallel-connected cells tend to even out and approach the ideal case.

Since each cell contributes only part of the load current, a battery made of parallel-connected cells will have a much longer life than would a single cell in the same application, though the voltage of the parallel-connected battery is the same as the voltage of a single cell.

Problems **1.** In the circuit shown, $E_{oc_1} = 1.5$ V, $R_{int_1} = 1$ Ω, $E_{oc_2} = 1.55$ V, and $R_{int_2} = 1.5\,\Omega$. Find V_l and I_t, with $R_l = 10\,\Omega$.

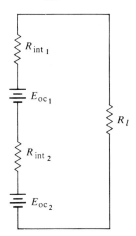

Circuit for Problems 1–4.

2. If R_{int_1} increases to $10\,\Omega$, what are the new V_l and I_t?

3. Using the circuit and values of Problem 1, except that $R_l = 50\,\Omega$, find V_l and I_t.

4. In Problem 1 how much heat energy in watts is dissipated in the internal resistance of each cell?

5. In the circuit shown, $E_{oc_1} = 1.5$ V, $E_{oc_2} = 1.5$ V, $R_{int_1} = 2\,\Omega$, $R_{int_2} = 2\,\Omega$, and $R_l = 6.5\,\Omega$. Calculate I_1, I_2, I_t, and V_l.

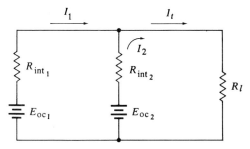

Circuit for Problems 5–8.

6. Calculate the power expended in R_l in Problem 5, and the power expended in R_{int} for each voltage source.

7. Recalculate I_1, I_2, I_t, and V_l for Problem 6, assuming $R_l = 14\,\Omega$.

8. Using the data of Problem 6, with $R_l = 6.5\,\Omega$ as before but with $R_{int_1} = R_{int_2} = 5\,\Omega$, recalculate I_1, I_2, I_t, and V_l.

CELL CLASSIFICATION.   Cells as voltage sources are usually classified as either primary or secondary cells. *Primary cells* are not rechargeable to any significant degree, while *secondary cells* may usually be recharged a nearly unlimited number of times. The most common example of a primary cell is the flashlight cell, while the most common example of secondary cells are the individual cells which make up the automobile battery.

**5-3
Cell Types**

All cells change chemical energy into electrical. Secondary cells can also change electrical energy into chemical, as when they are being recharged.

The molecules of some substances—particularly the compounds of metals —split, or dissociate, when dissolved in water or acids. If the split is uneven, so that some of the atoms have more than their original share of electrons while others have less, the result is two fragments which have some net charge. These charged fragments of the original molecules are called *ions*, and in the solution in which the molecule was dissolved they can travel from one point to another under the influence of an electric field. The solution is called an *electrolyte*.

If two conductors of different materials are immersed in this solution, the ions can react with them. Those ions which have an excess of electrons will transfer this excess to the conductor with which they react, while those ions which have a deficiency of electrons will make up that deficiency by taking electrons from the conductor with which they react. The two conductors will thus have different charges. If these charges are not lost through some external circuit, the conductor will then repel the ions and there will be no further reaction; all chemical action within the solution will stop.

The different charges on the two conductors constitute a potential difference between them. For most of the common materials used for the two conductors or for the electrolyte between them, that difference in potential is 1 to 2 V.

If the two conductors are connected to some external load, the difference in potential between them constitutes a voltage across the load, and current will flow through the load. This current is composed of electrons brought to one of the conductors by the ions carrying an excess of electrons. The electrons flow through the external circuit to the other conductor where they are available to be transferred to the ions that have a charge deficiency. As the process continues, more and more ions are able to migrate to the two conductors, or *poles* as they are properly termed. This means that the chemical reaction which is responsible for the transfer of charge to the poles can continue, but only for so long as there is an external circuit through which the electrons can travel from the negative terminal of the cell to the positive.

All cells, whether primary or secondary, function through a chemical reaction similar to the very general outline just given. In some the reaction produces substances which are gases, like hydrogen, and which leave the cell and enter the surrounding air. If this is the case, the reaction cannot be reversed by the charging process, since one of the substances required is no longer present. In other cells an end product of the reaction is a material which will not redissolve; it, too, is effectively no longer available, and the cell cannot be recharged. Cells of these types are primary cells. In others the materials required for the reaction remain available in a usable form; these are the secondary cells.

In the primary cells the total energy available is just that which was in the form of chemical energy in the original compounds in the cell. When the reaction is complete, no more energy can be converted into electricity by the cell. In the secondary cells, recharging can restore the original chemical compounds in which the energy is stored, so that over a period of time an almost unlimited amount of energy may be stored and reused, though there is, of course, a definite and usually rather low limit to the amount that can be stored at any one time.

In a third class of cell, the *fuel cell*, the reacting chemicals are added to the cell from an outside source. So long as the fuel tanks are kept full, such a cell can continue to convert the chemical energy in the fuel directly into electrical energy.

5-4
Primary Cells

THE CARBON–ZINC CELL.   The cheapest, most widely available, and consequently, the best-known primary cell is the *carbon–zinc cell* (Figure 5-5). It is also sometimes known as the Leclanche cell, from Georges Leclanche, who, in 1868, developed a cell essentially the same as the present version. Nearly all the cells that are ordinarily referred to as "flashlight batteries" are carbon–zinc cells.

The electrolyte in this type of cell is ammonium chloride, NH_4Cl. In solution this molecule breaks into two fragments: NH_4^+ and Cl^-. The NH_4^+ is ammonium with a deficiency of 1 electron, while the Cl^- is a chlorine atom with an excess of 1 electron. The negative pole of this cell is zinc, and the positive pole is carbon. The zinc pole, or *electrode*, dissolves in solution, giving off positive zinc ions, Zn^{++}. Each zinc ion that goes into solution, therefore, leaves behind it in the zinc electrode two electrons. The zinc electrode is, therefore, the negative terminal of the cell. The zinc ions,

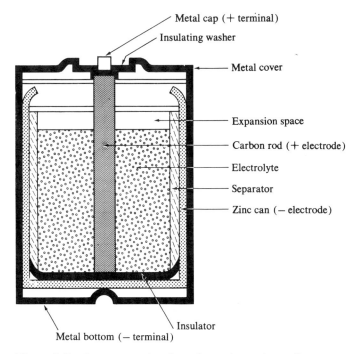

Metal cap (+ terminal)

Insulating washer

Metal cover

Expansion space

Carbon rod (+ electrode)

Electrolyte

Separator

Zinc can (− electrode)

Insulator

Metal bottom (− terminal)

Figure 5-5 A cutaway drawing of a carbon–zinc cell.

Zn^{++}, and the chlorine ions, Cl^-, are attracted to each other by their opposite charges, and combine, forming $ZnCl_2$. The two positive charges of the single zinc ion are canceled out by the single negative charge contributed by each of the chlorine ions, so that the $ZnCl_2$, zinc chloride, is electrically neutral. The reaction is shown in Figure 5-6.

The ammonium ions, NH_4^+, in the solution are repelled by the positive zinc ions going into solution at the negative pole of the cell, and migrate through the electrolyte to the carbon pole. On touching the carbon of this pole, the ammonium ions regain from it their lost electron. This permits the ammonium ion to split further, into ammonium gas, NH_3, and hydrogen, H, both electrically neutral. The carbon electrode of the cell, however, has to contribute the electron to permit this, and thus is left with an electron deficiency, which is a positive charge.

In this way the zinc electrode accumulates excess electrons and the carbon electrode sustains an electron deficiency so long as the reaction continues. The reaction depends on the movement of charged ions within the cell, and this will cease if the charge excesses and deficiencies of the two electrodes are not continually removed by permitting electron flow through some external

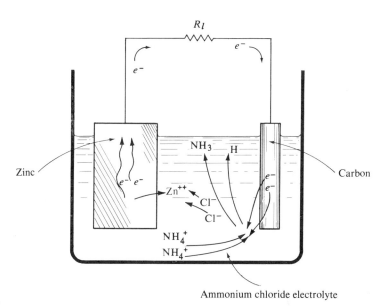

Figure 5-6   The chemical reaction of a carbon–zinc cell.

circuit. Thus, the reaction depends on cell use, and functions only when current is actually being drawn from the cell.

The zinc electrode is usually the cylindrical container for the remainder of the cell, so that the outside metallic body of the cell is the negative terminal. Within this container is a paste electrolyte, consisting of a mixture of ammonium chloride, water, granulated carbon, and powdered manganese dioxide. Sometimes the paste is made more gelatinous with corn starch or flour. Suspended down the center of this paste is a carbon rod which, together with the granulated carbon in the paste, serves as the positive terminal of the cell.

In the reaction that changes chemical energy to electrical, both ammonium gas and hydrogen are produced. The ammonium can combine with the water in the paste to form ammonium hydroxide; the hydrogen may, if permitted, coat the carbon pole with a layer of fine bubbles of the gas. This would interfere with the chemical reaction, and the cell would soon cease to function, so the manganese dioxide is added to the paste to combine with the hydrogen as it is produced to prevent this. This coating of the electrode with tiny hydrogen bubbles is called *polarization*, and, consequently, the manganese dioxide is known as a *depolarizer*.

In order to function as an electrolyte, the paste must contain moisture. If the cell is too tightly sealed, there is danger of case rupture if the current drain is so great that hydrogen is produced faster than it can be combined with the manganese dioxide; consequently, moisture can slowly escape as well as the excess hydrogen. In addition, impurities in the zinc can act as the positive poles of small local cells, and produce current which uses up the zinc without contributing to the output of the cell. Both of these factors combine to limit the useful life of the cell, regardless of use. Each size of zinc–carbon dry cell has a definite shelf life. The medium-size cells are useful for about a year after manufacture, but the smallest sizes may be good for only a few months. Dry cells are usually dated, and should be used as soon after manufacture as possible.

The output voltage of a zinc–carbon dry cell is approximately 1.5 to 1.6 V when new. The maximum continuous current rating depends on the cell size, ranging from a few mA for the smallest sizes up to about $\frac{1}{4}$ A for the large No. 6 cell. The size D flashlight cell has a current rating of 50 mA for approximately 60 hours of service.

CARBON–ZINC BATTERIES. Many applications require higher current or voltage than a single cell can supply. Manufacturers supply batteries made up of groups of cells in series, parallel, or series–parallel in a variety of combinations, case shapes, and terminal arrangements to meet nearly any need.

A type of construction often used in this type of battery is sometimes called the mini-max battery. In this construction the carbon and the zinc are in the form of flat plates, with the electrolyte paste sandwiched between the layers. Stacks of these layers, edge sealed and connected to external terminals, can be used in any desired arrangement.

THE ALKALINE CELL. Externally, the *alkaline cell* looks very much like the zinc–carbon cell. Internally, although the principle behind it is the same, the chemical reaction is different.

The positive electrode in this cell is compressed manganese dioxide, which also acts as a depolarizer. The negative electrode is zinc, usually surrounded by an outer case of steel. High-conductivity potassium hydroxide is the active material in the paste electrolyte.

Since this cell has a lower internal resistance than the zinc–carbon cell, it can operate at good efficiency even when delivering relatively large amounts of current. A new alkaline cell can provide more than ten times the service of an equivalent carbon–zinc cell. With light loads, or in terms of shelf life, the alkaline cell can still provide twice the service of the carbon–zinc cell.

THE MERCURY CELL. Although more expensive than either of the first two types of cell described, and with a lower terminal potential, the *mercury cell* still offers significant advantages in some applications.

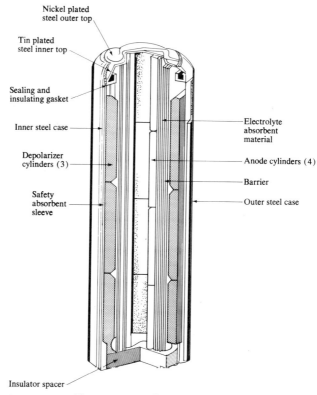

Nickel plated
steel outer top

Tin plated
steel inner top

Sealing and
insulating gasket

Inner steel case

Depolarizer
cylinders (3)

Safety
absorbent
sleeve

Electrolyte
absorbent
material

Anode cylinders (4)

Barrier

Outer steel case

Insulator spacer

Figure 5-7   The mercury cell.

Where shelf life is important, as in stand-by applications, the mercury cell is considerably superior to either the carbon–zinc or alkaline cell. They are reliable for up to five years in stand-by or insignificant current flow applications.

The output voltage of a mercury cell is much more constant as the cell ages than is the case with the other types. They may be used as voltage standards for comparison measurements, an application for which the alkaline and carbon–zinc cells are entirely unsuited.

The internal resistance and cost of mercury cells are both high. This high internal resistance makes the mercury cell unsuited for applications where large current drains are encountered, as well as where cost is a prime consideration.

The positive electrode and depolarizer in this cell is a dense structure of compressed red mercuric oxide. The negative terminal is zinc coated with mercury into which the zinc dissolves. The electrolyte is potassium hydroxide.

Often the completed cell as manufactured looks very much like a carbon–zinc or alkaline cell. Note carefully that the polarity of this cell is reversed compared to the others; the center top cap, which is the positive terminal on the other two cell types, is the negative terminal on the mercury cell (Figure 5-7).

SILVER OXIDE–ZINC CELL. *Silver oxide–zinc cells* are of the alkaline type. They have a silver oxide positive electrode and a zinc negative electrode, and use potassium or sodium hydroxide as the active ingredient in the electrolyte. The output voltage is 1.55 V at low current drains, and is sufficiently stable to serve as a voltage reference. Low internal resistance means they can deliver high currents for a short time. Cells of this type are often employed in hearing aids and in electric watches.

OTHER PRIMARY CELLS. The number of types of primary cell that have been used is nearly limitless. More may be expected. A few that have found sufficient application to be worth mentioning include the silver–zinc cell, the air cell, and the seawater cell.

The *silver–zinc cell* uses pure silver as one electrode and zinc as the other. Because of the silver electrode, the cost is high. The open-circuit voltage is high, about 1.7 to 1.8 V, dropping to approximately 1.5 V under load. This cell has the highest energy output per pound of cell of any primary cell. It is inconvenient, as the electrolyte must be added immediately prior to use. Where high energy stoage for a given weight and volume of cell is desired, the advantages of this cell often outweigh the disadvantages.

The *air cell* (Figure 5-8) is an alkaline cell, using zinc and carbon as the electrodes, and sodium hydroxide as the active electrolyte. The carbon electrode is porous, permitting air containing oxygen to be "breathed" in to prevent polarization by hydrogen gas. This gives the cell its name. No manganese dioxide is needed, and the supply of oxygen from the air is limitless. The electrolyte is usually liquid. The cells have a long life and low cost per ampere–hour. The output voltage is low, about 1.25 V, but it can be sustained for a long time. These cells are useful in such applications as power sources for aids-to-navigation lights and buoys, emergency lights, and signal lights.

The *seawater battery* is unique in its functioning and its applications. Each cell in this battery uses silver chloride as one electrode and magnesium as the other. The electrolyte is seawater, in which sodium chloride, or common salt, is the active ingredient. Used to power such underwater weapons as torpedoes, these cells are dry until the torpedo is launched. Seawater passing through the battery and out the discharge openings acts as the electrolyte, and

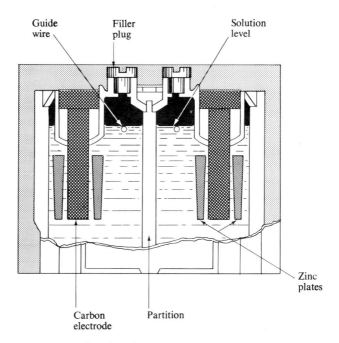

Figure 5-8   An air cell, which is useful mainly because of its long lifetime.

simultaneously carries away the waste products. The battery can continue to run until the silver chloride is completely used up, or, of course, until the torpedo hits a target. Batteries of these cells can produce voltages of up to 250 V and deliver currents of over 500 A for up to 15 minutes, sufficient time for the job for which they were designed.

5-5
Secondary Cells

LEAD–ACID CELLS.   By far the most frequently encountered secondary cell is the *lead–acid cell* (Figure 5-9), such as the cells that make up the automobile battery.

The electrodes consist of plates made of an open grid of a lead–antimony alloy into which the active material is pressed under pressure. This active material is usually in the form of lead oxide, which is then electrochemically transformed into lead peroxide, PbO_2, to form the positive plate, and spongy lead, Pb, to form the negative plate. Visual inspection can determine which is which; lead peroxide is a chocolate brown, while the spongy lead is a dull slate grey.

To increase total plate area, the plates are combined into elements consisting of multiple layers of interleaved positive and negative plates, kept from contact with each other by separators. The separators formerly were made of wood, but now are more commonly of glass fibre, rubber, or plastic. All the negative plates are strapped together and connected to the common negative cell terminal, while the positive plates are connected together and to the common positive terminal.

The elements of a cell are housed together in a case of hard rubber, glass, plastic, or other suitable material. The case usually contains compartments for several such cells, connected together to form a battery.

The electrolyte nearly fills the case compartment and completely covers the elements of the cell. It consists of a dilute solution of sulfuric acid, H_2SO_4.

When the cell is assembled, with the elements and electrolyte in place, the terminal potential is about 2.2 V. When a load is connected to the cell, the lead peroxide of the positive plate combines with the sulfuric acid of the electrolyte

Figure 5-9   The most common secondary cell, the lead–acid cell. When the starter motor is operated in an automobile, a current of several hundred amperes may be drawn from a battery composed of six cells like this one.

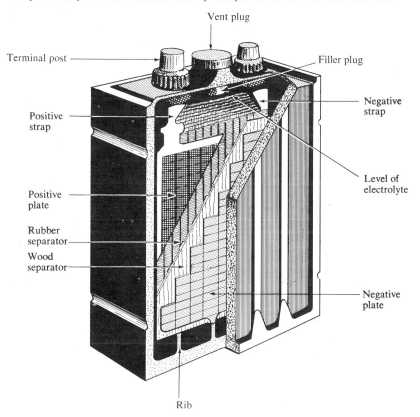

to form lead sulfate of the plate material and change to water the sulfuric acid which takes part in the reaction. There is a net loss of electrons from the plate material as this occurs, leaving this plate positive.

The spongy lead of the negative plate is meanwhile also combining with the sulfuric acid, to form lead sulfate and change the sulfuric acid to water. This occurs with a net gain of electrons to the plate material, making this plate negative. Note that both reactions make their respective plates lead sulfate and transform the sulfuric acid of the electrolyte to water. When both plates are of the same material, and the electrolyte is water, no further action can occur, and the cell is completely dead.

A lead–acid cell ought not to be left in a discharged condition for long, since the lead sulfate of which both plates consist, at least in part, in a discharged cell, may crystallize, and with time the crystals grow to larger size. If this occurs, there may be a physical warping or buckling of the grid into which the active material is pressed, and some of the active material may fall out of the grid. This can cause an accumulation of sludge at the bottom of the cell case which can cause a short between the positive and negative plates of the cell. Separators may also crack or split, permitting contact between the plates to cause a short.

The state of charge of a cell can be easily found with a *hydrometer* (Figure 5-10), which determines the specific gravity of the electrolyte. *Specific gravity* is the ratio between the weight of water and the weight of an equal volume of another substance. The specific gravity of sulfuric acid is 1.840, while the specific gravity of water is, of course, 1. The specific gravity of the dilute solution of sulfuric acid that is the electrolyte of a fully charged cell may vary from 1.275 to 1.300, depending on the manufacturing process and the temperature of the cell. As the cell is discharged, the sulfuric acid is transformed to water, and the specific gravity of the electrolyte decreases. A cell is considered half charged with a hydrometer reading of its specific gravity of 1.210, and fully discharged if the reading is between 1.120 and 1.150.

A cell may be charged by connecting to it a voltage source of slightly higher potential than the open-circuit cell potential so that the current flow through the cell is reversed. This converts the lead sulfate of the negative plate to spongy lead, and the lead sulfate of the positive plate to lead peroxide. Both reactions release sulfate ions to the electrolyte, reconstituting the original sulfuric acid electrolyte.

Heat is produced within the cell both by the *IR* drop of current flowing through the various components of the cell, and by the chemical reactions which are a part of the charge–discharge cycle. Materials are sometimes

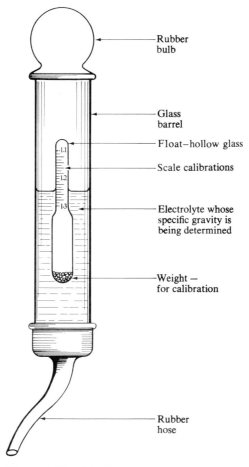

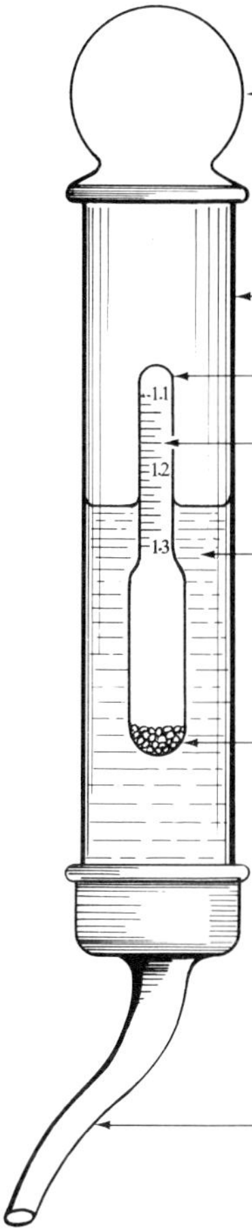
Rubber
bulb
Glass
barrel
Float–hollow glass
Scale calibrations
1.1
1.2
1.3
Electrolyte whose
specific gravity is
being determined
Weight –
for calibration
Rubber
hose

Figure 5-10 A hydrometer.

added to the grids in manufacture to reduce the *IR* drop, and thus permit higher charge–discharge rates. A cell may be charged or discharged at any rate that does not cause the internal temperature to rise above about 110°F (Fahrenheit).

Lead–acid batteries have a very low internal resistance and are, therefore, able to deliver large currents to a load with little internal heating. This, in addition to the fact that they may be recharged a nearly unlimited number of times, has made them suitable for such applications as providing the power to operate the electrical starter of a car. Currents of several hundred amperes may be drawn from the battery for short intervals as the starter motor is operated.

THE EDISON CELL.   The *Edison cell* is a nickel–iron cell with an alkaline electrolyte in which the active ingredient is potassium hydroxide. The positive plate consists of nickel oxide packed in small, perforated, nickel-plated tubes. The negative plate has iron as the active material in pockets in a nickel-plated plate.

When the cell is discharging current to a load, oxygen is transferred through the electrolyte from the nickel oxide to the iron, reducing the nickel oxide to metallic nickel, and oxidizing the iron to iron oxide, or rust. This process results in the transfer of electrons to the plate containing the iron, so it becomes the negative terminal of the cell, while a deficiency of electrons is occurring at the plate where the nickel oxide is being reduced to metallic nickel, so it becomes the positive plate.

Just as in the case of the other secondary cells, passing an electric current through the cell in a direction opposite to the discharge current reverses the chemical action of discharging. As the cell is recharged, the metallic nickel becomes the original nickel oxide, while the iron oxide in the other plate is reduced to metallic iron.

The internal resistance of the Edison cell is considerably higher than that for a lead–acid cell, thus making it less suitable for high-current applications. It is also considerably larger per ampere-hour of capacity than an equivalent lead–acid cell.

It is quite rugged and long lasting. Cells can be completely discharged and left in this condition for long periods without damage, something that is not true of the lead–acid cells. As with the lead–acid types, if the level of electrolyte falls, it should be brought up to the proper level with distilled water.

The state of charge cannot be determined from the specific gravity of the electrolyte, as this does not change sufficiently between charge and discharge. Instead, voltage readings of the cell may be taken and can serve as an indicator of the need for charge. The average voltage of a charged cell is usually taken as 1.2 to 1.3 V. When the voltage drops to 1.0 to 0.9 V, the cell may be considered discharged.

THE NICKEL–CADMIUM CELL.   In the *nickel–cadmium* cell, one electrode is nickel oxide, and the other is cadmium and iron, while the electrolyte is potassium hydroxide. This gives a cell with a voltage under load of about 1.25 V. (Figure 5-11)

The construction and internal chemical reactions of the nickel–cadmium cell are quite similar to those of the Edison cell. The internal resistance of these nickel–cadmium cells is much lower than that for the Edison cells, however, making them competitors to the lead–acid cells for the job of starting cars. They are also quite rugged and long lasting.

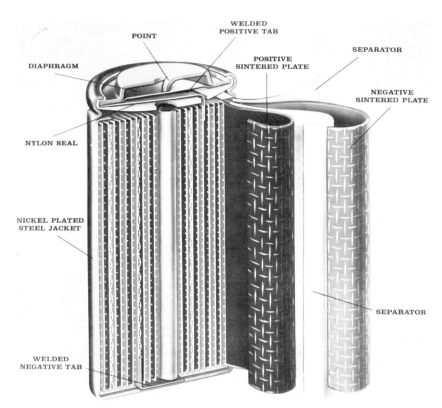

WELDED POSITIVE TAB

POINT

SEPARATOR

DIAPHRAGM

POSITIVE SINTERED PLATE

NEGATIVE SINTERED PLATE

NYLON SEAL

NICKEL PLATED STEEL JACKET

SEPARATOR

WELDED NEGATIVE TAB

Figure 5-11 A nickel–cadmium cell. This cell may be operated in any position Similar cells are used in many portable applications such as pocket calculators, cordless appliances, and communications systems. (Courtesy Marathon Battery Co.)

Small, sealed, rechargeable nickel–cadmium cells have been available for some years. The construction of these cells permits operation in any position without danger of spilling the electrolyte. They are small, convenient packages, with a long operating life and an indefinite storage life. They have a nominal output voltage of 1.25 V, and thus are not suitable as direct replacements for carbon–zinc flashlight cells, but they are admirably suited for many applications.

Primary cells, secondary cells, and fuel cells are all chemical cells. Nonchemical cells convert energy from such sources as light, heat, and atomic radiation directly into electrical power.

It was found a good many years ago that when light falls on the junction between a strip of selenium, which is a semiconductor element, and a strip of

5-6 Nonchemical Cells

iron, a potential of about 0.4 V is developed between the two strips. The amount of energy thus produced is slight since the cells have an efficiency of only about 1%, but for such applications as the photoelectric exposure meter it is adequate.

Later it was found that special silicon cells could be made by using wafer-thin strips of silicon infused with impurities. If opposing faces of these strips contain opposite-polarity impurities, the strips generate a potential when light strikes them. A series of these strips connected together make up a *solar battery*, which can operate with an efficiency of 10%. If the cost can be brought down, and if inexpensive storage of the energy produced during daylight hours can be found, these cells may provide the energy to initiate a technological revolution in areas of the world where such natural sources of power as coal or water are not available.

A number of different designs for cells utilizing the energy inherent in nuclear radiation to produce a potential have been developed. In some, a junction of two dissimilar semiconductor materials is bombarded by beta particles, which are high-speed electrons, from a radioactive material. The potential produced by a single cell is low, about 0.3 V, but the cells can be combined in series, parallel, or both to provide a battery with the desired electrical characteristics. They are expensive and can be hazardous to personnel, but they can operate for decades without attention. This is an area of technology where much more development seems unquestionably warranted.

Key Words **battery** a number of cells connected in series or parallel, according to intended use

cell a single unit of structure with a single chemical reaction producing the terminal voltage

charge current current that reverses the chemical reaction of a secondary cell, thus restoring energy to the cell

depolarizer a chemical that prevents the formation of hydrogen bubbles on an electrode

discharge current current which reduces the energy stored in a cell

electrode the positive or negative terminal of a power source

electrolyte a solution in which ions travel under the influence of an electric field

fuel cell a secondary cell in which reacting chemicals are added to the cell from an outside source

hydrometer   a device for determining the specific gravity of the electrolyte of a cell, and thus its state of charge

ion   an electrically charged molecule or atom that possesses either more or less than its original number of electrons, thus having either positive or negative net charge

net loop potential   the algebraic sum of the potentials in any closed loop

perfect voltage source   a theoretical source with no internal resistance, capable of delivering a fixed voltage in any load, at any current drawn by the load, and for any length of time

polarization   the coating of an electrode with tiny hydrogen bubbles

power supply   a source of dc voltage that is directly usable by electronic circuits. A voltage source may either depend on receiving power from an external source or be self-contained

practical voltage source   a source that contains internal conductors of some resistance, and which depends to some extent on the rate of a chemical reaction or on the conductivity of circuit elements

primary cell   a cell that is not rechargeable to a significant degree

secondary cell   a cell that can be recharged an almost unlimited number of times

series-aiding   power sources connected so that their total potential is the sum of the potentials of the individual sources

series-opposing   power sources connected so that their total potential is the difference between the sum of the potentials in each of the two polarities

specific gravity   the ratio between the weight of water and the weight of an equal volume of another substance

1.   A voltage source may receive its power from some external source on a continuing basis or be self-contained, in which case its energy is fixed.   **Summary of Concepts**

2.   The usual equivalent to a practical voltage source is a perfect voltage source with a series resistor connected internally between the perfect source and its external terminals.

3.   The open-circuit voltage of a source is the voltage at the terminals with no current being drawn by a load and, consequently, no voltage drop across the internal resistance of the source.

4.   All cells change chemical energy into electrical energy.

5.   Connecting cells in series to form a battery increases the terminal voltage to be applied to a load, but it does not increase the amount

of current that may be drawn by a load without exceeding the capabilities of the individual cells of the battery.

6. If two voltage sources are connected in parallel, the combination forms a series loop in which the two sources are in series-opposing, and the internal resistance of the two sources is in a simple series configuration.

7. Two perfect sources with equal potential and internal resistance have a net loop potential of zero and no loop current.

8. Used in the same manner, a battery of cells connected in parallel will have a longer life than any one of its component cells, although the voltage is the same in either case.

9. The molecules of some substances dissociate in water or acid. If the split is uneven—some atoms gain electrons and some atoms lose electrons—the dissociated fragments have a net positive or negative charge. These fragments are ions.

10. If conductors of different materials are immersed in an electrolyte, the ions of the electrolyte will react with the conductors to develop a potential.

11. If two conductors in an electrolyte solution are connected to an external load, the difference in potential between the conductors constitutes a voltage across the load, and current will flow through the load.

12. The chemical reaction that results in the transfer of charges to the poles of a cell will continue only as long as there is an external circuit through which the electrons can travel from the negative terminal to the positive.

13. A secondary cell may be charged by connecting it to a voltage source of slightly higher potential than the open-circuit cell, so that the current flow through the cell is reversed.

14. A lead — acid secondary cell may be charged or discharged at any rate that does not raise the internal temperature above 110°F.

15. Other energy sources include light, heat, and atomic radiation, all of which can be converted into electrical energy.

To Help You Review   *On a separate sheet of paper, fill in the blanks or answer the questions below. The number following each question refers to the section in the chapter where the correct answer can be found.*

1. What are the differences between a theoretically perfect voltage source and a practical voltage source? (5-1)

2. The two categories of power supplies are _____ and _____. (5-1)

3. What two facts do we need to know in order to calculate the internal resistance of a voltage source? (5-1)

4. What do *series-aiding* and *series-opposing* mean? (5-2)

5. How is the term *battery* often misused? (5-2)

6. What does net loop potential have to do with the operation of a voltage source? (5-2)

7. Explain briefly the conditions under which a cell or battery is discharged. When can a cell or battery be charged? (5-2)

8. Connected in parallel, three cells will have a _____ life than any of the three cells used separately. (5-2)

9. What is the most basic classification of cells? (5-3)

10. How are ions formed? (5-3)

11. What is an electrolyte? (5-3)

12. If the two conductors of a cell are connected to an external load, what causes current to flow through the load? What does this current consist of? (5-3)

13. Describe the basic functioning of a cell. (5-3)

14. Name two primary cells. Describe their construction and list their practical features. (5-4)

15. How can polarization be prevented in a cell? (5-4)

16. Describe two factors that limit the life of a carbon–zinc cell, regardless of use. (5-4)

17. Match the letters of the cells on the left with the characteristics on the right. (5-4) and (5-5)

    (a) carbon–zinc   1. Polarity reversed, compared to other cells

    (b) alkaline   2. Alkaline electrolyte with potassium hydroxide as the active ingredient

    (c) mercury   3. Sodium chloride is the active ingredient in the electrolyte

    (d) air   4. Used in navigation-aid lights because of its long lifetime

    (e) seawater   5. May be operated in any position without spilling the electrolyte

(f) nickel–cadmium

(g) Edison

(h) lead–acid

(i) silver oxide

6. The common flashlight "battery"

7. Can deliver high currents for short periods

8. The positive pole consists of compressed manganese dioxide

9. Delivers large currents with little internal heating

SIX
DC
MEASUREMENTS

THE D'ARSONVAL PRINCIPLE.   A few turns of wire wrapped around a soft iron nail and connected to a flashlight cell can make a temporary magnet of the nail. It is just as true that the coil with current from the cell running through it becomes a magnet without the nail, though the magnet thus formed is far weaker than if it had an iron core.

Magnets may attract or repel each other, depending on whether like or unlike poles face each other. It does not matter whether both magnets are of the same material; only the opposing polarities determine the direction of force between them, and only their magnetic strength and the distance between them determine the strength of the force between them.

Suppose we have a coil of fine wire, mounted so that it may turn freely between the poles of a strong magnet (Figure 6-1). If no current is flowing through the coil, it will experience no force;

6-1
Moving-Coil Meters

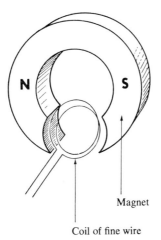

Magnet

Coil of fine wire

Figure 6-1 When current flows through the coil, it tends to rotate until its magnetic poles are aligned with the poles of the permanent magnet.

but if current flows through the coil, it becomes a weak magnet. If it is free to turn, it will tend to rotate so that its poles are in line with the poles of the larger magnet, just as a compass needle rotates to align itself with an external magnetic field. If it is not completely free to turn, but is restrained by springs, it will turn until the retarding force of increasing tension on the springs just balances the turning force created by the interaction of the magnetic field. This construction—a wire coil suspended between the poles of a permanent magnet—is based on the *d'Arsonval principle*. The design was invented by Arsène d'Arsonval, a French physicist.

The strength of the magnetic field produced by this coil of wire, which is to interact with the field of the permanent magnet, depends both on the number of turns of wire and on the amount of current flowing in the coil. Since the number of turns of wire is fixed, the angular displacement of the coil in turning against the springs depends only on the current flow. The instrument based on this principle is strictly a current-sensing device.

METER MOVEMENTS. In practice the d'Arsonval principle can be applied in a number of different ways. There are two general methods: the jeweled suspension with hairsprings and the taut-band suspension.

The jeweled suspension with hairsprings is the older and, perhaps because of this, the more widely used of the two designs (Figure 6-2). The rotating coil through which the current to be measured flows is wound on a rectangular aluminum bobbin, which is provided with hardened steel pivot points at top and bottom. The pivot points rest in jeweled bearings,

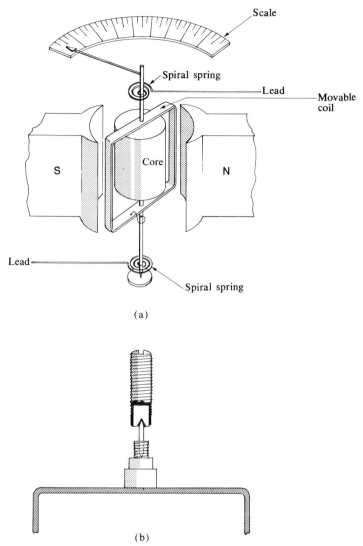

Figure 6-2   (a) The jeweled suspension meter with hairsprings.
(b) Detail of the jeweled pivot.

reducing friction to a very low level, but introducing the possibility of breakage of the jewels with even'a moderate impact. Current is fed to the coil through two very small spiral hairsprings, which also provide the retarding force necessary to make the angular deflection proportional to the current.

The taut-band suspension provides even less friction than the jeweled

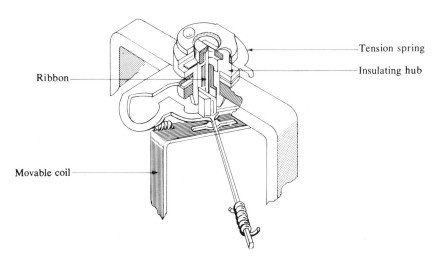

Figure 6-3   The taut-band suspension.

Figure 6-4 The pointer in a d'Arsonval movement must be balanced if readings are to be accurate.

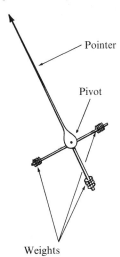

bearings. Instead of steel pivots in bearings, the moving coil is held in place by means of tightly stretched metal ribbons at the top and bottom (Figure 6-3). These ribbons also serve to provide the necessary two connections to the coil, as well as the retarding force needed.

For either type of suspension, the remainder of the construction of the meter movement is essentially similar. A permanent magnet surrounds the coil bobbin and its pivot supports. The design of this magnet may take a variety of forms; all perform the same function. Usually, a fixed-position iron core around which the coil bobbin rotates is used to concentrate the magnetic field of the coil. Affixed to the coil bobbin is a pointer; movement of this pointer across a scale is proportional to the degree of rotation of the coil, and, consequently, proportional to the amount of current flowing through the coil. The scale calibrations are made to suit the purpose to which the meter is to be put.

If the meter is to be used so that the needle rotates in a vertical plane, as most are, then it is necessary that the entire needle-and-bobbin structure be balanced. If it is not balanced, then the excess weight of the pointer will cause it to indicate a scale reading further left than it ought to be whenever the needle points to the left of center, and further to the right than it ought to be whenever the needle points to the right of center. A small cross of wire with wrapped movable weights is made a part of the rotating assembly to make possible the necessary balance (Figure 6-4). If the meter reading is not the same with the scale and pointer in a vertical plane as it is when they are horizontal, the weights on this cross need adjusting. The adjustment is not one for the average technician.

METER SENSITIVITY.   The pointer deflection that will be produced by a given current flowing through the coil depends on the number of turns of wire in the coil, the strength of the magnets that produce the magnetic field through which it rotates, and the retarding force provided by either hair-springs or taut-band suspension. These factors are all fixed and cannot in any practical way be altered for a given movement.

    The sensitivity of a meter movement is usually given in terms of the current flow through the coil which will produce full-scale deflection of the pointer. Movements are available having sensitivities ranging from a few μA up to 30 mA or more. Most commonly encountered are sensitivities of 10, 20, 50, 200, and 500 μA and 1 mA. The actual scale reading at full-scale deflection may, of course, be something quite different. A meter complete with scale is often designed for a particular function and to be used as part of a circuit which will include other components. A 0–1 mA meter movement may be purchased with a scale which reads 100 V full scale. This will be correct only if the basic meter movement is used in conjunction with the proper series resistance, mounted usually within the case and purchased as part of the complete meter, but sometimes designed to be mounted and used externally.

    The actual internal resistance of the basic meter movement is determined by the diameter and length of the wire used in winding the moving coil. The more sensitive meters will have the greatest number of turns of wire in the coil. This calls for many turns of fine wire; consequently, a high resistance is inevitable, often several thousand ohms. Less sensitive movements require fewer turns of wire in the coil, which makes possible the use of a larger-diameter conductor, thus reducing the coil resistance. A 30 mA movement may have a coil resistance of only a little over 1 Ω.

METHODS OF CURRENT MEASUREMENT.   If the current to be measured in a circuit is within the range of the movement of the meter, all that is necessary is to connect the meter to the circuit so that the current to be measured will flow through the moving coil. The resulting pointer deflection will indicate on the scale the magnitude of the current.

    This means that the circuit must be broken at the point at which the reading is desired, and the meter connected to bridge the break (Figure 6-5). Suppose a reading of the current through a particular resistor in a circuit is desired. The conductor connected to either resistor terminal must be

6-2
Current
Measurements

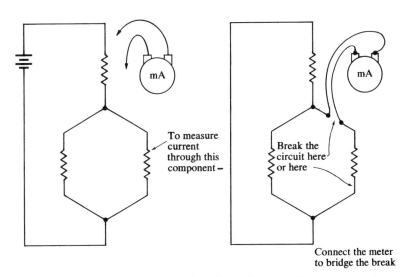

Figure 6-5   To get a current reading through a specific component in a circuit, break the circuit at either lead of the component and insert the meter in the break.

disconnected from the resistor. Then one lead from the meter is connected to the conductor, and the other meter lead to the resistor terminal from which the conductor was disconnected. Now the current previously flowing between the resistor and the conductor directly must flow through the meter movement, and the pointer deflection will indicate its magnitude.

Often, in a practical circuit, more than one conductor will be connected to a resistor terminal. If this is the case, then to determine the current through the resistor, *all* the conductors must be removed as a group. The meter will then have one lead connected to the resistor terminal, and the other to all conductors of the group simultaneously (Figure 6-6). Otherwise, the current read may be only part of the currents that sum at the junction.

The direction of current flow through the coil of the meter movement. determines the polarity of the magnetic field thus created and, consequently, determines whether the coil must rotate clockwise or counterclockwise to align its field with the field of the permanent magnet of the movement. If the meter is connected to the circuit with the incorrect polarity, the pointer will try to deflect in the wrong direction. It can move only a little below zero on the scale, since there are stops to prevent this movement.

Meter polarity is marked on the case or the meter terminals. Usually a small + sign is either stamped on the end of the threaded terminal of the meter or pressed into the plastic of the meter case adjacent to the

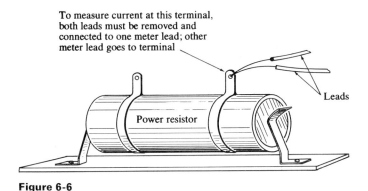

To measure current at this terminal, both leads must be removed and connected to one meter lead; other meter lead goes to terminal

Leads

Power resistor

Figure 6-6

positive terminal (Figure 6-7). The meter should be connected to the circuit so that the positive terminal of the meter goes through the circuit toward the positive terminal of the source, while the negative meter terminal connects to that part of the circuit which is the path to the common ground or negative terminal of the meter. If the source is negative, that is, if its common ground is connected to the positive source terminal, then the positive meter terminal connects to that part of the circuit with a path to common ground.

Note carefully that the meter is *not* to be connected between the source terminals. This would damage the movement, perhaps beyond repair, in a small fraction of a second. A current-measuring meter should be connected in a previously existing circuit *only*, by opening the circuit at the point where the measurement is to be made and inserting the meter electrically into the break, so that the current path is reestablished through the meter.

Currents greater than double the normal full-scale reading of the move-

Figure 6-7 When a meter is connected to a circuit, correct polarity is important. Examine meter before making any connections.

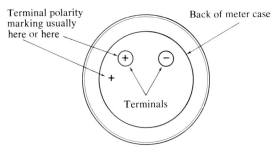

Terminal polarity marking usually here or here

Back of meter case

+

Terminals

ment will damage the meter. The very fine wire of the coil and the fine wires of the hairsprings can melt with excessive current. In addition, the violent movement of the pointer that accompanies such currents may bend the pointer, or even break it.

Before a meter is used in a particular measurement, a calculation (or at least a reasonably well-educated guess) ought to be made to determine the appropriate expected value of current. A meter that will have a full-scale reading greater than this current is then used.

If the current proves to be less than anticipated, so that the pointer deflection is too slight to give an accurate reading, a meter with higher current sensitivity can then be substituted.

A meter cannot be altered in any practical way to increase its sensitivity. It is easy to reduce the sensitivity of a meter movement, however. Suppose a resistance is placed in parallel with the coil of the meter movement. Some of the current will flow through the coil, causing deflection of the pointer; but some will flow through the parallel resistance, and this will cause no pointer deflection.

Suppose we are using a meter movement with a full-scale deflection of 1 mA and a coil resistance of 10 Ω. If we connect this meter to a circuit in which 1 mA of current is flowing, the pointer will read full scale. Presumably, the fact that the coil resistance of 10 Ω becomes a part of the circuit when the meter is connected to it to make the measurement does not significantly alter the current flow to be measured.

Now suppose we connect a 10 Ω resistor in parallel with the meter coil (Figure 6-8). This can be done, of course, by simply connecting the resistor between the meter terminals.

Now the current flow through the meter must divide in the parallel circuit we have formed. Since the two branches of this parallel bank—the coil and the resistor we have just added—have the same resistance, the current will divide equally between the two paths.

We presumed originally that the 10 Ω of the meter coil did not significantly affect the current being measured. If this is true, the 5 Ω of the parallel combination ought to affect it less. Therefore, the current being measured can be presumed to be unaffected by this change.

If the current being measured was 1 mA, then it would cause full-scale pointer deflection without the parallel resistor. With the parallel resistor, only 0.5 mA flows through the coil while 0.5 mA now flows through the resistor. Pointer deflection of the meter is, of course, proportional only to current flowing through the coil, not elsewhere in the circuit. Therefore, the pointer will now deflect only half-way.

This half-scale deflection still means that the current in the original

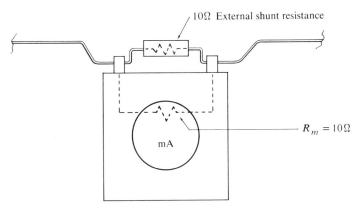

Figure 6-8 A resistor in parallel with a meter coil reduces the sensitivity of the meter, in this case by half. Thus, the meter reading must be doubled to give the true value of the current in the circuit.

circuit which we were trying to measure was 1 mA. Therefore, we can mark this point on the scale as 1 mA. A current in the original circuit that would cause full-scale pointer deflection would be 2 mA, since 1 mA would be flowing through the parallel resistor and 1 mA through the coil.

The addition of this parallel resistor has converted the original 0–1 mA meter into a 0–2 mA meter. This doubles the range of the meter. The resistor, as used in this application, is called a *meter shunt*. Meter shunts may be used to provide any current range greater than the original maximum range of the movement.

To calculate the appropriate value of a shunt, it is necessary to know either the internal resistance of the meter movement or its deflection sensitivity in millivolts. Current meters for use with external shunts to measure large currents are typically rated as having a full-scale deflection of 50 mV. This means that their internal resistance is such that 50 mV across their terminals will cause enough current to flow through the coil to cause full-scale deflection. The actual resistance depends on the sensitivity of the meter movement and can be calculated from Ohm's law if the sensitivity is known. Typically, 0–1 mA movements are used. If this is the case, a 50 mV 0–1 mA movement will have a coil resistance of

$$R = \frac{E}{I}$$

$$= \frac{0.05 \text{ V}}{0.001 \text{ A}}$$

$$= 50 \ \Omega$$

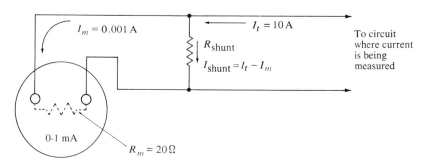

Figure 6-9

EXAMPLE   Suppose it is desired to use a 0–1 mA meter movement with an external shunt to make a 0–10 A meter. The resistance of the meter movement is 20 Ω (Figure 6-9). Find the proper shunt resistance.

Solution. When the meter current is 1 mA, the shunt current must be the remainder of the current desired to produce full-scale deflection. In this case it is 10 A. The difference between this and the 1 mA meter current is the shunt current. It is, therefore, 10.000 A minus 0.001 A, or 9.999 A. The shunt current is, therefore, 9,999 times the meter current, but since they are in parallel, they must have the same potential across their terminals. If the shunt is to carry 9,999 times the meter current, its resistance must be 1/9,999 of the meter resistance. Therefore,

$$R_{\text{shunt}} = \frac{20}{9,999}$$
$$= 0.002 \quad \text{(actually 0.0020002)}$$

It is also possible to state this in the form of an equation, based on the fact that with the meter resistance in parallel with the shunt resistance, the potential across them must be equal.

$$E_{\text{shunt}} = E_{\text{meter}}$$

From Ohm's law, and the fact that the shunt current is the maximum value of the desired range minus the maximum meter current,

$$R_{\text{shunt}}(I_{\text{max}} - I_{\text{meter}}) = I_{\text{meter}} R_{\text{meter}}$$
$$R_{\text{shunt}} = \frac{I_{\text{meter}} R_{\text{meter}}}{I_{\text{max}} - I_{\text{meter}}}$$

EXAMPLE   Suppose a meter movement with a full-scale deflection of 500 μA and a resistance of 90 Ω is to be used with a shunt to make a 0–20 mA milliammeter (Figure 6-10). What should be the value of the shunt resistance?

Solution.

$$R_{shunt} = \frac{I_{meter}\, R_{meter}}{I_{max} - I_{meter}}$$

$$= \frac{0.0005 \times 90}{0.020 - 0.0005}$$

$$= \frac{0.045}{0.0195}$$

$$= 2.308\ \Omega$$

A shunt resistance of this low value would, of course, have to be specially made. Usually, resistance wire—or in the case of shunts of very low value such as in the first example, copper conductor measured to the correct length for the proper resistance—can be used.

1. Given a 0–50 μA meter movement having a resistance of 100 Ω, what value of shunt resistor would convert this movement to a 0–5 A meter?   **Problems**

2. Given a 0–1 mA meter movement having a resistance of 23 Ω, what value of shunt resistor would convert this movement to a 0–100 mA meter?

3. When connected to a constant (low) voltage source, a 0–1 mA meter movement reads 0.8 mA. When this meter movement is in parallel with a 20 Ω resistor, the meter reads 0.4 mA. What is the resistance of the meter movement?

4. What value of shunt resistance could be used to convert a 0–1 mA movement to a 0–50 μA meter? Justify your answer.

5. Given a 0–100 μA meter movement with a resistance of 1000 Ω, what shunt is necessary to convert it to 0–0.1000 A meter? How much heat

Figure 6-10

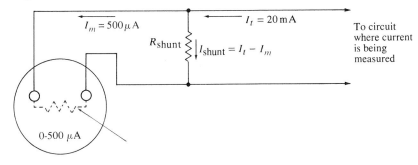

would be dissipated in the meter at maximum current? How much heat would be dissipated in the shunt resistance?

6-3
Voltage
Measurements

THE BASIC VOLTMETER. The d'Arsonval movement responds only to current, but Ohm's law shows that for a given resistance, the current is directly proportional to the applied voltage.

Consider a 0–500 μA meter movement with an internal resistance of 100 ohms. The voltage that must be applied across the internal coil resistance of 100 ohms to produce 500 μA of current flow through it is

$E = IR$

$\quad = (0.0005)(100)$

$\quad = 0.050$

$\quad = 50 \text{ mV}$

This meter movement can be used directly as a voltmeter with a range of 0–50 mV. We should note, too, that if we were to use it this way, it would be like connecting a 100 Ω resistor between the circuit points where the voltage was to be measured.

We seldom need to measure such low voltages, and we quite frequently need to measure voltages that are much higher. Also, we can seldom connect a 100 Ω resistance between the points in a circuit where the voltage is to be measured without significantly affecting the circuit, thus changing the voltage we are trying to measure.

Suppose we were to take the 0–500 μA, 100 Ω meter movement and connect a 9,900 Ω resistor in series with it (Figure 6-11). To cause a current flow of 500 μA through this series combination, we would need a voltage of

$E = IR$

$\quad = 0.0005(9,900 + 100)$

$\quad = 0.0005(10,000)$

$\quad = 5 \text{ V}$

Now the combination of the 0–500 μA meter movement with the series resistance can function as a voltmeter with a range of 0–5 V.

This enables us to measure the voltage of a flashlight cell or, indeed, any voltage between any two points in a circuit so long as it does not exceed 5 V. Note also that connecting the leads of this voltmeter between two points in a circuit is comparable, in its effect on the circuit, to connecting a 10 kΩ resistor between the two points. In many circuits this would have no significant effect.

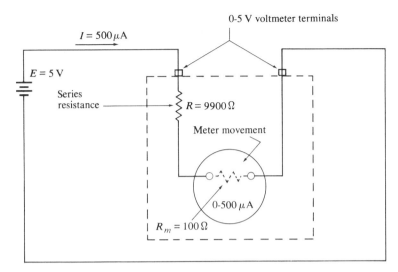

Figure 6-11   This meter movement with a series resistance is a voltmeter.

Usually, we are faced with the problem of finding the correct value of series resistance to convert a given meter movement into a voltmeter of a given range. The total series resistance—the sum of the series resistor plus the resistance of the movement—is the resistance through which the current to cause full-scale pointer deflection of the meter will flow when the desired maximum voltage is applied across it.

Suppose we wished to make a 0–100 V meter out of a 0–1 mA movement   EXAMPLE
with a coil resistance of 20 ohms. What value of series resistance should be used?

Solution.

$$R = \frac{E}{I}.$$

$$= \frac{100}{0.001}$$

$$= 100{,}000 \ \Omega \ \text{total resistance}$$

Since the meter resistance is 20 ohms, the correct value of series resistance is

$$R = 100{,}000 - 20$$

$$= 99{,}980 \ \Omega$$

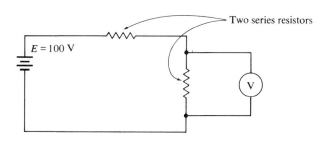

Figure 6-12

This figure is so close to the value of 100,000 Ω, differing by only a small fraction of a percent, that it would be foolish, in most practical applications, to attempt to get a precise value. After all, a 100 kΩ 1% resistor can vary $\pm 1000\ \Omega$ and still be within tolerance.

VOLTMETER SENSITIVITY.   To measure the voltage across a resistor or other component, a voltmeter is connected so that one lead of the meter goes to one component terminal, while the other voltmeter lead goes to the other component terminal. Thus, the voltmeter is effectively in parallel with the component, as in Figure 6-12.

Current flow through the coil of the meter is necessary before there can be any deflection of the pointer. This current is current that does not flow through the component across which the voltage is being measured, since the meter is in parallel. This represents additional circuit current.

If this additional current through the meter is small, the effect on the rest of the circuit will be slight; but if it is not small compared to the other circuit currents, then the effect can be considerable.

Suppose we have two 100 kΩ resistors connected in series, and the series combination connected to a 200 V source, as in Figure 6-13. We can easily calculate that the voltage across each of the resistors must be 100 V. Now suppose we try to measure the voltage across one of the resistors with a 0–100 V meter using a 0–1 mA movement.

A voltmeter with this range and using this movement will require a total series resistance, including the resistance of the movement, of 100 kΩ. If we are to measure the voltage across one of the resistors in the series string, we must place this meter with its total resistance of 100 kΩ across the resistor whose voltage we wish to measure.

The circuit is now a series–parallel arrangement. The combination of the 100 kΩ resistor across which we are trying to measure voltage, and the meter with which we are trying to measure it, makes a parallel bank

Figure 6-13

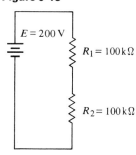

with a total resistance of 50 kΩ. This is shown in Figure 6-14. In combination with the other resistance of the original series string, the total resistance now seen by the voltage source is 150 kΩ, and the current drawn from the source by this total resistance is

$$I = \frac{E}{R}$$

$$= \frac{200 \text{ V}}{150 \text{ k}\Omega}$$

$$= 1.\overline{333} \text{ mA}$$

This is the current that must flow through the series resistor, and the voltage across it will be

$$E = IR$$

$$= 1.\overline{333} \times 100,000$$

$$= 133.33 \text{ V}$$

The voltage across the 50 kΩ total resistance of the parallel bank must be the difference between this voltage and the source potential of 200 V, or

$$E = 200 - 133.33$$

$$= 66.67 \text{ V}$$

The meter will read what the voltage actually is, and with the meter present the voltage actually is about 67 V. This represents a reduction of $\frac{1}{3}$ from the original voltage, and this would be an intolerable error. The error

Figure 6-14

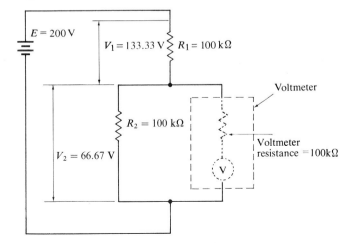

was caused by the effect of the meter current on the rest of the circuit voltages.

Now suppose we repeat the voltage measurement on the original circuit, this time using a 0–100 V meter based on a 10 μA movement.

The series resistance required to make a 0–100 V meter with a 10 μA movement is 10 MΩ. This is the effective meter resistance, and therefore the resistance which will be placed in parallel with the component across which the voltage is being measured.

Again, with the meter in place the original series circuit of two 100 kΩ resistors becomes a series–parallel arrangement, with the 10 MΩ of the meter in parallel with one of the resistors, as shown in Figure 6-15.

The total resistance of this parallel combination is now

$$R_t = \frac{R_1 R_2}{R_1 + R_2}$$

$$= \frac{(10^5)(10^7)}{(10^5) + (100 \times 10^5)}$$

$$= \frac{10^{12}}{101 \times 10^5}$$

$$= \frac{100}{101} \times 10^5$$

$$= 99{,}010 \ \Omega$$

Figure 6-15

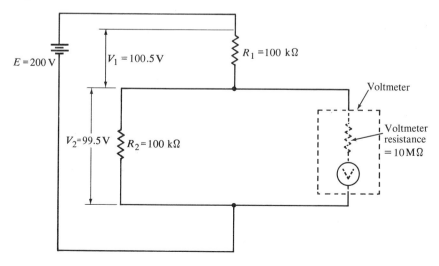

The total resistance of the circuit in which the measurement is being made is thus 199.01 kΩ, and the current from the 200 V source is

$$I = \frac{E}{R}$$

$$= \frac{200}{199.01}$$

$$= 1.005 \text{ mA}$$

This is the current from the voltage source and, consequently, the current that must flow through the series resistor. The voltage across it will be

$$E = IR$$

$$= (1.005)(100,000)$$

$$= 100.5 \text{ V}$$

The voltage across the combination of the meter and the other 100 kΩ resistor will be the difference between this *IR* drop and the source potential, or

$$E = 200 - 100.5$$

$$= 99.5 \text{ V}$$

The error is now $\frac{1}{2}\%$ and is, for most purposes, a quite tolerable error.

In the original circuit the calculated voltage across the original 100 kΩ series resistor was exactly 100 V. Measuring that voltage with a voltmeter using a 0–1 mA movement produced a reading of 67 V, an error of 33 V. Making the same measurement with a voltmeter using a 0–10 μA movement produced a reading of 99.5 V, an error of $\frac{1}{2}$ V.

Note that, since the original circuit composed of two 100 kΩ resistors in series was a symmetrical circuit, everything that has been said about measurements across one resistor applies as well to the other. Using the first voltmeter, we would get a reading of 67 V across *either* of the two resistors, since to make the reading on the second resistor we must move the meter to a new position, altering the circuit again. The two voltages thus obtained do not, obviously, sum to equal the source voltage. We might be tempted to conclude from this that Kirchhoff's current and voltage laws were not valid, if we did not take into account the effect of the meter used on the voltage being measured. Note also that the reading was not incorrect, but was an accurate representation of the actual value of the voltage *with the meter in the circuit*. If we are concerned with the value of the voltage without the meter in the circuit, then we must take into account the effect of the meter.

This effect is called *circuit loading*, and is an effect that will occur in voltage measurements whenever the voltmeter being used draws current from the source. Any simple voltmeter using a d'Arsonval movement and a series resistor to attain the proper range will draw current. The less current required to operate the meter, the less the effect of circuit loading.

The sensitivity of a meter, which includes both the movement and the necessary series resistance, is a measure of the effect it will have on a circuit. It is inversely proportional to the current required for full-scale deflection of the pointer; thus,

$$\text{Sensitivity} = \frac{1}{I_{\text{full scale}}}$$

but   and the reciprocal is

$$I = \frac{E}{R} \qquad\qquad \frac{1}{I} = \frac{R}{E}$$

Sensitivity of a voltmeter is therefore expressed in ohms/volt. For a meter using a basic 0–1 mA movement, the sensitivity is

$$\text{Sensitivity} = \frac{1}{I}$$

$$= \frac{1}{0.001}$$

$$= 1000 \ \Omega/\text{V}$$

For each volt of range, the resistance of such a meter is 1000 Ω. If the basic movement is converted with a series resistance into a voltmeter with a full-scale reading of 3 volts, the resistance of the movement and series resistance combined would be 3000 Ω. This holds true, of course, regardless of the actual voltage being measured; it is entirely due to the value of resistance of the movement and its series resistor. If we were to change the voltmeter to one with a different range, using the same basic movement, the total series resistance required for the new range will be the product of the full-scale reading in volts of the new range times the sensitivity in ohms/volt of the meter. Thus, for a voltmeter with a full-scale range of 10 volts the total voltmeter resistance, using the same movement as before, would be $10 \times 1000 = 10{,}000 \ \Omega$.

A *multirange voltmeter*, where different values of series resistor may be switched in or out to change the range of the meter to different values, usually has the meter sensitivity in ohms/volt marked on it. If it does, it is a simple matter to calculate the total meter resistance for a given range setting, and thus calculate the loading effect that may be expected from using the voltmeter to measure voltages in a given circuit.

A voltmeter having a sensitivity of 1000 ohms/volt is usually considered unsuitable for most work in electronics, since most electronic circuits involve low currents and high resistance. The loading effect from such a meter in these circuits produces significant errors.

A voltmeter using a 50 μA movement will have a sensitivity of 20,000 Ω/V, and, consequently, will produce much less loading effect on a circuit than will the less sensitive meter. The actual effect, of course, depends both on the resistance and current values in the circuit where the measurement is being made, and on the range setting of the meter. A 20,000 Ω/V meter set at a 1 V range presents a resistance of 20,000 Ω to a circuit in which it is being used to measure voltage, while the same instrument, set to a voltage range of 100 V, will appear to the circuit as a resistance of 2 MΩ. The loading effect will obviously be very much less when measurements are made at the higher voltage ranges. Readings made using the higher ranges seldom load a circuit significantly; readings made at low ranges using such an instrument—especially in high-resistance, low-current circuits—often are drastically affected by even this relatively sensitive instrument.

For this reason, *Vacuum Tube Voltmeters* (VTVM) and *Transistor Voltmeters* (TVM) have been developed. Through the use of more complex circuitry than we have yet laid the foundation for discussing, these instruments are able to function with very much less current drawn from the circuit under test than are the simple series voltmeters just discussed. For this reason they can be made to have much less loading effect on the circuit, particularly where voltage readings must be made using low ranges, than the simple voltmeters.

VOLTMETER ACCURACY.   A distinction needs to be made between accuracy of reading of a meter, and the error in measurements due to the loading effect of a voltmeter. In the first example chosen, where the voltage across one of two series 100 kΩ resistors connected to a 200 V source was measured using a 1000 ohm/volt meter, the reading obtained with the meter was 67 V, while the correct value of the voltage without the meter in place was shown by calculation to be 100 V.

This discrepancy between the calculated and measured values does not represent inaccuracy on the part of the meter. When the meter read 67 V, it was quite correct, since with the meter in the circuit that was the actual value of the voltage where it was measured. If the meter had read 70 volts, then it would have been inaccurate by approximately 3 V.

Accuracy depends on the care with which the manufacturer met tolerances in the production of the basic meter movement. Typically, the d'Arsonval movement has an accuracy of about 2%, which means that the reading may be in error by 2% of the full-scale value of the movement. The

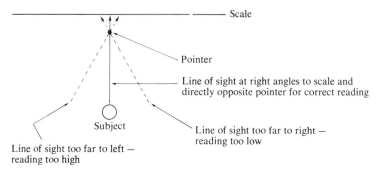

Figure 6-16   Even with a carefully manufactured meter, care must be taken to avoid parallax error or meter readings will be wrong.

necessary series resistor in a voltmeter introduces an additional source of inaccuracy; usually the value of such resistors is within 1% of the specified value. This permits the possibility of errors of 3% of the full-scale value for readings made with the voltmeter.

Accuracy of reading also enters into the final accuracy of a value obtained with such a meter. The position of the pointer can be determined by the eye only within limits, and much depends on the skill of the observer. If readings are taken from one side or the other, the position of the pointer will appear to change; this phenomenon is called *parallax* (Figure 6-16). Readings will be free of parallax error only if the position of the eye is directly opposite the pointer. For this reason, mirror scales are included in many instruments where the accuracy with which the meter is constructed warrants their use. (Such scales are also sometimes included in less accurate instruments, where the only thing that justifies their presence is sales appeal.) In use, the eye is positioned so that the pointer obscures its own reflection in the mirrored strip below the scale graduations on the face of the meter. This will occur if and only if the eye is directly opposite the pointer. Readings taken this way will be free of parallax error.

Accuracy depends on the inherent accuracy of the instrument, and the accuracy with which readings with it are made. Correctness depends on accuracy and the effect of the measuring instrument being measured. Correctness of voltage readings depends on the use of accurate instruments, accurately read, and with minimum loading effect on the circuit by the instrument.

Problems   **1.**   Given a 0–500 μA meter movement with an internal resistance of 75 Ω, find the correct value of series resistance required to make it a 0–250 V voltmeter.

2. Given a 0–1 mA meter movement with an internal resistance of 10 Ω, find the correct value of series resistance required to make it a 0–250 V voltmeter.

3. Which is the most important factor in determining the proper series resistance to make a voltmeter of a given range: the meter movement resistance, or the current required for full-scale deflection of the meter movement?

4. Consider the circuit of Figure 6-14, in which a 100 V source is connected to a simple series circuit consisting of two 1 MΩ resistors in series. A voltmeter with a series resistance of 1 MΩ is connected across one of the two resistors. What voltage would be calculated across each resistor with the voltmeter in place? When voltage is being measured with this voltmeter across one resistor, what voltage actually exists across the other resistor?

5. Suppose the two series resistors in Problem 4 (Figure 6-14) had been 1 kΩ resistors. What voltage would the voltmeter with an internal resistance of 1 MΩ measure across either of these resistors?

6. What should be the internal resistance for a voltmeter to be used in the circuit of Problem 4 if the error produced by meter loading is not to exceed 5%?

7. Express the sensitivity of the meter of Problem 4 in ohms/volt.

8. Express the sensitivity of the meter of Problem 6 in ohms/volt.

9. A voltmeter with a sensitivity of 1000 Ω/V is used on a 5 V range. What is the actual resistance of the meter on this range? What would be the total resistance of the same meter used on a 250 V range?

THE OHMMETER.   A voltmeter can be used to determine the value of an unknown resistance, in conjunction with a known current. If the current through the resistance is some fixed value, the voltage across it will be directly proportional to its resistance.

**6-4
Resistance
Measurements**

A milliammeter can be similarly used. If a known voltage is impressed across an unknown value of resistance, then the current through it as measured by the meter is inversely proportional to its resistance.

Both these methods involve calculations which, though not difficult, are inconvenient. There are two common circuits which are used to measure resistance directly.

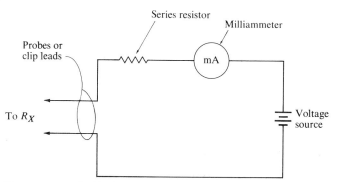

Figure 6-17   A simple series ohmmeter.

The *series ohmmeter* is the simplest circuit. It consists of a battery or other voltage source, a milliammeter, a series resistor, and probes or clip leads to connect the circuit to the unknown resistance (Figure 6-17).

Suppose the battery chosen is a 1.5 V cell, and the meter movement to be used is a 0–1 mA movement with an internal resistance of 25 Ω. The series resistance is chosen so that the total circuit resistance when the test leads are connected together without any resistance between them is such that the total circuit current will cause the meter to read exactly full scale. With the movement and battery specified, the total series resistance, including the meter movement itself, will then be 1500 Ω. Since the meter accounts for 25 Ω, the other series resistance required is 1475 Ω. Because resistors of this precise value are difficult to obtain, and because aging of the battery and consequent slight change in its voltage would require the use of a different value of resistance, it is customary to use a resistance of about 1400 Ω as a fixed resistor and place in series with it a rheostat of about 200 Ω maximum resistance. The circuit may now be adjusted so that the meter will read full scale when the leads are in contact with each other.

At this point the resistance between the two leads is zero, and the point on the scale indicated by the pointer should be marked zero. If the two leads are not in contact with each other, and if there is no current path between them, then the resistance between them is infinite, and the meter scale should be marked accordingly.

If a resistance of 1500 Ω is placed in series with the test leads, the total circuit resistance will be 3000 Ω, and 0.5 mA of current will flow. This will cause half-scale deflection of the meter, and this half-scale point should be marked 1500 Ω.

In a similar fashion, convenient points on the scale can be marked. A complete resistance scale can be marked off, and the value of an unknown resistance read directly from the pointer (Figure 6-18).

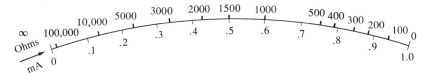

Figure 6-18   The scale of a series ohmmeter.

This simple ohmmeter will function well within its range. Resistance values much below 20 or 30 Ω are difficult to read since the pointer deflects nearly full scale, while resistance values above about 30,000 Ω are also difficult to read since the pointer barely moves. The range for high readings can be extended by using a higher-voltage battery or a more sensitive meter movement. The range for low readings could be extended by using a lower-voltage battery or a less sensitive meter movement. It is, of course, simple to make a highly sensitive meter movement less sensitive by using a current shunt in parallel with it.

SHUNT OHMMETER.   In a *shunt ohmmeter* circuit the battery, resistor, and milliammeter form a complete loop, in which current continuously flows. The test leads are connected in parallel with the meter, so that when a resistor of unknown value is connected to the leads, it is in parallel with the meter (Figure 6-19).

If the resistance of the unknown resistor is equal to the internal resistance of the meter, the current will divide, and the meter will read half scale. If the leads are shorted together, all the current will take the zero resistance path of the short circuit, and the meter will read zero. If the leads are separated, so the resistance between them is infinite, the circuit current, adjusted by the internal resistor, will all flow through the meter, and it will read full scale.

Figure 6-19   The shunt ohmmeter.

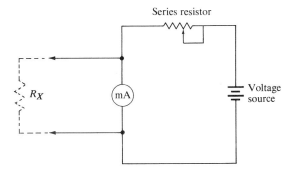

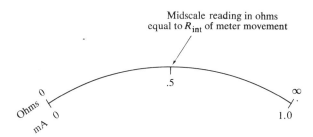

Figure 6-20   The scale of a shunt ohmmeter.

The scale reads opposite to the scale for the series ohmmeter. In the series ohmmeter the scale showed infinity to the left and zero to the right. In the shunt ohmmeter the scale shows zero to the left and infinity to the right (Figure 6-20).

In the series ohmmeter, center-scale reading corresponds to a resistance between the test leads equal in value to the internal series resistor of the ohmmeter circuit. In the shunt ohmmeter, center-scale reading corresponds to a resistance between the test leads equal to the meter resistance.

The meter resistance is very much smaller than any reasonable value for the series resistance in the series ohmmeter. Therefore, the shunt ohmmeter is much better adapted to low resistance readings. Readings as low as 0.1 ohm can be made with reasonable accuracy with this circuit.

The range of reading can be extended either by using a meter shunt—which has the effect of reducing the effective resistance of the meter and thus reducing the value of the center-scale reading—or by using a resistance in series with the meter movement. This has the effect of increasing the effective resistance of the meter, and the center-scale reading will be the sum of the resistance of the meter and the series resistor.

Note that current is continuously flowing in this circuit. If no switch is provided, the battery will soon be exhausted.

MULTIRANGE OHMMETERS. A circuit frequently found in multirange ohmmeters, particularly where they are combined in a single case with a multirange volt/milliammeter, is shown in Figure 6-21.

In this circuit the unknown resistance is connected in series with a range resistor, and the meter movement is connected directly across the range resistor. There is sufficient series resistance in the meter circuit so that it is actually best understood as a voltmeter connected across the range resistor. If the battery voltage is 1.5 V, then the meter circuit will have the proper series resistance to produce full-scale deflection when 1.5 V is impressed across the range resistor.

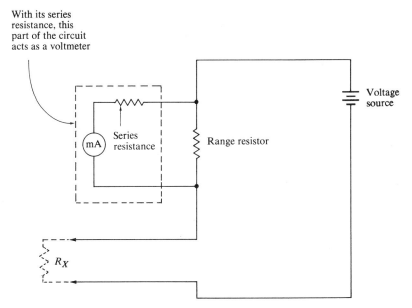

Figure 6-21   The multirange ohmmeter circuit.

If the test leads are shorted together, the full battery potential is placed across the range resistor, and the zero adjust is set for full-scale deflection of the meter. This corresponds to zero resistance between the test leads. When the test leads are separated, the resistance between them is infinite; the circuit from the battery is broken, and the meter will read all the way to the left. This corresponds to a resistance reading of infinity, and the scale will be so marked.

If a resistor of a value equal to the resistance of the range resistor is connected between the test leads, the voltage of the source will be divided equally between the range resistor and the resistor under test. Since half the maximum potential appears across the range resistor, the meter will read half scale. This marking on the scale should correspond to the value of the range resistor. By using range resistors in multiples of ten of the desired low-range midscale value, a single scale can be used for all ranges. The different values of range resistors are selected by a range switch on the front of the instrument case. They are usually marked $R \times 1$, $R \times 10$, $R \times 1000$, etc. If the pointer indicates 15 on the scale, and the range switch is in the $R \times 1$ position, the resistance being read is 15 Ω, while if the switch is set at $R \times 1000$, the resistance being read is 15,000 Ω (Figure 6-22).

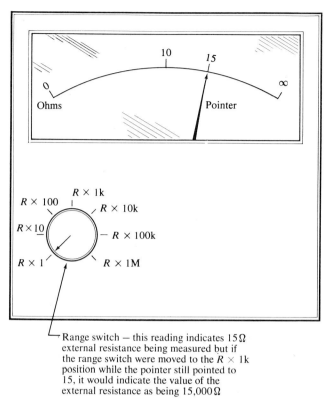

Range switch — this reading indicates 15 Ω
external resistance being measured but if
the range switch were moved to the R × 1k
position while the pointer still pointed to
15, it would indicate the value of the
external resistance as being 15,000 Ω

Figure 6-22   The range switch on a multirange ohmmeter
gives the meter a wide capability.

USING OHMMETERS.   There are two points to keep always in mind when
using ohmmeters. First, all commercial ohmmeters as parts of the complete
circuit of multirange, multifunction test instruments apply a voltage to the
circuit element under test, and cause current to flow through it if it does not
represent an open circuit. Second, if there is already current flowing
through the circuit element under test, or a potential across it, not only
will the ohmmeter reading have no relationship to any actual resistance in
the circuit, but the likelihood of damage to the meter, and particularly to
the range resistors on the low ranges, is very great.

Some circuits, particularly those in which there is a sensitive meter
movement, or one in which there are transistors, can be damaged by the
injudicious use of an ohmmeter. In most commercial ohmmeters the current
through a circuit element under test will be less on the higher ohmmeter
ranges and more on the lower. For the protection of the equipment

most tests should be made with the ohmmeter range switch at the $R \times 1000$ range or higher.

Ohmmeters are often used for simple *continuity tests,* where the only information needed is whether or not a complete circuit exists. If it is suspected that there may be a break in the wiring of a printed circuit board, or an open circuit condition in a coil, the ohmmeter, on nearly any range, will quickly determine if the suspected malfunction is present. Before the ohmmeter reading of zero resistance can be taken as an indication of continuity, however, it is necessary to determine whether there are any parallel current paths which might give a false indication. For example, let us make the unlikely assumption that a coil, which should have a low resistance so far as the ohmmeter is concerned, is in a circuit where it is actually in parallel with another coil, also having a low resistance. If the first coil is open, an ohmmeter reading taken across it will still show low resistance, because the ohmmeter will be reading the low resistance of the parallel path through the other coil. It would be necessary in this case to unsolder and disconnect at least one terminal of the suspected coil, so that its resistance could be determined in isolation from the rest of the circuit (Figure 6-23).

This holds true for all measurements taken with the ohmmeter. Where the component under test is part of a circuit, it is, in general, necessary

Figure 6-23 If an open condition is suspected in one of two coils mounted in parallel, disconnect one terminal of that coil in order to get an accurate reading of its resistance.

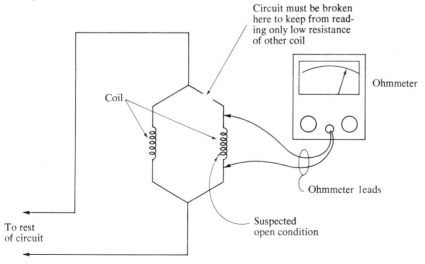

to disconnect one terminal of the component whose resistance is to be determined to prevent a false reading due to parallel current paths in the rest of the circuit. The exceptions to this are where knowledge of the circuit enables the technician to determine that there are no parallel current paths. Note that a parallel current path will cause the resistance reading to be lower than it should be, while the typical defects in resistive circuit elements will cause the resistance to increase. Thus, a lower-than-expected resistance reading almost certainly means a parallel current path exists, while a higher-than-expected reading almost certainly means the value of the resistance under test has increased. A normal or within-tolerance reading taken with the resistor in circuit may mean the value of the resistor being measured is within tolerance, but it may also occur because the value of the resistance has increased while parallel current paths containing resistance simultaneously cause low reading. If the two factors cancel each other out, a resistance reading may correspond to the marked value of the resistor, within tolerance, and the resistor still be well over tolerance. The only certain way to prevent this from occurring is to disconnect one end of the resistor before measuring its value with an ohmmeter.

A possible parallel path that can cause unsuspected erroneous indications is the technician's own body. The resistance between different points on the human body is roughly in the range of 10 kΩ to 100 kΩ, though this varies considerably, depending on the nature of the contacts, moisture on the skin, pressure, and several other factors which may change from day to day, even in the same person. If a technician makes a resistance measurement, holding the test leads on the resistor to be measured in such a way that he is in contact with both resistor terminals, then he provides a parallel high-resistance current path. This will not cause an electrical shock, since the potential across the meter leads in most ohmmeters is low; but if the measurement is being made on a high-resistance range, considerable error may result.

Always check the zero setting immediately before making a measurement, particularly if it has been necessary to change ranges. If the zero setting cannot be made with the adjustment provided, the battery is almost certainly exhausted and should be replaced.

In some tests the polarity of the voltage the ohmmeter applies to the circuit element under test is important. This always is the case when checking diodes or transistors with an ohmmeter.

It is easy to assume, where the ohmmeter represents one of the functions of a multimeter which has two test leads, one red and one black, that the red lead is connected to the positive terminal of the ohmmeter battery. This is a particularly tempting assumption where the red lead plugs into a jack on the face of the multimeter that is marked +V-mA-OHMS.

It is not always so. Manufacturers differ in their designs, and the ohmmeter can function with either polarity of leads, depending on the circuit design. The red lead may be positive, and it may be negative, so far as the polarity of potential it will apply to the circuit under test with the test instrument on OHMS function is concerned.

It is easy to determine, for any multimeter, what the test lead polarity on OHMS function actually is. All that is necessary is to connect the test leads to another voltmeter, set on a range low enough to give an indication but high enough to prevent damage to the voltmeter. For nearly all ohmmeters, this would be a 5–10 V range if the ohmmeter is on one of its low ranges, $R \times 1$ to $R \times 1000$. If the ohmmeter polarity is to be checked with its range switch set higher than $R \times 1000$, it would be safest to set the voltmeter to a range not less than 30 V, since in many cases higher-voltage ohmmeter batteries are automatically switched in as the range setting is increased. With the proper voltmeter, the direction of needle deflection is noted when the red, or +, lead of the ohmmeter is connected to the positive terminal of the voltmeter, while the other ohmmeter lead is connected to the voltmeter negative terminal.

If the deflection is upward, in the normal direction, then the red lead from the ohmmeter is, indeed, positive, and can be counted on to apply a positive potential to components under test, compared to the black lead. If, however, the deflection of the voltmeter needle is downward, but can be made to deflect upward when the ohmmeter leads are reversed, then the ohmmeter lead polarity is such that the red lead is negative, and the black positive.

Problems

1. A series ohmmeter uses a 10 mA movement with a 75 Ω internal resistor, and operates on a 3 V battery. Calculate the series resistance value that will cause a full-scale deflection when the test leads are shorted.

2. A series ohmmeter uses a 100 μA movement with a 500 Ω internal resistance, a 1.5 V battery, and a 14.5 kΩ series resistance. What value of an unknown resistor measured by the ohmmeter would cause a half-scale deflection? A 25% scale deflection? A 60% deflection?

3. What is the meter movement of a series ohmmeter that operates on a 1.25 V battery, has an internal movement resistance of 100 Ω and contains a series resistance of 2400 Ω?

4. Resistor R_x causes a 35% scale deflection, when measured by a series ohmmeter with a 250 μA movement, 650 Ω internal resistance, and an 11,350 Ω series resistance. Calculate the voltage of the battery used

by the ohmmeter and the value of R_x. Suppose that, in order to extend the range for low readings, we place a shunt resistor of 350 Ω across the meter movement and adjust the series resistance to bring the short-circuit ($R_x = 0$) deflection to full scale. What percentage of full-scale deflection would R_x now give? If instead, in order to extend the range of high readings, we triple the battery size and again adjust R_s, the series resistance, what deflection would R_x give? For both cases and the original meter, what value of R_x would give a half-scale deflection?

5. The shunt ohmmeter shown in Figure 6-19 has a meter movement of 0–10 μA, with a 50 Ω internal resistance, and operates on a battery of 9 V. Assuming R_s is sufficiently large so as not to significantly influence the calculations, determine the respective values of R_x that would give 10%, 50%, and 75% scale deflections.

6. A shunt ohmmeter has a 0–100 μA movement and operates on a 9 V battery. What is the internal resistance of the movement, if the center scale reads 25 Ω? If it is desired to increase the center scale reading, should a series resistance or shunt resistance be added to the meter's circuit? Calculate the value of the added resistance if the center scale is to be twice the original reading; fifteen times the original reading.

7. Suppose, for the shunt ohmmeter in Problem 6, it is desired to *reduce* the center scale reading. Should a shunt resistance or series resistance be added to the circuit? Calculate the value of the added resistance if a center scale resistance of $\frac{1}{2}$ the original center scale reading is desired; if $\frac{1}{10}$ the original reading is desired.

8. On a multirange ohmmeter the center scale reads 10, and the range switch has the settings of $R \times 0.1$, $R \times 1$, $R \times 10$, $R \times 100$, $R \times 1$ k, $R \times 5$ k, $R \times 10$ k, and $R \times 50$ k. What is the value of the range resistance for each setting?

9. On the multirange ohmmeter of Problem 8 the range switch is set to $R \times 5$ k, and the meter scale reads 15 when an unknown resistance is measured. What is the value of this resistance? What will this resistance read on the scale for each of the other multirange settings?

Key Words   **circuit loading**   the effect that occurs in voltage measurements when the voltmeter being used draws current from the source

meter shunt   a resistor used to increase the range of a meter

milliammeter   a meter used to measure low values of current

parallax   the apparent change in meter readings when taken from either side of the meter

series ohmmeter   a meter consisting of a battery, a milliammeter, a resistor, and probes or clip leads (which connect the meter circuit in series with an unknown resistance)

shunt ohmmeter circuit   a circuit in which battery, resistor, and milliammeter form a complete loop with continuous current flow

vacuum tube voltmeter   a meter that can function with much less current than a simple series voltmeter

1.   A few turns of wire wrapped around an iron nail and connected to a flashlight cell can make a temporary magnet of the nail.   **Summary of Concepts**

2.   Magnets attract or repel one another, depending on whether unlike or like poles face one another.

3.   The d'Arsonval principle makes use of magnetic attraction and repulsion to detect current and polarity.

4.   The deflection of the pointer of a d'Arsonval meter produced by a given current flowing through the coil depends on the number of turns of wire in the coil, the strength of the magnets that produce the magnetic field, and the retarding force of either the hairspring or taut-band suspension.

5.   The actual internal resistance of the basic meter movement is determined by the diameter and length of the wire used in winding the moving coil.

6.   The direction of current flow through the coil of the meter determines the polarity of the magnetic field and thus determines whether the moving coil will rotate clockwise or counterclockwise.

7.   A current-measuring meter must be connected only at the point where the measurement is to be made.

8.   A meter cannot be altered in any practical way to increase its sensitivity.

9.   To calculate the appropriate value of a meter shunt, it is necessary to know either the internal resistance of the meter movement or its deflection sensitivity in millivolts.

10.   To measure the voltage across a resistor or other component, a voltmeter is connected so that one lead of the meter goes to one component terminal and the other meter lead goes to the other component terminal.

11. The sensitivity of a meter is a measure of the effect it will have on a circuit. Sensitivity is inversely proportional to the current required for full-scale deflection of the pointer.

12. In an ohmmeter a mid-scale reading corresponds to a resistance between the test leads equal in value to the internal range resistor of the ohmmeter circuit.

13. Commercial ohmmeters apply a voltage to the circuit element under test and cause current to flow through it if the circuit is not open.

14. An ohmmeter is subject to severe damage if it is attached to a circuit that already has current flowing through it or a potential across it.

To Help You Review   *On a separate sheet of paper, fill in the blanks or answer the questions below. The number following each question refers to the section in the chapter where the correct answer can be found.*

1. What is needed to make a temporary magnet out of an iron nail? (6-1)

2. When do magnets attract each other? (6-1)

3. The strength of a magnetic field depends on _____ and _____ . (6-1)

4. The d'Arsonval principle can be applied in two general ways. Describe them. (6-1)

5. What determines pointer deflection in a meter? (6-2)

6. How is the sensitivity of a meter measured? (6-2)

7. Explain the actual internal resistance of the basic meter movement. (6-2)

8. What determines the direction of movement of a meter coil? (6-2)

9. Where should a meter be connected? (6-2)

10. In what way can the sensitivity of a meter be altered? (6-2)

11. What is a meter shunt? (6-2)

12. How is a voltmeter connected to measure voltage across a resistor? (6-3)

13. What is a circuit "loading" effect? (6-3)

14. What is inversely proportional to the current required for full-scale deflection of the pointer? (6-3)

15. What is a vacuum tube voltmeter and why is it used? (6-3)

16. In reading a meter, what error is often made? (6-3)

17. How can meter readings be free of parallax? (6-3)

18. What use does a milliammeter have in common with a voltmeter? (6-4)

19. What does a series ohmmeter consist of? (6-4)

20. Compare a series ohmmeter and a shunt ohmmeter with respect to center-scale reading. (6-4)

21. In a shunt ohmmeter, the test leads are connected in _____ with the meter. (6-4)

22. Commercial ohmmeters apply a _____ to the circuit element under test and cause _____ to flow through it. (6-4)

23. How can an ohmmeter be seriously damaged? (6-4)

This chapter will help you understand

☐ transformation solutions to resistance networks
☐ Thevenin's theorem and the Thevenin equivalent circuit
☐ Norton's theorem and the Norton equivalent circuit
☐ delta–wye and wye–delta transformations

**7-1
Superposition**

MULTIPLE VOLTAGE SOURCES. Circuits containing multiple voltage sources may not be directly solvable by simple series–parallel circuit reduction. They are often easily solved by the technique of *superposition*.

To use this method, the circuit is redrawn as many times as there are voltage sources in the original circuit. Each drawing shows only one of the voltage sources; each of the other sources is replaced by a short circuit. Each drawing is then a complete circuit, but with a single voltage source.

For each drawing, the current through each resistance may be calculated. Once the current through each circuit element is known for each voltage source, the results can be combined algebraically to give the actual circuit current through each resistor caused by all the voltage sources in the original circuit.

This is true because the current and voltage for each component are the algebraic sum of the effects produced by each voltage source acting separately.

Figure 7-1(a) contains what may appear at first glance to be a simple series–parallel circuit, but it contains two voltage sources. It cannot be reduced further by simple series–parallel reduction. No two resistors are in series with each other, so no reduction by combinations of series resistors is possible. No two resistors are in parallel with each other; R_2 and R_3 both have the point marked y as a common junction for their terminals, but the point marked x is not a common junction, since battery E_2 interposes. Therefore, no reduction by combinations of resistors in parallel is possible.

To solve this circuit by the method of superposition, we must make two drawings, one for each source. In each drawing, the other source is "killed" as a source of potential, but the circuit is otherwise unchanged from the original. To "kill" a source, we remove it as a source of potential, but not in any other way. In this example the sources were both voltage sources. This means that the effect of such internal resistance as they each might have was neglected; therefore, they can be replaced by short circuits. If the internal resistance was a significant factor for either source, the drawing replacing it as a source would still have to include its internal resistance as part of the circuit as redrawn.

The two drawings, each showing a single source, are shown in Figure 7-1(b) and (c). In 7-1(b) the drawing shows E_1 as the only source; the arrows showing conventional current flow indicate current in all three resistors

Figure 7-1 A circuit with multiple voltage sources is solved by the method of superposition.

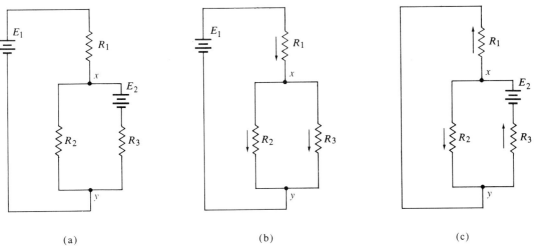

(a)   (b)   (c)

flowing downward toward the bottom of the page. R_2 and R_3 are in parallel with each other, while R_1 is in series with the parallel combination. Given the source potential and the resistance value of each circuit component, the current flow through each and the voltage across each resistor can be easily calculated.

Figure 7-1(c) shows E_2 as the only source. Note carefully that the direction of conventional current flow as indicated by the arrows is *not* the same in all cases as in the drawing of 7-1(b). Both drawings show the same direction of current flow through R_2, but both R_1 and R_3 show a direction of current flow in 7-1(c) that is opposite to that shown in 7-1(b). The combination of resistors in series and parallel is not the same in the drawing of 7-1(c) as it was in 7-1(b). In 7-1(c), R_1 and R_2 are in parallel with each other, and R_3 is in series with the parallel combination.

For R_1 and R_3, where the currents due to each of the two sources are not in the same direction, the total current due to both sources is the difference between the two values, and the direction of the final current is the direction of the individual source current having the greatest magnitude. For R_2 both currents are in the same direction, and this is the direction of the total current for that resistor. Its magnitude is the sum of the values due to each of the two sources.

EXAMPLE   Given the circuit of Figure 7-2(a) with the values of voltage and resistance as marked, calculate the voltage across and current through each resistor.

Solution.   The circuit is redrawn, so that each drawing shows a single source. Figure 7-2(b) shows only the 16 V source. R_2 and R_3 form a parallel bank whose resistance is

$$R_{2-3} = \frac{(3)(6)}{3+6}$$

$$= \frac{18}{9}$$

$$= 2\,\Omega$$

If the parallel bank is replaced by its equivalent resistance of 2 Ω, the total series resistance of the circuit is 8 Ω, and the current from the source will be 2 A. This current through R_1 will cause a 12 V *IR* drop across it, and the voltage remaining from the source voltage to appear across the parallel bank will be 4 V. This means there will be 4 V across each resistor in the parallel bank. Four volts across the 3 Ω resistor gives a current through it of

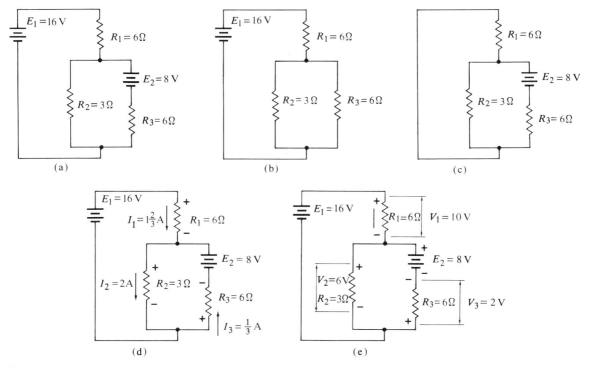

Figure 7-2

$$I = \frac{V}{R}$$

$$= \frac{4}{3}$$

$$= 1\tfrac{1}{3} \text{ A}$$

Four volts across the 6 Ω resistor gives a current through it of

$$I = \frac{V}{R}$$

$$= \frac{4}{6}$$

$$= \frac{2}{3} \text{ A}$$

The sum of the two branch currents is 2 A, satisfying Kirchhoff's current law.

The results are tabulated on the next page.

Circuit (b)

	R	V_b	I_b
R_1	$6\,\Omega$	12 V	2 A
R_2	$3\,\Omega$	4 V	$\frac{4}{3}$ A
R_3	$6\,\Omega$	4 V	$\frac{2}{3}$ A

For Figure 7-2(c) the calculation is done in exactly the same way. The results are tabulated below.

Circuit (c)

	R	V_c	I_c
R_1	$6\,\Omega$	2	$\frac{1}{3}$
R_2	$3\,\Omega$	2	$\frac{2}{3}$
R_3	$6\,\Omega$	6	1

If the currents and voltages are plotted on diagrams 7-2(b) and (c), it can be seen that Kirchhoff's current law is obeyed at each junction, and Kirchhoff's voltage law is true for each loop. If this were not so, the calculations would be in error.

Now the current and voltage for each resistor for each source are known. They may be combined, with due regard for direction of current and polarity of voltage, in the original circuit. The tabulation of the algebraic summation of voltages and currents follows.

Circuit (a) (both sources)

	R	$V_b + V_c$	$I_b + I_c$
R_1	$6\,\Omega$	$12 - 2 = 10$ V	$2 - \frac{1}{3} = 1\frac{2}{3}$ A
R_2	$3\,\Omega$	$4 + 2 = 6$ V	$\frac{4}{3} + \frac{2}{3} = 2$ A
R_3	$6\,\Omega$	$4 - 6 = -2$ V	$\frac{2}{3} - 1 = -\frac{1}{3}$ A

The polarity of voltage and direction of current shown in Figure 7-2(b) have been taken as positive, and those of (c) as either positive or negative, depending on whether they are the same as or different from those of (b). In the tabulation of voltages and currents for circuit (a), the original circuit, both voltage and current for R_3 are given as negative. This merely indicates the final current is in the opposite direction to that assumed in circuit (b). Total circuit currents are entered in Figure 7-2(d), and total circuit voltages are entered in Figure 7-2(e).

An important check is that Kirchhoff's laws not be violated in the currents and voltages shown as the final result in the original circuit. In this case they are not. Each loop in Figure 7-2(e) sums to zero voltage, and the currents at each junction in Figure 7-2(d) also sum to zero. If they did not, it would indicate an error in the calculations, although the fact that they do is not a guarantee that the results are correct.

VOLTAGE AND CURRENT SOURCES.   By definition, a voltage source is one which has no internal resistance, so that the voltage at the terminals remains constant regardless of how much current is delivered by the source. No real source is a perfect voltage source, though there are many that approach it quite closely up to some maximum current capability. With an electronically regulated power supply, the terminal voltage may vary only a small fraction of a percent over a wide range of currents. An automobile battery has a very low internal resistance; it, too, approaches being a voltage source even for quite large currents.

Current sources are less frequently encountered. A perfect current source would consist of an internal series resistance approaching infinity, and a perfect voltage source approaching infinity. For example, consider the current delivered to a load by an approximation to a current source composed of a voltage source with a potential of 10,000,000 V in series with a resistance of 100,000,000 ohms.

If we were to short the terminals of this current source together, the current flow between them would be limited by the internal resistance, and would be 100 mA. If we were to insert a 100 Ω resistor between the terminals, the current through it would still be 0.999999 A = 99.9999 mA. The change in current in going from zero resistance to 100 Ω resistance is not significant. Even substituting a 10,000 Ω resistor between the terminals changes the current but slightly; with this resistor in place the current is 99.9900 mA.

No practical source of power—whether battery, generator, or electronic circuit—is either a perfect voltage source or a constant current source, though there are many that approach one or the other of these ideal mathematical fictions over some range of operation. It is possible, and for some calculations highly desirable, to consider any practical power source either as a perfect voltage source with some series resistance, or as a constant current source with some parallel resistance.

Given the circuit of Figure 7-3(a), find the voltage across and current through   EXAMPLE
each component.

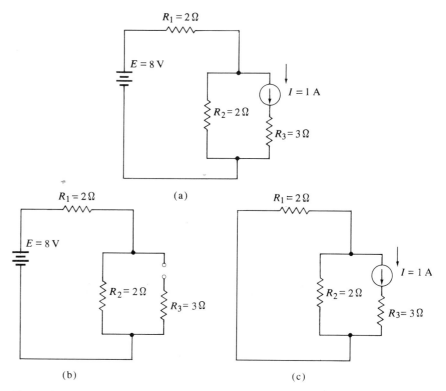

Figure 7-3

Solution. As before, the circuit is redrawn as many times as there are sources of voltage or current in the original circuit. Each drawing is to show only one power source, the others being replaced by their equivalent resistance.

Figure 7-3(b) shows the circuit redrawn with the 8 V voltage source as the only source. The current source has been replaced with its equivalent, an open circuit. As we have seen, the current source could be considered to be a series combination of a very high voltage source and a very high resistance. Thus, the equivalent resistance for a perfect current source is an open circuit.

Circuit (b) is now a simple series circuit, and voltages and currents for each resistor may be easily calculated. The results are tabulated below.

Circuit (b)

	R	I	V
R_1	$2\,\Omega$	2 A	4 V
R_2	$2\,\Omega$	2 A	4 V
R_3	$3\,\Omega$	0 A	0 V

Circuit (c) is a simple series–parallel circuit, containing a single current source. The current all flows through R_3, since it is in series with the source. With its resistance known, the IR drop across it can be easily calculated. R_1 and R_2 are in parallel with each other; the source current will divide between them so the two currents are inversely proportional to the resistances. Since the resistances in this case are equal, the currents will also be equal. The results are tabulated below.

Circuit (c)

	R	I	V
R_1	$2\,\Omega$	$\frac{1}{2}$ A	1 V
R_2	$2\,\Omega$	$-\frac{1}{2}$ A	-1 V
R_3	$3\,\Omega$	1 A	3 V

Now the results may be combined and tabulated for the original circuit (a), containing both sources. Due regard must, of course, be given for direction of current flow and polarity of IR drops. It will be observed that in the tabulation for circuit (c), R_2 is shown as having a negative I and V. This is because, for this resistor, the direction of current and polarity of potential are opposite to that for circuit (b). They combine as shown in this tabulation.

Circuit (a) (with both sources)

	R	I	V
R_1	$2\,\Omega$	$2+\frac{1}{2}=2.5$ A	$4+1=5$ V
R_2	$2\,\Omega$	$2-\frac{1}{2}=1.5$ A	$4-1=3$ V
R_3	$3\,\Omega$	$0+1=1$ A	$0+3=3$ V

Again, when the results are examined in the original circuit, it is apparent that at each junction the currents sum algebraically to zero, and in each loop the IR drops equal the source voltages in that loop.

Problems

1. Given the circuit shown (see next page), with $E_1 = 20$ V, $E_2 = 10$ V, $R_1 = 20$ kΩ, $R_2 = 10$ kΩ, and $R_3 = 10$ kΩ, calculate the voltage across and current through each resistor.

2. In the circuit shown (see next page), $E_1 = 22.5$ V, $E_2 = 7.2$ V, $R_1 = 2.2$ kΩ, $R_2 = 1.8$ kΩ, and $R_3 = 3.3$ kΩ, calculate the voltage across and current through each resistor.

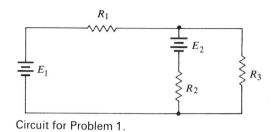

Circuit for Problem 1.

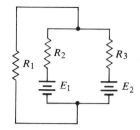

Circuit for Problem 2.

3. In the circuit shown, $E_1 = 10$ V, $E_2 = 12$ V, $R_1 = 3\,\Omega$, $R_2 = 6\,\Omega$, and $R_3 = 3\,\Omega$. Calculate voltage across and current through each resistor.

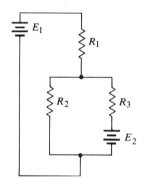

Circuit for Problem 3.

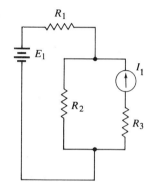

Circuit for Problem 4.

4. In the circuit shown, $E_1 = 100$ V, while I_1 is a current source with a constant current of 0.2 A. $R_1 = 10$ kΩ, $R_2 = 6.8$ kΩ, and $R_3 = 820\,\Omega$. Calculate the current through and voltage across each resistor.

5. In the circuit shown, $E_1 = 67$ V and $E_2 = 21$ V, while I_1 is a 125 mA constant current source. $R_1 = 1.5$ kΩ, $R_2 = 2.7$ kΩ, and $R_3 = 560\,\Omega$. Calculate the voltage across and current through each resistor.

Circuit for Problem 5.

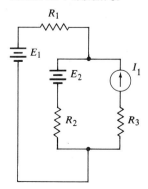

"BLACK-BOX" CIRCUITS. It is usually not necessary to find the voltage across and current through each component in a complex circuit. Suppose we have some complex resistive network, connected to one or more voltage or current sources. If the problem is to find the voltage and current for one component in that network, the labor involved can usually be greatly simplified by the application of *Thevenin's theorem*. Indeed, this is one of the most useful concepts in circuit analysis, though often not well understood.

7-2 Thevenin's Theorem

Given the circuit of Figure 7-4(a), in which there is a simple series–parallel circuit connected to a single voltage source, suppose that we are concerned only with the voltage across and current through the $6\,\Omega$ resistor, a part of the parallel bank. Now suppose further that we take the entire circuit, source and all, except for the $6\,\Omega$ resistor designated as the load resistor, R_l, and in our imaginations place the circuit in a large but unlabeled black box, as in Figure 7-4(b). The two conductors by which R_l is connected to the rest of the circuit are brought outside the box to two terminals. If the load resistor of $6\,\Omega$ is now connected to these terminals, the circuit will be electrically the same as before, and the voltage and current at this resistor will be unchanged.

Can we, by changing the value of the load resistor to any value (including

Figure 7-4   Using the "black box" concept to find the voltage and current for one component of a network.

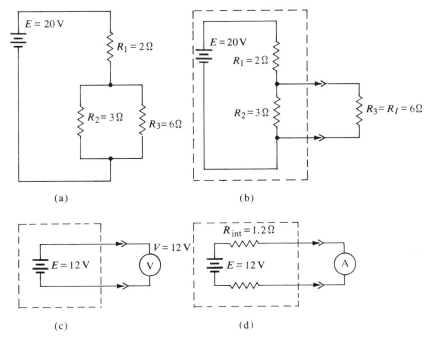

(a)   (b)

(c)   (d)

zero and infinity), determine exactly what circuit the box contains by measuring the resulting voltage and current at the terminals? Let us make some imaginary measurements and examine the conclusions.

First, remove the load resistor so that the resistance between the terminals is infinite. Knowing what is in the box, we can calculate that the voltage measured across the terminals would be 12 V. If this were our only measurement, we might conclude that the black box contained a 12 V source connected directly to the terminals, as in Figure 7-4(c).

Now let us try another measurement. The first measurement was with the terminals open, an infinite resistance between them. Now let us see what current flows between the terminals with zero resistance. We could do this by connecting an ammeter, with no significant internal resistance, directly between the terminals and measuring the current through it. Again, knowing what is in the box, we can calculate the result. Since, in the original circuit, the only thing between the ammeter and the 20 V source is the 2 Ω resistor, 10 A would flow through the meter.

Now what might we conclude? On the basis of the first measurement, it was decided that the box might contain a 12 V source connected directly to the terminals. If this were all, however, the current of our second measurement would have been infinite. The box still has to contain a voltage source of at least 12 V to account for the first reading, but how can we then account for the second? Obviously, something in the box limited the current. A series resistance between the source and the terminals could account for the second reading and would not affect the first since, with the load removed, no current would flow through it. The proper value of resistance, assuming the box contained a 12 V source, would be 1.2 Ω. This simple circuit, a 12 V source in series with a 1.2 Ω resistor, could account for both readings. See Figure 7-4(d).

Now what would happen if we tried some other value of load resistance? Suppose we insert the original 6 Ω resistor at the terminals of the new circuit as in Figure 7-4(d). The 6 Ω in series with the 1.2 Ω gives a total series resistance of 7.2 Ω. With a 12 V source, the current is $1\frac{2}{3}$ A, and the potential across the 6 Ω resistor is therefore 10 V.

Now let us try the 6 Ω resistor in the terminals of the original circuit in the black box of Figure 7-4(b). A little calculation shows the potential across it to be 10 V, and the current through it to be $1\frac{2}{3}$ A. This is exactly the same as with our conjectural circuit, the 12 V source in series with a 1.2 Ω resistor. We can experiment with various other values of load resistor in both circuits, in addition to the infinite, zero, and 6 Ω already tried. Each time, no matter what value is tried, we will find, with both the original circuit and the simple series circuit derived by deduction, exactly the same voltage and current at the load resistor.

This answers our original question: We could not tell exactly what was in the black box by any conceivable voltage and current measurements on any value of load resistance at its terminals. Instead, we found a simple series circuit with a single voltage source that acted in exactly the same way, so far as any load resistor was concerned. This new circuit was a simple equivalent to the original circuit.

It is important to note that the equivalent circuit is entirely independent of the value of the original load resistor and, indeed, is derived without any consideration of the load resistor. This makes the application of Thevenin's theorem so useful: by removing from consideration the load resistor itself, the original circuit is considerably simplified and thus much more amenable to calculation.

Now let's try a brief statement summarizing Thevenin's theorem. *Any two-terminal network can be replaced by an equivalent circuit consisting of a perfect voltage source, E_{Th}—with a voltage equal to the open-circuit voltage of the original circuit with the load resistor removed—in series with a resistance, R_{Th}, equal to the resistance measured back into the original network with the load resistance removed and all internal sources in the network removed and replaced with their equivalent internal resistances.*

This statement differs slightly from what we have done. Instead of measuring the resistance back into the circuit, with the load resistor removed and all voltage sources in the original network replaced by their equivalent resistance, we measured the current that flowed between the terminals when they were shorted together. As can be seen from Figure 7-5, E_{Th}, R_{Th}, and the short-circuit current are all related by Ohm's law; if two are known, the third is easily calculated.

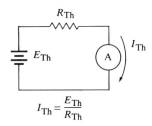

$$I_{Th} = \frac{E_{Th}}{R_{Th}}$$

Figure 7-5

Given the circuit of Figure 7-6(a), calculate the potential across R_l, the 6 ohm resistor.   EXAMPLE

Solution.   This is not a simple series–parallel circuit, since no two resistors are in series with each other, nor are any two in parallel with each other. It cannot, therefore, be solved by any series–parallel substitutions. It cannot be solved by the method of superposition, either, since there is only a single source.

It can be solved by the application of Thevenin's theorem. To calculate the Thevenin equivalent circuit, we need two quantities: the open-circuit voltage, and the Thevenin equivalent resistance.

The *Thevenin equivalent resistance* is that resistance which would be measured between the load terminals with the load removed and all sources in the network replaced by their equivalent resistances. Figure 7-6(b) shows the resulting circuit. Removal of the load resistor has made it a simple series–

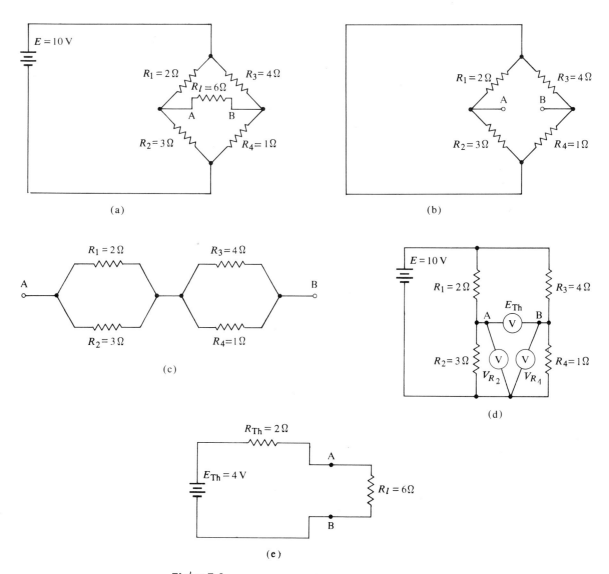

Figure 7-6

parallel circuit, and it is now easy to calculate the resistance that would be read by an ohmmeter connected between points A and B.

Examination of this circuit shows R_1 and R_2 are effectively in parallel with each other, and this parallel bank is in series with a parallel bank made up of R_3 and R_4, as in Figure 7-6(c). The total resistance between A and B is, therefore,

$$R_{\text{Th}} = \frac{R_1 R_2}{R_1 + R_2} + \frac{R_3 R_4}{R_3 + R_4}$$

$$= \frac{(2)(3)}{2 + 3} + \frac{(4)(1)}{4 + 1}$$

$$= 2 \, \Omega$$

This is the desired resistance for our Thevenin equivalent circuit.

The *Thevenin equivalent voltage* can also be easily determined. It is the open-circuit voltage with the load resistor removed. With this load resistor removed, the circuit becomes a simple series–parallel arrangement. In Figure 7-6(d) the circuit has been drawn. What is needed is the voltage that would be measured by a voltmeter connected between points A and B. The voltage between point A and the negative side of the source can be easily determined, as can the voltage between point B and the negative side of the source. The desired voltage between A and B is simply the difference between these two voltages.

The voltage between A and the common connection is most simply calculated on the basis of R_1 and R_2 acting as a voltage divider, with the voltage across R_2 being proportional to its share of the total series resistance in that string. The voltage between B and the common connection may be calculated in the same way. The result is

$$E_{\text{Th}} = \overline{V_{R_2} - V_{R_4}}$$

where the bar over the right side of the equation tells us it is the absolute value of the difference in voltages that is the value of E_{Th}. Thus,

$$E_{\text{Th}} = \frac{3}{5}(10) - \frac{1}{5}(10)$$

$$= 4 \, \text{V}$$

Now the *Thevenin equivalent circuit* may be drawn, and the appropriate values for E_{Th} and R_{Th} entered in it. It is shown in Figure 7-6(e) with the 6 Ω load resistor connected across the equivalent circuit terminals. The potential across the 6 Ω resistor, and current flow through it, may be calculated as follows:

$$I = \frac{E_{\text{Th}}}{R_{\text{Th}} + R} \qquad E_{R_l} = IR$$

$$= \frac{4}{8} \qquad\qquad = \tfrac{1}{2}(6)$$

$$= \tfrac{1}{2} \, \text{A} \qquad\qquad = 3 \, \text{V}$$

These are the values of voltage and current when the 6 Ω resistor is connected to the Thevenin circuit equivalent to the original circuit. The voltage across and current through any load resistor are the same in the equivalent circuit as they would be in the original circuit. Therefore, the voltage and current for the 6 Ω resistor in the original circuit are

$$I = \tfrac{1}{2} \text{ A} \qquad E = 3 \text{ V}$$

We have determined current and voltage for only one resistor in the circuit, and we know nothing about any other current or voltage except the source voltage. We cannot calculate them, using series–parallel substitutions, since we do not at this point have enough information. If current and voltage for the 6 Ω resistor are all the information we need, then the results are satisfactory, though we as yet have no means to check them.

We could select any other resistor in the original circuit to be considered a load resistor, and again apply Thevenin's theorem to the resulting circuit. With the removal of any other resistor, the circuit again would become a simple series–parallel circuit, and the calculations could be easily made. If we did this, we would know the voltage across and current through one more resistor, and this would then be sufficient to enable us to complete the solution to the network and handily calculate all voltages and currents.

Problems **1.** Given the circuit and values shown, calculate the voltage across and current through R_3, using Thevenin's theorem.

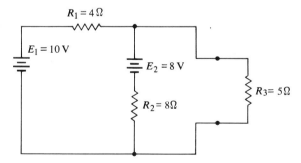

Circuit for Problems 1 and 2.

2. Given the circuit and values of Problem 1, calculate the voltage across and current through R_2, using Thevenin's theorem.

3. Given the circuit and values shown, calculate the voltage across and current through R_5, using Thevenin's theorem.

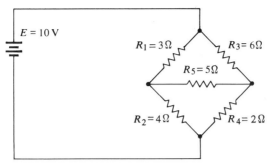

Circuit for Problems 3 and 4.

4. Given the circuit and values of Problem 3, calculate the voltage across and current through R_4, using Thevenin's theorem.

5. Given the circuit and values shown, calculate the voltage across and current through R_l, using Thevenin's theorem. Note that I_1 is a constant current source, and when Thevenin resistance R_{Th} is calculated, it must be replaced by an open circuit.

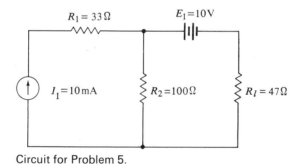

Circuit for Problem 5.

6. Given the circuit and values shown, calculate the voltage across and current through R_5, using Thevenin's theorem.

Circuit for Problems 6 and 7.

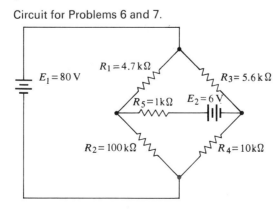

7. Given the circuit and values of Problem 6, calculate the voltage across and current through R_2, using Thevenin's theorem.

8. Using the results of Problems 6 and 7, calculate the current through R_1.

9. Calculate the voltage across R_3 and R_4, using the results of Problems 6, 7, and 8.

7-3
Norton's Theorem

We were unable, by any voltage and current measurements on a load connected at the terminals, to distinguish between the original network and the simple Thevenin equivalent circuit. There are an infinite number of circuits that could have been in the black box and presented precisely the same voltage and current to a load.

Suppose we had first measured the short-circuit current of the original circuit of Figure 7-4. We could have ascribed the 10 A reading to a 10 A constant current source within the box. When we read the open-circuit voltage and found it to be 12 V, we could have ascribed that to a parallel resistance between the load terminals, within the black box, through which all the 10 A produced by the constant current generator must flow with no external load resistor present, as in Figure 7-7.

This circuit consists of a constant current generator, producing a current equal to the short-circuit current of the original circuit. The short-circuit is, by definition, the current that would be measured by a suitable ammeter of zero internal resistance connected between the load terminals of the original circuit, with the load resistor removed.

Connected in parallel with this constant current generator is a resistor whose value is exactly the same, and is determined in the same way, as the internal series resistor for the Thevenin equivalent circuit.

This is the *Norton equivalent circuit.* Norton's theorem says, *Any two-terminal network can be replaced by an equivalent circuit consisting of a perfect current source, I_N—with a current equal to the short-circuit current*

Figure 7-7   A Norton equivalent circuit.

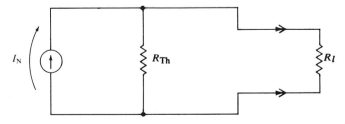

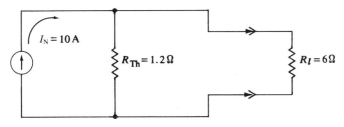

Figure 7-8

of the original circuit with the load resistor removed—in parallel with a resistance, R_{Th}, equal to the resistance measured back into the original network with the load resistance removed and all internal sources in the network removed and replaced with their equivalent internal resistances.

Since resistance R_{Th} has the same value in both equivalent circuits and is calculated in the same way for each, the same subscript has been used for both applications. Given the Thevenin equivalent circuit, it is easy to convert it to the Norton equivalent, and vice versa. They are related, as has already been suggested, by Ohm's law.

$$I_N = \frac{E_{Th}}{R_{Th}}$$

If we take the Norton equivalent circuit for the circuit of Figure 7-4 and connect to it the 6 Ω load resistor, it will be in parallel with the 1.2 Ω R_{Th}, as in Figure 7-8. Since we know total circuit current I_N, and wish to find load current I_l, it will be convenient to develop a relationship between them, based on the fact that the two resistances in parallel must have the same voltage across them. That is,

$$V_l = V_{Th}$$

Then, by Ohm's law,

$$I_l R_l = I_{Th} R_{Th}$$

We do not know I_{Th}, nor are we looking for it. But

$$I_{Th} + I_l = I_N$$

$$I_{Th} = I_N - I_l$$

Therefore,

$$I_l R_l = (I_N - I_l) R_{Th}$$

Solving this for I_l,

$$I_l = \frac{I_N R_{Th}}{R_l + R_{Th}}$$

This gives us the one unknown in terms of the three known values. Substituting values,

$$I_l = \frac{(10)(1.2)}{6 + 1.2}$$

$$= 1\frac{2}{3} \text{ A}$$

This is the same result as before, as it must be. Using this current, the voltage across the resistor is again found to be 10 V.

Thevenin's and Norton's theorems are obviously very closely related, and for a given problem either may be used. In general, Thevenin's is most frequently used when the problem involves a vacuum tube circuit, while Norton's is more often used with transistor circuits. If the nature of the original problem is such that the short-circuit current is more easily obtained than the open-circuit voltage, then Norton's is the obvious choice, though with any two of the three factors—E_{Th}, R_{Th}, and I_N—known, the other may be readily determined and either theorem applied.

Since many explanations of the operation of both vacuum tube and transistor circuits are based on applications of Thevenin's and Norton's theorems, both must be understood.

Problems **1.** Given the circuit and values shown, calculate the voltage across and current through R_l, using Norton's theorem.

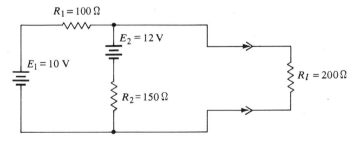

Circuit for Problems 1 and 2.

2. Given the circuit and values of Problem 1, calculate the voltage across and current through R_2, using Norton's theorem.

3. Given the circuit and values shown, calculate the voltage across and current through R_5, using Norton's theorem.

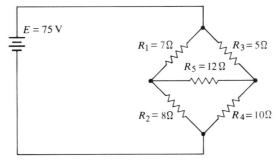

Circuit for Problems 3 and 4.

4. Given the circuit and values of Problem 3, calculate the voltage across and current through R_2, using Norton's theorem.

5. Given the circuit and values shown, calculate the voltage across and current through R_3, using Norton's theorem.

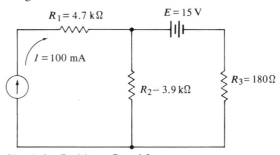

Circuit for Problems 5 and 6.

6. Given the circuit and values of Problem 5, calculate the voltage across and current through R_2, using Norton's theorem.

7. Given the circuit and values shown, calculate the voltage across and current through R_5, using Norton's theorem. *Hint:* That part of the circuit between points A and B may all be considered to be the load.

Circuit for Problems 7 and 8.

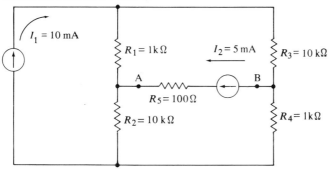

8. Given the circuit and values of Problem 7, calculate the voltage across and current through R_2, using Norton's theorem.

9. Using the results of Problems 7 and 8, calculate the current through R_1.

10. Using the results of Problems 7, 8, and 9, calculate the voltage across and current through R_3 and R_4.

7-4
Delta–Wye, Wye–
Delta Transforma-
tions

RESISTANCE EQUIVALENCES. Another method which can transform a circuit which is not a simple series–parallel circuit to a simple and easily solvable series–parallel circuit is the application of the *delta–wye, wye–delta transformations.*

Both delta and wye configurations are three-terminal networks, as seen in Figure 7-9. Between A and B on the wye network the resistance is

$$R_{AB} = R_A + R_B$$

while for the delta network, with two branches in parallel, the resistance between A and B is

$$R_{AB} = \frac{R_Z(R_X + R_Y)}{R_Z + (R_X + R_Y)}$$

If R_{AB} is to be the same for both configurations, then they must be equal. Therefore,

$$R_A + R_B = \frac{R_Z(R_X + R_Y)}{R_Z + (R_X + R_Y)}$$

Similarly, the resistance from B to C and from A to C can be calculated for both networks. The three resulting equations can be solved for each of the six unknowns, giving the following transformation equations.

Figure 7-9　Three-terminal networks.

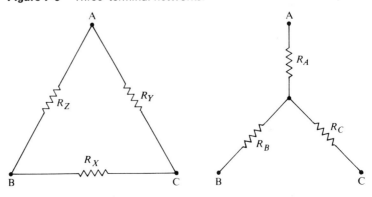

1. Given the delta, to find the corresponding wye:

$$R_A = \frac{R_Y R_Z}{R_X + R_Y + R_Z}$$

$$R_B = \frac{R_X R_Z}{R_X + R_Y + R_Z}$$

$$R_C = \frac{R_X R_Y}{R_X + R_Y + R_Z}$$

Note: In each case the product of the two resistors in the delta network tied to the same external point as the resistor in the wye equivalent that is being solved for is to be divided by the sum of the three resistors in the delta network.

2. Given the wye, to find the corresponding delta:

$$R_X = \frac{R_A R_B + R_B R_C + R_A R_C}{R_A}$$

$$R_Y = \frac{R_A R_B + R_B R_C + R_A R_C}{R_B}$$

$$R_Z = \frac{R_A R_B + R_B R_C + R_A R_C}{R_C}$$

Note: In each case the sum of the products of all the resistors in the wye network, taken two at a time, is divided by the wye resistor *not* tied to either external point common to the delta resistor being solved for.

Suppose the circuit of Figure 7-10(a) is given, with the values as indicated in the figure, and it is necessary to solve for all the voltages and currents. This is not a simple series–parallel circuit, so it cannot be solved by simple methods.   EXAMPLE

Solution.   First, we note that R_1, R_3, and R_5 are connected to points A, B, and C, as indicated in the figure, to form a delta configuration. If this delta configuration is replaced by a corresponding wye, the current through and voltage across the resistors in the original circuit not involved in the replacement will be unchanged. This means the voltage across and current through R_2 and R_4 will be the same in the original circuit as in the new, and also the total circuit current delivered to point A will be unchanged. If we know total circuit current and the current through R_2 and R_4, the remainder of the currents in the original circuit can be found by simple application of Kirchhoff's current law.

Therefore, we will make the transformation, as shown in Figure 7-10(b).

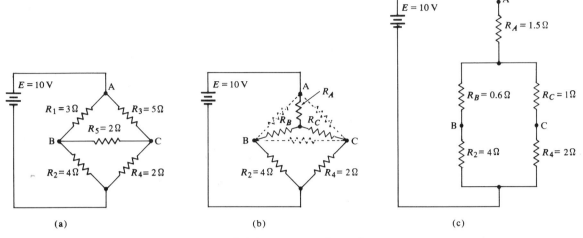

Figure 7-10　A delta–wye transformation.

The values for the wye resistors equivalent to the original delta configuration may be calculated from the transformation equations.

$$R_A = \frac{R_Y R_Z}{R_X + R_Y + R_Z} \qquad R_B = \frac{R_X R_Z}{R_X + R_Y + R_Z} \qquad R_C = \frac{R_X R_Y}{R_X + R_Y + R_Z}$$

$$= \frac{R_1 R_3}{R_1 + R_3 + R_5} \qquad = \frac{R_1 R_5}{R_1 + R_3 + R_5} \qquad = \frac{R_3 R_5}{R_1 + R_3 + R_5}$$

$$= \frac{(3)(5)}{3 + 5 + 2} \qquad = \frac{(3)(2)}{3 + 5 + 2} \qquad = \frac{(5)(2)}{3 + 5 + 2}$$

$$= \frac{15}{10} \qquad = \frac{6}{10} \qquad = \frac{10}{10}$$

$$= 1.5\,\Omega \qquad = 0.6\,\Omega \qquad = 1\,\Omega$$

These new values may be entered in the transformed circuit, as in Figure 7-10(c). Clearly, this transformed circuit is a simple series–parallel circuit, and is easily solved.

R_B and R_2 are in series with each other, for a total resistance of 4.6 Ω, while R_C and R_4 are in series for a total of 3 Ω. These two pairs of series resistors form a parallel bank, with an equivalent resistance given by

$$R_{eq} = \frac{(4.6)(3)}{4.6 + 3}$$

$$= \frac{13.8}{7.6}$$

$$= 1.816\,\Omega$$

This resistance is in series with R_A, giving a total circuit resistance of $3.316\,\Omega$. The total circuit current is, therefore,

$$I = \frac{E}{R}$$

$$= \frac{10}{3.316}$$

$$= 3.016\ \text{A}$$

This current, flowing through series resistance R_A, will produce a voltage drop of

$$V_A = IR$$

$$= (3.016)(1.5)$$

$$= 4.524\ \text{V}$$

The voltage drop across the parallel bank must therefore be the source voltage minus this drop, or

$$V_{\text{parallel bank}} = 10 - 4.524$$

$$= 5.476\ \text{V}$$

This voltage, applied across each branch of the parallel bank, will cause current flow in each branch. For the branch containing R_2, the current is

$$I_2 = \frac{V}{R}$$

$$= \frac{5.476}{4.6}$$

$$= 1.19\ \text{A}$$

For the branch containing R_4,

$$I_4 = \frac{V}{R}$$

$$= \frac{5.476}{3}$$

$$= 1.825\ \text{A}$$

We now know the total circuit current and the current through both R_2 and R_4. These values are correct for the transformed circuit, but they must also be correct for the original circuit, since neither R_2 nor R_4 was a part of the transformation. Therefore, we now know enough about the voltages and currents in the original circuit to calculate them all easily.

If the current through R_2 is 1.19 A, then the voltage across it must be

$$V_2 = I_2 R_2$$
$$= (1.19)(4)$$
$$= 4.76 \text{ V}$$

and the voltage across R_1 in the original circuit must be this much less than the source voltage, or

$$V_1 = 10 - 4.76$$
$$= 5.24 \text{ V}$$

If the current through R_4 is 1.825 A, then the voltage across it must be

$$V_4 = I_4 R_4$$
$$= (1.825)(2)$$
$$= 3.65 \text{ V}$$

and the voltage across R_3 in the original circuit must be this much less than the source voltage, or

$$V_3 = 10 - 3.65$$
$$= 6.35 \text{ V}$$

The voltage across R_5 must be the difference between the voltage across R_2 and the voltage across R_4, or

$$V_5 = 4.76 - 3.65$$
$$= 1.11 \text{ V}$$

With the voltage across R_1, R_3, and R_5 in the original circuit known, the currents through them may be easily calculated by Ohm's law.

$$I_1 = \frac{V_1}{R_1} \qquad I_3 = \frac{V_3}{R_3} \qquad I_5 = \frac{V_5}{R_5}$$
$$= \frac{5.24}{3} \qquad\quad = \frac{6.35}{5} \qquad\quad = \frac{1.11}{2}$$
$$= 1.747 \text{ A} \qquad = 1.27 \text{ A} \qquad = 0.555 \text{ A}$$

Now all currents and voltages have been found. As a check, we should sum the currents at each junction, since they must be in accord with Kirchhoff's current law.

The total circuit current of 3.016 A enters junction A, and the currents leaving the junction are, by our calculations, 1.747 A and 1.27 A. The sum of these currents is

$$1.747 + 1.27 = 3.017 \text{ A}$$

The discrepancy of one digit in the last significant figure indicates only that some of the intermediate results have been rounded off.

At junction B, I_1 enters, while I_2 and I_5 leave. Thus,

$$1.747 = 0.555 + 1.19$$

$$= 1.745$$

Again, the results are satisfactory, since the only difference is the natural result of rounding off.

At junction C, I_3 and I_5 enter, while I_4 leaves. Thus,

$$1.27 + 0.555 = 1.825$$

$$1.825 = 1.825$$

Our conclusions are found to be in accord with Ohm's law and with Kirchhoff's laws, and may therefore be accepted as correct.

Given the circuit of Figure 7-11(a), with the values shown on the figure, calculate the current through each component.   EXAMPLE

Solution.   The circuit is not a simple series–parallel circuit, but it can be solved in a number of different ways. Application of Thevenin's or Norton's theorems would solve the circuit, but each would have to be applied twice to achieve a complete solution. Other methods, not yet discussed, are presented in the next chapter. Of the methods so far presented, wye–delta or delta–wye transformations can be easily used. The previous example used a delta–wye transformation; this example will be based on a wye–delta transformation.

Examination of the circuit of Figure 7-11(a) shows that R_1, R_3 and R_5 form a delta configuration which could be replaced by a wye, and R_5, R_2, and R_4 form another delta configuration which could be replaced by a wye. Though it may seem less obvious at first glance, R_1, R_5, and R_2 form a wye configuration which can be replaced by a delta. In addition, R_3, R_5, and R_4 form a wye configuration. It is this last wye configuration which we have chosen to illustrate the method of solution by wye–delta transformation.

Points A, B, and C have been identified on the original circuit of Figure 7-11(a), showing the external terminations of the chosen wye configuration. In Figure 7-11(b) the circuit has been redrawn to show more clearly the actual wye configuration formed by R_3, R_5, and R_4. Note that none of the electrical connections has been changed between the two figures; only the physical placement of the resistors in the drawing is changed. Points A, B, and C in both figures are the same, with the same resistors connected to them.

In Figure 7-11(c) the original wye has been replaced by the corresponding delta. The values for the delta resistors, R_X, R_Y, and R_Z, are calculated from the transformation equations, as follows.

$$R_X = \frac{R_A\,R_B + R_B\,R_C + R_A\,R_C}{R_A}$$

$$= \frac{(4)\,(7) + (7)\,(9) + (4)\,(9)}{4}$$

$$= \frac{127}{4}$$

$$= 31.75\ \Omega$$

$$R_Y = \frac{R_A\,R_B + R_B\,R_C + R_A\,R_C}{R_B}$$

$$= \frac{127}{7}$$

$$= 18.14\ \Omega$$

Figure 7-11   A wye–delta transformation.

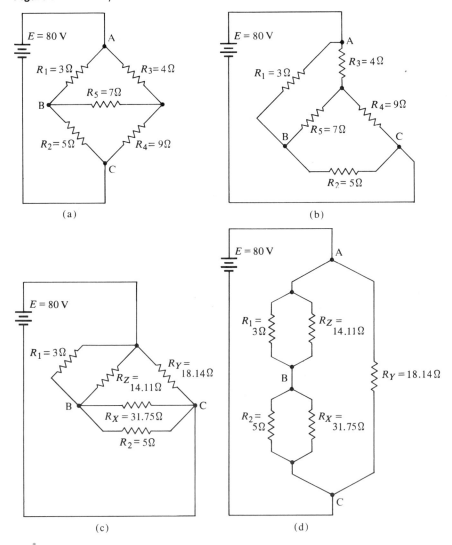

$$R_Z = \frac{R_A\,R_B + R_B\,R_C + R_A\,R_C}{R_C}$$

$$= \frac{127}{9}$$

$$= 14.11\ \Omega$$

Since it may be difficult to see that this is now a simple series–parallel circuit, it has been redrawn in Figure 7-11(d). The electrical relationships between components in (d) and (c) are the same; only the placement of the resistors on the drawing has been changed. Clearly, this is now a simple circuit which may be solved by series–parallel reduction.

We need the total circuit current, and the current through R_1 and R_2, since they are the only parts of the circuit of Figure 7-11(c) that are also part of the original circuit of Figure 7-11(a).

In the circuit of Figure 7-12(a) the combination of R_1 and R_Z in parallel has a resistance of $2.47\,\Omega$, and the combination of R_2 and R_X in parallel has a resistance of $4.32\,\Omega$. Since these two equivalent resistances are in series with each other and the 80 V source, it is now possible to calculate the voltage across each. The voltage between points A and B is thus 29.10 V and between B and C 50.89 V.

Figure 7-12

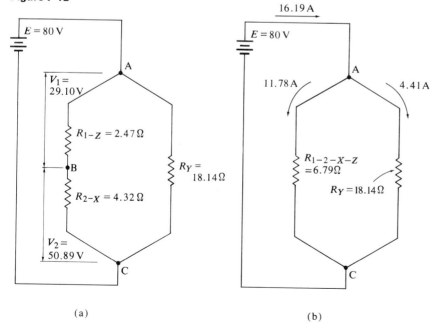

(a)   (b)

The total resistance of this branch of the parallel network to which the circuit reduces, seen in Figure 7-12(b), is 6.79 Ω. The current through this branch is thus 11.78 A, while the resistance of the other branch of 18.41 Ω permits a current of 4.41 A. The total circuit current is thus the sum of the two, or 16.19 A.

This is about as far as we can usefully go with the circuit obtained from the original by the wye–delta substitution. We have determined from the delta substitution the voltage between points A and B, and between B and C, as well as the total circuit current. If this information is plotted on the original circuit, as in Figure 7-13, it is evident that the remainder of the voltages and currents can be easily determined.

The voltage between A and B is the voltage across R_1 in the original circuit. Its resistance is 3 Ω, and the voltage across it is 29.10 V; therefore, the current through it is 9.70 A. This is entered in the figure as I_1.

Since the current flowing into the junction of point A is the total circuit current $I_t = 16.19$ A, and $I_1 = 9.70$ A is flowing away from the junction, then the other current leaving the junction, the current through R_3, must be the difference between the two, or $I_3 = 16.19 - 9.70 = 6.49$ A.

Similarly, currents summed at point B in accord with Kirchhoff's current law give a value for current I_5 through R_5 of 0.48 A, and currents may be

Figure 7-13

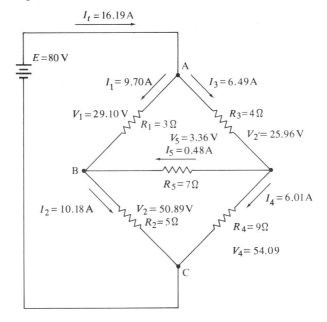

summed at either of the other two junctions in the circuit to give a value of $I_4 = 6.01$ A.

With the currents all known, any voltages still unknown may be readily calculated by using Ohm's law. This has been done, and the results entered in Figure 7-13. The results are seen to be in accord with Ohm's law, and with Kirchhoff's laws, to the degree of accuracy that may be expected with calculations rounded off to no more than three significant figures.

Problems

1. Completely solve the circuit shown, using a delta–wye transformation across the network between points A, B, and C.

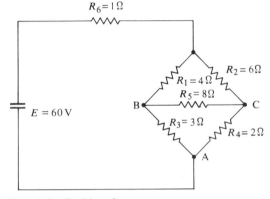

Circuit for Problem 1.

2. Completely solve the circuit shown, using a wye–delta transformation across the network between points A, B, and C.

Circuit for Problem 2.

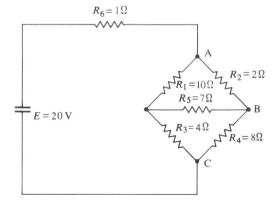

3. Completely solve the circuit shown, using a wye–delta transformation across the network formed by R_4, R_6, and R_7.

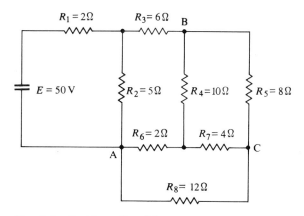

Circuit for Problems 3 and 4.

4. Completely solve the circuit of Problem 3, using a delta–wye transformation across the delta network formed by R_4, R_5, and R_7.

5. Reduce the circuit shown in (a) to the five-resistor, simple bridge circuit shown in (b), using successive wye–delta tranformations. *Hint:* Begin with the wye network of R_4, R_5, and R_7.

Circuit for Problem 5.

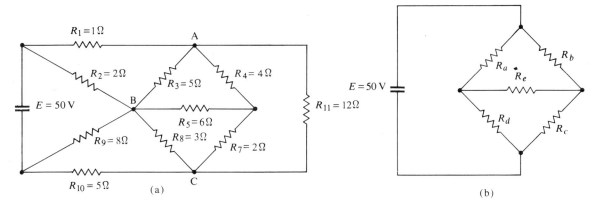

6. Using successive delta–wye transformations on the circuit shown, determine the currents flowing through R_1 and R_2, and the voltage drops across each. *Hint:* Start with the delta network of R_6, R_7, and R_{10}.

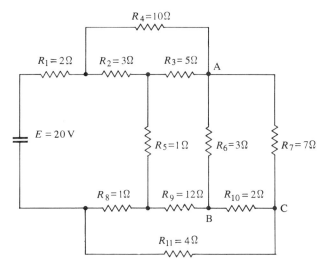

$R_4 = 10\,\Omega$

$R_1 = 2\,\Omega$ $R_2 = 3\,\Omega$ $R_3 = 5\,\Omega$ A

$E = 20\ \text{V}$

$R_5 = 1\,\Omega$ $R_6 = 3\,\Omega$ $R_7 = 7\,\Omega$

$R_8 = 1\,\Omega$ $R_9 = 12\,\Omega$ $R_{10} = 2\,\Omega$ C

B

$R_{11} = 4\,\Omega$

Circuit for Problem 6.

delta–wye, wye–delta transformations   a method for tranforming a complex   **Key Words**
circuit into an easily solvable series–parallel circuit

delta and wye configurations   three-terminal networks

Norton equivalent circuit   a constant current generator with a resistor
connected in parallel. The generator produces a current equal to the
short circuit current of the original circuit.

short-circuit current   current that would be measured by a suitable ammeter
of zero internal resistance connected between the load terminals of the
original circuit with the load resistor removed

superposition   a method for solving circuits that contain multiple voltage
sources. Each source is solved separately, and the results are summed
algebraically.

Thevenin equivalent resistance   resistance measured between the load
terminals with the load removed and all sources in the network replaced
by their equivalent resistances

Thevenin equivalent voltage   open-circuit voltage with the load resistor
removed

1.   Once the current through each circuit element is known for each voltage   **Summary**
source of a multiple source circuit, the results can be combined   **of Concepts**
algebraically to give the actual current through each resistor caused by
all the voltage sources in the original circuit.

2. It is possible to consider any two-terminal network either as a perfect voltage source with some series resistance, or as a constant current source with some parallel resistance.

3. Thevenin's theorem states that any two-terminal network can be replaced by an equivalent circuit consisting of a perfect voltage source (E_{Th}) with the voltage equal to the open-circuit voltage of the original circuit with the load resistor removed, in series with a resistance (R_{Th}) equal to the resistance measured back into the original network with the load resistance removed, and all internal sources in the network removed and replaced with their equivalent internal resistances.

4. Norton's theorem says that any two-terminal network can be replaced by an equivalent circuit consisting of a perfect current source (I_N) with a current equal to the short-circuit current of the original circuit with the load resistor removed, in parallel with a resistance (R_{Th}) that is equal to the resistance measured back into the original network with the load resistance removed, and all internal sources in the network removed and replaced with their equivalent internal resistances.

5. Thevenin's theorem is most frequently used when the problem involves a vacuum tube circuit. Norton's theorem is more often used with transistor circuits. In general, if short-circuit current can be measured more easily than open-circuit voltage, then Norton's theorem is obviously easier to work with. But always remember that if any two of the three factors—E_{Th}, R_{Th}, and I_N—are known, you can *always* determine the unknown value and work with either theorem.

To Help You Review   *On a separate sheet of paper, fill in the blanks or answer the questions below. The number following each question refers to the section in the chapter where the correct answer can be found.*

1. What method does the following statement describe? To use this method, the circuit is redrawn as many times as there are voltage sources in the original circuit. (7-1)

2. When it is removed as a source of potential, a source is said to be _____. (7-1)

3. We can consider a practical power source as a perfect voltage source with some _____ resistance, or as a constant current source with some _____ resistance. (7-1)

4. According to Thevenin's theorem, what does an equivalent circuit consist of? (7-2)

5. What must the voltage of an equivalent circuit equal? (7-2)

6. In an equivalent circuit, what is removed? (7-2)

7. How is an equivalent circuit connected to the original circuit? (7-2)

8. What is accomplished in an equivalent circuit by removing the load resistor and replacing all the original voltage sources with their equivalent resistances? (7-2)

9. What is the Thevenin equivalent resistance? (7-2)

10. Is the voltage across any load resistor in an equivalent circuit the same as, more than, or less than the voltage in the original circuit? (7-2)

11. What is a short-circuit current? (7-2)

12. What does the Norton equivalent circuit consist of? (7-3)

13. How is the Norton equivalent circuit connected with the original circuit? (7-3)

14. Thevenin's and Norton's theorems are closely related. When would you be most likely to use Thevenin's theorem? Norton's theorem? (7-3)

15. Delta and wye configurations are _____-terminal networks. (7-4)

EIGHT

RESISTIVE NETWORKS —KIRCHHOFF'S SOLUTIONS

This chapter will help you understand

☐ how to solve equations involving resistive networks, using
   —branch current analysis
   —mesh analysis
   —nodal analysis

8-1
Branch Current
Analysis

CIRCUIT CONVENTIONS.   If we can write as many equations as there are different independent variables in a problem, we can, in general, solve the resulting equations to find the values of each of the variables.

Consider the example of the simple series–parallel circuit of Figure 8-1. The values and circuit were chosen so that the currents and voltages are immediately apparent. The equivalent resistance of the parallel bank is 2 Ω, and this, in series with 2 Ω resistor R_1, gives a total circuit resistance of 4 Ω. With a source voltage of 8 V, the total current must be 2 A. This will produce a 4 V IR drop across R_1, leaving 4 V across the parallel bank. This gives a current of $\frac{2}{3}$ A through the 6 Ω resistor, and a current of $1\frac{1}{3}$ A through the 3 Ω resistor.

Now let us use this same problem to illustrate another method. *Branch current analysis* is the most general of all methods, and

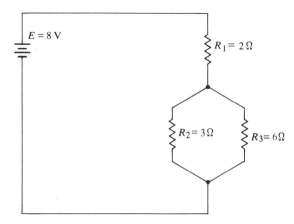

Figure 8-1   A simple series–parallel circuit.

can be used to solve very complex circuits, though it will become apparent that it is not the easiest method to use on our simple example. In spite of this, this simple example will serve to illustrate the method more clearly than the more complex problems for which it is most frequently used.

Step one is to examine the original circuit and draw arrows indicating the direction of assumed current flow. It does not matter at this stage if the arrows really go in the right direction or not; if they do not, the answer will be negative for the current indicated by the wrong arrows. It is a simple matter then to reverse the arrows. It will be helpful, too, to indicate the polarity of the expected potential across each resistor, and such sources as may be in the circuit, by putting a + at one end and a − at the other (Figure 8-2). Again, any errors at this stage do not matter. The main point is that it *is* essential to be consistent throughout the entire solution of the problem. Changing our minds about a current direction in the middle of the problem *will* prove disastrous to the final result.

Step two is to determine the minimum number of variables. Since the circuit as drawn encloses two separate areas, A and B, we can expect a minimum of two variables.

We are going to solve for the current through each resistor, but while there are three resistors, there are not three independent variables. If we know any two of the currents, we can calculate the third; therefore, any two are independent variables and the third is dependent. Two equations will therefore be sufficient, if they are independent equations, and will enable us to solve for the two currents included in them.

Step three is to write the equations. We may choose any two of the

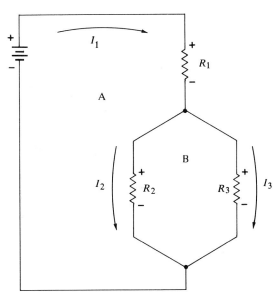

Figure 8-2 The circuit of Figure 8-1 redrawn. Direction of assumed current flow and polarities of all circuit elements are indicated.

currents as our variables, and write the other current in terms of these two, since

$$I_t = I_1 = I_2 + I_3$$

The equations themselves are based on Kirchhoff's voltage law, which says the algebraic sum of the voltages in any complete loop in any circuit is zero. Since there are two unknowns, we need two equations, so we will write two loop equations, as follows.

$$V_1 + V_2 - E = 0 \qquad V_1 + V_3 - E = 0$$

where V_1, V_2, and V_3 represent the voltage across R_1, R_2, and R_3, respectively. But by Ohm's law, for any resistor,

$$V = IR$$

Therefore, making the substitutions,

$$R_1(I_2 + I_3) + I_2 R_2 - E = 0 \qquad R_1(I_2 + I_3) + I_3 R_3 - E = 0$$

Now, substituting for R_1, R_2, and R_3 their values as given in the statement of the problem,

$$2(I_2 + I_3) + 3I_2 - 8 = 0 \qquad 2(I_2 + I_3) + 6I_3 - 8 = 0$$

These equations may usually be written directly from inspection of the circuit.

Step four is to solve the equations for I_2 and I_3. Any of the usual mathematical procedures may be followed. The example is continued, using the subtraction method. The equations are first simplified.

$$5I_2 + 2I_3 = 8 \qquad I_2 + 4I_3 = 4$$

The left-hand equation may be multiplied by two, and the right-hand equation subtracted from it, as follows.

$$2(5I_2 + 2I_3 = 8) = 10I_2 + 4I_3 = 16$$
$$\text{(minus)} \quad I_2 + 4I_3 = 4$$
$$\overline{9I_2 = 12}$$

Therefore,

$$I_2 = 1\frac{1}{3}$$

If this value is substituted back into one of the original equations, I_3 will be the only unknown, and may be easily solved for.

$$I_2 + 4I_3 = 4$$

$$I_3 = \frac{4 - I_2}{4}$$

$$= \frac{4 - 4/3}{4}$$

$$= \frac{8/3}{4}$$

$$= \frac{2}{3} \text{ A}$$

The total current is the sum of I_2 and I_3, and is therefore 2 A. This result agrees completely with our original calculation, based on series–parallel reduction. Though this method of applying Kirchhoff's laws to the writing of simultaneous equations, and then solving them, proved much more cumbersome for this problem than the series–parallel analysis, the method has applications where no other way will work.

Where more complex circuits are involved, loops may be written as voltage equations that do not contain a voltage source. It is also important that the proper sign for each term be used, since any error here will invalidate the entire result. It is desirable, therefore, to establish some standard procedures to minimize the possibility of such error.

The first recommended step was to draw current arrows beside each component, and to label each component with a + at one terminal and a − at the other to indicate polarity. Actually, there is a certain amount of duplication in this procedure, since if we only marked a + at one end, the other end would inevitably have to be −, and there is no real need for both a current arrow and a polarity marking, since they carry the same information. Still, using both the current arrow and the polarity marking seems to reduce errors for most students.

Now we are going to trace loops through the circuit so we may write the necessary voltage equations, using *IR* drops. Usually, the most convenient place to start a loop is just past any source that may be in the loop, so that the source voltage will be the last potential encountered in the loop. It is not mathematically better; mathematically, any term in the

Figure 8-3   When traversing a resistive circuit, the trace must match one of these four conditions. There are no other possibilities.

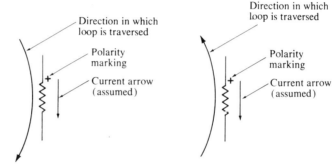

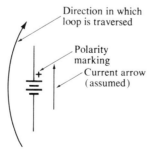

(a) Resistive circuit element — loop traversed with current arrow gives positive term in voltage equation

(b) Resistive circuit element — loop traversed against current arrow gives negative term in voltage equation

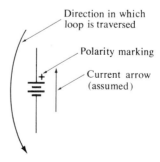

(c) Voltage source — loop traversed with current arrow gives negative term in voltage equation

(d) Voltage source — loop traversed against current arrow gives positive term in voltage equation

equation may be first, but standardizing procedure saves errors, and is well worth while.

In traversing a loop back to the starting point, we will be moving through many components in a complex circuit. There are only a few possibilities, in terms of polarity of component and the proper algebraic sign to be associated with the voltage across the component.

For resistive circuits the component may be a resistor, or it may be a source. We may traverse through the component in the direction of the assumed current arrow, or against the arrow. That exhausts the possibilities (Figure 8-3).

If we are going with the arrow when traversing a resistive component in a loop, the resistor represents a voltage drop, and the voltage source a voltage gain. Mathematically, the two have opposite signs. Usually, in writing the voltage equations, terms representing an *IR* drop are called positive, and terms representing the voltage gain of a source are marked negative.

In some circuits we may, in traversing a loop, go through a resistor against the designated current arrow. We must give the opposite sign to the term in the equation resulting from this. If going through a resistive circuit element with the arrow gives a positive voltage term, then going through a resistive circuit element against the arrow must give a negative voltage term. Similarly, if going through a voltage source with the arrow gives a negative voltage term, then going through a voltage source against the arrow must give a positive voltage term. For easy reference see Table 8-1.

TABLE 8-1   Polarity Signs of Voltages across Resistive Circuit Components

	Voltage Source	Resistor
With the arrow	−	+
Against the arrow	+	−

Again, the only really important thing is consistency. If you reverse all the signs in an equation, the value of the unknowns in that equation is not changed. Consequently, you may reverse all the signs in the above tabulation, and still have perfectly valid equations that will lead to the correct current values. We have, in the first example, based the current arrows on conventional current flow. We could have based the arrows on electron flow, and while this would have resulted in changed signs in each term, it would not have changed the calculated current values.

Since each equation is an independent entity, and the sign of each term in it may be changed without affecting any of the other equations, it is even possible to write one equation using conventional current flow and another using electron flow, or write one using the convention of signs suggested in the tabulation and another equation using the opposite convention, and still get correct current values. This is not recommended, as it does nothing to reduce confusion.

EXAMPLE   Given the circuit of Figure 8-4, find the current value and direction for each resistor.

Solution.   This is not a simple circuit. It could be solved by a combination of the method of superposition and the application of Thevenin's theorem or wye–delta transformations. Considerable labor would be involved. For this example the least laborious method is the solution of simultaneous voltage equations written in accord with Kirchhoff's laws.

First polarities and current arrows are marked on the drawing, as in Figure 8-5. There may be some doubt as to the actual current directions; examination of the circuit shows that source E_2 would, by itself, cause current flow through R_1 and R_4 opposite to the direction assumed. Since E_2 has a considerably higher potential than E_1, this may well occur; it does not matter, since the only consequence would be a negative value for the currents in our solution. We could choose directions at random, or even show all the currents at a junction as entering.

Examination of the circuit shows that it encloses three areas on the plane of the paper; consequently, there are three independent currents. If we choose I_1, I_2, and I_5 as independent currents, then the current through R_3 is $I_2 + I_5$, and the current through R_4 is $I_2 - I_5$. These may be marked on the drawing, as in Figure 8-5.

Figure 8-4   The easiest way to solve this circuit is with simultaneous voltage equations.

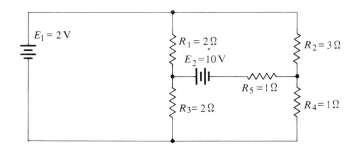

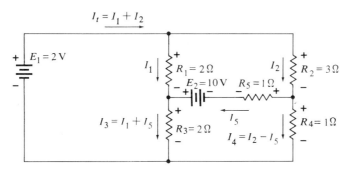

Figure 8-5 The circuit of Figure 8-4 with assumed current flow, component polarities, and independent currents marked.

Now we may choose the loops and write the equations. Any three independent loops may be chosen; a large number of loops are possible. Perhaps the simplest procedure is to mark loops in each of the areas enclosed by the elements of the circuit. These loops are shown added to the drawing of the circuit in Figure 8-6.

We may now proceed to write voltage equations for each loop. For Loop 1, the voltage drop across R_1 plus the voltage drop across R_3 minus the source voltage in the loop, E_1, must, by Kirchhoff's voltage law, be equal to zero. Algebraically, this is

$$I_1 R_1 + (I_1 + I_5)R_3 - E_1 = 0$$

Substituting the resistance values, this becomes

$$2I_1 + (I_1 + I_5)2 - 2 = 0 \qquad \text{(Loop 1)}$$

Figure 8-6 Three independent loops indicated for the circuit of Figure 8-4.

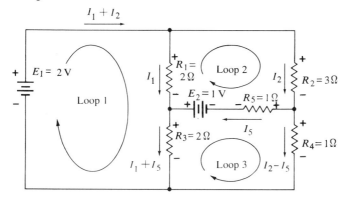

Equations for the other two loops may be written directly.

$$-2I_1 + 3I_2 + I_5 - 10 = 0 \qquad \text{(Loop 2)}$$

$$-I_5 + (I_2 - I_5) - 2(I_1 + I_5) + 10 = 0 \qquad \text{(Loop 3)}$$

In writing these voltage equations, the conventions suggested in Table 8-1 have been followed. For example, in the equation for Loop 2, the first term is the voltage across R_1. It is preceded by a minus sign, since we are traversing the loop against the arrow through a resistor. Similarly, the term for the source voltage in the equation for Loop 3 (the $+10$, just to the left of the equal sign) is positive, since we are traversing a voltage source against the current arrow.

Given the three loop equations, they may now be solved by any convenient means to give values for I_1, I_2, and I_5. First, the equations may be put in normal form, as follows.

$$2I_1 \qquad\quad + \; I_5 = \quad 1 \qquad \text{(Loop 1)}$$

$$-2I_1 + 3I_2 + I_5 = \quad 10 \qquad \text{(Loop 2)}$$

$$-2I_1 + \; I_2 - 4I_5 = \; -10 \qquad \text{(Loop 3)}$$

The first equation added to the second gives

$$3I_2 + 2I_5 = 11$$

and the first equation added to the third gives

$$I_2 - 3I_5 = -9$$

If the second of these new equations is multiplied by -3 and subtracted from the first, the result is

$$11I_5 = 38$$

$$I_5 = \frac{38}{11} = 3.45 \text{ A}$$

Since $I_2 - 3I_5 = -9$, the value of I_5 may be substituted in this equation to give the value of I_2.

$$I_2 = 3I_5 - 9 = 3\left(\frac{38}{11}\right) - 9 = \frac{15}{11} = 1.36 \text{ A}$$

Since $2I_1 + I_5 = 1$, the value of I_5 may be substituted in this equation to give the value of I_1.

$$I_1 = \frac{1 - I_5}{2} = \frac{1 - 38/11}{2} = -\frac{27}{22} = -1.23 \text{ A}$$

Solving for the other current values,

$$I_3 = I_1 + I_5 = -\frac{27}{22} + \frac{38}{11} = \frac{49}{22} = 2.23 \text{ A}$$

$$I_4 = I_2 - I_5 = \frac{15}{11} - \frac{38}{11} = -\frac{23}{11} = -2.09 \text{ A}$$

Note that I_1 and I_4 are negative. This simply means that the arrow indicating current direction in the original circuit diagram was drawn in the wrong direction. Redrawn with the correct polarity, the arrows are indicated in Figure 8-7.

The voltage across each resistor may be calculated from the current through it times its resistance, and the tabulated results are shown below.

	R	I	V
R_1	2	1.23	2.46
R_2	3	1.36	4.09
R_3	2	2.23	4.46
R_4	1	2.09	2.09
R_5	1	3.45	3.45

Solution. The solution to the three loop equations of this example could have been achieved using determinants. An illustration of the method follows.

First, the three original loop equations are repeated, for convenience.

$$2I_1 \qquad + I_5 = \quad 1 \qquad \text{(Loop 1)}$$

$$-2I_1 + 3I_2 + I_5 = \quad 10 \qquad \text{(Loop 2)}$$

$$-2I_1 + \quad I_2 - 4I_5 = -10 \qquad \text{(Loop 3)}$$

Figure 8-7 The circuit of Figure 8-4 with actual—not assumed—direction of current and component polarity.

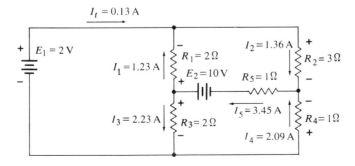

Now the determinant for the solution of I_1 may be written.

$$I_1 = \frac{\begin{vmatrix} 1 & 0 & 1 \\ -10 & 1 & -4 \\ 10 & 3 & 1 \end{vmatrix}}{\begin{vmatrix} 2 & 0 & 1 \\ -2 & 1 & -4 \\ -2 & 3 & 1 \end{vmatrix}}$$

Note that the numerator is a determinant in which the numbers in the I_1 column (the first column) have been replaced by the numerical values to the right of the equal sign in the original three equations. The other two columns, the I_2 and I_5 columns, contain the numerical coefficients of I_2 and I_5, arranged in the same order as in the original equations. Where a term is missing, as is the I_2 term in the equation for Loop 1, a coefficient of zero is entered in its place in the determinant. The denominator is a determinant in which the numerical coefficients of the currents in the original loop equations are entered in positions corresponding to their positions in the original equations.

Now the numerical value of each of the two determinants may be calculated. The products of the diagonals downward to the right are summed and entered as indicated by the arrows. Each diagonal is identified by its numbered arrow, and the corresponding products are identified by the circled number just above their value in the indicated sum.

$$I_1 = \frac{\overset{①\quad②\quad③}{(1 + 0 - 30)} - (\qquad)}{\overset{①\quad②\quad③}{(2 + 0 - 6)} - (\qquad)}$$

In the same way, the product of the diagonals upward to the right are summed and entered as indicated by the arrows. Again, each diagonal is identified by its numbered arrow, and the corresponding products are identified by the circled number just above their value in the indicated sum.

$$I_1 = \frac{\begin{array}{ccc} 1 & 0 & 1 \\ -10 & 1 & -4 \\ 10 & 3 & 1 \end{array}}{\begin{array}{ccc} 2 & 0 & 1 \\ -2 & 1 & -4 \\ -2 & 3 & 1 \end{array}} = \frac{\overset{①\;②\;③}{(1 + 0 - 30) - (10 + 0 - 12)}}{\underset{①\;②\;③}{(2 + 0 - 6) - (-2 + 0 - 24)}}$$

Now the value of the sums and differences of these products may be calculated, and the final fraction converted to a decimal to give a value for I_1.

$$I_1 = \frac{(-29) - (-2)}{(-4) - (-26)} = \frac{-27}{+22} = -1.23 \text{ A}$$

The determinants for I_2 and I_5 may be set up and solved in exactly the same way. It is not necessary to recalculate the determinant of the denominator, since it is the same for all three variables. It is often desirable, however, to recalculate it simply to insure against the possibility of error.

$$I_2 = \frac{\begin{vmatrix} 2 & 1 & 1 \\ -2 & -10 & -4 \\ -2 & 10 & 1 \end{vmatrix}}{+22} = \frac{(-20 + 8 - 20) - (20 - 2 - 80)}{+22}$$

$$= \frac{(-32) - (-62)}{+22} = \frac{+30}{+22} = 1.36 \text{ A}$$

$$I_5 = \frac{\begin{vmatrix} 2 & 0 & 1 \\ -2 & 1 & -10 \\ -2 & 3 & 10 \end{vmatrix}}{+22} = \frac{(20 + 0 - 6) - (-2 + 0 - 60)}{+22}$$

$$= \frac{(14) - (-62)}{+22} = \frac{+76}{+22} = 3.45 \text{ A}$$

Obviously, the results are the same as obtained by the previous method of calculation. They must be, if they are without error. Any method of calculation that is mathematically sound will yield the same result. The choice of method should be based on the problem itself. Since the coefficients of the variables in the sort of problem likely to be encountered in a practical situation in electronics will not usually be small whole numbers, the use of determinants is frequently the method of choice. The actual calculations may be made using a small electronic calculator, with less chance of error than with most other methods, since the results of the intermediate steps are stored in the calculator's memory until needed.

Problems   **1.**   Using branch current analysis, solve the circuit shown.

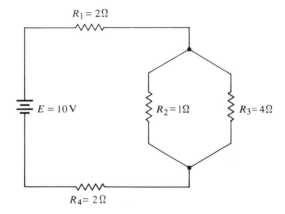

Circuit for Problem 1.

2.   Using branch current analysis, solve the circuit shown.

Circuit for Problem 2.

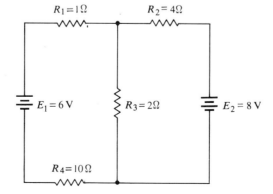

3. Solve the circuit shown, using branch current analysis.

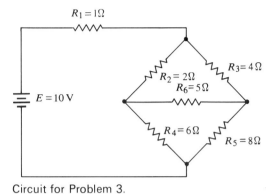

Circuit for Problem 3.

4. Solve the circuit shown, using branch current analysis.

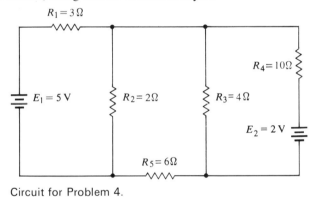

Circuit for Problem 4.

5. Using branch current analysis, solve the circuit shown.

Circuit for Problem 5.

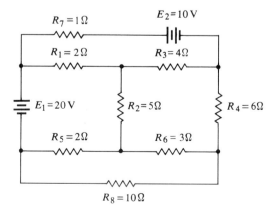

6. Using branch current analysis, solve the circuit shown. *Hint:* Redraw the circuit without a crossover.

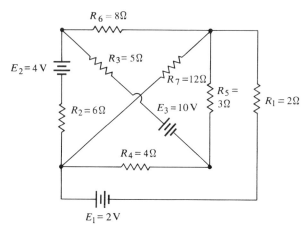

Circuit for Problem 6.

8-2
Mesh Analysis

LIMITATIONS OF MESH ANALYSIS. *Mesh analysis* is similar to branch current analysis, in that it is a method of writing equations, based on Kirchhoff's laws, that may be solved for currents. Branch current analysis is applicable to any network; mesh analysis is applicable only to networks which may be drawn on a plane surface with no crossovers. Since the majority of networks are in this category, mesh analysis is widely applicable.

In branch current analysis we considered the current through each resistor as a single current, and solved for it. In mesh analysis we are going to consider each loop as having its own current, and any resistor that is between two loops will carry a current equal to the algebraic sum of the two loop currents.

Consider the circuit of Figure 8-8. It is a simple series–parallel circuit, and since the circuit constants are the same as those chosen for Figure 8-1, we already know each of the currents. First, draw a current arrow, as shown, in each "window" in the network. A *window* is simply any closed area bounded by the network. The current arrow may be drawn in any arbitrary direction, but it is usually less confusing to draw it in the direction of conventional current flow that would be caused by any voltage sources included in the loop. In the circuit of this example, there are two windows, and the two loop currents have been drawn clockwise.

Now we may write the mesh equations. Each equation will have one term that is the product of the loop current times the sum of the resistance in that loop. There will be another term for each resistor that also carries another loop current. If the two currents are in the same direction, it will be positive; if they are in opposite directions, it will be negative. The term will be the other loop current times the sum of the resistances common to the two loops. The algebraic sum of the loop current terms for each loop is set equal to the sum of the source voltages in the loop. The mesh equations for this circuit are

$$5I_1 - 3I_2 = 8$$
$$-3I_1 + 9I_2 = 0$$

These are written directly by inspection of the circuit. The first equation is written for the first loop. The sum of the resistors through which I_1 flows is 5 Ω, so the first term is $5I_1$. The 3 Ω resistor has both I_1 and I_2 currents, so the equation contains the term $3I_2$. It is negative, since for that resistor, I_2 flows opposite to I_1. The algebraic sum of these terms is set equal to the source voltage in that loop.

The second equation is written for the second loop. The sum of the resistances in that loop through which I_2 flows is 9 Ω, so the equation must contain the term $9I_2$. The term for the loop current itself will always be positive. The 3 Ω resistor is the only resistor in that loop through which another loop current, I_1, flows. Therefore, we write term $-3I_1$ in this equation, and it is negative since the direction of the two loop currents through this resistor are opposite. It is set equal to zero since there is no source in this loop.

Figure 8-8 A series–parallel circuit with loop currents indicated for each window of the circuit.

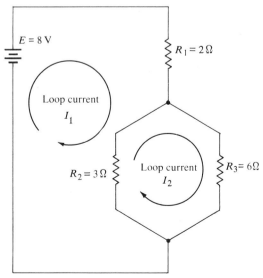

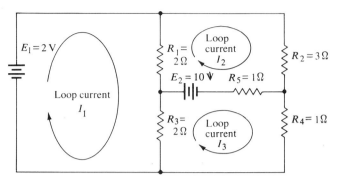

Figure 8-9 The circuit of Figure 8-4. A loop current is indicated for each window.

The two equations are easily solvable, and the values obtained are

$$I_1 = 2 \text{ A} \quad \text{and} \quad I_2 = \tfrac{2}{3} \text{ A}$$

I_1 is the current through the source and through the 2 Ω resistor. I_2 is the current through the 6 Ω resistor. To find the current through the 3 Ω resistor, we observe that it is the difference between I_1 and I_2. It is, therefore, $1\tfrac{1}{3}$ A, and since the magnitude of I_1 is greater than that of I_2, the resulting current is in the direction of I_1. The results of this calculation are, of course, the same as those achieved with the first method of analysis, the use of branch currents.

Similarly, the more complex circuit of Figure 8-4 has been redrawn as Figure 8-9. The application of the method of mesh analysis is the same in this problem as it was in the simpler example. There are three windows; consequently, there will be three loop currents. It is important to note that there are no crossovers in the drawing. If there were, it would have to be drawn without crossovers, if possible. If it could not be redrawn without crossovers, then the method of mesh analysis would not be applicable, and the circuit would have to be solved by using branch current analysis.

The three loop currents are drawn, as in Figure 8-9. Since all three loops contain a source, they were each drawn to conform to the direction of conventional current flow from the source within the loop.

With the loop currents drawn, the mesh equations may be written directly. They are

$$4I_1 - 2I_2 + 2I_3 = 2$$
$$-2I_1 + 6I_2 + I_3 = 10$$
$$2I_1 + I_2 + 4I_3 = 10$$

These equations may be solved by any convenient method, and the results are

$$I_1 = \frac{3}{22} \text{ A}$$

$$I_2 = \frac{30}{22} \text{ A}$$

$$I_3 = \frac{46}{22} \text{ A}$$

The fractional answers have purposely not been reduced, since to find the actual resistor currents, they must be added and subtracted. From Figure 8-4 it is apparent that the resistor currents must be computed as follows.

$$I_{R_1} = I_2 - I_1 = \frac{30}{22} - \frac{3}{22} = \frac{27}{22} = 1.23 \text{ A}$$

$$I_{R_2} = I_2 \qquad = \frac{30}{22} \qquad\qquad = 1.36 \text{ A}$$

$$I_{R_3} = I_1 + I_3 = \frac{3}{22} + \frac{46}{22} = \frac{49}{22} = 2.23 \text{ A}$$

$$I_{R_4} = I_3 \qquad = \frac{46}{22} \qquad\qquad = 2.09 \text{ A}$$

$$I_{R_5} = I_2 + I_3 = \frac{30}{22} + \frac{46}{22} = \frac{76}{22} = 3.45 \text{ A}$$

The results are in exact agreement with the results obtained on the same circuit using the method of branch analysis, as they must be. For most students this method, once learned, is simpler to apply than the method of branch currents. It is also readily suited to computer solutions, and for those students interested in programming, this method provides useful material.

1. Use mesh analysis to solve the circuit shown.   **Problems**

Circuit for Problem 1.

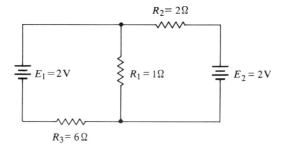

2. Use mesh analysis to solve the circuit shown.

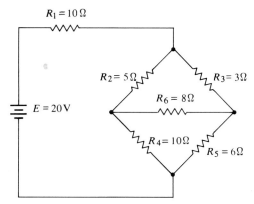

Circuit for Problem 2.

3. Use mesh analysis to solve the circuit shown.

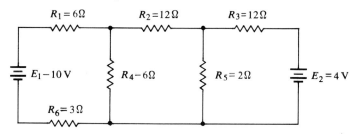

Circuit for Problem 3.

4. Solve the circuit shown, using mesh analysis.

Circuit for Problem 4.

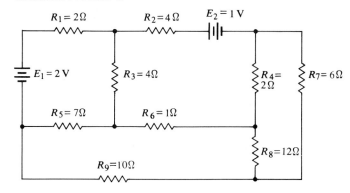

5. Solve the circuit shown, using mesh analysis.

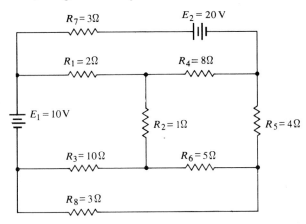

Circuit for Problem 5.

6. Using mesh analysis, solve the circuit shown.

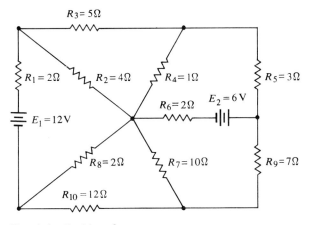

Circuit for Problem 6.

THE METHOD OF NODAL ANALYSIS. In branch current and mesh analysis methods, voltage equations were written in terms of current and resistance, and the resulting equations were solved for currents. In the method of *nodal analysis,* current equations are written in terms of voltage and resistance, and the resulting equations are solved for voltages. Each method has its role; nodal analysis is most useful where the sources are current sources. If they are voltage sources, then the circuit must be redrawn with current sources equivalent to the original voltage sources.

8-3
Nodal Analysis

Any voltage source shown with a series resistance can be redrawn as an equivalent current source with a parallel resistance. If the voltage source is considered as a Thevenin equivalent circuit, then it is transformed into a Norton equivalent circuit (Figure 8-10). In the Thevenin equivalent circuit, voltage source E_{Th} is in series with resistance R_{Th}. If the terminals of this Thevenin equivalent are shorted, current I_N will flow. A constant current generator with current I_N and resistance R_{Th} in parallel will deliver to any load the same current at the same voltage as the original series voltage source and resistor.

The original circuit with a voltage source is nearly the same simple series–parallel circuit that has been used as a first example both for branch current analysis and for mesh analysis. It is shown again in Figure 8-11. To be solved by using nodal analysis, it must first be redrawn with the voltage source replaced with an equivalent current source.

The voltage source in the original circuit is in series with a 1 Ω resistor. If the voltage source with its series resistor is considered to be a Thevenin

Figure 8-10   Thevenin and Norton equivalent circuits.

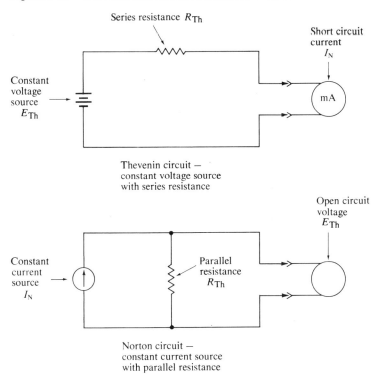

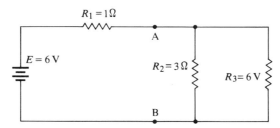

Figure 8-11   A simple series–parallel circuit.

equivalent circuit, and connected to the rest of the circuit at the points A and B, then it may be replaced with an equivalent circuit at the same points without change in voltage or current in the remainder of the circuit.

The short-circuit current of a Thevenin equivalent circuit consisting of a 6 V source in series with a 1 Ω resistor is, by Ohm's law, 6 A. The Norton equivalent to this circuit is therefore a 6 A constant current generator in parallel with the same 1 Ω resistor. The original circuit may now be redrawn with the equivalent current source connected to points A and B, as shown in Figure 8-12.

A *node* is defined as a junction of two or more branches. The circuit as redrawn with the current source in place has two nodes. One node is selected as the reference node, and the voltage at the other node is to be determined by comparison with the reference node.

By Kirchhoff's current law the current entering the node must be equal to the current leaving. The current entering the node is the 6 A from the constant current generator. The current leaving the node is the sum of the currents through the resistors to the reference node. Written as an equation, this is

$$I_1 + I_2 + I_3 = 6$$

Figure 8-12   The circuit of Figure 8-11 redrawn with a constant current source equivalent to the original voltage source.

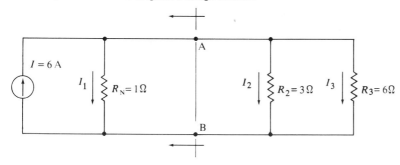

By Ohm's law the current through any resistor is

$$I = \frac{V}{R}$$

and for each resistor in this network, V is the same. By substitution

$$\frac{V}{R_1} + \frac{V}{R_2} + \frac{V}{R_3} = 6$$

Since the value of each resistor is known, this becomes

$$\frac{V}{1} + \frac{V}{3} + \frac{V}{6} = 6$$

Since there is only one unknown in this equation, it may be readily solved, and the result is

$$V = 4 \text{ V}$$

With this voltage known, the current through the two resistors which were originally connected between this node and the reference node may be calculated. The two currents are

$$I_2 = 1\frac{1}{3} \text{ A}$$

$$I_3 = \frac{2}{3} \text{ A}$$

The current through the 1 Ω resistor in parallel with the 6 A constant current generator in the circuit as redrawn so that nodal analysis might be applied is *not* the same as the current through the same 1 Ω resistor in series with a 6 V source in the original circuit. In the circuit with the constant current generator this resistor has a potential of 4 V across it, and a consequent current flow through it of 4 A. In the original circuit the potential across it may be easily seen to be 2 V, the difference between the source potential and the voltage across the parallel bank (Figure 8-13).

Figure 8-13   The circuit of Figure 8-11 obeys Kirchhoff's current law.

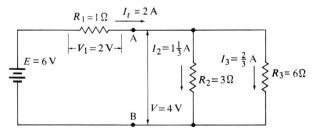

This means the actual current through this resistor in the original circuit is 2 A, and this is correct in satisfying Kirchhoff's current law for the original circuit.

It is not always necessary, or even desirable, that voltage sources be converted to current sources before nodal analysis is applied to a circuit. Some circuits may be solved most readily by retaining voltage sources. An example, and a common one, is the bridge circuit of Figure 8-14.

There are four nodes in this circuit. If the node which is the common connection of R_2, R_4, and the negative terminal of the voltage source is chosen as the reference node, then the node consisting of the positive terminal of the voltage source and the common connection of R_1 and R_3 is at a known potential of 10 V with respect to the reference node. Thus, even though it is a four-node circuit, only two of the nodes are at unknown potentials compared to the reference node, and the system may be solved with two equations in two unknowns.

The first step in the solution is to label the nodes and draw current arrows. Node 1 is assumed to be at some potential intermediate between the 10 V node and the reference node. Therefore the arrow representing the current through R_1 is drawn from the 10 V node to node 1, and the arrow representing the current through R_2 is drawn from node 1 to the reference node.

Figure 8-14   Voltage sources may be retained when nodal analysis is applied to a bridge circuit.

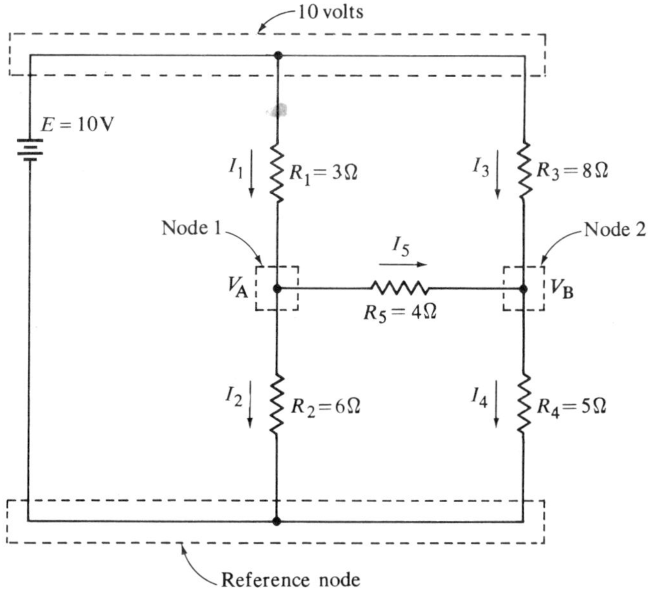

Similarly, node 2 is assumed to be at an intermediate potential, and the current arrows for R_3 and R_4 are drawn accordingly. The potential at node 1, V_A, has been arbitrarily assumed to be more positive than the potential at node 2, V_B. Therefore the current arrow for R_5 has been drawn *from* node 1 *to* node 2.

With the voltage at node 1 designated V_A and the voltage at node 2 designated V_B, the voltage across each resistor may now be written. The voltage across R_2 is of course V_A, and similarly the voltage across R_4 is V_B. The voltage across R_1 is the difference in potential between the two nodes to which it is connected. Since V_A was assumed to be less positive than the 10 V node, this potential across R_1 is $10 - V_A$. Similarly, the potential across R_3 is $10 - V_B$. Since node 1 was assumed to be more positive than node 2 when the current arrow directions were designated, the potential across R_5 is written as $V_A - V_B$.

Now, by Ohm's law, each current may be designated in terms of voltage and resistance.

$$I_1 = \frac{10 - V_A}{3} \qquad I_3 = \frac{10 - V_B}{8} \qquad I_5 = \frac{V_A - V_B}{4}$$

$$I_2 = \frac{V_A}{6} \qquad I_4 = \frac{V_B}{5}$$

By Kirchhoff's current law, for node 1

$$I_1 - I_2 - I_5 = 0$$

and, by substitution,

$$\frac{10 - V_A}{3} - \frac{V_A}{6} - \frac{V_A - V_B}{4} = 0$$

This reduces to

$$9V_A - 3V_B = 40$$

By Kirchhoff's current law, for node 2

$$I_5 + I_3 - I_4 = 0$$

and, by substitution,

$$\frac{V_A - V_B}{4} + \frac{10 - V_B}{8} - \frac{V_B}{5} = 0$$

which reduces to

$$10V_A - 23V_B = -50$$

These two equations, based on currents and with voltages as the unknowns, may be solved by any convenient means. For the sake of clarity, the two equations are repeated together and solved using determinants.

$$9V_A - 3V_B = 40$$

$$10V_A - 23V_B = -50$$

$$V_A = \frac{\begin{vmatrix} 40 & -3 \\ -50 & -23 \end{vmatrix}}{\begin{vmatrix} 9 & -3 \\ 10 & -23 \end{vmatrix}} = \frac{(-920) - (+150)}{(-207) - (-30)} = \frac{-1070}{-177} \doteq 6.0452 \text{ V}$$

$$V_B = \frac{\begin{vmatrix} 9 & 40 \\ 10 & -50 \end{vmatrix}}{\begin{vmatrix} 9 & -3 \\ 10 & -23 \end{vmatrix}} = \frac{(-450) - (+400)}{(-207) - (-30)} = \frac{-850}{-177} = 4.8023 \text{ V}$$

Now the voltage at each node is known in relation to the reference node. Each current may be calculated from the original current equations.

$$I_1 = \frac{10 - V_A}{3} = \frac{10 - 6.0452}{3} = 1.3183 \text{ A}$$

$$I_2 = \frac{V_A}{6} = \frac{6.0452}{6} = 1.0075 \text{ A}$$

$$I_3 = \frac{10 - V_B}{8} = \frac{10 - 4.8023}{8} = 0.6497 \text{ A}$$

$$I_4 = \frac{V_B}{5} = \frac{4.8023}{5} = 0.9605 \text{ A}$$

$$I_5 = \frac{V_A - V_B}{4} = \frac{6.0452 - 4.8023}{4} = 0.3107 \text{ A}$$

The current flow through each resistor, as just calculated, and the voltage across each resistor have been entered on the circuit diagram in Figure 8-15. As a necessary check, it may be seen that Kirchhoff's current law is satisfied at each junction, and Kirchhoff's voltage law is satisfied for any loop through the circuit.

A few precautions may be noted, particularly where both voltage and current sources are involved. Where a current is shown, whether the current is designated in terms of voltage and resistance or in terms of current from a current source, the current arrow must flow *from* the more positive node *to* the less positive node. This, of course, is where the direction of the current arrow follows conventional current rather than electron flow.

If, as with the other forms of analysis based on Kirchhoff's laws, a current is calculated as negative, it simply means the original direction assumed for current flow was wrong. As before, the direction of flow indicated by the arrow may be reversed and the value of the current then entered as positive.

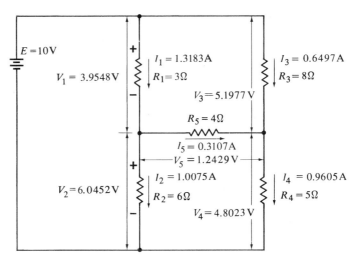

Figure 8-15

It is necessary that the results be checked against Kirchhoff's and Ohm's laws. Each junction must be checked to insure that the currents sum to zero, and each loop must be checked to insure that the algebraic sum of the voltages is zero. In the example just given, all voltages and currents were calculated to four digits past the decimal point. This was done primarily to aid in the checking process (and would not have been done if an electronic calculator had not been immediately at hand). The accuracy with which the original data was known did not, of course, justify this degree of precision. In any practical problem, the results ought to be rounded off to a degree of precision commensurate with the accuracy of the original data.

Problems   **1.**   Using nodal analysis, solve the circuit shown.

Circuit for Problem 1.

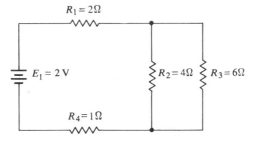

2. Using nodal analysis, solve the circuit shown.

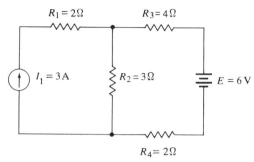

Circuit for Problem 2.

3. Solve the circuit shown, using nodal analysis.

Circuit for Problem 3.

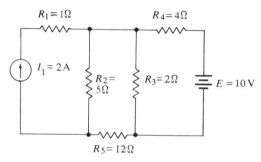

4. Solve the circuit shown, using nodal analysis.

Circuit for Problem 4.

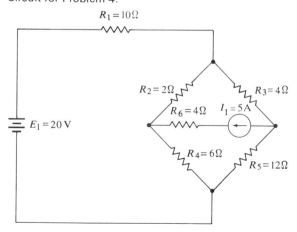

5. Using nodal analysis, solve the circuit shown.

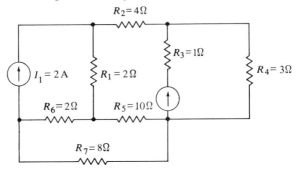

Circuit for Problem 5.

6. Using nodal analysis, solve the circuit shown.

Circuit for Problem 6.

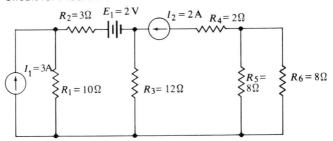

7. The circuit shown is called an incremental model of a transistor amplifier. Using nodal analysis, derive the equations for the voltages at points B, E, and C on the circuit, in terms of i_s, and the resistances R_1, R_2, R_3, r_b, r_e, and r_c.

Circuit for Problem 7.

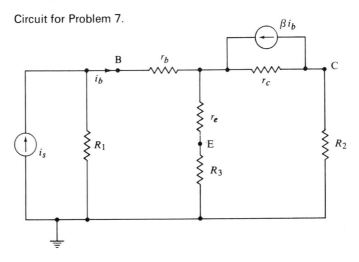

branch current analysis   a method of solving circuits, usually very complex **Key Words**
ones, by considering each branch as a single current and then
algebraically combining the single-current results

mesh analysis   a method of solving any network that can be drawn without
crossovers on a plane surface

node   the junction of two or more branches

nodal analysis   a method of solving circuits in which current equations
are written in terms of voltage and resistance and the resulting
equations are solved for voltages. Nodal analysis is most useful in
circuits where the sources are current, not voltage sources.

window   any closed area bounded by a network

1.   If we can write as many equations as there are independent variables **Summary**
in a problem, we can solve the resulting equations to find the value **of Concepts**
of each of the variables.

2.   In writing voltage equations, terms representing *IR* drops are marked
positive, and terms representing voltage gains are marked *negative.*

3.   While branch current analysis is applicable to any network, mesh
analysis is applicable only to networks that may be drawn without
crossovers on a plane surface.

4.   Each mesh equation has one term that is the product of the loop
current times the sum of the resistance in that loop. There must be
another term for each resistor in that loop that also carries another loop
current.

5.   In branch current and mesh analysis, voltage equations are written in
terms of current and resistance, and the resulting equations are solved
for currents.

6.   Nodal analysis is most useful where the sources are current sources.
If the sources are voltage sources, then the circuit may be redrawn
with current sources equivalent to the original voltage sources.

On a separate sheet of paper, fill in the blanks or answer the questions below. **To Help You Review**
The number following each question refers to the section in the chapter where
the correct answer can be found.

1.   If you can write an equation for each of five variables in a problem,
what should you be able to do? (8-1)

2. In writing voltage equations, terms representing a voltage drop are marked _____, while terms representing a voltage gain are marked _____. (8-1)

3. In what way are mesh analysis and branch current analysis similar? How do these methods differ? (8-2)

4. What is a "window"? (8-2)

5. In mesh analysis if two currents are in the same direction, terms for each resistor that carries another loop current are _____. If the currents are in the opposite direction, the terms are _____. (8-2)

6. In branch current and mesh analysis, voltage equations are written in terms of _____ and _____. In nodal analysis the equations are written in terms of _____ and _____. (8-3)

7. What is a node?

PART 2
REACTIVE CIRCUITS

NINE
MAGNETISM AND ELECTRO-MAGNETIC INDUCTION

THE MAGNETIC PHENOMENON.   Magnetism was probably among the first electrical phenomena to be discovered, and certainly among the last to be understood. Some naturally occurring materials are magnetic, including magnetite, an iron ore. The earth has a magnetic field that has been used for centuries as a basis for marine navigation.

Magnetism is now known to be an effect associated with moving charges of electricity. Atoms consist of a central nucleus and electrons in orbit around the nucleus. The electrons themselves have a property called *spin,* which seems to imply that they are spinning like tops as they move in orbit about the nucleus (Figure 9-1). This is quite similar to the way the earth revolves on its axis as it moves in orbit around the sun; but this is too simple to be fully true, as it neglects the wave aspects of the nature of electrons.

9-1
Magnetism

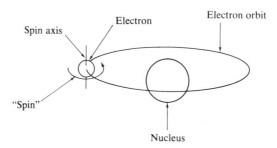

Figure 9-1   In an atom an electron not only orbits
the nucleus but also "spins" on its axis.

MAGNETIC MATERIALS.   Each spinning electron in orbit about its nucleus
can act as a tiny magnet. Spins in opposing directions give rise to fields of
opposite polarity. In most materials the magnetic effect resulting from the
spin and orbital motion of these moving charges is weak, and the random
alignment of the spins and orbital motions of electrons of adjacent atoms
prevents the magnetic fields from combining.

In the group of materials called *ferromagnetic* materials, there are many
unpaired electrons with spins in the same direction in each atom. This
results in a strong magnetic effect.

Magnetic materials are usually classified in the following three groups.

1. *Ferromagnetic materials* include iron, steel, and such alloys as Alnico
   and Permalloy. They become strongly magnetized in the same direction
   as the magnetizing field.
2. *Paramagnetic materials* include aluminum, platinum, manganese,
   chromium, nitrogen, and uranium, as well as others. They become
   weakly magnetized in the same direction as the magnetizing field.
3. *Diamagnetic materials* include all materials in which ferromagnetic or
   paramagnetic effects are not noted. Among the diamagnetic materials
   are copper, bismuth, antimony, zinc, mercury, gold, and silver. These
   materials become very weakly magnetized in the direction opposite
   to the magnetizing field.

MAGNETIC DOMAINS.   Ferromagnetism is by far the most important
magnetic effect associated with materials, at least so far as electronics is
concerned. The reason is that in these materials adjacent atoms are
magnetically linked together by an effect called *exchange coupling* so that
large groups of atoms all have their magnetic fields aligned in the same
direction. These groups of atoms with their aligned magnetic fields are
called *domains,* and each domain acts like a small but powerful magnet.

Ordinarily, the magnetic domains in a piece of iron are randomly aligned with each other, so there is no net external effect. If the piece of iron is placed in an external magnetic field, the domains aligned with the field grow by realignment of atoms at the borders of the domain, while the other domains are consequently reduced in size (Figure 9-2).

In soft iron the domains resume their random orientations as soon as the external magnetic field is removed. In hard steel the domains retain their alignment, and the piece of steel becomes a permanent magnet.

MAGNETIC FIELDS.   The external effect of the spinning electrons in orbit about their atoms, and its much stronger manifestation—the total of the individual effects in a permanent magnet—is called a *magnetic field*.

It is what is called a *dipole field*. An electric field can be the result of a single kind of charge, and is thus of a single polarity. A magnetic field is always associated with two poles.*

The earth is a gigantic magnet with its own magnetic field. A bar of steel that has been magnetized will tend to align itself to this field, with the result that one end of the steel magnet points toward one of the earth's

*The possible August 1975 discovery of a monopole may change this.

Figure 9-2   The influence of an external magnetic field on ferromagnetic material results in a net external field.

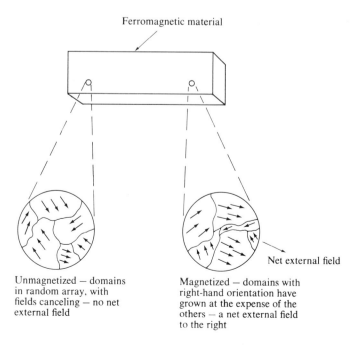

Ferromagnetic material

Net external field

Unmagnetized — domains
in random array, with
fields canceling — no net
external field

Magnetized — domains with
right-hand orientation have
grown at the expense of the
others — a net external field
to the right

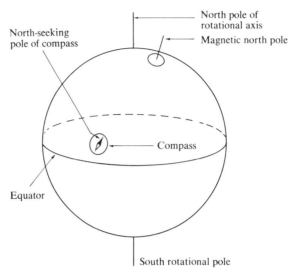

Figure 9-3   A compass needle points to the magnetic north pole, which is close to the geographic north pole.

magnetic poles, while the other end of the magnet points at the earth's other magnetic pole.

Since the earth's magnetic poles approximately coincide with the poles of rotation, this phenomenon has been used since the second century A.D. as an aid to navigation—the compass. A compass is simply a sliver or needle of magnetic material, mounted so it may turn freely to align its magnetic field to the earth's field (Figure 9-3).

The end of a magnet that points to the magnetic pole of the earth near the north geographic pole is called the *north-seeking pole*. The opposite end is, of course, the *south-seeking pole*. The terms are usually abbreviated, and the poles of a magnet are usually simply called the north pole (N) and the south pole (S).

Just as a force of attraction exists between opposite charges and a force of repulsion between like charges, a force of attraction exists between opposite magnetic poles and a force of repulsion between like poles. This is sketched in Figure 9-4.

RULE   *A north pole and a south pole attract each other. A north pole repels another north pole, while a south pole repels another south pole.*

MAGNETIC FIELD LINES.   If a sheet of paper or glass is placed over a bar magnet and iron filings are sprinkled on the sheet, the iron filings will

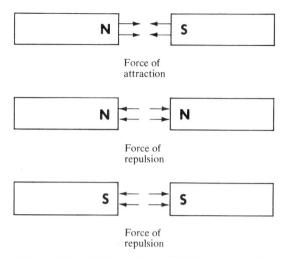

Figure 9-4 Unlike poles (N, S) attract. Like poles (N, N or S, S) repel.

tend to become individual magnets because of the field of the bar magnet. If the sheet is tapped, these individual magnetized filings will tend to cling together end to end, N to S, and align themselves with the field of the bar magnet. The result is that they will appear to define curved lines extending outward from each pole, and, where they do not run off the edge of the sheet, from one pole to the other (Figure 9-5).

This phenomenon has given rise to the concept of field lines, or *lines of flux*. This is a very useful concept mathematically, but flux lines have no more physical reality than do contour lines on a map. In fact, flux lines serve much the same purpose, though in a slightly different way.

Closely spaced contour lines on a map indicate steep terrain, and a ball placed on the actual slope will roll at right angles to the direction of the imaginary lines. Where the contour lines change curvature, the path of the ball may change direction. so as to always cross contour lines at right angles to their direction.

Magnetic flux lines indicate field strength. Where they are close together, the field is intense; as they become more widely spaced, the field they represent is weaker. Unlike contour lines, which are drawn at right angles to the slope they represent, magnetic flux lines are drawn in the direction of the field. A ball of iron placed in a magnetic field will move parallel to the direction of the flux lines. Where the lines curve, the path of the ball will also curve.

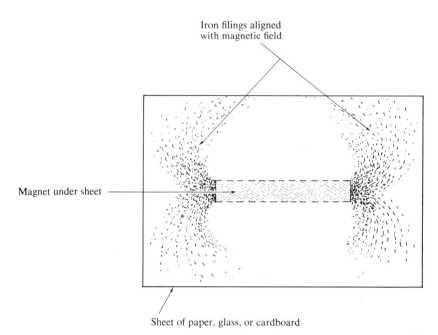

Iron filings aligned
with magnetic field

Magnet under sheet ——

Sheet of paper, glass, or cardboard

Figure 9-5 Lines of flux do not have physical existence, but we can "see" them following the method described in the text.

9-2
Magnetic Effects of
Electric Currents

THE FIELD AROUND A CURRENT. Just as the spinning charges in orbit around the nucleus of an atom produce a magnetic field, so the movement of charges through a conductor—an electric current—produces a magnetic field.

Think of the flux lines indicating the strength and direction of a magnetic field around a bar magnet as continuous, from the N pole of the magnet, curving through space to the S pole, and continuing through the body of the magnet back to the N pole again. The polarity of the magnetic field indicated by these lines is usually shown by arrowheads on the lines, pointing from N to S where the flux lines are outside the body of the magnet. You can see this in Figure 9-6.

The magnetic field generated by a current flowing through a conductor can also be indicated by lines of force. Pass a wire conductor vertically through a sheet of paper and sprinkle iron filings on the paper. Since the effect is comparatively weak, the current in the wire must be intense. The iron filings will form concentric circles about the conductor, a pattern indicating flux lines.

Just as the flux lines from a bar magnet have a north-to-south polarity, so the flux lines about a conductor have a direction of polarity. The right hand may be placed on the conductor with the thumb pointing in the direction of conventional current flow, and the fingers will circle the conductor in the direction of polarity of the flux lines about the conductor. Figure 9-7 shows this *right-hand rule*.

COILS. If a loop is made in a wire to form a coil of one turn, the flux lines from opposite points on the coil will be in the same direction. This may be seen by applying the right-hand rule. If the loop is held vertically and at right angles to the observer, so that the direction of conventional current through the loop is counterclockwise, the right-hand rule applied to the right side of the coil, where current is ascending, will indicate a direction of flux through the coil and in the direction of the observer. The right-hand rule applied to the left side of the coil, where the current is descending, will also show a direction of flux through the coil and in the direction of the observer.

The direction of external flux in a bar magnet is from N to S; consequently, the direction of internal flux is from S to N. The end of the magnet from which the flux lines emerge is the N pole. The same is true of the coil. In the case of the single-turn coil, the end of the coil facing the observer is the source of emerging flux lines and is, consequently, the N pole of the coil (Figure 9-8).

Figure 9-6 The field of this bar magnet is continuous; the flux lines flow from the N pole through space to the S pole, and then through the magnet to the N pole. Arrowheads mark the polarity of the field.

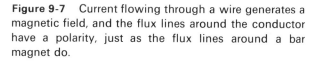

Figure 9-7 Current flowing through a wire generates a magnetic field, and the flux lines around the conductor have a polarity, just as the flux lines around a bar magnet do.

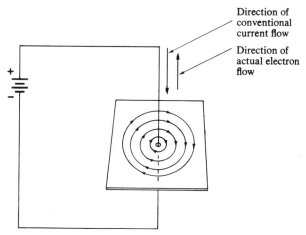

Direction of conventional current flow

Direction of actual electron flow

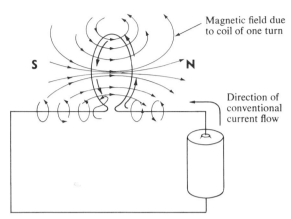

Figure 9-8 The polarity of flux lines in a one-turn coil.

The external magnetic field generated by a coil of one turn is weak, but it can be greatly increased by increasing the number of turns in the coil. Each turn generates a field of the same polarity as every other turn. Consequently, the net external field is the sum of the fields from each turn. The external field from such a coil is exactly the same as the external field that would be produced by a cylindrical magnet of the same shape (Figure 9-9).

If the coil is wrapped around a core of ferromagnetic material, the domains of the ferromagnetic material that are aligned with the field of the coil grow at the expense of those not so aligned, and the flux from these domains adds to the field produced by the coil. The total external flux from such a combination can be very much greater than the flux produced by the coil alone. This fact forms the basis for the *electromagnet*.

The electromagnet in its most simple and obvious form may vary from the small electromagnets that, with a sliding core, actuate the valves on a modern washer to the huge electromagnets that lift tons of scrap iron at a salvage yard. An electromagnet, whatever its size, consists of a soft iron core around which a coil of many turns of wire is wrapped. When current flows through the coil, the domains in the core align, and the external magnetic field thus produced can, by induction, pick up ferromagnetic materials.

MAGNETIC INDUCTION. When a ferromagnetic material is placed within a field of magnetic flux such as is present at the pole of an electromagnet, the magnetic domains in the ferromagnetic material are realigned. If the pole the material is facing is a N pole, with the flux lines emerging from the pole, the domains in the previously unmagnetized ferromagnetic material are realigned in the direction of the field. For each domain the realignment is such that it presents a S pole to the facing N pole, so the field lines emerging from the N pole of the electromagnet enter the domain. As the domains align, the material itself becomes a magnet, with its S pole facing the N pole of the electromagnet. There is thus a force of attraction between the electromagnet and the ferromagnetic material within its field of flux. If the S pole of the electromagnet faces the ferromagnetic material, the domains in the previously unmagnetized material are realigned to present a N pole to the facing S pole of the electromagnet. Thus, the direction of the magnetism induced in any ferromagnetic material within the influence of some external field is always such as to produce a force of attraction between the material and the external field.

MOTOR ACTION.   The d'Arsonval meter movement previously discussed is a tiny motor, capable of only part of a revolution. Current flowing through the moving coil of the meter movement makes a magnet of it, and the poles of the magnetic field of the coil tend to realign themselves with the field of the permanent magnet of the meter. If the coil was not restrained by the hairsprings, it would rotate until the two fields were aligned, but there the rotation would stop.

If we want continuous rotation of a current-carrying coil in a stationary magnetic field, there must be some arrangement for changing the direction of polarity of the magnetic field of the current-carrying coil at the instant

Figure 9-9   The external field of a coil is shaped like the field of a bar magnet.

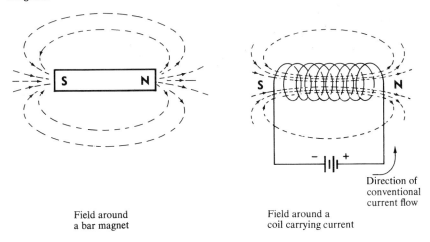

Field around
a bar magnet

Field around a
coil carrying current

Direction of
conventional
current flow

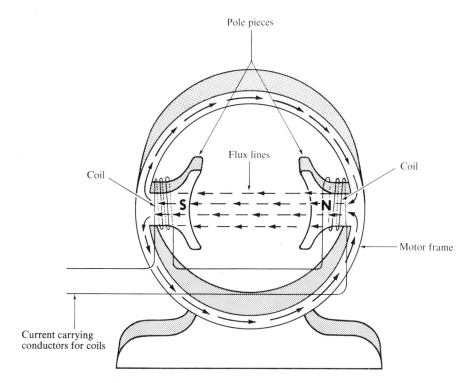

Figure 9-10   In an electric motor, flux lines travel through the motor frame.

of alignment. If this is done, the attractive forces that cause the poles of the coil to align themselves with the opposite poles of the stationary magnetic field become repulsive forces. For example, as the N pole of the field of the current-carrying coil is attracted toward the S pole of the stationary magnetic field and moves into alignment with it, the direction of current through the coil is suddenly reversed. Now the face of the coil that was the N pole becomes a S pole and is repelled by the S pole of the stationary magnetic field. The coil thus continues to rotate past the point of alignment at which it would otherwise have stopped.

This action must continue as the coil rotates. Another half revolution brings the new S pole of the coil into alignment facing the N pole of the external magnetic field, and again rotation will stop if there is no reversal of current in the coil.

In a practical motor the external stationary field is produced by current flowing through two coils called the *field coils*. These coils are opposite each other inside the motor frame. They are both wound around iron cores called *pole pieces*. Each coil and pole piece is either a N or S pole for the magnetic field inside the motor frame. Since the flux lines must be continuous, the motor frame itself provides the necessary path. A single line of flux can be traced from the N pole piece, through the space inside the motor frame which is filled by the rotating coil, to the S pole piece, and then through the iron motor frame back to the N pole piece (Figure 9-10).

In the space inside the motor frame between the pole pieces is a rotating metal frame called an *armature,* on which the rotating coil is wound. The armature is mounted on bearings at each end so that it can rotate freely. Like the pole pieces and the motor frame, the armature must be made of a ferromagnetic material.

The ferromagnetic material of the armature and pole pieces greatly intensifies the magnetic field produced by current flowing through the coils, just as in the case of the simple electromagnet. The forces of attraction or repulsion which cause rotation of the armature can be considerable. The air gap between the pole pieces and the metal of the armature is made as small as practical, which also increases the force.

The necessary switching action to reverse the direction of current in the rotating coil is performed by two curved metal segments mounted on the armature shaft so they rotate with the armature but are insulated from it. These two metal segments together are called the *commutator,* and the two terminals of the coil wound on the armature are connected to the two commutator segments (Figure 9-11).

Figure 9-11 The armature, commutator, and coil of a motor.

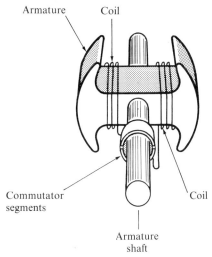

Fixed to the motor frame but insulated from it are two carbon rods, called *brushes,* which make continuous contact with the commutator as the armature rotates. The brushes carry current from whatever external power source is used to the armature coil. As the armature rotates, each brush makes contact with first one commutator segment and then the other. Each time the two brushes change segments, the direction of current flow through the armature coil changes (Figure 9-12).

To provide for more even and continuous torque, most motors have more than one pair of poles and one coil on the armature. Many coils may be wound at different angles on the armature.

There are many different designs for motors. All electric motors, however, are based on the same principle, the attraction and repulsion between the poles of electromagnets.

9-3
Magnetic
Measurements

Unfortunately, several systems of units are used in the measurement of magnetic quantities. Also unfortunately, the names of the units are men's names, used to honor the men who laid the foundations on which electrical technology is based, but confusing to the student first approaching the

Figure 9-12   A complete electric motor.

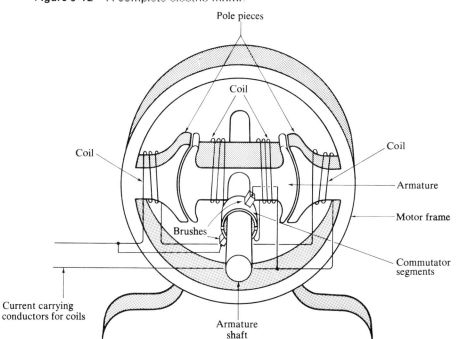

subject. It is as though we had to measure distances using three different sets of units, called the Smith, the Jones, and the Paderewski, and to remember that five Smiths equal one Johnson, but ten Joneses equal one O'Reilly.

FLUX. The entire group of lines of flux that flow out of the N pole of a magnet constitute the *flux* of the magnet, and the symbol to represent that flux is the Greek letter ϕ (phi). In the English system the unit by which flux is measured is the *line*. In the CGS (centimeter-gram-second) system flux is measured with a unit equivalent in size to the line but called the *maxwell* (Mx). In the MKS (meter-kilogram-second) system the unit is 10^8 lines (or maxwells), and it is called the *weber* (Wb). In all three systems the symbol is ϕ. Unfortunately, if a quantity is given as $\phi = 13$, it can mean a flux of 13 lines or a flux of 1,300,000,000 lines, depending on whether the original value is in maxwells or webers.

In this book the explanations and problems are all based on the MKS system, but the other units are still in use and cannot be ignored.

As might be expected from the number of lines of flux 1 Wb represents, it is an inconveniently large unit. Thus, in the MKS system flux is often given in microwebers (μWb). A flux of 1 μWb $= 10^2$ lines $= 10^2$ maxwells.

FLUX DENSITY. Two magnets are of equal strength if they have the same flux (the same total number of lines of flux emerging from their N poles). But if the area of the pole face of one magnet is half that of the other, then the concentration of lines of force must be twice as great in the magnet with the smaller pole face. This degree of concentration of flux is the *flux density,* for which the symbol is B. The unit is lines/in.^{2} in the English system, lines/cm^2 in the CGS system, and webers/m^2 in the MKS system.

The name for lines/cm^2, the flux density unit in the CGS system, is the *gauss* (G), while the MKS unit of webers/m^2 is the *tesla* (T). Table 9-1 shows how all these units are related.

TABLE 9-1   Units of Flux and Flux Density

	Symbol	MKS	CGS	English
Flux	ϕ	weber (Wb)	maxwell (Mx)	line
Flux Density	B	tesla (T)	gauss (G)	lines/in.^{2}

1 weber $= 10^8$ maxwells $= 10^8$ lines
1 tesla $= 10^4$ gauss $= 6.45 \times 10^4$ lines/in.^{2}

The flux density is, by definition, flux per unit area. In the form of an equation, this is

$$B = \frac{\phi}{A}$$

where A stands for area in the appropriate units—m² in the MKS system, cm² in the CGS system, and in.² in the English.

EXAMPLE   Suppose a magnet has a pole face area of 6.5×10^{-4} m² (about 1 in²) and a total flux of 500 μWb. Calculate the flux density.

Solution.

$$A = 6.5 \times 10^{-4} \text{ m}^2$$

$$\phi = 500 \times 10^{-6} \text{ Wb} = 5 \times 10^{-4} \text{ Wb}$$

Substituting in the equation,

$$B = \frac{5 \times 10^{-4}}{6.5 \times 10^{-4}}$$

$$= 0.77 \text{ T}$$

Magnetic flux and flux density are independent of the origin of the magnetic field. A bar magnet and an electromagnet produce the same kind of field, which is measured in the same units.

MAGNETIZING FORCE.   With a coil as the source of the magnetic flux, the strength of the magnetic field depends on the strength of the current. The more current flowing in the coil, the stronger the resulting magnetic field. The strength of the field also depends on the number of turns of the coil. Each turn of the coil acts as a magnet, and the fields from each turn combine to give the total field of the coil. The coil produces a magnetic field like the field of a bar magnet, with a strength proportional to the product of the number of amperes of current flowing in the coil times the number of turns in the coil. The number of ampere–turns is the unit of *magnetic potential, magnetizing force, or magnetomotive force* (mmf).

Magnetomotive force is measured in *ampere–turns (NI)* in the MKS system, and in *gilberts* (Gb) in the CGS system; 1 ampere–turn equals 1.26 gilberts.

EXAMPLE   Calculate in both MKS units and CGS units the mmf of a coil of 200 turns in which a current of 250 mA is flowing.

Solution.

$$NI = N \times I = 200 \times 0.25 = 50 \text{ A}$$

Both *NI* and mmf are used to indicate magnetomotive force in ampere–turns. The result of this calculation is 50 A, where the A stands for ampere–turns, though it is the same abbreviation that is used for amperes. The result in gilberts is

$$\text{mmf} = NI(1.26) = 50 \times 1.26 = 63 \text{ Gb}$$

FIELD INTENSITY (*H*).   The mmf of a coil is the total magnetizing force of the coil. But mmf says nothing about how large or small a volume of space that force is concentrated in. The mmf of a short coil, measured from end to end, is concentrated, while the mmf of a longer coil is spread over a longer distance, and must therefore have a lesser field intensity. In MKS units the *field intensity* is

$$H = \frac{NI}{L}$$

where *NI* is the number of ampere–turns (A) in the coil, and *L* is the length in meters between poles of the coil. If the coil has an air core, the poles are the ends of the coil; but if the coil has a ferromagnetic core, the poles are the ends of the core, since the core concentrates the flux of the coil.

In the CGS system the unit for *H* is *oersted* (Oe), which equals 1 Gb/cm. To convert the MKS unit of *H* into the corresponding number of oersteds, note that 1 unit of *H* measured in ampere–turns per meter is the same as 0.0126 Oe.

Given the field intensity *H* for a certain coil is 2000 A/m, calculate the   EXAMPLE
corresponding value of field intensity in CGS units.

Solution

$$\text{Oe} = 0.0126 \text{ A/m}$$
$$= 0.0126 \times 2000 = 25.2 \text{ Oe}$$

PERMEABILITY (*μ*).   The quantity *H* specifies how much field intensity is available to produce magnetic flux, but it does not by itself tell us how much flux will be produced. Much depends on the material in the core of the coil. A ferromagnetic material already consists of magnetic domains, each of which has some inherent flux, regardless of any mmf from the coil surrounding it. If the field intensity of the coil, which tells us how the mmf is concentrated in the core, is sufficient to cause some domains to grow, then the core exhibits a magnetism of its own, and the total flux from the coil with its core is much greater than the flux of the coil alone.

The quality of the ferromagnetic material which relates to the ease with which the flux appears to be concentrated by it is called *permeability* (μ). Permeability relates flux density to field intensity as follows.

$$B = \mu H$$

If, of course, we know B and H for a ferromagnetic core, then

$$\mu = \frac{B}{H}$$

This factor, μ, is the absolute permeability, not permeability compared to any other material. It is given in units of B/H.

In the CGS system the units for flux density and field intensity have been chosen so that B measured in gauss divided by H measured in oersteds gives μ the value 1 when the coil has no core—in other words, when the "core" is air or a vacuum. Thus, in the CGS system a field intensity of 20 oersteds produces a flux of 20 gauss where there is no core (the presence of air in the core is not considered significant).

With this system the permeability of another material may be compared with that of air or free space, which are taken to be the same. Since the permeability of air is 1, the relative permeability of any substance will be the same as the absolute permeability as measured in B/H units.

Since in the MKS system the size of the units for flux density and field intensity were not deliberately chosen to make B/H equal to 1 for air, the absolute value of μ in this system is *not* the same as the relative permeability.

The permeability of air or a vacuum, where B and H are given in teslas and ampere–turns/meter respectively, is $4\pi \times 10^{-7}$, which is the same as 1.26×10^{-6}, and is given the symbol μ_o.

If the relative permeability (μ_r) of a ferromagnetic material is known, the absolute permeability in B/H units may be calculated from

$$\mu = \mu_r \mu_o$$

Permeability is not a property merely of the kind of ferromagnetic material used in a core, but of its condition as well. It is flux density per field intensity, but the flux density does not change directly with the field intensity, particularly at high field intensities.

The reason, as we have seen, that a ferromagnetic material appears to concentrate lines of flux is that the domains inherent in the material grow to align themselves with the external field. Their fields then add to the external field, but there is a limit to this process. When all the domains within the core have aligned themselves with the field, then any further increase in the field will produce no further increase in flux density, except so far as the relatively much weaker field of the coil contributes to the total.

Figure 9-13 A *B–H* curve. Flux density *B* on the vertical axis is plotted against field intensity *H* on the horizontal axis. The curve marks values of μ, permeability. Point *a* is saturation, the point at which nearly all the domains are aligned and beyond which flux density cannot increase very much. μ varies near zero, depending on previous magnetization, so no values are shown.

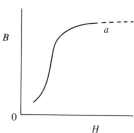

If we plot flux density (B) on the vertical axis of a graph against field intensity (H) on the horizontal axis, we get a graph like that shown in Figure 9-13. Note that the curve, called a *B/H curve,* flattens out at the top. The field intensity continues to increase, but the flux density does not increase rapidly after a certain level, called *saturation,* is reached. This is the point where nearly all the domains have been aligned, and quite naturally there is little more in the way of domain alignment that the external field can do.

Mathematically, the slope of this curve at any point is the value of *B/H* at that point. But as we have seen, *B/H* is the value of permeability μ. Clearly, μ is not the same for high levels of *H* as it is for low levels.

The curve starts at zero only for cores with no residual magnetism. That is, if some of the domains are already aligned, then even when field intensity *H* is zero, with no current flowing through the coil, the flux density at the poles of the core is not zero. Therefore, for this curve no attempt is made to show the behavior near zero.

Problems

1. Convert the following flux (ϕ) and flux density (B) values into the other two systems of units:

(a) 12 μWb   (b) 42,000 lines   (c) 3 T

(d) 3.2×10^3 Mx   (e) 7.5×10^5 G   (f) 8.65×10^6 lines/in.^{2}

2. What is the flux density of a magnet if it has a pole face area of 15.4×10^{-4} m^2 and a total flux of 2000 μWb?

3. Suppose a magnet has a circular pole face with a diameter of 2.5 in. and total flux density measured at 4×10^4 lines/in.^{2} Calculate the total flux of the magnet. Express the answer in MKS units.

4. Calculate in both MKS units and CGS units the mmf of a coil of 3500 turns in which a current of 5 mA is flowing.

5. Suppose a coil has a current of 400 mA and an mmf of 151.2 Gb. Calculate the number of turns that it must have.

6. Field intensity *H* of a coil is 12.4 Oe. Express this value in MKS units.

7. Consider a coil 0.2 m long, with 7500 turns, carrying a current of 200 mA. Calculate the value of the coil's field intensity in CGS units.

8. Suppose we wish to build a coil that will have a field intensity of 3500 A/m when a current of 50 mA flows through it. If the coil is

to be 10 cm long, how many turns will it have? On the other hand, if it is to have 20,000 turns, what will be the length of the coil?

9. The relative permeability of a ferromagnetic material is 54,100. What is the absolute permeability in the CGS and MKS systems?

10. The absolute permeability of a ferromagnetic material is 0.000136 in the MKS system. What is the relative permeability μ_r of the material?

11. The field intensity of a coil wrapped around a ferromagnetic core is 1450 A/m, and the corresponding flux density is 45.675 T. Calculate the relative permeability of the core. Assume linearity in the relationship between B and H.

12. The relative permeability of a ferromagnetic core material is 1500. Suppose a coil of 1000 turns is wrapped around a piece of that material 10 cm long, and carries a current of 150 mA. Calculate the corresponding flux density B in both CGS and MKS units. Assume linearity in the relationship between B and H.

9-4
Hysteresis

THE B/H CURVE The word *hysteresis* comes from the Greek *hysterein,* which means "to lag behind." It is quite applicable to the situation that occurs when field intensity H starts at zero, builds to a maximum with one polarity, then drops to zero to build to a maximum with the opposite polarity, then drops again to zero.

Consider the drawing of Figure 9-14(a). This shows the B/H curve for a ferromagnetic material starting with no residual magnetism; the field intensity increases from zero to the value that will produce saturation, at the point marked *a* on the curve. So far, the curve is the same as before.

Now field intensity H is decreased to zero. As the field intensity decreases, the domain alignment becomes less ordered. As H decreases, more and more of the domains change to a random alignment, but not all will do so; and as the field intensity reaches zero, some significant number of domains remain aligned to the polarity with which the field had been applied.

This is seen in Figure 9-14(b) as the point *b* on the curve. The field intensity at this point is zero, but some residual magnetism still exists in the core, with a flux density measured from the intersection of the axes to point *b*. This remaining flux density retained by the material is its *retentivity,* which differs with different materials. For any material the retentivity also is determined by the magnitude of the original field

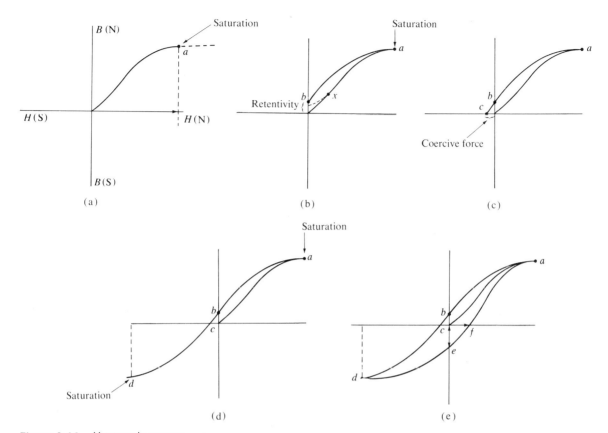

Figure 9-14   Hysteresis curves.

intensity H. If the field intensity reached only the point x on the graph, then dropped to zero, the B/H curve would have followed the course of the dashed line, and would obviously have retained less residual magnetism. To talk about the retentivity of a material, we must specify that the B/H curve reaches saturation before H is reduced to zero. Otherwise, the retentivity may have any value from the maximum for the material down to zero. Retentivity is low for soft ferromagnetic materials such as iron, and high for hard materials such as steel.

For this reason, if we wish to make an electromagnet that loses its flux when the current is turned off, we will choose a core material of soft iron or a similar ferromagnetic material with low retentivity. Otherwise, the electromagnet may not release its load as the coil current is cut off. On the other hand, if we wish to make a permanent magnet of a bar of ferromagnetic material, we will choose hard steel. It has a high retentivity and will, therefore, continue to exhibit a high flux density even after the current has been turned off. A piece of steel may be removed from the coil and used elsewhere as a magnet, since it retains its high flux density for a very long time. But physical accidents, such as a hard rap with a hammer, may shift many or all of the domains into a random order, thus reducing the flux density, perhaps to zero.

In Figure 9-14(c) the polarity of the applied field has been reversed, field intensity H has been increased just to the point where those domains still retaining the original alignment have been reordered, and flux density B has dropped to zero. The value of field intensity required to reduce the flux density to zero is called the *coercive force,* indicated by the point c on the graph.

If field intensity H is increased with the new polarity, as shown in Figure 9-14(d), to a value sufficiently great, the domains in the ferromagnetic core will realign themselves with it, and the value of B will increase to saturation. This will magnetize the core with the opposite polarity to that shown in Figure 9-14(a).

In Figure 9-14(e), the field intensity has been changed from the value which produces saturation with the polarity just shown, down through zero, and back to the original value of Figure 9-14(a). As this occurs, flux density B also reverses polarity, but its value lags behind the changing field intensity H. As the field intensity reaches zero, the core still retains some flux density, as shown by the point e on the graph. The flux density is reduced to zero only as the field intensity reaches the value indicated by the point f. As the field intensity continues to increase with the polarity of the first drawing, the flux density increases again to saturation point a on the diagram, and the curve now forms a complete loop. This loop is called the *hysteresis loop*.

HYSTERESIS LOSSES.   In the realignment of domains accompanying the change in flux density and flux polarity, a considerable loss of energy occurs. Much of this energy is used to overcome the internal friction of the molecular dipoles. The larger the area enclosed by the hysteresis loop, the greater the energy losses. Losses are greater for hard ferromagnetic materials such as steel than for softer magnetic materials. When the magnetizing force varies at a slow rate, the losses are seldom significant. But in many electronic circuits the magnetizing force goes through the complete cycle of polarities which generates the complete hysteresis loop millions of times a second, and the losses can be considerable. These losses appear as heat in the core material and also act as a load on the coil generating the changing magnetic field.

RELUCTANCE. *Reluctance* is related to permeability in much the same way that resistance is related to conductance. The greater the permeability of a material, the less its reluctance; and the less its permeability, the greater its reluctance. Ferromagnetic materials have a high permeability and a low reluctance. The permeability of air or a vacuum is low, and, consequently, the reluctance is high.

9-5
Magnetic Circuits

Given the *resistivity* (ρ) of a material, and its length and cross-sectional area, we can calculate its resistance as in the equation

$$R = \rho \, \frac{l}{A}$$

The reluctance ($\mathscr{R}$) of a given core of any material for which the permeability is known can be calculated as follows.

$$\mathscr{R} = \frac{l}{\mu A}$$

where $\mathscr{R}$ is the reluctance, l the length, A the cross-sectional area, and μ the permeability. If the quantities are all in MKS units, the unit of reluctance $\mathscr{R}$ is the *rel,* though there is no widely accepted unit.

Note that both resistance and reluctance are directly proportional to length and inversely proportional to area.

MAGNETIC AND ELECTRIC EQUIVALENTS. If reluctance is the magnetic equivalent of the electrical quantity resistance, then we might expect the existence of other equivalents. There are many.

In electricity the potential of a source is the cause of the flow of current in a circuit in which the opposition is resistance. The potential of the source is often called electromotive force, abbreviated emf.

In a magnetic circuit the corresponding quantity is magnetomotive force, abbreviated mmf.

In an electric circuit emf produces current in a material having resistance. The current is directly proportional to the emf and inversely proportional to the resistance.

$$I = \frac{E}{R}$$

In a magnetic circuit mmf produces flux in a material having reluctance. The flux is directly proportional to the mmf and inversely proportional to the reluctance.

$$\phi = \frac{\text{mmf}}{\mathscr{R}}$$

This is Ohm's law for magnetic circuits. The circuit is the flux path, just as the circuit for flow of current is the current path.

MAGNETIC CIRCUITS. The analogy between magnetic circuits and electric circuits can be carried further. Just as there is an Ohm's law for magnetic circuits that is, in its mathematical form, identical to Ohm's law for electric circuits, so there are laws for magnetic circuits analogous to Kirchhoff's laws for electric circuits.

Kirchhoff's voltage law states that the algebraic sum of the voltages encountered in traversing a complete loop in any circuit is zero.

The corresponding statement for magnetic circuits is known as Ampere's circuital law. It may be stated in a fashion similar to the voltage law; that is, the algebraic sum of the mmfs encountered in traversing a complete loop in any magnetic circuit is zero.

We may also find a statement about magnetic circuits corresponding to Kirchhoff's current law, which states that the algebraic sum of the currents at any junction is zero. The corresponding statement about the magnetic circuit says that the algebraic sum of the flux at any junction is zero.

All of the calculations we did on series and parallel circuits and the more complex calculations on networks using simultaneous linear equations to solve for currents and voltages were based on nothing more than Ohm's law and Kirchhoff's laws. This also applies to Thevenin's and Norton's theorems and to delta–wye transformations.

Since there are in magnetic circuits exact parallels to the laws on which network analysis is based, the analogy could be continued. Given more time and space, we could, for example, find correspondences in magnetic network analysis to Norton's theorem. However, not all elements of an electric circuit can be present in a magnetic circuit. There is no exact parallel in a magnetic circuit to the simple switch of the electric circuit, since there is no such thing as a magnetic insulator. This is because the permeability of a vacuum or air is 1, and not zero.

AIR GAPS. Consider the simple series magnetic circuit of Figure 9-15(a). The current flowing through the coil creates an mmf, and the reluctance of the ferromagnetic core determines the flux according to Ohm's law for magnetic circuits. Note, too, that if the resistance of the coil wire and the internal resistance of the battery were not taken into consideration, we might conclude that the current through the coil was infinite. It is not. The coil has some resistance, and the battery has some equivalent internal resistance; these limit the coil current.

This is a magnetic circuit equivalent to a simple series circuit consisting

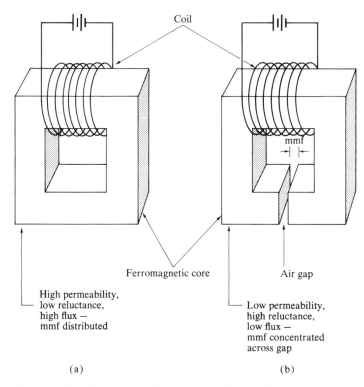

Figure 9-15   An air gap alters a magnetic circuit.

of a single source of emf and a single resistance. Since the permeability of the ferromagnetic core is high and the reluctance, therefore, low, for a reasonable number of ampere–turns NI in the coil producing the mmf, the flux in the core will be high.

In Figure 9-15(b) the magnetic circuit has been changed by the introduction of an *air gap*. This is the magnetic equivalent of an electric circuit with two resistors in series with each other. In such a circuit the total resistance is the sum of the individual resistances.

In our series magnetic circuit with two reluctances, the reluctance of the air gap and the reluctance of the ferromagnetic core material for the remainder of the circuit, the same thing is true. The total reluctance is the sum of the reluctances of the two circuit elements, the core and the gap.

The reluctance of a circuit element in a magnetic circuit is, as we have seen, directly proportional to the length and inversely proportional to the product of the permeability and cross-sectional area of the element. The air gap is such a circuit element, with a very low permeability and, consequently, a very high reluctance.

The reluctance of the remainder of the core is usually not significant compared to the reluctance of an air gap. If the air gap is short, its reluctance will be less than if it is long, but the total reluctance of the magnetic circuit has been greatly increased by the air gap.

If we insert a high resistance in a series circuit without changing the battery voltage, we will expect a considerable reduction in current. That is in correspondence with what happens here. The air gap represents a high reluctance, and there is, consequently, a considerable reduction in flux.

We would also expect—in a series electric circuit with two resistances, one much higher than the other—that the greater voltage drop would appear across the higher value of resistance. The correspondence holds; since the air gap represents nearly all the reluctance in the magnetic circuit, nearly all the mmf appears across the gap. With a narrow gap this can represent a high concentration of mmf in a narrow space. This concentration of mmf in a narrow space by an air gap, or by the insertion in a magnetic circuit of a material of low permeability, is the basis for a tape recording "head." The head records a pattern of magnetization on the tape passing across it, in exact conformity to the variations in current in a coil producing the mmf which, because of the circuit through the ferromagnetic core, then appears across the gap.

Problems

1. A core of ferromagnetic material has a length of 12 cm, a permeability of 0.0124, and a cross-sectional area of 5 cm². Calculate the value of its reluctance in MKS units.

2. A cylindrical core of ferromagnetic material has a length of 20 cm, a relative permeability of 8500, and a diameter of 3 cm. Calculate the value of its reluctance in MKS units.

3. The mmf across a portion of a magnetic circuit is 4200 A. The reluctance of that same portion is 0.5×10^4 rels. Calculate the flux in MKS and CGS units.

4. Consider the magnetic circuit shown, consisting of a coil and a ferromagnetic core 30 cm long, a cross-sectional area of 10 cm², and a relative permeability of 120,000. The coil has 5000 turns and a current of 200 mA flowing through it. Calculate the flux through the circuit.

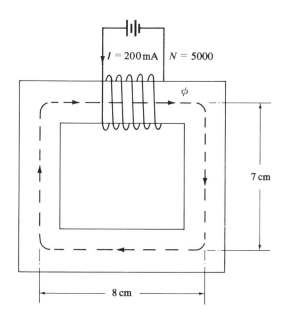

Magnetic circuit for Problem 4.

5. Consider this simple magnetic circuit with a single air gap. The core forms a rectangle 8 cm long and 5 cm wide, and has a cross-sectional area of 10 cm². The core material has a relative permeability of 45,000. The air gap is 2 cm. If the mmf of the coil is 9500 A, calculate the flux through the circuitry and the mmf across each portion of the circuit.

Magnetic circuit for Problem 5.

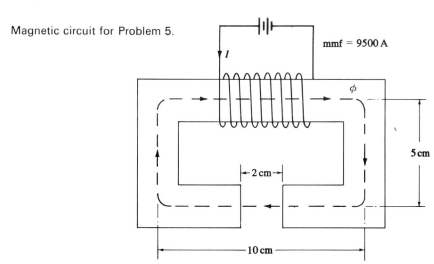

6. Consider the magnetic circuit with a double air gap. Given the dimensions of the magnet and air gaps on the diagram, a core cross-sectional area of 15 cm², a relative permeability of the core material of 25,000, and a coil mmf of 1500 A, calculate the flux through the circuit and the mmf across each portion of the circuit.

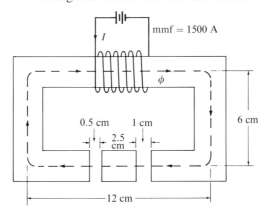

Magnetic circuit for Problem 6.

7. Consider the magnetic circuit shown, which has an air gap of 2.5 cm. A 2 cm portion of the core is composed of a different ferromagnetic material (relative permeability of 1000) from that of the rest of the core. The core's relative permeability is 30,000. Given the dimensions shown in the diagram, a core cross-section of 20 cm², a coil current of 150 mA, and a measured mmf across the air gap of 2500 A, calculate the number of turns N in the coil, the mmf of the coil, the flux through the circuit, and the mmf across each portion of the circuit.

Magnetic circuit for Problem 7.

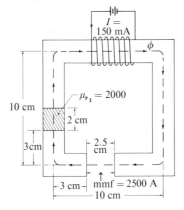

8. Consider a magnetic circuit with two mmf sources. The mmf of one coil (mmf$_1$) is equal to 9000 A, and the mmf of the other coil (mmf$_2$) is equal to 4500 A. There are two portions of ferromagnetic material with different permeabilities. One portion has relative permeability μ_{r_1} of 2000, and the other has relative permeability μ_{r_2} of 1000. Given the dimensions shown in the diagram and a cross-sectional area of 10 cm^2, calculate the total flux flowing through each portion of the circuit, as well as the respective mmfs. *Hint:* Use superposition as you would if it were an electric circuit. Note also that the currents in the coils give resultant flux flows in the directions shown in the diagram. Keep track of the directions of the flows as you superimpose. Assume also that the reluctance of the core is negligible.

Magnetic circuit for Problem 8.

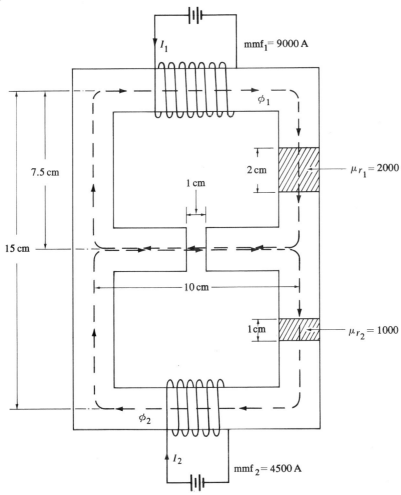

9-6
Electric Effects of
Magnetic Currents

INDUCED VOLTAGE. The reciprocal comparison between electric and magnetic circuits discussed in the previous section can be carried farther.

We have already seen that a current flowing in a conductor produces a magnetic field. It is reasonable to expect a magnetic field to be able to produce a current in a conductor. It can, and does, but one element in the way in which it does so baffled early experimenters for a considerable time. Simply having a powerful magnet near a conductor does nothing, though it seemed reasonable to the researchers of the time that it would. They tried, to no avail, to detect some slight current in conductors near the most powerful magnets they could construct.

By accident it was discovered that the one thing necessary before a magnetic field could produce current in a conductor was relative motion between the two. Once this was discovered, progress was rapid indeed.

If a conductor is placed between the poles of a powerful magnet, as in Figure 9-16(a), and the ends of the conductor are connected to a very sensitive microammeter, there will be no deflection of the microammeter pointer so long as neither the conductor nor the magnet is moved.

If the conductor is moved up or down between the poles of a magnet so placed that the flux lines between the poles are horizontal, then the pointer of the microammeter will deflect, as in Figure 9-16(b). It will deflect in one direction for upward motion and in the other for downward,

Figure 9-16 A magnetic field can generate an electric current.

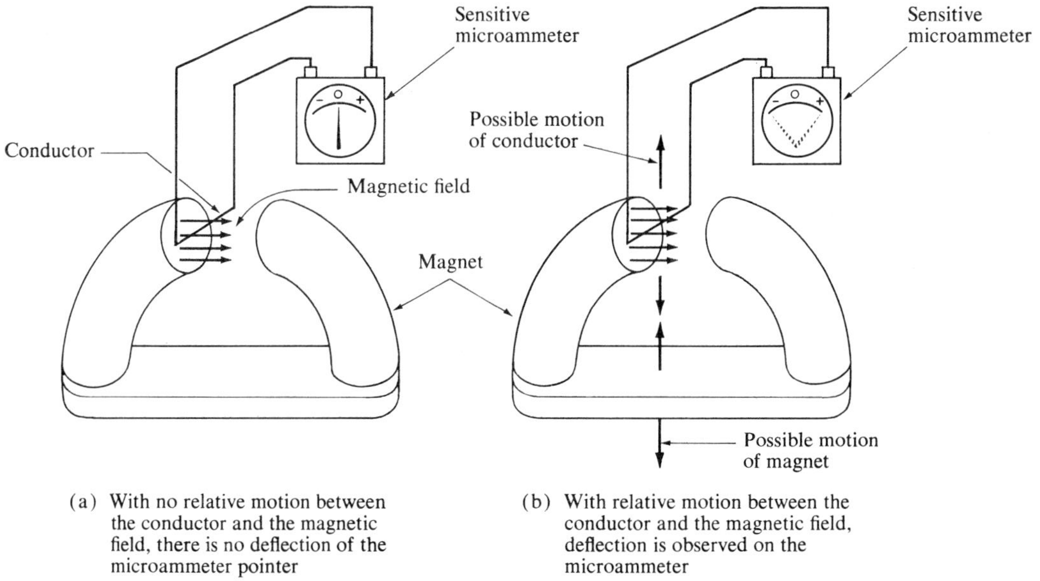

(a) With no relative motion between the conductor and the magnetic field, there is no deflection of the microammeter pointer

(b) With relative motion between the conductor and the magnetic field, deflection is observed on the microammeter and the amount of deflection will be proportional to the rapidity of the movement.

If the movement of the conductor is back and forth between the poles and parallel to the horizontal flux lines, there will be no deflection of the pointer, no matter how rapid the movement. Similarly, if the conductor is slid back and forth in the direction of its own length, no deflection will be observed.

If the conductor is held stationary, and the magnet moved, the results will be similar. Only when the movement causes the flux lines to cut across the conductor will deflection of the microammeter pointer be observed.

The results of the above observations (and others, as well) can be summarized in a single statement.

RULE   *When there is relative motion between a charge and a magnetic field, a force is exerted between the charge and the field at right angles to the direction of relative motion, and at right angles to the direction of flux of the field. If the charge is not constrained, it will move in the direction of the force.*

If we continue with the notion of lines of flux—which, to repeat, have no more real existence than contour lines on a map, but are as useful in understanding the terrain—then we can say that the conductor must cut across the lines of flux to cause the electrons in the conductor to move. The electrons in the conductor are unconstrained charges, at least along the length of the conductor. If the two ends of the conductor are, as in this case, connected through some low-resistance device such as our microammeter to form a complete circuit, then there will be a current flow in the conductor, continuing as long as the motion of the conductor across the lines of flux continues.

If the ends of the conductor were open, so that no complete circuit existed, then the free electrons in the conductor would be impelled to move along its length and create an excess of electrons at one end of the conductor and a deficiency at the other. The excess negative charge at one conductor terminal and the negative charge deficiency, which is the same as a positive charge, at the other terminal constitute a potential between them.

When the conductor was moved back and forth between the poles of the magnet, the free electrons in it were moving parallel to the lines of flux; consequently, there was no relative motion between them. Thus, no force was exerted on the charges by the field. Only if the conductor moves so there is relative motion between the charges in it and the field will there be any current flow through the conductor, or any potential at its terminals.

When the conductor was moved along its length through the field, there was actually relative motion between the free electrons in it and the field, but the force resulting from that motion on the electrons did not push them along the length of the conductor. Since the force is exerted at right angles to the direction of motion, which was along the length of the conductor, the force was at right angles to that length and did succeed in crowding electrons up against one side of the conductor and creating a deficiency at the other; but it did not succeed in moving them along the conductor length or in creating a potential difference between the terminals.

LENZ'S LAW. We have already seen that there is a magnetic field associated with current flowing in a conductor. When the conductor of our demonstration was connected to the microammeter and moved through the field of the magnet at right angles to the flux lines, current flowed in it. That current generated in its own magnetic field.

We saw earlier that the magnetic field around a conductor could be greatly enhanced by winding the conductor into a coil. A long coil carrying current will have a magnetic field around it similar to the field of a bar magnet, with the poles at the ends of the coil.

Consider the illustration of Figure 9-17. It shows a coil of wire wound around a hollow tube of nonmagnetic material. The coil terminals are connected to a resistor. If a magnet is moved toward the end of the coil, as shown, so that the N pole of the magnet starts to enter the open end of the coil, the flux of the magnet must cut across the turns of the coil. This, as we have seen, will cause a current to flow in the coil and through the resistor connected across its terminals.

If we now pull the magnet back from the coil, the flux lines from the magnet must cut across the turns of the coil in the opposite direction. This will cause a flow of current in the coil and through the resistor in the opposite direction.

No matter which way current flows through a resistor, energy is expended. We could, theoretically, use the heat from a resistor to boil water, and use the steam to run an engine which could do work.

If our engine could do work, it had to take energy from the steam. If the steam contained energy, it must have been the heat energy from the resistor. The heat energy produced in the resistor was the consequence

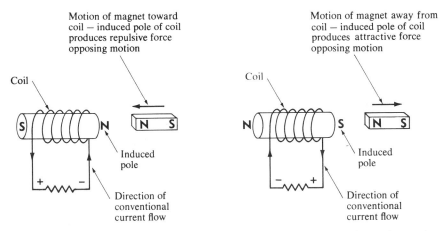

Figure 9-17 The direction of induced current flow in the coil depends on the direction in which the magnet is moved.

of current flow through its resistance, and that energy had to come from somewhere. The answer is, it came from our muscles, as we alternately pushed and pulled on the magnet, producing the changing flux which generated the current in the coil and through the resistor.

To do work takes effort. Effort is expended in causing motion against opposition. If, therefore, work is to come from our muscles as we alternately push and pull on the magnet, there must be opposition to that motion *in each direction*. It must be opposition in each direction since energy is expended in the resistor independently of the direction of current through it. This is an inevitable consequence of the *law of conservation of energy*. If there were some way we could get energy to boil water out of this system without putting an equal amount of energy into the system somewhere, we would have a perpetual motion machine.

The current flowing in the simple series circuit consisting of the coil and the resistor must generate a magnetic field about the coil, with its poles at the ends of the coil. If the field produced by the coil current caused an S pole at the end of the coil into which we are moving the N pole of the magnet, no energy would need to be produced by our muscles since there would be a force of attraction between the two opposite poles. This would be a clear violation of the law of conservation of energy, and the laws of nature are not subject to violation as are man's (though they are often misunderstood and may be *apparently* violated).

The polarity for the magnetic field of the coil would, in this instance, be N when the incoming pole of the permanent magnet was N. The two poles would then repel, and our muscles would need to do work to push the two opposing poles toward each other. This would not violate the law of conservation of energy, and is even required by it, as we have seen.

When we pull the magnet away from the coil, again we must do work. We must, therefore, be separating unlike poles. Since the pole of the permanent magnet that we are moving away from the coil is an N pole, then during that movement the adjacent pole of the coil must be S. If it were not, it would be a violation of the law of conservation of energy.

This principle, first enunciated by Lenz, is known as *Lenz's law: The direction of the induced current must be such that its own magnetic field will oppose the action that produced the induced current.*

It is for this reason that the most popular invention of all time will not work. Nearly everyone has at some time thought of driving an electric generator with an electric motor, and using the output of the generator to run the motor, with enough left over to be independent of the power utilities. The reason it will not work is that a generator is simply a large-scale and relatively complex system for moving conductors rapidly through a magnetic field, and the output current of the generator is the sum of the currents produced in all the conductors as they cut through the flux of the field. But the current flowing through these conductors makes magnets of them, and, by Lenz's law, we must always be moving these magnets through the generator field so that like poles are approaching each other or unlike poles are moving away from each other. Thus, the action is always working against a force, and the motor must do work to cause the conductors in the generator to move through the field. The amount of work that must be done will depend on the strength of the magnetic field around the conductors, and this, in turn, depends on the current flow through them.

If there is no load connected to the generator terminals, there will be no current through the internal conductors moving through the field, and, consequently, no field will be produced by them. Therefore, no work need be done in moving the conductors, and the armature of the generator will move freely.

As soon as a load is connected to the generator, current will flow through it and, consequently, through the internal conductors of the generator. The intensity of the magnetic field around the conductors will be directly proportional to the current flow through them. The force required to be produced by the motor driving the generator will be, therefore, directly proportional to the energy expended in the load, since with greater load current, stronger magnetic fields within the generator must be moved in opposition to each other.

There are always frictional losses in any moving system. The motor will have to produce power to overcome these losses, in addition to the power required to cause the generator armature to rotate against the kind of magnetic opposition we have just discussed. Our invention, therefore, not only will not be able to produce any excess power to light our homes, it will not even run itself.

FARADAY'S LAW. When we first tried the experiment of moving a conductor at right angles to the flux of a magnetic field, we noted that the largest current through the conductor was obtained with the most rapid motion. Clearly, then, the current must be some mathematical function of the rate of movement.

We could experiment further and try moving our conductor through the flux of magnetic fields of various intensities. If we were to do so, we would discover that, not surprisingly, the more intense the field strength, the more the current for a given rate of relative movement and, consequently, the higher the potential that would appear across a load.

We know that current flowing through a conductor generates a magnetic field about the conductor, and winding the conductor into a coil concentrates the field. It seems natural to suspect that winding our conductor into a coil and moving it through the field of the permanent magnet might enhance the voltage, and again, experiment confirms it. We must, of course, take the precaution of making sure that opposite sides of the coil are cut by the flux in opposite directions. This is clear, for if we are facing the open end of a single-loop coil, current must be flowing down the side of the coil opposite the side in which it is flowing up. If the coil is made to rotate between the poles so that one side of the coil is passing the S pole moving upward at the instant the other side of the coil is passing the N pole moving downward, then the condition is met (Figure 9-18). If a coil of 1 turn produces an emf of 1 V when cutting the flux of a given magnet at a given rate, then a coil of 2 turns will give an emf of 2 V when cutting through the same flux at the same rate.

The experimenting was done long ago, much of it by Faraday, and the results are known as *Faraday's law*.

$$e \text{ (volts)} = \frac{d\phi \text{ (in webers)}}{dt \text{ (in seconds)}} \times N$$

where e is the induced voltage, N the number of turns in the coil, and the fraction $d\phi/dt$ is the rate of relative motion between the lines of flux and the conductors of the coil. In this equation, and for the first but not by any means the last time we encountered it, e is a lower-case

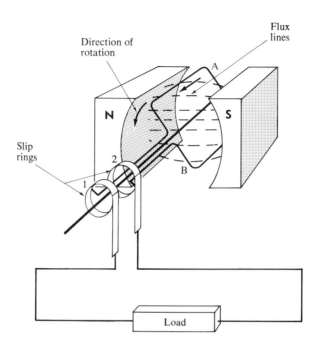

Figure 9-18   A single-loop ac generator.

instead of a capital letter. This convention is used to indicate a changing
voltage, since the rate at which flux is cut by the coil is not the same
for different positions of the coil even though the rate of rotation may be
constant. For example, when a single-turn coil is in the position shown in
Figure 9-19, the line of motion of the upper and lower conductors of the
coil is along the lines of flux, and not cutting across them. Consequently,
the voltage at the coil terminals at that instant is zero.

The fraction $d\phi/dt$ is *not* $d \times \phi$ divided by $d \times t$. The d in both
numerator and denominator stands for "delta," which means a *change*. It
could be read as "the rate of change of flux compared to time," or, perhaps
more usefully, "*the rate of change of flux* in webers per second." This is an
instantaneous value, which means that it is simply the value at one and
only one instant. A rate of change of flux of 60 Wb/sec doesn't mean the
flux has to be 60 Wb, or that it has to continue for one second. If you
are driving at a rate of 60 miles per hour (mph), that doesn't mean
you are driving 60 miles, or that you must keep it up for 1 hour. What
your speedometer tells you is also an instantaneous rate, and could be
written as ds/dt, where the s stands for distance. The whole fraction would
be read as "the rate of change of distance with respect to time" or "the
rate of change of distance in miles per hour."

Suppose a coil of 25 turns is rotating in a magnetic field so that it cuts   EXAMPLE
the flux lines at a rate of 10 Wb/sec. What is the potential at the coil
terminals at the instant this occurs?

Solution.

$$e = N \times \frac{d\phi}{dt} = (25)(10) = 250 \text{ V}$$

1.   At a particular instant a coil of 2500 turns rotating in a magnetic field is   **Problems**
     cutting the field's flux lines at a rate of 25 Wb/sec. What is the
     instantaneous potential at the coil terminals?

2.   Suppose a coil is cutting across the flux lines of a large magnetic
     field at a constant rate of 8×10^5 Mx every 0.1 sec. If the resultant
     potential at the coil terminals measures at 120 V, how many turns
     must there be in the coil?

Figure 9-19   At this instant, the rotation of the coil
is such that the movement of the upper and lower
conductors is parallel to the lines of flux. Since the
coil does not cut the flux lines, the voltage at the
coil terminals at this instant is zero.

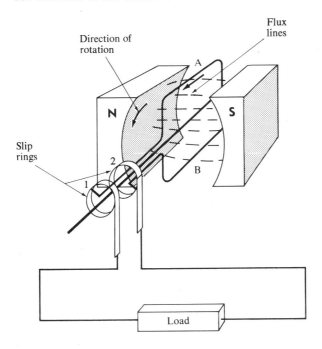

EDDY CURRENTS.   There are two major causes of energy losses in magnetic materials where the flux is changing. One we have already seen—hysteresis. The losses from this cause can easily be kept low where the rate of change of flux is relatively low, through the use of soft iron and its alloys. But hysteresis is not the only serious cause of energy losses in most applications.

Most ferromagnetic materials are conductors. If they are in a rapidly varying magnetic field, currents will be induced in them just as in any conductor in the field. But currents in the core represent energy losses in the system since, by Lenz's law, the direction of the currents must be such as to create a magnetic field opposing the original field. The losses show both as energy lost by the source of the original varying magnetic field, and as heat in the core. Both conditions are undesirable.

If the currents circulating in the core, or *eddy currents* as they are usually termed, can be broken up into smaller currents, the power involved in them will be very much less for several reasons. Therefore, magnetic core materials to be used where the flux is changing at moderate rates are usually made up of thin layers, or *laminations*. The laminations are usually of silicon steel, an alloy with high permeability, low retentivity and coercive force—and, therefore, little area enclosed in the hysteresis loop and, consequently, low hysteresis losses.

The power involved in a flow of current, whether eddy currents or regular circuit currents, is proportional to the square of the currents. For example, the power involved in a current of 4 A through a resistance of 1 Ω is 16 W. If the current is broken up into four smaller currents of 1 A each, through a resistance of 1 ohm, the total current is the same, but the power in each current is only 1 W, and the sum of the powers involved in the four currents is, therefore, 4 W, a significant reduction.

The laminations are therefore insulated from each other by very thin layers of varnish, and are not made in complete loops, but in segments which are stacked to form the desired shapes.

If the rate of change of flux is to be high, as is often the case in electronic circuits, then a material with minimal hysteresis losses and no eddy current losses is required. A class of ferromagnetic materials known as *ferrites* gives the required qualities. Ferrites are actually in the class of ceramic materials, composed of oxides of nickel and zinc, or manganese and zinc. They are nonconducting and, consequently, not subject to eddy current losses. They can be manufactured with almost any desired hysteresis characteristics.

For intermediate frequency applications a core is sometimes used which is composed of powdered iron, with each granule insulated from the others. This is done by mixing the granules of iron powder with a non-conducting matrix material, then forming the resulting mixture into the desired shape and hardening it by heat or pressure. The resulting core may have little physical strength, but can have excellent electrical characteristics.

Key Words

ampere's circuital law   states that the algebraic sum of the mmf encountered in transversing a complete loop is zero

armature   the rotating ferromagnetic frame on which the coil of an electric motor is wound

B/H curve   the curve formed by plotting flux density on the vertical axis against field intensity on the horizontal axis

brushes   two carbon rods that make continuous contact with the commutator as the armature rotates. The brushes carry current from the external power source to the armature coil.

commutator   two curved metal segments, mounted on the armature shaft, which reverse the direction of the current

diamagnetic materials   become very weakly magnetized in the opposite direction to the magnetizing field

domain   a group of atoms with aligned magnetic fields

eddy currents   currents circulating in the magnetic core

electromagnet   a magnet based on the fact that current flowing through a wire conductor has an associated magnetic field. These magnets are useful because the magnetic effects can be turned on and off as the current is turned on and off.

exchange coupling   the linking together of adjacent atoms so that their magnetic fields are aligned

Faraday's law   states that current is a mathematical function of the rate of change of flux:

$$e \text{ (volts)} = \frac{d\phi \text{ (webers)}}{dt \text{ (seconds)}} \times N$$

ferrites   a nonconducting class of ferromagnetic metals not subject to significant eddy current losses

ferromagnetic materials   become strongly magnetized in the same direction as the magnetizing field

field intensity (*H*)   the degree of concentration of mmf in space

flux (*ϕ*)   the entire group of magnetic field lines

flux density (*B*)   the degree of concentration of flux

flux lines   indicate magnetic field strength—when close together the field is intense, and when widely spaced the field is weak

gauss (G)   the unit of flux density (lines/cm^2) in the CGS system

hysteresis   a "lagging behind" of domain alignments as field intensity changes

hysteresis loop   the curve produced by plotting B against H for a complete cycle

Lenz's law   states that the direction of induced current must be such that its own magnetic field will oppose the action that produced the induced current

line   the unit of flux in the English system

magnetic field   the external effect of the spinning electrons in orbit about their atoms, plus the total of the individual effects in a permanent magnet

magnetomotive force (mmf)   the strength of a magnetic field, which is proportional to the number of amperes of current flowing in the coil times the number of turns in the coil. Also called *magnetizing force* and *magnetic potential*

maxwell (Mx)   the unit of flux in the CGS system

north-seeking pole   the end of a magnet that aligns with the earth's magnetic north pole

oersted (Oe)   the unit of field intensity in the CGS system

paramagnetic materials   become weakly magnetized in the same direction as the magnetizing field

permeability (μ)   the measure of the ease with which flux concentrates in ferromagnetic materials

pole pieces   iron cores in an electric motor. Each is either a N or S pole for the magnetic field within the motor.

reluctance   the opposite of permeability. Ferromagnetic materials have low reluctance and high permeability.

retentivity   the flux density remaining when field intensity is at zero

tesla (T)   the unit of flux density (webers/m^2) in the MKS system

weber (Wb)   the unit of flux in the MKS system

Summary of Concepts

1. Magnetism is an effect associated with moving charges of electricity.

2. Electron spins in opposing directions give rise to fields of opposite polarity, thus canceling magnetic fields.

3. In ferromagnetic materials many unpaired electrons in each atom have spins in the same direction.

4. In soft iron, domains resume their random orientations when an

external magnetic field is removed. In hard steel the domains retain their alignment, and the steel is permanently magnetized.

5. The earth is a giant magnet with its own magnetic field.

6. A north-seeking pole and a south-seeking pole attract each other.

7. A north-seeking pole repels another N pole. Similarly, a south-seeking pole repels another S pole.

8. An electric current produces a magnetic field.

9. Flux lines around a conductor have a direction of polarity.

10. If a loop is made in a conductor to form a coil of one turn, the flux lines from opposite points on the coil will be in the same direction.

11. The external magnetic field of a coil is greatly increased by increasing the number of turns in the coil.

12. The direction of the magnetism induced in any ferromagnetic material within the influence of some external field always produces a force of attraction between the material and the external field.

13. All electric motors are based on the principle of attraction and repulsion between magnetic fields.

14. With a coil as the source of magnetic flux, the strength of the magnetic field depends on the strength of the current and on the number of turns in the coil.

15. In the realignment of domains accompanying a change in flux density and flux polarity, a considerable loss of energy due to hysteresis occurs.

16. Both resistance and reluctance are directly proportional to length and inversely proportional to area.

17. Magnetic circuits are analogous to electric circuits. Magnetomotive force corresponds to electromotive force, for instance. Magnetic circuits are solved by using laws and methods that correspond to the laws and methods we use to solve electric circuits.

18. When there is a motion between a charge and a magnetic field, a force is exerted between the charge and the field at right angles to the direction of the relative motion and at right angles to the flux of the field. If the charge is not constrained, it will move in the direction of the force.

19. Lenz's law states that the direction of induced current must be such that its own magnetic field opposes the action that produced the induced current.

20. Faraday's law states that the induced voltage equals the rate of change of flux in webers/second.

21. If eddy currents (currents circulating in the core) can be broken up into smaller currents, the power involved in them will be considerably less.

To Help You Review   *On a separate sheet of paper, fill in the blanks or answer the questions below. The number following each question refers to the section in the chapter where the correct answer can be found.*

1. Magnetism is an effect associated with _____ . (9-1)

2. What is the important characteristic of ferromagnetic materials? (9-1)

3. Describe and compare ferromagnetic, paramagnetic, and diamagnetic materials. (9-1)

4. What does "exchange coupling" mean? (9-1)

5. What is a domain? (9-1)

6. Describe the earth's magnetism in terms of polarity. (9-1)

7. Describe what happens when iron filings are sprinkled on a sheet of paper placed over a bar magnet and the sheet of paper is tapped. (9-1)

8. How can you demonstrate the magnetic field generated by a current flowing through a conductor? (9-2)

9. What do we know about the flux lines of a one-turn coil? (9-2)

10. What is the relationship between the number of turns in a coil and its external magnetic field? (9-2)

11. The direction of magnetism induced in any ferromagnetic material produces an attraction between the _____ and the _____ . (9-2)

12. Describe briefly pole pieces, armature, and commutator. (9-2)

13. What basic principle underlies all electric motors? (9-2)

14. What is flux? (9-3)

15. The Greek letter ϕ is the symbol for what? (9-3)

16. Fill in the blanks: (9-3)

Symbol	_____	CGS	English
ϕ	weber	_____	line
_____	_____	gauss	_____

17. What is field intensity? How is it calculated? (9-3)

18. _____ relates flux density to field intensity. (9-3)

19. If flux density is plotted against field intensity, the resulting curve is a _____ curve. Describe this curve. (9-3)

20. The term *hysteresis* comes from the Greek, "to lag behind." How is this term applicable in describing a certain situation in field intensity? (9-4)

21. What is a hysteresis loop? (9-4)

22. Supply the magnetic equivalents for each of these electrical terms and statements:

  (a) electromotive force
  (b) $I = E/R$
  (c) Kirchhoff's voltage law
  (d) "the algebraic sum of the currents at any junction is zero" (9-5)

23. In a series magnetic circuit with two reluctances, the total reluctance equals _____ . (9-5)

24. What is the opposite of reluctance? (9-5)

25. What happens when there is relative motion between a charge and a magnetic field? (9-6)

26. Using Figure 9-15, describe Lenz's law in your own words. (9-6)

27. What law follows from Lenz's law? What does this law attempt to show? (9-6)

28. What are two major causes of energy losses in magnetic materials. (9-7)

29. Describe the qualities of ferrites. (9-7)

30. Why are magnetic core materials usually made up of laminations? (9-7)

TEN

ALTERNATING CURRENT AND VOLTAGE

This chapter will help you understand

☐ the principle of ac generator operation
☐ the sinusoidal waveform
☐ phasor representation
☐ peak, p–p, and rms ac voltages

10-1
The Single-Loop AC Generator

THE GENERATOR PRINCIPLE. As we have already seen, if a conductor cuts through the lines of flux of a magnetic field, a potential will appear at the conductor terminals. The potential depends on the rate at which the flux is cut. If the conductor is wound into a coil, the magnitude of its terminal voltage is given by the equation known as Faraday's law.

$$e = N \frac{d\phi}{dt}$$

where e is the induced voltage, N is the number of turns in the coil, and $d\phi/dt$ is the rate at which flux is cut in webers/second.

A SIMPLE AC GENERATOR.   Figure 10-1(a) shows a simplified version of a single-loop ac generator. The loop rotates around the axis shown by the dashed line x–x'. The flux of the magnetic field in which it rotates can be considered to be everywhere vertical and with the lines of flux all parallel to each other. The loop is, of course, made of a conducting material. It is almost invariably of copper wire. The two ends of the loop are connected to the slip rings, with the side of the loop marked A connected to slip ring 1 and the other side of the loop, B, connected to slip ring 2. A brush, usually made of graphite, a form of carbon which is both a reasonably good conductor and a lubricant, is fixed in position at each slip ring. The slip ring rotates under it, and the brush maintains electrical contact with it as it rotates. Each brush is connected to one terminal of the load resistor. This arrangement permits continuous rotation of the loop, but at all times keeps side A of the loop connected to the terminal of load resistor R_1, marked a, and the side of the loop marked B connected to the terminal of the load resistor marked b.

Suppose the loop is in continuous rotation at some constant rate of turning. If we consider the rate at which it is cutting across the lines of flux at different positions, we can determine the magnitude and direction of the induced current at different parts of the complete cycle of revolution.

Figure 10-1   A single-loop ac generator. (a) and (c) No load current and no load potential. (b) and (d) Maximum load current and maximum load potential.

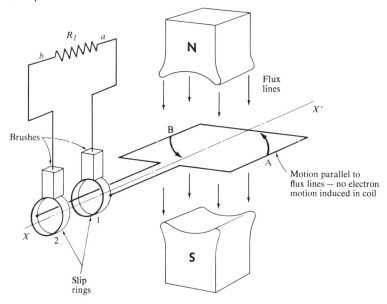

Figure 10-1(a)   No load current and no load potential.

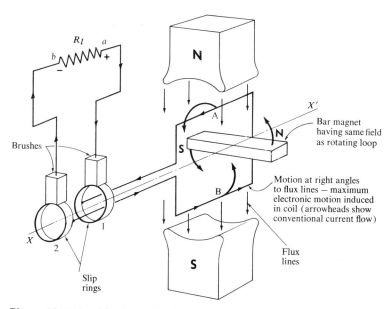

Figure 10-1(b)   Maximum load current and maximum load potential.

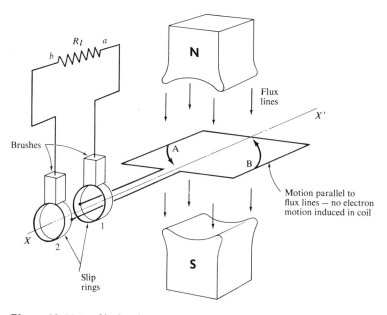

Figure 10-1(c)   No load current and no load potential.

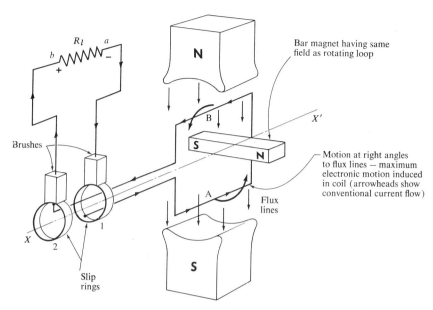

Figure 10-1(d) Maximum load current and maximum load potential.

Consider the instant when the loop has reached the position shown in Figure 10-1(a). The loop is horizontal, and at that instant conductor A is moving straight up while conductor B is moving straight down. The lines of flux are also vertical, so the motion of the two conductors is at that instant parallel to the lines of flux, and not cutting across them. Therefore, at that instant there will be no current induced in either of the two marked conductors. There will be no load current, and thus no potential across the load.

When the loop has reached the position shown in Figure 10-1(b), the loop is vertical and the conductors are moving at that instant at right angles to the direction of flux. In this position they are cutting across the flux lines at the maximum rate. Therefore, the maximum current will be induced in the coil and will flow through the load resistor, and the maximum potential voltage will appear across the load resistor.

Since, by Lenz's law, the direction of the induced current in a coil must be such as to oppose the motion creating it, the magnetic field of the coil caused by coil current must oppose the rotation of the coil. The field of a coil carrying current is through its ends, one end of the coil being an N pole, and the other S. The coil could be replaced by a bar magnet having the same shape, and the shape of the field would be unchanged. It can be seen from Figure 10-1(b), that if this were done, the bar magnet would then be rotating in place of the coil in such a way that its N pole would be approaching the N pole of the generator, and the magnet's S pole would be approaching the S pole of the generator.

If this is true—and it must be if the law of conservation of energy is not to be violated—then to produce this field the coil current must be through conductor A *toward* slip ring 1, and through conductor B *away* from slip ring 2. This is true if conventional current notation is used, as can be seen from the right-hand rule. The actual electron flow is, of course, in the opposite direction.

This means the direction of conventional current flow, at that instant, must be *from* slip ring 1, through the load from *a* to *b*, and *to* slip ring 2. Therefore, the *a* end of R_l is positive and the *b* end negative.

As the loop continues to rotate, it will reach the position of Figure 10-1(c). Again, the loop is horizontal. Conductor A is now moving down through the flux, and conductor B is moving up, but in both cases the motions are parallel to the lines of flux. Since, at that instant, no flux lines are being cut by the conductors, no induced current is flowing in the coil. There is, therefore, no current flowing through the load resistor at that instant, and no potential across it.

After three-fourths of a complete revolution, the loop has reached the position shown in Figure 10-1(d). It is again vertical, and again the two conductors are cutting across the flux lines at the maximum rate. Again, the maximum coil current will be induced, the maximum load current will flow, and the maximum potential will appear across the load resistor.

This time, however, conductor A is at the bottom of the loop, while conductor B is at the top. Lenz's law still applies; therefore, the coil current must be producing a magnetic field opposing the coil motion. Again, *like* poles must be approaching each other. Applying the right-hand rule, we can see that the direction of coil current must now be through conductor A *away* from slip ring 1, and through conductor B *toward* slip ring 2. Again, this is the direction of conventional current flow. The actual electron flow is in the opposite direction.

This means the direction of conventional current flow, at that instant, must be from slip ring 2, through the load from *b* to *a*, and to slip ring 1. Therefore, the *b* end of R_l is positive, and the *a* end is negative.

If we continue the rotation to the original position, everything that was said about that position still applies, and at that instant the load voltage must be zero.

We may plot the results, as seen in Figure 10-2. The vertical axis of our graph indicates the amount and polarity of the voltage across the

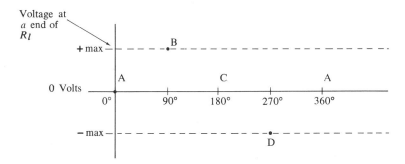

Figure 10-2   Plot of voltage resulting from movement of loop in
Figure 10-1.

load resistor, measured against the *b* terminal of the resistor as reference.
The graph therefore shows whether the *a* terminal of R_l is positive or
negative with respect to that common reference, and by how much.

The horizontal axis of our graph shows the position of the coil for
each voltage. It is calibrated in degrees of rotation, starting with 0° at the
left side. The original position of the coil, as shown in Figure 10-1(a), is
taken as the reference position, and this is the position for 0°. Each
quarter of a revolution is 90°; therefore, the 90° division on the horizontal
axis of the graph corresponds to the position of the coil shown in Figure
10-1(b). Similarly, 180° corresponds to the position of (c) and 270° to the
position of (d). Since 360° is a full circle, the position and, consequently,
the load voltage must at that instant be the same as for 0°.

If the voltages obtained at each position are marked at the appropriate
points on the scale, the voltage will be shown as zero at 0°, 180°, and
360°. At 90°, the voltage was maximum with the *a* end of the resistor
positive, and the voltage is marked B on the graph to correspond to the
position at which it occurred. Similarly, the voltage at 270° of rotation is
marked D on the graph to correspond to the instantaneous position of
rotation at which it occurred.

We know five points on the graph, but this is not enough information
to complete the graph by connecting these points with a line. We can
easily see from Figure 10-1 that at all the intermediate degrees of
rotation for which we did not plot voltages the conductors must be
moving so as to cut lines of flux. Only at the two instants during
which the loop was horizontal could the conductors be moving parallel
to the flux lines. In all other possible positions the conductors had to
be moving at some angle to the flux lines and, therefore, cutting across
them at some rate. Since the potential across the resistor at any instant
is proportional to the rate at which flux is being cut at that instant,

there must be some potential across the resistor at points on the graph other than those marked A, C, or D.

We need to find the load resistor potential at intermediate points to complete the graph. Let us consider what must be occurring between the coil and the flux it is cutting at some intermediate position.

Figure 10-3(a) shows an end view of the single-loop generator of Figure 10-1. Let us consider only a single conductor, starting at point A and rotating toward point B. At any position intermediate between these two points, the loop must have rotated through some angle θ, measured from the initial position.

As it is rotating, it has some angular velocity. The exact speed at which the conductor itself is moving depends on the number of revolutions it makes per unit time, and on the diameter of the loop. Let us assume that the circumference of the circle through which the conductor moves in a complete revolution of the loop is 10 cm, and also that a revolution takes 0.1 sec. If the conductor travels 10 cm in 0.1 sec, then it travels 100 cm = 1 m in 1 sec. This is true whether the path of the conductor is a straight or curved line. It is just as though you drove your car forty mph for 1 hr. At the end of the 1 hr, you would have driven 40 miles, even though you might not be 40 miles from your point of starting. You could have driven in circles.

Thus, the linear speed of the conductor at any instant is 1 m/sec, whether the actual path of the conductor is a straight or curved line. This is shown on the drawing of Figure 10-3(a) as the straight arrow pointing in the direction of motion of the conductor.

Figure 10-3   End view of the single-loop generator in Figure 10-1.

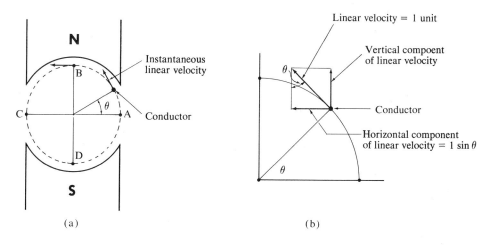

(a)   (b)

In Figure 10-3(b) the essential geometry is shown, with everything else removed for the sake of clarity. The coil of which the conductor is a part is shown as having rotated through an angle θ, which may be any angle between 0° and 90°. The instantaneous value of its linear velocity is 1 m/sec, as shown by the arrow identified on the drawing.

For any angle θ between 0° and 90°, that arrow showing the linear velocity is neither parallel nor at right angles to the direction of the lines of flux, but cuts across the flux at the angle θ itself. The rate of flux cutting is the same as the number of flux lines that would be cut by the conductor traveling in the direction of its instantaneous linear velocity for one second, even though it may not travel in that direction for a full second. This is like saying that a car is doing forty miles per hour because if it continued at that rate of motion for one hour it would go forty miles. It is not necessary to go the full forty miles to be going at that rate for an instant.

The arrow showing the direction of the instantaneous value of the linear velocity of the conductor may be broken into two components. The vertical component is parallel to the flux lines, and cuts none of them. The horizontal component cuts the flux lines at right angles. If the length of the arrow is drawn proportional to the value of the velocity it represents, and the lines of flux are drawn to the same scale, then the horizontal component of the arrow will cut a number of lines exactly equal to the lines cut by the original arrow at the angle θ.

If the arrow whose length is proportional to the linear velocity of the conductor is laid off at the angle θ, it is the diagonal of a rectangle whose vertical sides are the length of the vertical component of motion, and whose horizontal sides are the length of the horizontal component of motion.

The diagonal divides the rectangle into two right triangles. If the length of the diagonal which forms the hypotenuse of the triangles is divided by the length of the side opposite the angle θ in either triangle, the result is, by definition, the sine of the angle θ.

$$\text{Sin } \theta = \frac{\text{Opposite side}}{\text{Hypotenuse}} = \frac{\text{Horizontal component of velocity}}{\text{Linear velocity}}$$

We assumed the circumference of the circle traced out by the rotating loop and its rate of rotation were such that at any instant the linear velocity of a conductor was 1 m/sec. Now let us assume the flux through which the conductor moves in 1 sec is 1 Wb when it is moving at this velocity at right angles to the flux.

If this is true, then the voltage at the coil terminals can be found from Faraday's law.

$$e = N \frac{d\phi}{dt}$$

where N for this coil is 1, and the rate of change of flux, $d\phi/dt$, is also 1.

$$e = (1)(1) = 1 \text{ V}$$

This can occur only when the linear velocity is measured at right angles to the flux. This is only when the conductor is, at the instant of measurement, at the positions shown in Figures 10-1(b) and (d). This is the peak voltage, and Figure 10-2 shows it marked on the graph plotting the voltage across the load as a function of the coil position.

But for all intermediate positions, the horizontal component of velocity has a length proportional to the number of flux lines being cut. If the horizontal component were as long as the linear velocity of the conductor, then it would cut the same number of lines of flux per second. This occurs at 90° and 270°. If that length of arrow represents the cutting of enough lines to produce a terminal voltage of 1 V, then a line half that long would represent a terminal voltage of $\frac{1}{2}$ V. For any length of line the terminal voltage is proportional to its length.

The length of this horizontal component of the linear velocity of the conductor is the sine of the angle of rotation, θ, as we have seen. Therefore,

Horizontal component of velocity = Linear velocity × sin θ

In our case, where the linear velocity is 1,

Horizontal component of velocity = 1 sin θ

The maximum voltage produced, which occurs at 90° and 270°, is directly proportional to the length of the linear velocity arrow. The voltage at any instant is proportional to the length of the arrow representing the horizontal component of velocity. Therefore,

$$e = E_{max} \sin \theta$$

where e is the voltage at any instant, and E_{max} is the maximum value of the voltage.

Values of sin θ for any angle are to be found in tables in trigonometry books, or in any set of math tables. If we now wish to complete the graph started in Figure 10-2a, we may. If we continue with the assumption that $E_{max} = 1$, then the value of the sine of the angle θ as found in the table will be the value of the instantaneous voltage. Values of sin θ at 15° intervals are shown in Table 10-1.

TABLE 10-1   Values of Sin θ

θ	Sin θ	θ	Sin θ	θ	Sin θ	θ	Sin θ
0°	0	15°	0.259	30°	0.500	45°	0.707
60°	0.866	75°	0.966	90°	1.000		

These values may be plotted as voltages on the graph, as seen in Figure 10-4. The line connecting points A and B on the original graph of Figure 10-2 can now be seen to be a smooth curve that starts with a relatively steep slope that becomes less and less as the height of the curve increases. At the maximum value, the curve is parallel to the *x*-axis.

As rotation of the loop continues from 90° to 180°, the angle at which the conductor is cutting across the flux lines gradually decreases, from the right angle between the motion of the conductor and the direction of the flux when the conductor is at the 90° position, to parallel motion between the two when the conductor is at 180°. As the angle changes, the horizontal component of the motion must decrease, causing the voltage to decrease in proportion.

It is apparent that the change in voltage between 90° and 180° is a mirror image of the change in voltage between 0° and 90°. But it is also apparent that the change in voltage between 180° and 360° is a mirror image of the change between 0° and 180°. Therefore, the whole cycle of change in voltage that occurs during a single rotation of the simple single-loop generator can be traced out, as seen in Figure 10-5.

This is a *sine curve*. It can be obtained mathematically by simply plotting the sine of all angles between 0° and 360°. It can be obtained

Figure 10-4   Values of E_{max} sin θ plotted for $0° \leq \theta \leq 90°$, where $E_{max} = 1$ V.

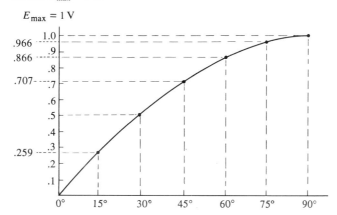

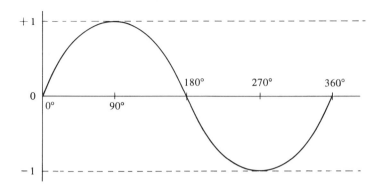

Figure 10-5 One cycle of change in voltage, which occurs during a single rotation of the single-loop generator.

electrically by rotating a loop of wire in a magnetic field of parallel lines of flux, and plotting the terminal voltages or current through a resistive load. It is certainly one of the most important curves in electronics.

Problems   1. Suppose the maximum voltage produced across the terminals of a single-loop ac generator is 60 V. Plot the curve of the terminal voltage through one complete cycle of the generator loop, at positions of every 15° around the circle that the loop makes.

   2. Assume that the conductor of a single-loop ac generator, with a constant linear velocity of 1 m/sec, is cutting across magnetic flux at a rate of 2.5 Wb/sec at the instant it is moving at right angles to the flux. Calculate and plot the values of the rate of change of flux, $d\phi/dt$, and the voltage output, as the loop makes one complete cycle, for positions of every 15°.

10-2
Sinusoidal Waveform

THE SINE WAVE.   The voltage generated by a single loop rotating in a magnetic field with parallel flux lines is not the only source of the sine curve. If a pointer is affixed to the end of a vibrating prong of a tuning fork, and a glass plate coated with a thin layer of soot is pulled at a constant rate past the pointer so that it traces out a path in the soot, the waveform thus traced is a sine curve. A graph showing the displacement from its center position of the pendulum of a clock as it swings is a sine curve. A graph showing the velocity at each instant of the pendulum is also a sine curve, though it is zero when the displacement is a maximum, and a maximum when the displacement is zero. Indeed, the physical phenomena which can be described, at least in part, by a sine wave plotted against position, or time, are nearly limitless.

The current that we have described as the coil current and, consequently, the current through the load resistor in the single-loop generator is called *ac current,* where the letters *ac* stand for *alternating current.* It is, of course, redundant to use the phrase "ac current," and it seems confusing to hear the phrase "ac voltage," which would seem to mean alternating current voltage.

The term *ac* is used to refer to either a voltage or current that has a waveform similar to the sine curve. Where a voltage or current is unchanging, as from a battery, and would graph as a horizontal straight line, it is referred to as dc, including either dc voltage or dc current.

The graph of a sine wave is shown in Figure 10-6. It shows two sets of measurements along the horizontal axis, not just one. One set of calibrations is in degrees, as we have done before; the full cycle is, as always, 360°. The other set of calibrations is in terms of time.

FREQUENCY. Though we have plotted out a single cycle, a sine wave is not presumed to have any beginning or ending. If the sine wave in question represents the voltage variations in one cycle for our single-loop generator, the generator had been running before the one cycle we plotted, and continued to run after we had made our measurements.

The frequency of a sinusoidal waveform is simply the number of cycles of that waveform that would occur in one second if the wave were to

Figure 10-6   The graph of a sine wave.

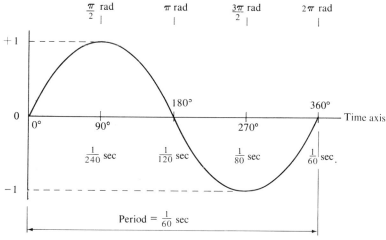

continue that long. It does not, of course, need to continue for a full second, any more than you must drive for an hour before you can be going 60 mph.

The waveform of the voltage present at our wall plugs from the utilities is sinusoidal. *Sinusoidal* means having the shape of a sine wave, and going through the same variations. A sine wave must always start and end at zero, by mathematical definition. A sinusoidal wave is not subject to this restriction, but if it does start at zero, then it is everywhere coincident with a sine waveform.

The sinusoidal voltage at our wall plugs varies back and forth through a complete cycle 60 times a second. Its frequency is, therefore, 60 cycles per second, or 60 Hz. (*Hz* is the abbreviation for *hertz*.) The frequencies of ac voltages and currents encountered vary from the frequency of dc, which is zero Hz, through the audio range of frequencies—which is usually considered to be from about 20 Hz up to about 20 kHz (k stands for thousands, so 20 kHz is the same as 20,000 cycles per second)—on up to frequencies of hundreds of millions of Hz.

PERIOD. In ac the *period* is the time required for one complete cycle. If the ac referred to is the power line voltage, then the time required for one cycle is 1/60 sec. This is the other set of calibrations on the horizontal axis of the graph of Figure 10-4. At the right of the graph, at the point on the horizontal axis coinciding with the 360° mark, the time 1/60 sec is indicated. This is the time required for one cycle at this frequency. Intermediate points are fractions of that time. The time for one-half cycle is, therefore, half of 1/60 sec, or 1/120 sec. The time for 1° of rotation of the loop of the generator is 1/360 of 1/60, which is 1/21600 sec, or about 46.3 μsec.

These divisions are time, and are coincident with the degree markings. The horizontal axis on this graph, which we will see again and again, is therefore called the *time axis*. For a constant angular velocity of rotation, the position from some predetermined reference position depends on how long the rotation has been going on. If, for example, we could physically manage the job of marking the position of the rotating coil of our single-loop generator when it was rotating at a frequency of 60 Hz, and then 46.3 μsec later measure the angle through which it had rotated, we would find it to be 1°.

We use degrees and time units interchangeably. For a constant rate of rotation, 360° is the time of 1 period. At the power line frequency of 60 Hz, 360° equals 1/60 sec, and is interchangeable with it.

Period and frequency have a reciprocal relationship with each other.

That is,

$$f = \frac{1}{T} \text{ and } T = \frac{1}{f}$$

where f is the frequency in Hz, and T is the period.

PHASE.   Suppose we had two single-loop generators, both running at exactly the same speed so that the frequency of the ac from each was exactly the same. But suppose they had been started at slightly different times. Then, if the sinusoidal curves representing the voltage output of the generators were both plotted on the same graph, they would not be superimposed. Figure 10-7 shows such a situation. One waveform is taken as the reference, and the single cycle of its voltage is plotted, starting with zero voltage at zero time.

At the instant the reference waveform from the first generator is zero at the start of its cycle, the voltage from the second generator is +1 V. When the voltage from the reference generator has risen to 1 V, the output of the second generator has dropped to 0 V. If we examine the quarter cycle just before the one used as a reference, it is apparent that the shape of the waveform showing voltage variations for the second generator

Figure 10-7   Sinusoidal waveforms from two single-loop generators are out of step—that is, they show a phase angle difference.

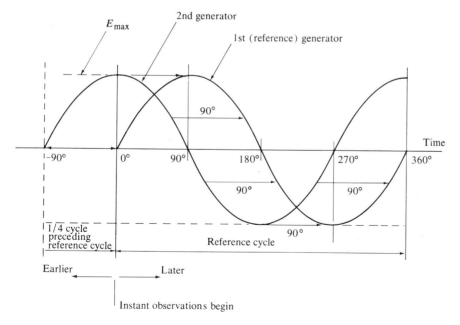

is sinusoidal, but it is everywhere out of step with the reference. If we could somehow pick up the line showing the second generator voltage and push it to the right one quarter of a cycle, which is 90°, then the two would everywhere coincide.

For each point on the reference waveform, there is a corresponding point on the second generator waveform, but it is 90° to the *left* of the reference waveform.

We could describe this situation more concisely by saying there is a 90° *phase* difference between the two waveforms. The phase difference—or, more accurately, *phase angle* difference—is a measure of how far two waves are out of step with each other. If the phase difference is 0°, then the two waves are not out of step, but have their maximum values at the same instant and are both zero at the same instant. If the phase angle is 90°, as in the case just discussed, then when one is at a maximum, either positive or negative, the other is at zero. A phase difference of 180° means that they are the precise opposite of each other. They both are zero at the same time, but when one is at a positive maximum value, the other is at its negative maximum value. If they have the same maximum and minimum voltage values, the sum of the two will always be zero, and they will cancel each other out completely.

Phase angles may be of any value. A phase difference of 30° means one wave is 30° before or after the other. If it is before the reference waveform, it is said to be a *leading* phase angle, or a *positive* phase angle. If it occurs later than the reference waveform, it is said to be *lagging*, and may be specified as a *negative* phase difference.

If two waveforms are combined in phase, they everywhere add, and the sum is the sum of the two. Waveforms with an E_{max} of 2 V and 3 V combining in phase would produce a single sinusoidal waveform of the common phase with an $E_{max} = 5$ V.

If two waveforms are combined 180° out of phase, they are of opposite polarity at every instant. If they are also of equal magnitude, then they cancel, and their sum is zero. If they are not equal, then the sum is the difference between them. If one has an $E_{max} = 3$ V and the other has an $E_{max} = 5$ V, then the sum of the two will have an $E_{max} = 2$ V.

If two waves are between 0° and 180° out of phase, then they will combine to produce a single sinusoidal waveform. It will have an E_{max} between the sum and difference of the E_{max} of the two original sinusoids, and it will have a phase angle with respect to a reference that will be between the phase angles of the two original waves measured to that same reference.

1. For each of the following sinusoidal waveforms, calculate the frequency and the period:

(a) 40 cycles every 25 seconds   (b) 200 cycles every 10^{-5} sec

(c) 10,000 cycles every 12 minutes   (d) 0.1 cycle in 3 sec

(e) 0.0001 cycle in 25 μsec   (f) 36 cycles in one minute

(g) 10^6 cycles every $\frac{1}{2}$ hour   (h) 650 cycles in 0.015 msec

2. Consider two sinusoidal waveforms with the same frequency f, but out of phase. Given t_1, the time in the first cycle that one waveform has its first peak, and t_2, the time in the first cycle that the other waveform has its first peak relative to some initial time t_0, calculate the phase angle between them and note the direction of the phase difference for the following cases:

(a) $f = 60$ Hz   (b) $f = 10^3$ Hz   (c) $f = 5$ Hz
     $t_1 = 4.167$ msec $t_1 = 0.25$ msec $t_1 = 0.15$ sec
     $t_2 = 2.083$ msec $t_2 = 0.4$ msec $t_2 = 0.05$ sec

(d) $f = 200$ Hz   (e) $f = 40,000$ Hz   (f) $f = 1$ MHz
     $t_1 = 0.5$ msec $t_1 = 6.25$ μsec $t_1 = 0.35$ μsec
     $t_2 = 1.25$ msec $t_2 = 4.167$ μsec $t_2 = 0.25$ μsec

10-3
Phasor
Representation

VECTORS. Some quantities are sufficiently represented by a single number—the resistance of a 10 Ω resistor, for example. Such quantities are *scalar*. Other quantities require more information. If someone says there is a force of ten pounds pushing a sliding weight, and asks you to describe the resulting motion, you would certainly have to find out in what direction the force was acting. Such a quantity is a *vector*, for which both magnitude and direction must be known before the effect of the quantity can be known.

A vector may be plotted on paper by drawing an arrow whose length is proportional to the magnitude of the quantity in question and whose direction is the direction of the quantity. In this way such quantities may be added, subtracted, multiplied, and divided.

PHASORS. Consider the drawing of Figure 10-8. It shows a circle divided into four *quadrants* by two lines. Where the lines intersect the circle, the circle degrees are marked, with $0°$ on the right side of the circle. This is the reference, by convention.

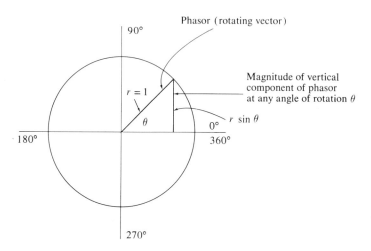

Figure 10-8   Graphic representation of a phasor.

From the center of the circle to its circumference, an arrow is drawn. This arrow is sometimes called a *radius vector* (*r*), but is not really properly called a vector, since the direction it points changes with time.

The initial position of the radius vector is taken to be from the center of the circle pointing to the right, toward 0°. As it rotates through the angle θ, a perpendicular dropped to the horizontal axis from the point where the radius vector touches the circumference of the circle will have a length equal to $r \sin \theta$. If the length of the radius vector is taken as 1, then the length of the perpendicular is $\sin \theta$. If the length of the radius vector is taken to be E_{max}, then the length of the perpendicular is equal to $E_{max} \sin \theta$. But this is the value of the voltage at any instant, where the waveform is a sinusoid.

Since the radius vector is rotating, it is more properly called a *phasor*. If the phasor represents 60 Hz ac, it is rotating at the rate of 60 revolutions per second. Any voltage or any current may be represented by a phasor, with a length equal to E_{max} or I_{max}, rotating through one complete revolution for each cycle of the voltage or current.

RADIANS.   The angle through which a radius vector has rotated at any instant may be measured in the familiar degree notation, but it is sometimes more convenient to measure angles in *radians*.

Consider the drawing of Figure 10-9, showing a circle with a radius *r*. Laid off on the circumference from the endpoint of *r* is a distance *s*, that satisfies the relationship $s = r$.

If the endpoint of *s* is joined to the center of the circle, then the angle included at the center of the circle is, by definition, 1 *radian* (rad).

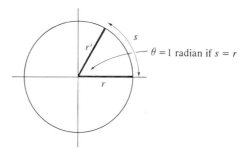

Figure 10-9 One radian is the angular part of a circle that includes an arc equal to the radius of the circle. Thus 1 rad = 57.3°.

Since the circumference of the circle is π times the diameter, it is 2π times the radius. Since the circumference contains the radius 2π times, the distance s can be marked off 2π times before the circle is completed.

Since the angle θ marked off by the radii and the distance s on the circumference is 1 rad, the complete circle must contain 2π rad. Therefore,

$$2\pi \text{ rad} = 360°$$

and

$$\pi \text{ rad} = 180°$$

Therefore,

$$1 \text{ rad} = \frac{180°}{\pi} = 57.2958° \cong 57.3°$$

or

$$1° = \frac{\pi}{180°} = 0.01745 \text{ rad}$$

Look back at Figure 10-6, which has been marked off in radians as well as degrees. The initial position of 0° is also 0 rad. 90° corresponds to $\pi/2$ rad, 180° to π rad, and 270° to $3\pi/2$ rad. 360° is, of course, 2π rad.

Smaller angles as well can be given as simple fractions involving π when the angular measure is in radians. A tabulation of some common values follows in Table 10-2.

TABLE 10-2   Angular Measure in Degrees and Radians

θ	θ(rad)	θ	θ(rad)	θ	θ(rad)	θ	θ(rad)
1°	$\pi/180$	5°	$\pi/36$	15°	$\pi/12$	30°	$\pi/6$
45°	$\pi/4$	60°	$\pi/3$	75°	$5\pi/12$	90°	$\pi/2$

ANGULAR VELOCITY. The radius vector, or phasor, is considered to be rotating at a rate that will permit one complete revolution in the time it takes for one cycle of the waveform represented by the phasor. For the sake of convenience in mathematical manipulation, it is often more desirable to discuss the rate of rotation of the phasor in terms of angular velocity instead of speed.

Since

$$e = E_{\text{max}} \sin \theta$$

the voltage e at any instant is a function of θ. That is the same as saying that time—since we are talking about instants—on one side of the equation is equal to degrees on the other side of the equation. But degrees are a measure of position.

We have already seen that our graph showing sinusoidal voltages or currents has a time base that may be marked off in degrees of rotation or in seconds. The correspondence exists for angles of rotation measured in radians as well as angles measured in degrees.

Angular velocity is simply the rate of rotation measured in terms of the change in the angle θ from zero to its position at some time t after the time when the phasor was in the reference position. A phasor that starts at reference time t_0, in the reference position, and rotates at a rate of 720°/sec for a time of 2 sec will have made four complete revolutions and be again in the reference position. If the same phasor rotates for 1 sec, it will make two revolutions and be in the reference position. If it rotates for 0.1 sec, it will have rotated 72°. This time it will not be in the reference position, but will be at an angle $\theta = 72°$ to the reference position.

Each time, to ascertain the final position of the phasor, we multiplied the angular velocity by the time. This is nothing more than the familiar

Rate × Time = Distance traveled

and in this case,

Angular velocity × Time = Angle completed

But we are concerned with position, not simply the total angle completed. If, at the end of some time t, the phasor is back in the reference position, the instantaneous value of the voltage it represents is zero, regardless of how many times the phasor had rotated during the time t. We therefore subtract from the total angle as many multiples of 360° as possible until the remainder is less than 360°, or 2π rad. This remainder is the position of the phasor at the end of the time t.

The symbol for angular velocity is ω (the Greek letter omega). It is in rad/sec, or in deg/sec. The product ωt has the dimension of an angle, as can be seen.

$$\omega t = \frac{\text{rad}}{\text{sec}} \times \text{sec} = \text{rad}$$

or

$$\omega t = \frac{\text{deg}}{\text{sec}} \times \text{sec} = \text{deg}$$

We may therefore write ωt as an angle, and the sine of that angle is $\sin \omega t$.

The instantaneous value of the voltage represented by a phasor rotating with an angular velocity ω for some time t is given by $e = E_{\max} \sin \omega t$ (Figure 10-10).

PHASE ANGLES. If, at the time t_0, the phasor does not start at the reference position but at some other position, it will have some value for the sine of the angle it makes at that instant with the horizontal axis. This value is proportional to the instantaneous value of the voltage, which will not at that instant be zero, but may be either positive or negative.

The initial angle the phasor makes with the reference axis is its *phase angle*. If the phasor is at the reference axis at t_0, its position at any instant is ωt. Suppose its initial position with respect to the reference axis is 30° above the axis. Then it will continually be ahead of a similar phasor starting at the reference position with an angular velocity ω, by a

Figure 10-10   Use of graphic representation of a phasor to represent instantaneous value of voltage.

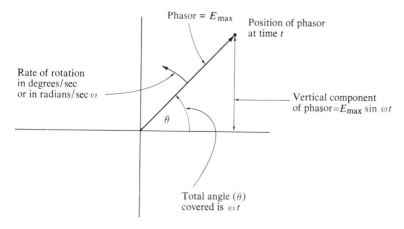

constant amount. That amount would, of course, be its initial lead over the reference phasor.

This initial lead, which will be maintained over any reference phasor starting from the horizontal axis at the same time and with the same angular velocity ω, is the phase angle with respect to that reference. The symbol used to represent it is ϕ.

The angle a phasor with some initial phase angle will make with the reference axis at any instant t is the same as that of a reference phasor starting from the reference and with the same angular velocity *plus the phase angle* ϕ. Thus,

$$e = E_{max}\sin(\omega t + \phi)$$

since $(\omega t + \phi)$ is the whole angle between the phasor and the reference axis at the time t.

Problems

1. Let r be the radius of a circle, and s be a section of the circle's circumference. For each of the following sets of values calculate the number of radians in the portion of the circle circumscribed by s:

(a) $r = 3, s = 6$ (b) $r = 1.5, s = 9$ (c) $r = 30, s = 22$

(d) $r = 0.1, s = 0.001$ (e) $r = 3, s = \pi$ (f) $r = 2.1, s =$
                                                    0.036645

2. Calculate the radian equivalent to the following degree values of θ:

(a) $\theta = 10°$ (b) $\theta = 230°$ (c) $\theta = 72°$

(d) $\theta = 12.5°$ (e) $\theta = 330°$ (f) $\theta = 23°$

3. Convert the following radian angles to degrees:

(a) $\pi/8$ (b) 0.5 (c) $13\pi/8$

(d) 0.1 (e) $3\pi/16$ (f) 0.4π

4. Consider a phasor moving at an angular velocity ω. For the following cases determine the position of the phasor, in degrees, at a time t after the phasor was in its reference position:

(a) $\omega = 2$ rad/sec, $t = 1/3$ sec

(b) $\omega = 40$ deg/sec, $t = 3.4$ sec

(c) $\omega = 220\pi$ rad/sec, $t = 0.02$ sec

(d) $\omega = 14\pi$ rad/sec, $t = 8$ sec

(e) $\omega = 72$ deg/sec, $t = 17$ sec

(f) $\omega = 0.0015$ rad/sec, $t = 2.5$ hr

5. For each of the following sets of values calculate the instantaneous value of the voltage, at a time t, represented by a phasor rotating with an angular velocity ω, and given by the equation $e = E_{max} \sin \omega t$:

(a) $E_{max} = 90$ V, $\omega = \pi$ rad/sec, $t = 1.5$ sec

(b) $E_{max} = 9$ V, $\omega = 3\pi/8$ rad/sec, $t = 4$ sec

(c) $E_{max} = 30$ V, $\omega = 4000\pi$ rad/sec, $t = 0.12$ msec

(d) $E_{max} = 500$ V, $\omega = 40$ deg/sec, $t = 3.5$ sec

(e) $E_{max} = 2$ V, $\omega = 200\pi$ rad/sec, $t = 25$ msec

(f) $E_{max} = 100$ V, $\omega = 22\pi$ rad/sec, $t = 7.576$ msec

6. If the instantaneous voltage at a time t is given by the equation $e = E_{max} \sin (\omega t + \phi)$, complete the following table, where f is the frequency, t_1 is the time when e is at its first positive peak, t_2 is the time when e is at its first negative peak, t_3 is the time when e first reaches 0.707 its maximum positive value, and e_1 is the value of e at the time $t = \frac{1}{2} T$ ($T =$ the period of the sinusoid).

	E_{max}	ω	ϕ	t_1	t_2	t_3	T	f	e_1
(a)		3π rad/sec	$30°$						-30 V
(b)	750 V				94.445 μsec			5000 Hz	
(c)	9 V	420π rad/sec		1.984 msec					
(d)	400 V		$-45°$					2.5 MKz	
(e)						0.3806 msec	2.778 msec		31.2 V
(f)	12 V		$72°$				22.22 μsec		

**10-4
Phasors and
Sinusoids**

PHASORS PROJECTED.   Suppose we imagine the artificial situation of the drawing of Figure 10-11. A spotlight is shining on a screen, but interposed between the light and the screen is a rotating arrow representing a phasor. Suppose we imagine that only the head of the arrow and the point about which it rotates cast a shadow on the screen. As the arrow rotates, the shadow of its tip would move up and down equal distances from the shadow of the point about which it rotates, the central axis.

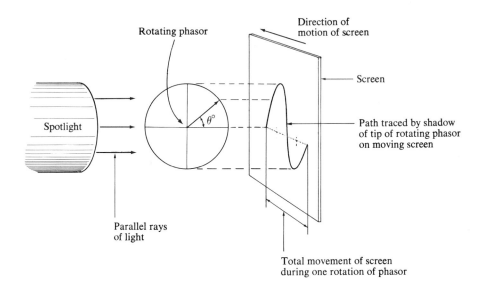

Figure 10-11   Tracing a sinusoidal shadow.

Now suppose further that we move the screen to the left, at a constant rate, so the shadow is tracing out the combination of the vertical component of motion of the arrowhead and the horizontal motion of the screen.

The result would be a sinusoid. Whether it would be a true sine wave or not would depend on whether or not the arrow had been in the horizontal position pointing to the right as the motion of the screen was started. If the arrow had been straight up, the path traced by its shadow would have been that of a *cosine wave,* which has the same shape as a sine wave, but is 90° out of phase with it.

The important point is that the sine wave depiction of the variations in voltage and current that are ac can be derived from the phasor representation of the same thing. It is true, too, that the phasor representation of ac variations can be derived from their representation as a sinusoid with position (or its equivalent at a constant rate, time) plotted on the horizontal axis, and value in volts or amperes—upward for positive and downward for negative—plotted on the vertical axis.

The two representations are thus equivalent, and may be used interchangeably, in whichever form is most convenient to the problem at hand.

Phasors may be used to represent not only voltages and currents, but other time-varying electrical quantities as well. By using the phasor concept, we can easily make calculations involving these quantities—calculations which might be quite lengthy and difficult otherwise. In Chapters 15, 16, and 17 we will use phasors to make calculations with ac voltages and currents similar to the dc analysis already performed in Chapters 7 and 8. The major reason for the work we have done with dc analysis of resistive circuits was to prepare for analysis of the far more frequently encountered ac circuits. This ac analysis becomes mathematically comparable to the dc analysis when phasors are used to represent ac quantities.

THE UNDERLYING REALITY.   It is sometimes difficult, after all the complexities of phasors and sinusoids, to remember what it is we are really talking about. We are most definitely *not* talking about sinusoids wiggling their way down a conductor, or the arrows of phasors shooting through it. Both phasors and sinusoids are *symbolic* representations of the variations occurring in the physical phenomena they represent. The underlying reality of electrons surging back and forth through a conductor or circuit element, alternately creating charge excesses and deficiencies at the terminals of the component, is what we are representing by the mathematical symbology of phasors and sinusoids.

The electron motion is the reality; phasors and sinusoids are just two of many possible ways to describe it. They are ways that lend themselves to relatively simple mathematical manipulations, with results that are in agreement with the underlying reality of electron motion. They are, therefore, useful, and we use them. They are, themselves, only symbols convenient to manipulate; and if we change from one set of symbols to another, we do not affect the reality they represent.

PEAK. The *peak value* of an ac voltage is the same as E_{max}. It is the maximum value at 90° and 270°, whether positive or negative. The two are equal in a sine wave (Figure 10-12).

P–P. *Peak-to-peak voltage* for an ac sinusoidal wave is the difference between the positive peak and the negative peak voltages, though the two do not occur at the same time. For a true sinusoidal wave the voltages of the positive and negative peaks are equal in absolute value,

10-5
Peak, P–P, and RMS

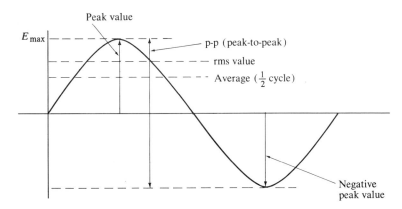

Figure 10-12   The value of an ac voltage may be specified in different ways, and the value of a given voltage varies depending on the method used to specify the voltage.

though opposite in sign. Therefore, twice the peak value is equal to the peak-to-peak value. The abbreviation for peak-to-peak is p–p.

AVERAGE.   The *average value of a sinusoidal waveform* over one full cycle is zero, and this is not useful in computations. The average value taken over one-half cycle is not zero, and is therefore meaningful.

The average value is the average of all the values of a sine wave for one-half alternation. We cannot by any simple means take the average of *all* the values, for they are infinite in number. We can get a very close approximation by averaging a number of the values. If we take the average of the values for each 5° between 0° and 180°, it is about 0.636. The more exact figure, obtained by the methods of calculus, is 0.637. This is the value of the average compared to the peak. If the peak value of a voltage is 100 V, then the average for one-half cycle is 63.7 V.

RMS AND EQUIVALENT.   The value of an ac voltage which can do the same work over a period of time as a steady and unvarying dc voltage plays a role in many calculations. If an ac voltage source is connected to a resistor, the alternating current flow through the resistor produces heat. This production of heat is at a zero rate during the instants the voltage and consequent current are zero (0°, 180°, 360°, . . .). The production of heat is at a maximum rate during the instants the voltage and consequent current are maximum (90°, 270°, . . .).

The alternations of heat production thus occur twice during each cycle. For 60 Hz ac, peaks of heat production within the resistor are occurring 120 times/sec, with zero heat production occurring at instants between.

The resistor cannot heat up and cool down that fast, of course. Its temperature will rise until, over a period of time which is at least a significant fraction of a second, the average value of the internal production of heat matches the rate at which heat is lost to the surroundings.

The heat produced internally in the resistor at any instant is proportional to the power expended in it by the current flow through it. Power is proportional to the *square* of the current flow. If, therefore, we wish to find the value of the dc voltage which will produce currents through the resistor at the same rate of power dissipation as the ac, then we must find the *root-mean-square* (rms) value of the ac.

The term root-mean-square comes from the principles behind the mathematical process by which it is calculated. We can arrive at a very close approximation of the correct value by taking instantaneous values of the voltage at selected intervals throughout the *entire* cycle, squaring these values, averaging the squares, and taking the square root of that average. The fact that the squares of the values are to be averaged is what permits the use of the full cycle, since the square of either a positive or a negative voltage will be positive. This is reasonable, since heat will be produced and power dissipated in the resistor regardless of the direction of current flow through it.

The value obtained by this mathematical process described by the term rms is

$$E_{rms} = 0.707\, E_{max}$$

where E_{rms} is the rms value of the ac voltage. Suppose an ac voltage has a peak value of 200 V. Its rms value could be calculated, using the above equation, and would be 141.4 V.

The voltage measured at our wall plugs is approximately 120 V ac. That is the rms value. When an ac voltage is given, if it is not specifically said to be peak, p–p, instantaneous, or some other particular specification, then it is taken to be rms. Usually, for the sake of clarity, where there is the possibility of doubt, rms will also be specified. This is a little like the sign of a number—if it is positive, nothing need be said and the sign may be omitted, but if it is negative the sign must be shown. Any voltage not specifically stated in some other system is to be taken to be an rms value.

The peak value of an rms voltage may be calculated from the relationship

$$E_{max} = 1.414\, E_{rms}$$

For the power line voltage of a nominal 120 V rms, the peak value is $1.414 \times 120 \cong 170$ V.

The rms value of an ac voltage is sometimes also called the *equivalent* since it is the voltage of the dc which can do the same work as the ac.

It is this that makes it possible to use the rms value of ac in power calculations, just as though it were dc. For example, the power dissipated in a 10 Ω resistor by a voltage of 5 V dc is

$$P = \frac{5^2}{10} = 2.5 \text{ W}$$

and the power dissipated in a 10 Ω resistor by a voltage of 5 V ac rms is likewise

$$P = \frac{5^2}{10} = 2.5 \text{ W}$$

Rms and dc can be used interchangeably in power calculations.

If peak voltage is used to calculate power in ac circuits, the result is exactly twice the rms power. This is the correct value for the peak power, but it is an instantaneous value and *not* an effective value. The reason peak power is double the rms power comes from the fact that power is proportional to the square of the voltage; and if we square 1.414, the conversion factor between peak and rms, the result is 2.000.

If p–p voltages are used to calculate power, the results will be 4 times peak power and 8 times rms, or effective, power. There seems little practical use for this calculation, except to note that an rms power of 8 W can be given as 64 W p p power, a much larger number and, therefore, for some purposes a more impressive way to describe the same 8 W. Advantage has been taken of this sometimes in advertising the capabilities of home stereo amplifiers and similar equipment.

Problems **1.** For the following ac sinusoidal voltages calculate the peak value, peak-to-peak voltage, average value over $\frac{1}{2}$ cycle, and rms value:

(a) 20 sin 2πt   (b) 120 sin (3πt/8 + 30°)   (c) 32 sin 60t

(d) $\frac{1}{2}$ sin 30t   (e) 75 sin (60t + 120°)   (f) 9 sin πt/8

2. Given the rms voltage values below, calculate the corresponding peak voltage values, peak-to-peak voltages, average values over $\frac{1}{2}$ cycle, and the rms power dissipated in a 20 Ω resistor:

(a) 70.7 V   (b) 8.484 μV   (c) 50.904 V   (d) 707 mV

(e) 1.414 V   (f) 1696.8 V   (g) 42.42 V   (h) 6.363 V

3. For each of the waveforms shown, calculate the peak voltage, peak-to-peak voltage, rms voltage, and the power that would be dissipated if the signal were applied across a 50 Ω resistor. *Hint:* For the waveforms in (d) and (e), apply the definition of rms as given in the text, averaging the voltage values over time for a complete cycle.

Waveforms for Problem 3.

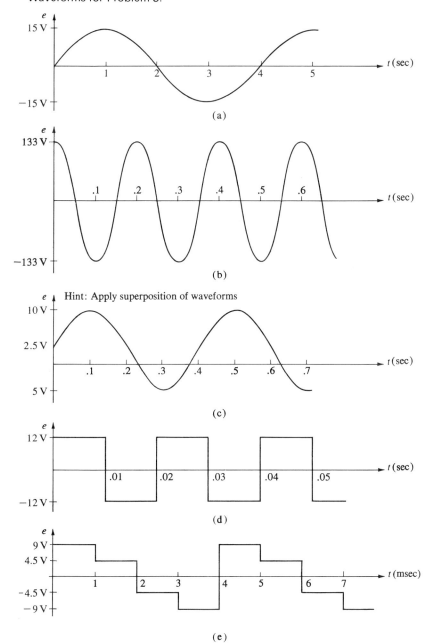

(a)

(b)

Hint: Apply superposition of waveforms

(c)

(d)

(e)

Key Words   **ac**   these letters stand for *alternating current*, but the term ac is used to refer to either a current or a voltage that has a waveform similar to the sine curve

angular velocity   the rate of rotation measured in terms of change in the angle θ from zero to its position at some time after the time when the phasor was in the reference position

dc   these letters stand for *direct current*, but the term dc is used to refer to either an unchanging voltage or an unchanging current that graphs as a horizontal straight line

leading phase angle   describes the situation in which a waveform comes before the reference waveform

negative phase difference   the opposite of leading phase angle—that is, a waveform comes after the reference waveform

peak voltage   has maximum value at 90° and 270°, whether positive or negative

p–p   for an ac sinusoidal wave, the difference between the positive peak and the negative peak. Peak-to-peak value is twice peak value because positive and negative peaks are of equal value.

period   the time required for one complete ac cycle

phase angle   the initial angle the phasor makes with the reference axis

phase difference   the measure of how far two waves are out of step with each other

phasor   a quantity that is described by its magnitude and variation in time

radian   the angle formed by joining to the center of a circle the two end points of a segment of the circumference equal in length to the radius. A radian is about 57.3°.

root-mean-square (rms)   a method of finding a dc value that produces currents through a resistor at the same rate of power dissipation as a given ac. Rms value is found by taking instantaneous values of the voltage at selected intervals throughout the cycle, squaring the values, averaging the sum of the squares, and then taking the square root of this average.

scalar   a quantity that can be described fully by a single number

vector   a quantity that is described by its magnitude and direction. In other words, a quantity that cannot be described by one number

Summary of Concepts

1.   The linear speed of a conductor in a rotating loop at any instant depends on the number of revolutions it makes per unit time and on the diameter of the loop.

2. The frequency of a sinusoidal waveform is simply the number of cycles of the waveform that would occur in one second if the wave were to continue that long.

3. Any voltage or current may be represented by a phasor, with a length equal to E_{max} or I_{max}, rotating through one complete revolution for each cycle of the voltage or current.

4. A radius vector, or phasor, is considered to be rotating at the rate that permits one complete revolution in the time it takes to complete one cycle of the waveform represented by the phasor.

5. The sine wave depiction of the ac variations in voltage and current can be derived from the phasor representation of the same thing.

6. The phasor representation of ac variations can be derived from their representation as a sinusoid with position plotted on the horizontal axis and value in volts plotted on the vertical axis.

7. The average value of a sinusoidal waveform is the average of all the values of the sine wave through one-half cycle.

8. Any ac voltage not specifically labeled otherwise should be considered an rms value.

9. If peak voltage is used to calculate power in ac circuits, the result is exactly twice rms power.

10. If p–p voltage is used to calculate ac power, the result is four times peak power and eight times rms power.

On a separate sheet of paper, fill in the blanks or answer the questions below. **To Help You Review**
The number following each question refers to the section in the chapter where the correct answer can be found.

1. The linear speed at which a conductor is moving depends on _____ and _____ . (10-1)

2. The rate of flux cutting is the same as _____ . (10-1)

3. What is a sine curve? (10-1)

4. Define the term ac. (10-1)

5. The frequency of a _____ is the number of cycles that would occur in one second if the _____ were to continue for that long. (10-2)

6. What does sinusoidal mean? (10-2)

7. What does time axis refer to? (10-2)

8. What is phase? (10-2)

9. Vectors can be plotted on paper. Can scalars? Explain. (10-3)

10. Draw a sketch that explains what a radian is. (10-3)

11. At what rate is a phasor considered to be rotating? (10-3)

12. What is angular velocity? (10-3)

13. What can phasor representation of ac variations be derived from? (10-4)

14. Describe three kinds of voltage values. (10-5)

15. How do we arrive at rms values? (10-5)

16. Peak voltage, if used to calculate ac power, gives results _____ times rms power. (10-5)

17. Power calculations based on p–p voltages are _____ times calculations based on peak voltages, and _____ times calculations based on rms voltages. (10-5)

This chapter will help you understand

☐ the operating principles of ac meter movements

☐ electronic amplification in voltmeters

☐ the use of an oscilloscope in charting waveforms

☐ voltage, frequency, and phase measurement with an oscilloscope

ELEVEN
AC
MEASUREMENTS

RECTIFIER-TYPE METERS.   The vast majority of ac reading meters contain a *rectifier* that converts the incoming alternating current to a pulsating direct current.

11-1

AC Meters

The rectifier is a nonlinear circuit element. It functions as a switch, approximately, permitting current to flow in one direction much more readily than in the other.

A perfect rectifier would have infinite resistance to the flow of current in one direction, like an open switch. In the other direction, the resistance would be zero, like a closed switch. There is no such thing as a perfect rectifier. Practical rectifiers have some resistance in the conducting direction and permit the flow of some leakage current in the nonconducting direction.

If a perfect rectifier were connected in series between an ac source and a resistive load, the load current would appear only during that half-cycle of the ac when the polarity across the rectifier was in the conducting direction. During the other half-cycle, when the polarity of voltage across the rectifier was in the nonconducting direction, no significant load current could flow. Therefore, the voltage across the load would appear during one half-cycle, but not during the other, and the load voltage would always be in the same polarity.

This load voltage, as seen in Figure 11-1, shows only a single polarity. Whether it is positive or negative depends on the polarity of connection of the rectifier. Since it is, in either event, a unidirectional current, it is a form of dc, called *pulsating dc*.

If this pulsating dc is applied to a d'Arsonval meter movement, the flow of current in the moving coil will always be in the same direction. The polarity of the magnetic field around the coil as a consequence of this current flow through it will always be the same, and the consequent force and direction of movement of the pointer due to that force will always be in the same direction.

If the needle is deflected upward during each positive half cycle, and does not have time to fall back to the zero position between impulses, it will show some net positive movement. If the ac to be measured by this meter is at the power line frequency of 60 Hz, then there will be no time for significant return of the needle between impulses, since the impulses occur 60 times each second. The inertia of the pointer, moving coil, and other parts of the moving mechanical portion of the meter cannot respond that rapidly.

If ac is applied to a d'Arsonval meter movement without the rectifier, the net movement of the needle is zero, since each impulse in one direction

Figure 11-1   A rectifier converts ac to pulsating dc. The arrow above the rectifier shows the direction in which it will conduct, using conventional current flow.

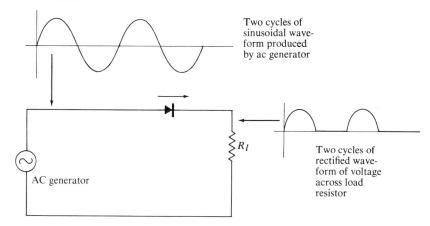

is followed 1/120 sec later by an impulse of equal magnitude in the opposite direction. The pointer can do nothing except quiver about the zero position. If we apply an ac voltage of much lower frequency, 5 to 10 Hz, this quivering can be seen; but regardless of the magnitude of the potential applied, there will be no useful net pointer deflection.

If such a low frequency is applied to a meter through a series rectifier, the tendency of the pointer to fall back to zero between impulses will be apparent, since the pointer will appear to vibrate; but there will be some net movement, and it will be proportional to the magnitude of the current flow through the moving coil.

It can be shown that the net force acting on the pointer through the moving coil is proportional to the average value of the current through one full cycle. Since there is no current flow through the coil during one half-cycle, and the average value of the current during the half-cycle when current does flow is $0.637 I_{max}$, the net average value of current for the full cycle must be half of that figure, or $0.318 I_{max}$.

The important thing to note is that the force acting to deflect the pointer is proportional to the average value of current, and *not* to the rms value. The meter will almost invariably be calibrated in rms values. This is possible since, with a sinusoidal waveform, the ratio between average current and rms current is a constant; but this is true *only* for sinusoidal waveforms. If the waveform is not sinusoidal, the deflection of the pointer will still be proportional to the average value of the current, but rms values have no meaning for nonsinusoidal currents.

The accuracy of a meter using a rectifier is dependent not only on the accuracy of the meter movement and the accuracy with which the values of any multiplier resistors have been selected, but on the accuracy of the rectifier as well. The error in the rectifier may add to the error in the meter. Thus, if a meter with an inherent accuracy of 1% is used with a rectifier whose accuracy is 2%, the accuracy of the combination will not be greater than 3%. The same meter used for dc measurements without the rectifier would be able to give readings to within 1%.

The common VOM, or *volt-ohm-milliammeter,* usually has both ac and dc functions, with a variety of ranges. When the basic meter movement is used on the dc ranges, the rectifier built into the case is switched out of the circuit by the function switch. The accuracy of the meter in this application may be 2%, depending on the instrument and the care with which it has been manufactured. When the same instrument is switched on to an ac function, the rectifier is switched into the circuit, and the accuracy of the instrument is now limited by the accuracy of the rectifier, as well as that of the rest of the components. Typically, a meter that is claimed by its manufacturer to have an inherent accuracy of 2% on the dc functions will have an accuracy of not more than 3% on the ac functions.

The sensitivity of such a meter will be less on the ac ranges than on the dc since the need for calibration requires circuit compensations that are not needed on dc.

The characteristics of rectifiers as used on meters are not sufficiently stable and predictable to enable the manufacturer to avoid the necessity for individual calibration. It is also unfortunately true that, particularly with the older copper-oxide rectifiers, changes in characteristics of the rectifier with time are inevitable. Some way in which compensation may be made to recalibrate the meter must be included in the design.

Usually, this calibration compensation takes the form of both series and shunt resistors. A resistor between the rectifier and the meter can be used, if it is adjustable, to compensate for changes in the resistance of the rectifier in the conducting direction. The addition of this resistance means that part of the energy in the current drawn from the circuit under test is dissipated in this resistance, as well as the resistance of the rectifier, and this is waste energy so far as deflection of the pointer is concerned. For this reason alone, the sensitivity of the meter, in terms of amount of pointer deflection for energy drawn from the circuit being tested, must always be less than for comparable dc measurements.

Since the rectifier is not a perfect switch, but one whose resistance in the conduction direction depends on the potential across it, the current flow in the circuit of which it is a part is not simply directly proportional to the applied potential. The resistance of a rectifier will be much greater for low potentials across it than for high. This means that the current in the circuit and through the meter movement will be proportionately less for low potentials, and the meter sensitivity low for low potentials. The calibrations will thus necessarily be crowded at the low end, to compensate for this low sensitivity.

If a shunt resistor is placed across the meter, the current through the shunt added to the current through the meter movement provides increased current through the rectifier. This means that, for low levels of potential measured, the part of the potential that appears across the rectifier will be greater, and the effect of its higher resistance at low potentials will be less. The meter scale will thus appear to be less crowded at the low end, and the difference in calibration between scales for various ranges will not be as great.

Usually, even with the compensation of this shunt resistor, there will need to be a separately calibrated scale for low ac voltage reading, and sometimes the two lowest ranges are separately calibrated. Care is required in reading since it is very easy to read the wrong scale, and a significant error may be involved.

The effect of both series and shunt resistors on the sensitivity of the VOM when it is used in the ac ranges is to reduce it. An instrument rated at 20,000 Ω/V when used on the dc ranges will usually have a sensitivity of not more than 10,000 Ω/V when used on the ac ranges, and it may be much less.

This means that the loading effect of such an instrument on the circuit under test will be at least twice as great on ac functions as it will on the corresponding dc functions.

AC CURRENT MEASUREMENTS. Most VOMs do not have internal provision for ac current measurements. Such measurements are simply made, however, by inserting a low value of resistance between the two points between which the current is to be determined, and using the ac volts function to measure the potential across the resistor. The simple application of Ohm's law leads to quick calculation of the current.

OTHER METER TYPES. A number of meter types which do not use the d'Arsonval movement and which are suitable for direct ac measurements have been developed. Among them are the iron-vane movements and the electrodynamometer movements.

The *iron-vane movements* depend for their operation on the fact that a piece of ferromagnetic material placed in a magnetic field will be magnetized by that field, with a polarity which, as we have seen, results in an attractive force toward the magnetizing field. If two such pieces of ferromagnetic material are placed in such a field, they will both be magnetized with the same polarity. But if they are adjacent to each other, and magnetized with the same polarity, then there must be a force of repulsion between them.

In the practical application of this principle, magnetizing force is furnished by the current to be measured flowing through a coil surrounding two pieces of soft iron. One piece of material is fixed in position; the other is free to rotate. The rotating vane has a pointer affixed to it (Figure 11-2). When current is flowing through the coil, the fixed and the movable vane both become magnetized with a like polarity and, consequently, repel each other. The movable vane pivots away from its resting position, restrained by springs, and moves against the springs by an amount proportional to the strength of the magnetizing field. The pointer attached to this vane indicates the degree of deflection, with whatever calibrations are suitable to the intended use.

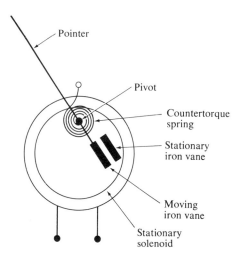

Figure 11-2   An iron-vane meter movement.

Though the polarity of the magnetizing field is constantly changing, the induced magnetization in the two vanes is also changing, keeping step with the magnetizing field, so the force between the vanes is always one of repulsion.

This movement has some severe limitations. It requires a rather large amount of power from the circuit where the measurements are being made, since the only magnetic field present is from the flow of magnetizing current through the coil, and not an interaction between that field and the field of a permanent magnet, as in the case of the d'Arsonval movement. Consequently, this iron-vane movement has less sensitivity than a comparable d'Arsonval movement.

In addition, the hysteresis losses in the iron vanes become considerable at high frequencies. Since the hysteresis losses are a function of frequency, such an instrument can be expected to be correct only at the frequencies for which it is calibrated, typically a rather narrow range of low frequencies. If the instrument is to be used only on 60 Hz power line frequencies, and on circuits where the sensitivity of the movement is not important, these factors do not represent a drawback. For use in most electronic applications, particularly in test instruments where measurements are to be made under a wide range of conditions, they are not usually considered suitable.

THERMOCOUPLE AMMETERS.   For use over a wide range of high frequencies, *thermocouple ammeters* have proven useful. They are based on the principle that a junction of dissimilar metals will, when heated, develop a potential between them. The principle of a typical thermocouple ammeter is shown in Figure 11-3. The current to be measured flows through the resistance wire and heats it according to the rms value of the current. This, of course, is independent of the direction of flow, and whether it is ac or dc. The heat at the junction of the two dissimilar materials of the thermocouple produces a current flow through the thermocouple circuit. This current flow is dc, regardless of the source of the heat. It is proportional only to the amount of heat produced by current flowing through the resistance wire.

The current through the thermocouple circuit is dc, and therefore may be read by a meter utilizing the standard d'Arsonval movement. The scale must be specially calibrated for a particular thermocouple. The thermocouple itself need not be physically near the movement; this arrangement lends itself well to remote readings of high-frequency currents.

Since full-scale readings are typically near the temperature at which the thermocouple resistance wire will melt, such thermocouples are liable to burn out at only moderate overloads. They must also draw considerable power from the circuit under test, which is not significant at high power levels of the current to be measured, but would not be suitable for use in test instruments. This type of meter is, therefore, limited to special applications, though it is unquestionably the best instrument for the direct measurement of current in high-power, high-frequency circuits.

THE ELECTRODYNAMOMETER MOVEMENT. The *electrodynamometer movement* shown in Figure 11-4 is similar in principle to the d'Arsonval

Figure 11-3 The principle of the thermocouple ammeter. The current to be measured flows through the resistance wire. At the thermocouple, the heat produces a dc current flow that moves the pointer of a d'Arsonval movement.

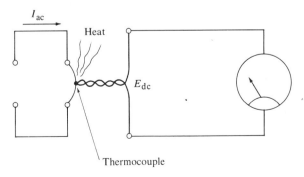

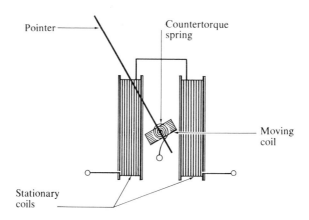

Figure 11-4   An electrodynamometer movement.

movement except that in place of a permanent magnet to produce the field against which the field of the moving coil reacts, the external field is produced by the current to be measured.

Usually, the movable coil is situated between a pair of fixed coils. The fixed coils and the movable coil may be connected in series. The magnetic field due to the current in the fixed coil will tend to align itself to the magnetic field produced by the fixed coils. The movable coil is restrained by springs, and will deflect against the springs by an amount proportional to the force due to the interaction of the magnetic fields. The indications of this instrument are of true effective (rms) values.

Since no iron is present in the magnetic field, no hysteresis losses are evident, but other factors limit the frequency response of this instrument. It may be used interchangeably for both dc and ac measurements, up to the limit of its frequency response.

The sensitivity is poor, since the only power to deflect the pointer comes from the interaction of two relatively weak magnetic fields. Typically, such an instrument is unlikely to have a sensitivity in excess of 1000 Ω/V, and it may be much less. Therefore, it is unsuitable for measurements on circuits where the loading effect might be significant.

THE ELECTRODYNAMOMETER WATTMETER.   If the coils are not connected in series with each other—as when the electrodynamometer is used as a voltmeter—but are connected so the current through the fixed coils is proportional to the load current while the current through the moving coil is proportional to the load voltage, the resulting indication of the pointer will be proportional to the product of load voltage and current, and will therefore be an indication of the power consumed by the load.

The *electrodynamometer wattmeter* will have four terminals for connection to the circuit under test. Two of the terminals will be for the fixed coils, called the *current coils,* while the other two will be for the moving coil, called the *potential* or *voltage coil.* There are two points to remember when using the electrodynamometer. First, the polarity of connection of the coils is important, since this determines whether the pointer deflection will be clockwise or counterclockwise. Usually, ± markings are engraved on both voltage and current terminals, so that appropriate connections may be made. It is also of importance to note that a multiplier resistor is required for the potential coil. The connection to the load for the potential coil should be made so that the multiplier resistor is connected to the side of the line *opposite* the side to which the current coils are connected, as in Figure 11-5. This is necessary to keep the potential difference between the two coils to a minimum.

The scale markings of an electrodynamometer wattmeter are crowded at the low end. This is because the torque to deflect the pointer comes from the interaction of two magnetic fields, both of which depend on the quantities being measured. At low power levels, the current through the fixed coils is low, and therefore the magnetic field produced by that current will be low. If the voltage is also low, as it may be where low power levels are being read, the field from the moving coil will also be weak. The interaction of the two weak fields will produce only a slight deflection. This crowding at the low end of the scale divisions is, therefore, a characteristic of the instrument.

ELECTRONIC VOLTMETERS.   In the voltmeters discussed so far, where the movement is entirely electromechanical, power must be drawn from the circuit under test. This is because even in the most sensitive movement,

11-2
Electronic Meters

Figure 11-5   An electrodynamometer wattmeter.

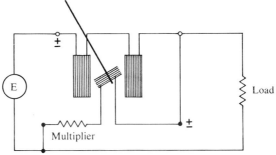

the pointer must be deflected against the restraining force of the hair-springs to achieve a full-scale reading. This power and the restraining force of the hairsprings can be reduced only to a certain value before the friction of the bearings on which the moving mechanical assemblage is mounted becomes a significant factor.

If a separate power source is used to produce the required pointer deflection, and this power source is derived from batteries or from the utility line, then power from the circuit under test need be used only to *control* the pointer deflection. This is achieved by electronic amplification.

Amplification may be defined as the use of a weak force to control a stronger force. The weak force in the power drawn from the circuit under test may be used to control the much stronger force derived from the power supply of the *electronic voltmeter*. The power required to move the pointer of the meter, or to drive a digital display, does not come from the circuit under test.

Electronic voltmeters may be constructed with almost any desired sensitivity. One type of instrument, called the *differential voltmeter,* presents a theoretically infinite resistance to the circuit under test. In practical terms the loading effect of this instrument in most circuits is of no consequence and may be disregarded.

Most electronic voltmeters do present some finite resistance to the circuit being tested. It is usually quite high, ranging from 11 MΩ on all ranges for the most popular and least expensive meters up to several hundred megohms for some of the better quality meters. Since the input resistance of these instruments usually does not change when the range switch position is changed, the concept of sensitivity rated in Ω/V does not apply to them. In practice the actual Ω/V sensitivity of these instruments is highest on the low voltage ranges, and on the high voltage ranges may actually be less than for a comparable electromechanical voltmeter without amplification. Where voltage measurements are to be made on high-voltage, high-resistance circuits, the loading effect may well be less with the electromechanical voltmeter.

AC MEASUREMENTS.   Where electronic voltmeters are used to make ac measurements, the necessary rectification of the voltage being measured can be done *after* amplification. This means that the inherent loss of power in the signal being measured due to the loss of each alternate half-cycle in rectification is of no consequence, since the power loss can be made up for with more amplification.

With electromechanical movements all the power to deflect the pointer had to come from the signal. The pointer deflection of such a movement when the signal had been rectified was proportional to the average power during one half-cycle, not the rms value, though the instrument might be calibrated in rms values.

In electronic voltmeters the voltage being measured is used only to control the current which will deflect the pointer. These instruments usually respond to the *peak* value of the half-cycle of the ac being measured, not the average value nor the rms value.

In both instruments—the electromechanical movement that responds to average values, and the electronic instrument that responds to peak values—the rms calibrations are meaningful only when the waveform of the voltage being measured is sinusoidal.

Consider the confusion that would result from reading the rms scale when making voltage measurements on the waveforms shown in Figure 11-6, using both types of instrument.

In Figure 11-6(a) the waveform shown is a series of narrow voltage spikes, both positive and negative, of equal amplitude. The spikes are of short duration, compared to the repetition rate of the waveform, and during most of the time the voltage is zero. Such a waveform applied to a resistor will do little to heat it, since there will be no current flow through the resistor during all the time the voltage is zero. Figure 11-6(b) shows a waveform in which the peak value is the same as in Figure 11-6(a). In this, however, the voltage remains at the peak level during nearly the entire time, either positive or negative. If this voltage were applied to a resistor, peak current would flow nearly all the time, and the resistor would get much hotter than in the previous example, using the spike waveform with the same peak amplitude.

If both voltages were measured with an electronic voltmeter that responded to the peak value, the reading for each waveform would be the same, since they have the same peak value. If, however, the scale on which they were read was calibrated in rms values, the reading obtained in each case would be 70.7 V, since that is the rms value of a sinusoidal waveform with a peak value of 100 V.

Now suppose the first waveform, the narrow positive and negative spikes, were to be read on an electromechanical meter, which with its rectifier responded to the average value of the current. If the actual average were assumed to be 10 V—and it might well be considerably lower if the spikes were narrow enough—the needle would swing upscale to a point corresponding to an average voltage of 10 V. If the instrument were calibrated in rms values, this would correspond to a scale calibration of approximately 11.1 V. Since the average voltage is 0.637 times peak, and rms is 0.707 times peak for sinusoidal waveforms, the ratio between

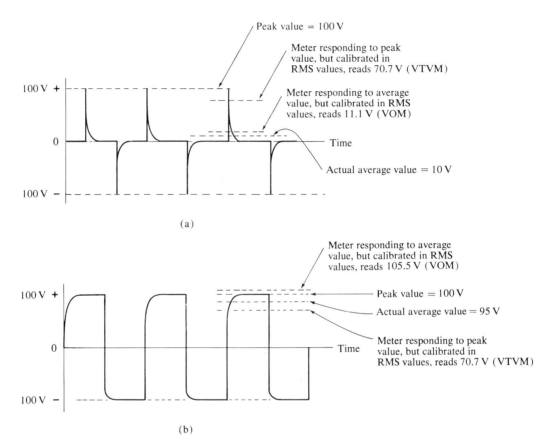

Figure 11-6 In either of the situations graphed above, the RMS scale of a VOM or a VTVM will not give a meaningful reading.

average voltage and rms voltage is approximately 1.11, yielding the 11.1 V reading if the average voltage is 10 V.

But there is a considerable disagreement between the reading of 70.7 V rms taken with the electronic voltmeter and the reading of 11.1 V rms taken with the electromechanical movement. Neither is giving us a true or meaningful value according to the scale calibrations, but neither instrument is wrong, either. If we are aware that the electronic voltmeter is responding to peak values of the voltage being measured, then we can either multiply the reading of 70.7 by 1.414 to convert it to peak voltage and find the true value of 100 V, or we can use the appropriate scale on the instrument, if it has one. If we are aware also that the electromechanical meter is responding to the average value of the voltage, we can divide the rms reading of 11.1 V by 1.11, the ratio between rms and average, and find that the average value of this voltage is 10 V. Unfortunately, this last fact is seldom what we want to know. Usually, knowledge of the peak value is much more important.

If we were to make similar measurements on the voltage waveform of Figure 11-6(b), the results would be the opposite. Again, the electronic voltmeter would respond to the peak voltage of the waveform, and on the rms calibrated voltage scale, the pointer would deflect to point to 70.7 V, the rms value of a sinusoidal voltage waveform with a peak value of 100 V. But this is not a sinusoidal voltage waveform.

The electromechanical movement would respond to the average value of one half-cycle. Since, for this nearly rectangular waveform, the average value of the half-cycle voltage is very nearly equal to that of the peak voltage, the reading would be quite high. If the average value was equal to 95 V, then the pointer would deflect to read 105.5 V, approximately. This is because the rms value of a sinusoidal waveform with an average value of 95 V would be 105.5 V. The peak value of a sinusoidal waveform with an average value of 95 V would be about 149 V, but the peak value of this voltage waveform is 100 V. This is not a sinusoidal voltage waveform.

Usually, with a nonsinusoidal waveform, the peak or p–p voltage is much more important than the average value. Therefore, electronic volt-meters are the most suitable type of metered instrument to use.

Electronic voltmeters require care and attention if they are to give consistently accurate results. If the major electronic components are vacuum tubes, they must be allowed to warm up before dependable readings may be made. If the pointer reading is not adjusted to zero with no voltage applied, the measurements taken will be incorrect. Electronic test instruments in general are more likely to require calibration at regular intervals than are simpler electromechanical meters. They are also more expensive, but their extra sensitivity, and the reduction of circuit loading, as well as the fact that most respond to the peak value of the voltage waveform being measured, make them essential tools.

GRAPHICAL SIGNAL PRESENTATION.   We could draw our own graph of any waveform, sinusoidal or nonsinusoidal, by taking measurements of the exact value of the voltage at appropriate time intervals and plotting the results on a graph. If the vertical axis of the graph is divided into voltage readings with zero in the middle, positive above zero, and negative below, and the horizontal axis is divided into units of time, then the resulting graph will be like the ones we have been using.

11-3
The Oscilloscope

But we would encounter problems in making the necessary measurements. For one thing, the voltages we would be trying to measure vary quite rapidly. If the voltage waveform is at a frequency of 60 Hz, then one complete cycle time is only 1/60 sec, and the problem of identifying the correct instant at which to make a measurement and then trying to make it would be impossible with any ordinary meter, or even an electronic voltmeter. The meter pointer cannot respond with the necessary speed. Even if it could, our eyes could not read the result.

The *oscilloscope* is a device which can draw such a graph for us quickly and accurately.

Inside the oscilloscope an electron beam passes between two sets of plates, then strikes the inside of the faceplate. The inside of the faceplate is coated with a phosphor that glows when struck by electrons. The point of light thus created is visible to the operator.

The two sets of plates between which the electron beam passes control its motion. One set of plates, called the *vertical deflection plates,* controls the motion up or down of the electron beam. Varying voltages applied to this plate can cause the electron beam to strike the top or bottom of the phosphor-coated screen, or anywhere in between. The other set of plates, called the *horizontal deflection plates,* controls the motion of the electron beam to the right or left. Varying voltages applied to this plate can cause the electron beam to strike the right or left side of the phosphor-coated screen, or anywhere in between. If appropriate voltages are applied to each set of plates, the endpoint of the electron beam can appear anywhere on the face of the tube containing it, called the *cathode ray tube* (CRT). See Figure 11-7.

If we apply a voltage waveform called a *sawtooth wave* to the horizontal deflection plates, the electron beam sweeps across the screen from left to right at a constant rate, then quickly flies back to the left side of the screen, only to repeat the motion. We can make this motion as slow or as rapid as we like, within quite wide limits.

If the beam sweeps across the face of the screen slowly enough, we can see the motion as a tiny point of light. If the motion is sufficiently rapid, we no longer see a point of light. Instead, a combination of persistence of vision and the fact that the phosphor continues to glow for a fraction of a second after being struck by electrons causes us to see a continuous line of light, as though it were drawn across the face of the tube.

Suppose we apply a 60 Hz sinusoidal voltage waveform to the vertical deflection plates while at the same time applying a sawtooth waveform with a rate of 60 repetitions per second to the horizontal deflection plates.

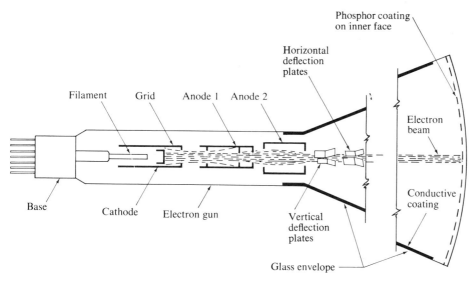

Figure 11-7 A cathode ray tube (CRT). Supporting structures and internal connections are not shown.

If the beam starts its travel at the left side of the face of the tube just as a single cycle of the 60 Hz signal impressed on the vertical deflection plates starts, and reaches the end of its travel at the right side of the face of the tube just at the end of a single cycle of the voltage impressed on the vertical deflection plates, the beam will trace out exactly the same sinusoidal pattern we have previously and laboriously graphed.

If this occurs in 1/60 second, and does not occur again, we would see it only as a single and unrecognizable flash of light. If, however, the beam is caused to return to the left side of the screen and, during the next 1/60 sec, again move at an even rate to the right side of the screen, while the sinusoidal voltage continues to be impressed on the vertical deflection plates, again the same path will be traced out by the electron beam. If this pattern is continued, and if each cycle of the waveform presented to the vertical deflection plates is similarly displayed, the eye will blend all the separate images into a single whole, and the appearance will be that of a single continuous graph of the sinusoidal voltage.

This can occur whenever the waveform being presented to the vertical deflection plates is one that continuously repeats a pattern. It need not be sinusoidal, but can be any waveform, so long as it repeats the same pattern long enough for it to be recognized.

If the pattern is to be displayed on the face of the oscilloscope as a single stationary pattern, it is necessary that the trace start at the same point in each repetition of the waveform, and end at the same point. The repetition rate of the sawtooth waveform that drives the beam from left to right across the face of the tube must be matched exactly to the repetition rate of the waveform to be viewed. It need not have a duration exactly equal to the length of one repetition of the waveform; it may be any whole number of waves. For example, the sweep rate to view the 60 Hz power line waveform may be adjusted to 1/30 sec to view two complete cycles of the waveform, or 1/20 sec to view three complete cycles, and so on.

The horizontal sweep voltage that determines the horizontal axis of the graph being drawn by the oscilloscope must sweep at a constant rate if the waveform is to be presented without distortion. On the graphs that we drew the horizontal axis was calibrated either in degrees or in time units. We found the two were interchangeable since the position of the phasor whose angle was represented in degrees was a constant function of time, and if the angle was known, the time was determined, and vice versa. Since the horizontal sweep voltage is equivalent to the horizontal axis of our graph, it is known as the *time base*.

For some special purposes the voltage to be viewed may be applied directly to the vertical deflection plates. This is not usually the case, since with this method only a narrow range of voltages will produce deflection within the limits of the tube, and the small voltages likely to be of the most interest could not be seen at all, since the deflection of the beam they would produce would be too slight.

Nearly all oscilloscopes have some means for accurately amplifying the signal to be presented to the vertical deflection plates. With this and some means of easily adjusting the repetition rate of the horizontal sweep voltage, the oscilloscope can draw graphs of waveforms accurately over a wide range of amplitudes and frequencies.

COMMERCIAL OSCILLOSCOPES.   Except for a few special-purpose instruments, all commercial oscilloscopes perform much the same functions in much the same way. Differences are in such details as control nomenclature, range of frequency of operation, precision of adjustment and calibration, and stability of operation. Precision and stability are of the utmost importance, and while they add to the cost of the instrument, they add more to its usefulness.

The controls of nearly all oscilloscopes can be grouped into four categories. They are static beam controls, vertical input controls, horizontal input controls, and sweep controls (Figure 11-8).

The *static beam controls* are those which control the resting position of the electron beam, its intensity, and its focus. The resting position

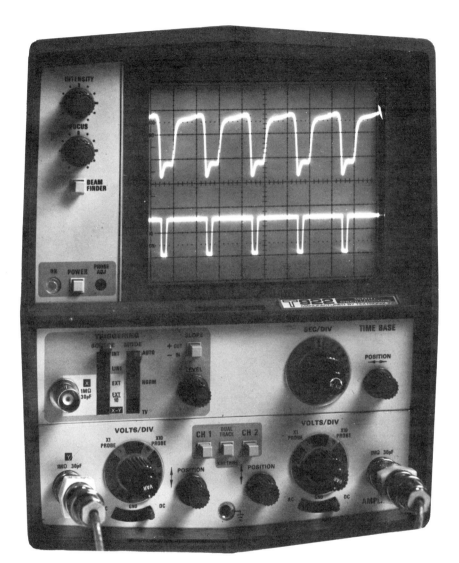

Figure 11-8   This dual trace oscilloscope is the latest example of the kind of oscilloscope usually found in college laboratories. It can accept two separate input signals and display them simultaneously. It is thus easy to compare the input and output signals from a circuit under investigation. The input impedance is relatively low, but with special probes that come with the instrument, it is comparable to an electronic multimeter. It has both calibrated sweep and calibrated vertical deflection amplifiers. The sweep rate can be as low as 0.5 sec/div or as high as 20 nsec/div. The vertical sensitivity for both inputs ranges from 2 mV/div to 10 V/div. When the special probes are used, the sensitivity is decreased by a factor of 10, and the vertical sensitivity becomes 20 mV/div to 100 V/div. Since the screen is eight divisions high, signal voltages up to 800 V p-p can be observed. Frequencies from dc to 15 MHz are observable with this instrument. The claimed accuracy is 3%. (All rights reserved by Tektronix Inc.)

of the electron beam is controlled by a vertical position control and a horizontal position control. They may be used to position the beam anywhere on the face of the CRT or beyond it. If the intensity is turned up, and no beam is visible, the chances are that the position controls need to be adjusted to bring the beam back onto the faceplate of the CRT. The intensity controls the brightness of the display. It should be adjusted for comfortable viewing, but if the other controls are adjusted so that the electron beam is not sweeping across the face of the CRT, the intensity should be turned down. The electron beam can damage the phosphor on the inside of the faceplate if it is left in one place with the intensity too high for very long.

The *vertical input controls* function in much the same way as the volume control on a radio. They determine the height of the display for a given voltage of the signal to be displayed. They are usually calibrated controls, marked in volts/cm. If the display of a waveform on the face of the CRT is observed to be 3 cm high when the vertical input V/cm switch is in the 0.5 V/cm position, then the p–p voltage of the signal being displayed is $3 \times 0.5 = 1.5$ V.

The *horizontal input controls* may be used to feed in to the horizontal deflection plates a signal to be displayed. While it is highly desirable that an oscilloscope be able to do this, the function is not often used. Most frequently, the oscilloscope is operated with the horizontal input controls switched into the position that feeds the internally generated sweep sawtooth voltage into the horizontal deflection plates, and disconnects the horizontal input jack from the internal circuitry of the oscilloscope.

The *sweep controls* are used to control the repetition rate of the sawtooth voltage which provides the time base for the graph to be drawn by the oscilloscope. It also provides for keeping the sweep voltage precisely and automatically in step with the frequency of the signal presented to the vertical input terminals, which, of course, is the signal to be displayed. This is called *synchronization,* and on some oscilloscopes is performed automatically, while on others it calls for manual adjustments.

No two manufacturers use the same control layout, though usually the static beam controls are grouped near the face of the CRT, while the vertical input and its associated controls are in the lower left corner of the front panel of the oscilloscope. For specific nomenclature of controls, and proper operation of them, the operating manual of the particular model of oscilloscope being used should be consulted.

VOLTAGE MEASUREMENTS.   All voltage measurements with oscilloscopes are p–p measurements, for the very simple reason that the positive and negative peaks of the signal are the only reference points for measurement that can be accurately located on the display. There is no magic line across the graph of a waveform as drawn by an oscilloscope to indicate the rms level or the average value of the signal.

There are two general methods of measuring the peak–peak value of voltages with oscilloscopes. With less expensive oscilloscopes an unknown voltage is measured by comparison with a known voltage. With more expensive oscilloscopes the settings of the controls determine directly and accurately the sensitivity of the instrument, usually in V/cm of vertical deflection of the signal as seen on the faceplate. With either method a transparent plastic screen with ruled or engraved lines on it, called a *graticule,* provides the scale on which measurements are made.

For oscilloscopes using the comparison method of measurement a source of calibrating voltage is usually provided. This may be simply a signal voltage of known amplitude brought out to a front panel jack where it may be connected to the vertical input, or it may be a wide range of switch-selected voltages to be used for comparison with an unknown voltage.

In the simplest method a known voltage, usually 1 V p–p, is brought out to a front panel terminal. The vertical input probe is touched to the test voltage terminal, and the resulting deflection of the CRT beam is noted. Assume the controls of the vertical input section are adjusted so that the p–p height of the known 1 V test signal is 1 inch. If the adjustment of the controls is unchanged, an unknown voltage that produces a vertical deflection of 2 in. must be 2 V p–p, while a signal producing a vertical deflection of $\frac{1}{2}$ in. would be $\frac{1}{2}$ V p–p.

There are usually two controls for adjusting the sensitivity of the amplifier between the vertical signal input and the vertical deflection plates. One is a continuous adjustment that is usually not calibrated, even on the more expensive oscilloscopes. It has various names on different models by different manufacturers. We will call it the *vertical vernier adjustment.* Whatever its name, it is a continuous gain adjustment for the vertical amplifier.

The other control is a switch which controls the sensitivity of the amplifier in multiples of ten. It is called an *attenuator switch* and usually has a minimum of three positions for this *decade switching.* They are most often labeled × 1, × 10, and × 100. The × 1 position is the most sensitive. If a given signal at the vertical input terminals produces a deflection of 4 in. with the attenuator switch in the × 1 position, the display height will be $\frac{4}{10}$ in. high with the attenuator switch in the × 10 position; and in the × 100 position the display will be hardly visible, being only $\frac{4}{100}$ in. high.

If a 1 V p–p signal at the vertical input terminals produces a deflection of 4 in. with the attenuator switch in the × 1 position, a signal that produces the same 4 in. of deflection with the attenuator switch in the × 10 position must be ten times as great, or 10 V p–p. If the attenuator is switched to the × 100 position, without change in the setting of the vertical vernier adjustment, the same four inches of deflection would indicate a voltage of 100 V p–p at the vertical input terminals.

If the original setting of the vernier adjustment had been to produce a deflection of $\frac{1}{2}$ in. with the 1 V p–p calibration voltage on the × 1 setting of the attenuator, then a deflection of 4 in. at the same attenuator setting would indicate an 8 V p–p signal at the vertical input terminals. If the 4 in. deflection was obtained at the × 10 position of the attenuator, the signal at the vertical input must be 80 V p–p; and if the attenuator was in the × 100 setting for this same reading, the corresponding signal at the vertical input must have been 800 V p–p.

We can go the other way just as well. Suppose we set the deflection on the screen for 4 inches, using the same 1 V p–p calibration voltage, and with the attenuator in the × 10 position, assuming the vertical amplifier has sufficient gain to permit this. Then a deflection of 1 in. at the same setting of the attenuator would indicate a voltage of 0.25 V p–p at the vertical input terminals, while this same reading at an attenuator setting of × 1 would indicate an input signal of 0.025 V p–p.

With this system even a simple and inexpensive oscilloscope can read a wide range of voltages easily. With a little practice the method, though it often seems confusing at first, becomes very simple to use.

There are several limitations to the accuracy with which an oscilloscope can be used to read voltages, however. First, the accuracy of this system is limited to the accuracy with which the calibration voltage is known. It will usually have an inherent error of somewhere between 1% and 5%, depending on the circuitry used inside the oscilloscope to generate it. Then there is a limit to the accuracy with which the oscilloscope can be adjusted to a given deflection with that calibration voltage. Since the line on the face of the CRT produced by the electron beam has a finite width, and is seldom quite as sharply defined as we would like, it is difficult to achieve a setting accuracy of more than about 2%. If the position of the attenuator switch must be changed between the calibration setting and the observation of the waveform under test, any errors in the switching ratio will affect the reading obtained. Since there are many factors involved in this switching ratio, accuracy of decade switching is probably not greater than 2% in most cases, and may be considerably less. Just as there is a setting error in setting the height of the display of the calibration voltage, so there can be expected to be a reading error of the final signal to be measured. Usually, the same person will make both the calibration setting and the final reading, and make the same minor errors of judgment in reading both. The errors thus made tend to cancel since the person who tends to set the calibration voltage a little above the line will tend to read the final signal for a little less than it is. The cumulative effect of these errors means that we can expect errors of 5%, and in some cases even more, in measuring the p–p value of voltages with the oscilloscope.

Another, and potentially even more serious, source of error is in the difference in frequency between the calibration signal and the signal whose voltage is to be read. The vertical amplifier in the oscilloscope will not respond in the same way to all frequencies, though the amount of error introduced is in inverse proportion to the cost of the instrument. A good oscilloscope may provide the same amplification within a few percent to signals ranging from dc to 5 MHz or more, while a poor oscilloscope may vary by as much as 50% at frequencies no lower than 20 Hz and no higher than 300 kHz. If accuracy of reading signal voltages is desired, then the frequency of the signal to be read must be within the frequency range of the particular oscilloscope being used. If it is not, compensation can be made, but the results are not likely to be very precise.

Better quality oscilloscopes usually have direct voltage calibrations on the attenuator switch. They will be marked on the switch, usually in terms of V/cm of vertical deflection. There may be a large number of such settings, so that a wide range of voltages may be read. The calibrations are meaningful only for a single position of the vertical vernier adjustment. This position will be indicated, usually by a neon lamp which glows when the vernier adjustment is *not* in the position for which the calibrations are accurate.

This is the simplest adjustment to use. The operator need only note the number of V/cm corresponding to the position of the attenuator switch, which will be marked on the front panel of the oscilloscope. Then the number of V/cm is multiplied by the number of centimeters of height of the display, and the result is the voltage p–p of the waveform being displayed.

Most of the causes for error already mentioned still apply. In addition, calibration errors in the oscilloscope itself since the last time the necessary internal adjustments were made may be involved. The usual system is to have only a single internal adjustment for all scales, with frequency compensation settings for each position of the attenuator switch. It is seldom that the frequency compensation settings are off, but it is fairly often that the single internal gain adjustment is off. If it is, then all the voltage readings, on any position of the attenuator switch, will be off by the same amount and in the same direction. This is of no consequence if the readings are only for comparison with each other, but is of considerable consequence if they are to be compared to some set standard.

Usually, an oscilloscope equipped with a calibrated attenuator switch will have available on the front panel of the instrument one or more sources of calibration voltage which can be used to check the accuracy of the attenuator switch settings. If this is used, or if the readings are checked with an accurate peak-reading voltmeter, then the results can be dependable, and accuracy sufficient for most purposes can be obtained.

One obvious superiority of the oscilloscope over any other test instrument is the fact that the actual shape of the waveform is visible. If there is any departure of the waveform from the desired—any distortion—it can be seen, and from the nature of the distortion its cause can often be deduced. The problems of the disparity between the readings of the electronic voltmeter and the electromechanical movement when reading nonsinusoidal voltage waveforms could quickly be resolved.

The loading effect of most oscilloscopes is greater than for electronic voltmeters. Most oscilloscopes are the equivalent of approximately 2 MΩ to the circuit to which they are connected, though with the use of special probes rather than a direct connection the loading effect can usually be reduced to insignificance.

FREQUENCY AND PERIOD MEASUREMENTS. If the oscilloscope has a calibrated time base, the period for a single repetition of a waveform can usually be read to a moderate degree of accuracy. Errors of approximately 2% to 10% may be expected, depending on the skill of the operator and the accuracy with which the instrument attains its indicated calibration.

The horizontal axis is, of course, the calibrated time base. The positions of the sweep control switch are calibrated in terms of time per centimeter of horizontal measurement along the axis. If the sweep control switch is set in a position marked 0.1 msec/cm, and the signal is observed to have a length measured along the horizontal axis of 2.5 cm between corresponding points on adjacent cycles, then the time per cycle is

$$\text{cm} \times \frac{\text{sec}}{\text{cm}} = \text{sec}$$

$$2.5 \times 0.0001 = 0.00025 \text{ sec}$$

The frequency is the reciprocal of the period T.

$$f = \frac{1}{T} = \frac{1}{0.00025} = \frac{1}{0.25 \times 10^{-3}} = 4 \times 10^3 = 4000 \text{ Hz}$$

If the time base is not calibrated, or if there are questions about the validity of the calibrations, external sources may be used to provide markers which take the place of calibrations in the instrument itself. The appearance of the markers on the faceplate depends on the type of marker generator used, and on how it is used. Often the markers will be short spikes sticking up from the signal itself, or they may be either bright or dark spots at equal intervals along the base line.

A far more accurate method, which can be used with any oscilloscope having provisions for both vertical and horizontal inputs, is the comparison method where a signal of unknown frequency is compared directly to a signal of known frequency. Particular patterns showing simple integral frequency ratios are used. They are known as *Lissajous patterns*.

The signal whose frequency is to be determined is usually fed into the vertical amplifier input, and the signal with which it is to be compared is fed into the horizontal input. The electron beam in the CRT will be influenced by both signals simultaneously. The internal sweep circuitry is not in operation as this is done, since switching the horizontal input selector to receive the external signal from the known frequency signal source disables the sweep, and leaves only the signal presented to the horizontal input to influence the voltage on the horizontal deflection plates.

Let us suppose the two signals are at exactly the same frequency and also exactly in step with each other. Then, when the signal at the vertical input is zero at the start of a cycle, the signal at the horizontal input is also zero at the start of a cycle. With both inputs having an instantaneous value of zero, there will be no deflecting voltage on the deflection plates, and the spot will be at that instant in the center of the screen. As the signals both start to increase in the positive direction with the start of the cycle, the spot will be moved upward by the vertical input signal, and simultaneously moved to the right by an exactly equal amount by the horizontal input signal. The result is motion in a straight line, from the center of the screen upward and to the right. When both inputs have simultaneously reached the peak of the cycle at the 90° point, the spot will have been deflected up at an angle of 45° (assuming both signals have equal amplitude) and in a straight line from the resting point.

As the voltages of both signals drop toward zero, in the 90° to 180° quarter of their cycle, the spot will move back along the same path to the starting point.

During the second half-cycle, the action is the same as during the first, but with the polarities reversed. Instead of moving up and to the right, the spot will move down and to the left. During the course of a full cycle, the electron beam will trace out a diagonal line on the screen of the CRT. If the deflections caused by the two signals are equal, then the line will make an angle of 45° with the horizontal axis. Figure 11-9 plots this in detail. Corresponding points are identified by numbers on each of the two waveforms, the signal at the vertical input, shown at the left, and the signal at the horizontal input, shown below. The two waveforms are plotted on the same time base.

When the voltage presented at the vertical input is at the point marked 1 on the vertical input waveform, the voltage at the horizontal input is also at the point marked 1 on the plot of its graph. If we extend a horizontal line from the point marked 1 on the vertical input waveform graph, and a vertical line from the corresponding point 1 on the horizontal input

Figure 11-9   Tracing of sinusoidal input signals on a CRT screen.

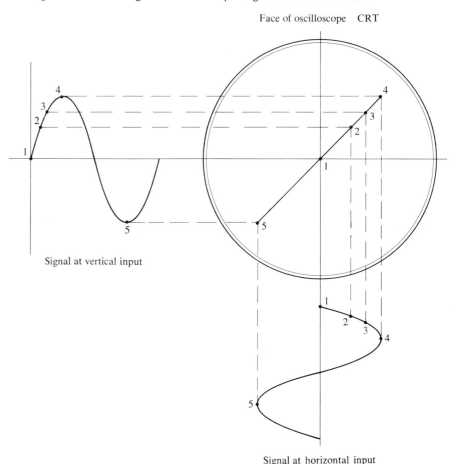

waveform, then the intersection of the two lines locates the position of the spot of light on the face of the CRT at that instant. Similarly, by means of this kind of geometric projection the position of the spot of light at the instant identified by the number 2 on the drawings of the two waveforms can be found. Since at that instant the point marked 2 on the vertical input waveform is above the base line, and the point marked 2 on the horizontal input waveform is to the right of the base line, the spot will have moved both up and to the right, to the position marked 2 on the plot of the position of the spot on the face of the CRT.

This same geometric projection can be continued for any number of points along the base line, so long as corresponding points are taken on both vertical and horizontal input waveforms, and the complete projection will be a diagonal line.

If the two waveforms are not in step, but are out of step by 90° or 270°, the geometric projection as shown in Figure 11-10 demonstrates that the result of the combined motions on the spot on the face of the CRT is to cause it to trace out a circle. If the two waveforms are 180° out of phase with each other, then the result of the combined motions on the spot is to cause it to trace out a diagonal line similar to the first example, but slanting in the opposite direction.

If the two signals are nearly but not exactly the same frequency, they will at some times be in the same relative phase, and at other times not. The result will be that the figure on the face of the CRT will assume the configurations shown, together with all possible intermediate stages. If we start at the instant the figure is a diagonal line slanting to the right, we see it change to a narrow ellipse, and the ellipse gradually broaden into a circle. The circle then narrows through elliptical shapes of decreasing width, then becomes again for an instant a single line before it again opens to an ellipse to retrace the pattern of shapes just seen. Watching the changing pattern, one gets the illusion of seeing a rotating figure of a circle, seen sometimes at right angles to its plane, and sometimes edge on.

By adjusting the frequency of one of the two signals so that they are identical, the figure will appear to stop rotating. It may stop in any position, but whatever position the pattern attains when it is stopped, the two frequencies are identical. The result is a one-to-one Lissajous pattern, and when that pattern is observed, it may be taken as proof that the two frequencies are the same.

Even though the figure may not be absolutely still, but appear to be rotating at some slow rate, the frequencies may still be compared. The time required for the pattern to go through its complete change of appearance from a diagonal line slanting upward to the right, through the

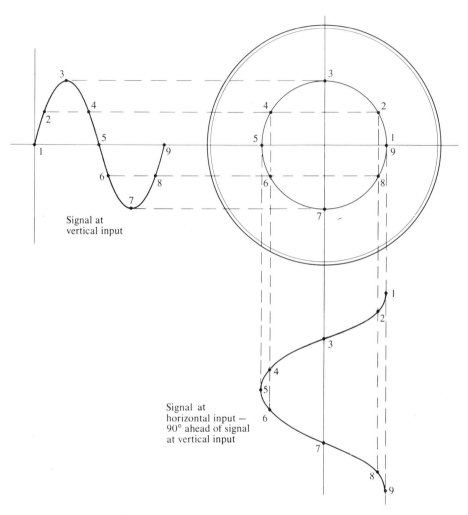

Figure 11-10   Tracing of out-of-phase sinusoidal signals on a CRT screen.

ellipses and circle, to a slanting line downward to the right, and back
again to the original pattern, indicates the time required for one complete
change of phase between the unknown frequency and the reference. If the
complete change of phase takes five seconds, then the frequency difference
between the two signals is 1/5 Hz. For most purposes, this is more
accuracy than would be required, though much greater accuracy is easily
obtained. Note that the accuracy of this method does not depend on any
accuracy of calibration of the oscilloscope. All that the oscilloscope is
required to do is present the display. All the accuracy is dependent on the
precision with which the frequency standard is known.

We are not limited to a one-to-one Lissajous pattern for frequency comparison. Two-to-one or one-to-two patterns are easily used, as are 3 to 2, 3 to 1, 4 to 3, and so on. The only limit is the practical difficulty of recognizing the pattern. See Figure 11-11.

If we imagine the pattern, assumed to be nearly stationary, is enclosed in a rectangle, the sides of which just touch the pattern, it is usually easy to count the number of points at which one vertical side of the rectangle touches the pattern and the points at which one horizontal side of the rectangle is in contact with the pattern, as in Figure 11-12. The ratio between horizontal and vertical points of tangency is the same as the ratio between vertical and horizontal frequencies.

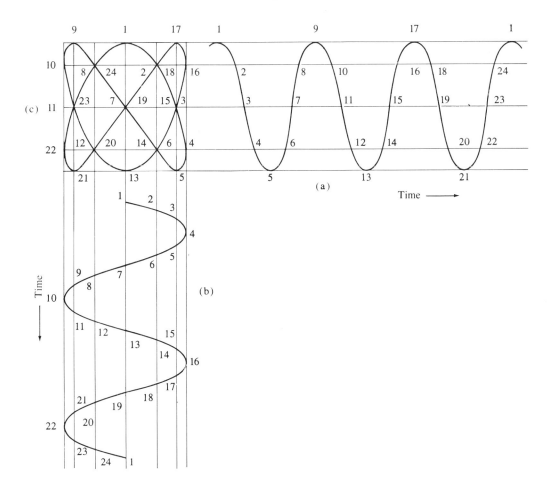

Figure 11-11 A 3-to-2 Lissajous pattern. (a) Signal on vertical deflection plates. (b) Signal on horizontal deflection plates. (c) Lissajous figure.

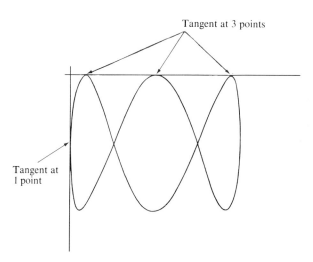

Figure 11-12   This Lissajous figure has one horizontal point of tangency and three vertical points of tangency with its imaginary rectangular "frame." Thus, for this figure vertical frequency is three times horizontal frequency.

$$\frac{f_v}{f_h} = \frac{\tan_h}{\tan_v}$$

where f_v is the frequency of the signal being fed into the vertical input, f_h is the frequency of the signal being fed into the horizontal input, $\tan_h$ is the number of points at which the figure is tangent to an imaginary horizontal line just touching the top or bottom of the figure, and $\tan_v$ is the number of points at which the figure is tangent to an imaginary vertical line just touching either side of the figure.

It should be noted that this is an inverse relationship. If there are more points of horizontal than vertical tangency, then the vertical frequency is the greater of the two. This method is far preferable to attempting to remember a multitude of Lissajous patterns, any of which may be encountered in an infinite variety of positions.

Phase measurements may also be made with an oscilloscope. There are two general methods by which this may be done. One is to display a 1–1 Lissajous pattern of the reference phase and the signal to which it is to be compared. This can be any figure from a diagonal line to a circle. If the two are in phase, the figure will be a line slanting diagonally upward to the right.

If the two are not in phase, the value of the phase angle between them may be calculated from a comparison between the amplitude of the figure and the height of the point where the figure crosses the vertical axis. It is important that the resting position of the beam be at the intersection of the vertical and horizontal axes before this measurement is made.

The measurement is shown in Figure 11-13. In this figure two distances are marked off. The distance A is where the figure crosses its own vertical centerline. If the figure is properly centered on its axes, this distance will be the *y*-intercept. The distance B is the distance from the centerline to the top of the figure. It is most conveniently measured along the *y*-axis. The phase angle between the signal and its reference phase is given by

$$\sin \theta = \frac{A}{B}$$

Figure 11-13 One method for making a phase measurement with an oscilloscope. This method does not tell the direction of phase shift, so if the nature of the circuit is unknown, the method cannot be used.

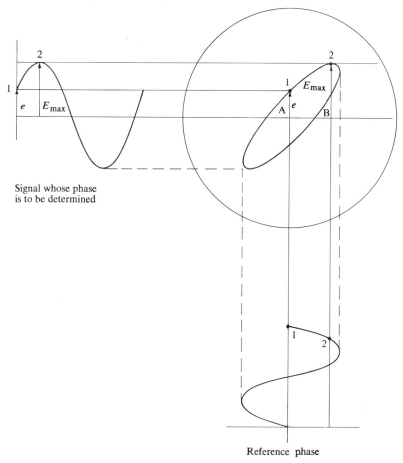

where θ is the phase angle. The geometry of this may be seen from the consideration that B is the maximum vertical displacement of the signal, and is therefore proportional to E_{max} for the signal being fed into the vertical input terminals of the oscilloscope. A is proportional to the instantaneous value of the vertical input signal at the instant the voltage from the reference phase signal being fed into the horizontal input is zero. But this instant is zero on the time base against which the phase is being measured. Since

$$e = E_{max} \sin \theta$$

then

$$\sin \theta = \frac{e}{E_{max}}$$

where θ is the phase angle when the instantaneous voltage is e. But this instant is when the reference phase is zero. And since the two distances A and B are proportional to e and E_{max}, respectively, the ratio A/B must be the sine of the phase angle. Note that the two distances A and B may be measured in any units; it is not necessary to calibrate the scope to read voltages, since the only thing of importance is the ratio between the voltages, not their value.

For this method to succeed, it is essential that any phase shift introduced into the signal between the vertical input terminals and the deflection plates of the oscilloscopes be exactly matched by the phase shift introduced into the reference signal between the horizontal input terminals and the horizontal deflection plates. This is not always the case, since many oscilloscopes do not have identical vertical and horizontal deflection amplifiers. Since the phase shift which may occur in an amplifier depends on the frequency of the signal it is amplifying, it is difficult to compensate for this. If the two amplifiers are identical, or if neither introduces any phase shift, then no compensation need be made and this method may be used with confidence. A simple means of checking is to feed the identical signal into both amplifiers by connecting it to vertical and horizontal input terminals simultaneously, and to observe the Lissajous pattern produced. It should be a diagonal line, slanting upward to the right. If it is not, then the amount by which it is not is an indication of the relative phase shift introduced into the two signals by the oscilloscope.

This method does not give the *direction* of the phase shift. If the nature of the circuit in which the signal has been shifted in phase compared to the reference is known, the direction of the expected phase shift may be already inferred. If the nature of the circuit is not known, then some other means must be used to determine the direction of phase shift.

The second method of determining phase shift with an oscilloscope gives both the direction and magnitude of the phase shift. It is a simple and direct method, but it is applicable to an oscilloscope with provision for external synchronization. Most commercial oscilloscopes have such provision.

In use, the external synchronization signal terminal on the oscilloscope is connected to a point in the circuit at which the phase reference signal exists, and the sync selector is switched to external. The signal must be present at that point with sufficient amplitude to successfully synchronize the trace on the scope to itself.

The vertical input terminals of the oscilloscope are connected to the same point. The trace on the oscilloscope is then adjusted for convenient viewing and centered vertically on the face of the CRT. The trace is then expanded so that a complete cycle occupies some known distance along the time base, and starts at some known division on the face of the CRT. For example, the trace may be so adjusted that a complete cycle of the reference phase waveform occupies a distance of 12 divisions measured horizontally along the face of the CRT. Each division then represents $360°/12$, or $30°$. A convenient reference point on the trace is then noted. Usually, it is most convenient to adjust the waveform being viewed so that the $180°$ point on it crosses the center of the screen (Figure 11-14).

Figure 11-14   Another method for measuring phase shift with an oscilloscope. Unlike the method pictured in Figure 11-13, this method tells direction as well as magnitude of the shift. This method can be used only on oscilloscopes with provision for external synchronization.

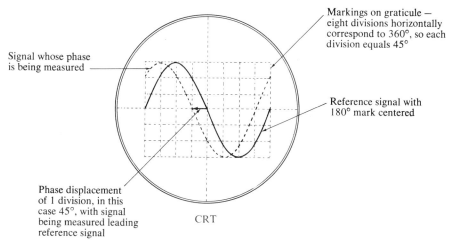

Signal whose phase is being measured

Markings on graticule — eight divisions horizontally correspond to 360°, so each division equals 45°

Reference signal with 180° mark centered

Phase displacement of 1 division, in this case 45°, with signal being measured leading reference signal

CRT

Now, with no change in any of the settings of the oscilloscope sweep, sync, or position controls, the test leads from the oscilloscope vertical input terminals are moved to the point on the circuit where the signal whose relative phase is to be determined exists. The oscilloscope external sync is still connected to the point in the circuit where the reference phase signal is, and the trace on the face of the CRT is still being started at an instant determined by that signal and, consequently, by the reference phase signal.

The signal whose phase is to be determined is now presented to view. If it is ahead of the reference phase signal, it will appear to the left of the position which had been occupied by the reference phase signal. If it is behind the reference signal, it will be to the right.

Again, a convenient point is the 180° division, where the electron beam presenting the waveform on the face of the CRT crosses the horizontal axis moving downward from left to right. The difference between this point and the point where the waveform of the reference phase crosses the axis is the phase angle, in whatever units the horizontal axis was calibrated. For example, suppose we had set the waveform of the reference phase to occupy 12 divisions, or 30° to a division. If the new waveform crosses the horizontal axis two divisions to the left of the original crossing for the reference, it leads that reference by 60°. If, on the other hand, it crossed 1.5 divisions to the right of the reference, it would be thus shown to lag by 45°.

This method is particularly applicable to *dual trace oscilloscopes,* where both the reference phase and the unknown phase can be seen simultaneously.

If accuracy is to be obtained with this method, it is essential that the trace be centered vertically, and that there be no vertical or horizontal drift in the position of the trace between the time the reference phase is set and the time the position of the unknown phase is determined. A simple way to ascertain if drift has occurred is to reconnect the scope to the original position where it was showing the reference phase after the position of the unknown phase has been noted, and see if the reference phase is still in exactly the same position on the face of the CRT as before. If it is not, the reading and the results calculated from it are probably not valid.

Phase shift within the oscilloscope vertical amplifier is not a factor, since such phase shift as may occur will be the same for both reference and unknown phases, and will have no effect on the difference in phase between them. A possible factor, however, is the effect of the oscilloscope itself, and the test probe with which it is connected to the circuit, on the phase shift at either the point where the reference phase was chosen or the point at which the unknown phase was measured. This is a form of circuit loading, affecting phase, not amplitude, and is usually not a factor. If the frequency of the signal being compared is fairly high, however, it may be a significant factor. Probes are available for most oscilloscopes, however, which will minimize any errors resulting from this cause.

Problems

1. On an oscilloscope screen a reference signal of 10 V p–p causes a vertical deflection of 2 in. with an attenuator setting of × 1. What is the p–p voltage of a test signal that causes a deflection of 3 in. when the attenuator is in the × 10 position?

2. A reference signal of 2 V p–p causes a deflection of 4 in. with the attenuator at × 100. What is the p–p voltage of a test signal that causes a 0.5 in. deflection at the × 1 position?

3. A reference signal of 10 V p–p causes a deflection of 2 in. at the attenuator × 1 position. If a test signal of 425 V p–p is to be measured, what will be the deflection on the screen with the attenuator at × 100?

4. A reference signal of 5 V p–p causes a deflection of 4 in. at the attenuator × 1 position. With the attenuator at × 100, what is the p–p voltage of a test signal which causes a deflection of 2.25 in.?

5. For each of the waveforms as shown on a calibrated oscilloscope screen, determine the frequency and period, given the sweep control switch position in each case: (a) 1 msec/cm, (b) 0.001 μsec/cm, (c) 0.01 sec/cm, and (d) 0.25 μsec/cm.

Waveforms for Problem 5.

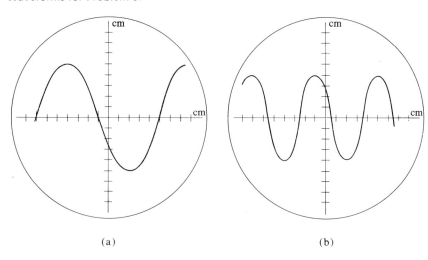

(a)   (b)

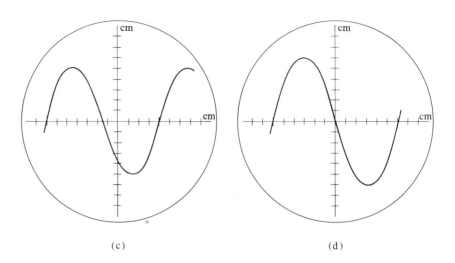

(c)   (d)

6. For each of the Lissajous figures illustrated, determine the frequency of the horizontal input signal f_h, given f_v, the frequency of the vertical input signal.

Lissajous figures for Problem 6.

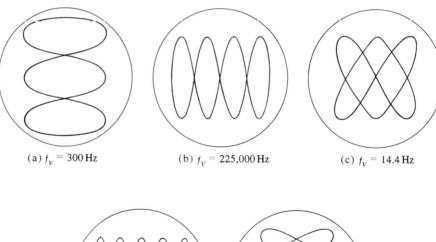

(a) $f_v = 300\,\text{Hz}$ (b) $f_v = 225{,}000\,\text{Hz}$ (c) $f_v = 14.4\,\text{Hz}$

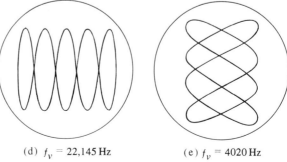

(d) $f_v = 22{,}145\,\text{Hz}$ (e) $f_v = 4020\,\text{Hz}$

7. Suppose the signal fed into the horizontal input of an oscilloscope has a frequency of 200 Hz, and the signal fed into the vertical input has a frequency of 500 Hz. Assuming that both signals are of equal amplitude, plot the resulting Lissajous figure by applying the method shown in Figures 11-9 and 11-10.

8. From each of the six Lissajous figures on an oscilloscope screen, determine the phase angle between the horizontal and the vertical input signals.

Lissajous figures for Problem 8.

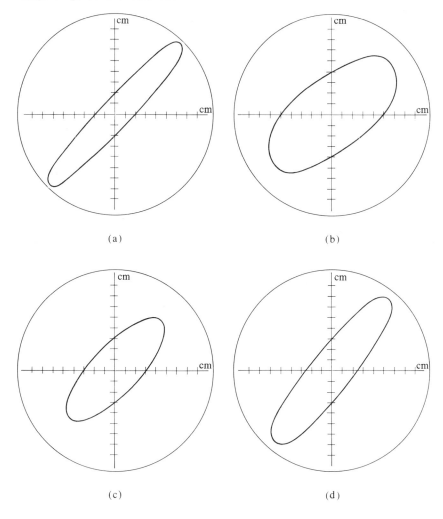

(a)

(b)

(c)

(d)

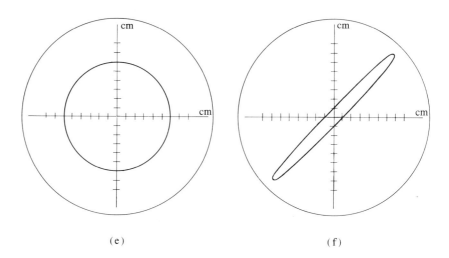

(e)   (f)

9. Each of the waveforms illustrated shows a reference signal (smooth line) and a test signal (broken line) on the face of an oscilloscope. Determine the magnitude and direction of the corresponding phase shift between the two signals in each case.

Waveforms for Problem 9.

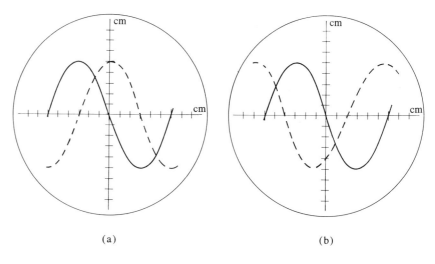

(a)   (b)

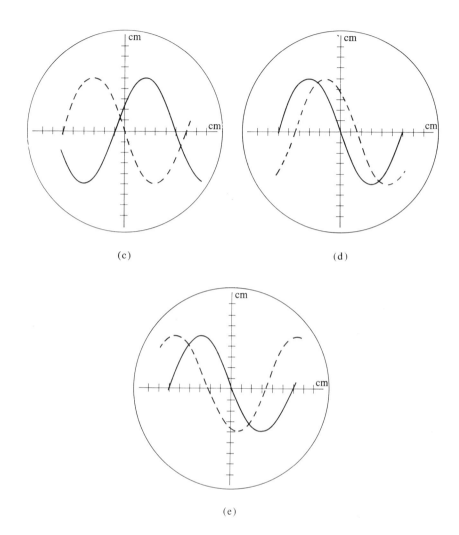

(c)　　　　　　　　　　　　　　　(d)

(e)

attenuator　the switch used to control the sensitivity of the vertical amplifier **Key Words**
　　of an oscilloscope, in multiples of ten
CRT (cathode ray tube)　the "picture" tube in an oscilloscope. Its phosphor-
　　coated face glows where the electron beam strikes it.
electrodynamometer movement　this movement is suitable for both ac and
　　dc measurements and is similar to the d'Arsonval movement except
　　that the current being measured produces the external field
electronic amplification　the use of a weak force to control a stronger force
graticule　a transparent plastic screen with ruled lines, on which oscilloscope
　　measurements are made

horizontal deflection plates   this two-plate set controls the left–right motion of the electron beam through a CRT

iron-vane movement   this movement is used in some meters and is suitable for direct ac measurements, but it has low sensitivity and, at high frequencies, considerable hysteresis losses

Lissajous patterns   patterns that show integral frequency ratios and that are used to make frequency measurements on an oscilloscope

oscilloscope   a device that can "draw" a quick, accurate graph by recording a moving dot of light on a phosphor-coated screen. Oscilloscopes allow us to make measurements that would be difficult or impossible with other instruments.

rectifier   a nonlinear circuit element that permits current to flow in one direction much more easily than in the other. Rectifiers are used in ac-reading meters to convert ac into pulsating dc.

static beam controls   oscilloscope controls that regulate the resting position, intensity, and focus of the electron beam

sweep controls   oscilloscope controls that govern the repetition rate of the sawtooth voltage that provides the time base for the graph drawn by the oscilloscope. These controls also keep the sweep voltage synchronized with the voltage that is to be displayed.

time base   the horizontal sweep voltage is called the time base because it is equivalent to the horizontal axis of the graph being drawn by the oscilloscope

vertical deflection plates   control the up–down motion of the electron beam through a CRT

vertical input controls   oscilloscope controls that determine the height of the display for a given voltage of the signal to be displayed

vertical vernier adjustment   the continuous gain adjustment for the vertical amplifier, usually used with the attenuator switch to regulate the signal fed to the vertical deflection plates and thus to determine the height of the display

VOM (volt-ohm-milliammeter)   a type of meter having both ac and dc functions and a variety of ranges. The function switch cuts the built-in rectifier out of the circuit for dc measurements and switches the rectifier into the circuit for ac measurements.

Summary of Concepts

1.   If a pulsating dc current is applied to a d'Arsonval meter movement, the flow of current in the coil will always be in the same direction.

2.   The net force acting to deflect the pointer in a meter is proportional to the average value of current (*not* to rms value).

3.   Rms values have no meaning for nonsinusoidal waveforms.

4.   The sensitivity of a rectifier-type meter in terms of amount of pointer deflection for energy being drawn from the circuit being tested is always less than for comparable dc measurements.

5.   The resistance of a rectifier is much greater for low potentials across it than for high.

6.   If a shunt resistor is placed across a VOM, the current through the shunt added to the current through the meter movement provides increased current through the rectifier.

7.   Both series and shunt resistors reduce VOM sensitivity in the ac ranges. The loading effect of such a meter is twice as great on ac functions as it will be for corresponding dc functions.

8.   Operation of an iron-vane movement depends on the fact that a piece of ferromagnetic material placed in a magnetic field will be magnetized with a polarity that results in an attractive force toward the magnetizing field.

9.   An iron-vane movement has less sensitivity than a comparable d'Arsonval movement.

10.   Hysteresis losses in an iron-vane movement are considerable at high frequencies.

11.   Thermocouple ammeters are based on the principle that a junction of dissimilar metals will, when heated, develop a potential between the metals.

12.   Any current—ac or dc—through a thermocouple produces heat, and the heat produces a dc current that may be read by a meter utilizing the standard d'Arsonval movement.

13.   The electrodynamometer movement is similar in principle to the d'Arsonval movement, except that in place of a permanent magnet to produce the field against which the field of the moving coil reacts, the external field is produced by the current to be measured.

14.   The scale markings of an electrodynamometer wattmeter are crowded at the low end. Thus, interaction of two weak fields produces only slight pointer deflection.

15.   Most electronic voltmeters present some finite resistance to the circuit being tested.

16. When electronic voltmeters are used to make ac measurements, the necessary rectification of the voltage being measured can be done *after* amplification.

17. For ac measurements, electronic voltmeters usually respond to the peak value of the half-cycle being measured, and *not* to the average or rms values.

18. If a single, stationary pattern is to be displayed on an oscilloscope, the trace must start and end at the same point in each repetition of the waveform.

19. All oscilloscope voltage measurements are p–p because only the positive and negative peaks of the waveform can be accurately located on the display.

20. One advantage the oscilloscope has over every other test instrument is that, with the oscilloscope, the actual shape of the waveform is visible.

To Help You Review   *On a separate sheet of paper, fill in the blanks or answer the questions below. The number following each question refers to the section in the chapter where the correct answer can be found.*

1. What is the role of the rectifier in an ac-reading meter? (11-1)

2. What is pulsating dc, and what is its effect on a d'Arsonval meter movement? (11-1)

3. The net force acting on a pointer through a moving coil is proportional to _____ . (11-1)

4. What happens to the current when a shunt resistor is placed across a VOM? (11-1)

5. What effect do series and shunt resistors have on the sensitivity of a VOM? (11-1)

6. Name three meter types that do not use the d'Arsonval movement. (11-1)

7. Iron-vane movements have serious limitations. What are they? (11-1)

8. What kind of meter movement is based on the principle that a junction of dissimilar metals will, when heated, develop a potential between the metals? (11-1)

9. What are two limitations of the thermocouple ammeter? (11-1)

10. The _____ movement is similar to the d'Arsonval movement, except that in place of the permanent magnet, the external field is produced by the current to be measured. (11-1)

11. Why are the scale markings of an electrodynamometer wattmeter crowded at the low end? (11-1)

12. What is electronic amplification? (11-2)

13. Indicate whether the voltmeter movement described in each statement below is electronic or electromechanical. (11-2)

(a) Power must be drawn from the circuit under test.

(b) Power from the circuit under test is used only to control pointer deflection.

(c) On high-voltage, high-resistance circuits, the loading effect may be less.

(d) When the signal has been rectified, pointer deflection is proportional to the average power during one half-cycle.

(e) The voltage being measured is used only to control the current that deflects the pointer.

(f) Instruments with this movement usually respond to the peak value of the half-cycle of the ac being measured.

(g) When measuring ac, the voltage can be rectified after amplification.

(h) More likely to require calibration at regular intervals.

14. How does an oscilloscope "draw a graph"? (11-3)

15. Define the following terms as they apply to the oscilloscope. (11-3)

(a) vertical deflection

(b) sawtooth wave

(c) cathode ray tube

(d) time base

(e) sweep controls

(f) vertical input controls

(g) graticule

(h) static beam controls

16. Complete this statement: In order to display a single stationary pattern on an oscilloscope, it is necessary that _____ . (11-3)

17. Why must all oscilloscope voltage measurements be peak-peak? (11-3)

18. What is the vertical vernier adjustment on an oscilloscope, and what is its function? (11-3)

TWELVE

CAPACITANCE AND CAPACITORS

This chapter will help you understand

- [ ] a simple capacitor
- [ ] dielectrics and the dielectric constant
- [ ] capacitive circuits in series and parallel
- [ ] *RC* circuits and time constants
- [ ] practical capacitors and their uses
- [ ] capacitor defects

12-1
Capacitance

CAPACITANCE DEFINED. With the advent of integrated circuits some of the old definitions need refining. It used to be satisfactory to define circuit elements in terms of their construction. With this sort of definition, we would say a capacitor was two conductors separated by a dielectric, where a dielectric is an insulating material, including a vacuum. This definition is true as far as it goes, but electronic technology has gone beyond it.

A more useful definition of a capacitor is in terms of how it acts. If we define a capacitor as we defined a resistor, in terms of the relationship between voltage and current in it as a two-terminal circuit element, then this definition is more useful, and it covers devices that function as capacitors regardless of how they are constructed.

A capacitor is any two-terminal circuit element in which the current is directly proportional to the rate of change of voltage between the terminals.

Mathematically this is

$$i_C = C\frac{dv}{dt}$$

where i_C is the instantaneous value of the current flow between the capacitor terminals, C is a proportionality factor called the capacitance, and dv/dt is the *rate of change* of the voltage in volts per second.

This is similar to our definition of resistance, in which we said a resistor was a two-terminal circuit element in which the current is directly proportional to the instantaneous *value* of the voltage. With this new circuit element, the only change is that the value of the voltage has no effect on the current. Only the *rate of change* of voltage is significant. But this, as we shall see, is a very significant difference.

Between the two terminals of this thing we call a capacitor, there can be very many different things, including some complex integrated circuits. Regardless of the mechanism by which the effect is produced, if a two-terminal circuit element fits our definition of a capacitor, then it will function as a capacitor in any circuit to which it is connected.

THE SIMPLE CAPACITOR. The least complex structure which acts as a capacitor, and still the most commonly encountered kind of capacitor, is illustrated in Figure 12-1. Two metal plates are shown, facing each other but not touching. They are connected to opposite terminals of a source of voltage.

That metal plate which is connected to the negative terminal of the source of voltage will have an excess of electrons, while the plate which is connected

Figure 12-1   A simple capacitor.

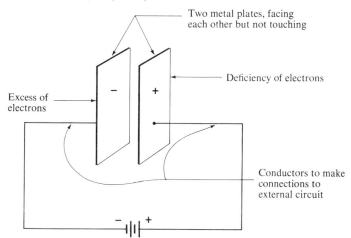

to the positive terminal will lose electrons, and end with a deficiency, which constitutes a positive charge.

Suppose only one plate were connected to the negative voltage source terminal. It would have an excess of electrons, since the voltage source would "inject" electrons into it until the mutual repulsion of the electrons in the plate was exerting as much force pushing the electrons back into the voltage source as the source was exerting in pushing electrons into the plate.

The number of electrons in excess that the plate could hold would depend on its size and on the force with which the voltage source was injecting electrons into it. Since the electrons exert such a strong repulsive force on each other, they are repelled away from the interior of the metal plate and tend to be concentrated at its surface. Its surface area, and not its volume, is thus the most significant aspect of its size. Thus, a plate of a given area, when connected to a negative voltage source terminal of a given voltage, will accumulate some excess negative charge. Once the charge is accumulated, there will be no further flow of electrons from the voltage source to the plate, and so long as the voltage of the source is maintained, there will be no flow of electrons from the plate back to the voltage source.

The charge thus accumulated by a single isolated plate is very small, and is usually not considered. But suppose we now bring near this charged plate another, which is connected to the positive terminal of the same voltage source. This new plate has, by the same process, lost electrons to the voltage source, and now has some net positive charge.

If the two plates are close to each other, electrons in the negatively charged plate will be attracted to the nearby presence of positive charge in the other plate. This will change the previous balance, in which the number of electrons the voltage source had been able to inject into the plate was determined by how hard the tightly packed electrons in the plate were pushing back against the voltage of the source. The effect of this mutual repulsion is counter-balanced by the effect of the attraction of the electrons to the nearby positive plate. Now a new balance will be achieved, with many more electrons in the negative plate than before.

The same thing will occur in the positive plate. It was positive because the attractive force of the positive terminal of the voltage source withdrew electrons from it. The number of electrons withdrawn was determined by the source voltage. When the force attracting electrons back to the positive plate equaled the force of the voltage source in removing electrons, a balance was achieved, and no more electrons would leave the positive plate. When the charged negative plate was brought near the positive plate, this previous balance was upset, and electrons in the positive plate now experienced both an attractive force toward the voltage source terminal and a repulsion from the negatively charged plate. The net effect of the mutual force between the plates, due to the electric field between them, is to considerably increase the quantity of charge that will be in excess in the negative plate and exist as a charge deficiency in the other plate.

Suppose the source is connected to the two plates at a time when they have no previous charge difference, and when they are near each other. At the instant the voltage source is connected, electrons will flow from the positive plate toward the positive terminal of the voltage source, and from the negative terminal of the voltage source to the negative plate. This flow will continue, though not at a constant rate, until by mutual repulsion electrons are being impelled back from the negative plate toward the negative voltage source terminal with exactly the same force with which the negative terminal is attempting to force them into the plate. At the positive voltage source terminal, electrons are being attracted toward the terminal with a force exactly balanced by the force with which the electron charge deficiency of the plate is attracting them back to it.

If, during this process, 1 coulomb (C) of electrons has thus been effectively transferred from the positive plate to the negative, so that a charge deficiency of 1 C exists in the positive plate while a charge excess of 1 C exists in the negative plate, we say the capacitor has been charged with a charge of 1 C.

The actual charge depends on two factors. One is the source potential. If we double the source potential, we will transfer twice as much charge, and if we reduce the source potential, the amount of charge transferred will be proportionately reduced. The other factor is the innate capacity of the two plates to store charge. This capacity depends on the area of the plates, the distance between them, and the nature of the material between them. The capacity can be increased by increasing the area of the plates, by decreasing the space between them, and by changing the nature of the material between them, the dielectric.

For a given capacitor

$$Q = CE$$

where Q is the charge transferred, E is the source potential, and C is the physical constant called the capacity of the capacitor.

This can also be written as

$$C = \frac{Q}{E}$$

Since Q is in coulombs and E is in volts, C has the dimensions of coulombs per volt (C/V).

The unit of capacity is the farad (F). It is entirely too large a unit to be practical. The microfarad (μF) and picofarad (pF) are commonly used.

1 microfarad $= 1 \, \mu F = 10^{-6}$ F

1 picofarad $\;\; = 1 \, pF = 10^{-12}$ F

The micromicrofarad ($\mu\mu$F) is still sometimes encountered as a unit. It is identical to the pF, being 10^{-12} F.

Problems   **1.**   What is the value of a capacitor that charges up to 0.025 C when a voltage of 100 V is placed across its terminals?

2.   What is the value of a capacitor that charges up to 1.44×10^{-9} C when a voltage of 120 V is placed across its terminals?

3.   A 300 V source is placed across the terminals of a 400 μF capacitor. What is the value of the charge held by the capacitor?

4.   What voltage is necessary to charge a 0.012 μF capacitor to 4.2 μC?

12-2
Dielectrics

NATURE OF DIELECTRICS.   An electric field exists between the plates of a charged capacitor. An electron placed between the plates would move toward the positive plate and away from the negative plate, if it were unconstrained.

If an insulator is placed between the plates of a charged capacitor, the electrons in it will experience a force impelling them away from the negative plate and toward the positive plate. They are not unconstrained, since in an insulator the electrons are not free to move away from their parent atoms. They will continue to revolve about their parent atoms, but the orbits will be distorted. That part of the orbit of each electron which brings it closest to the negative plate will be slightly compressed, so that it does not move as far in that direction as it would if the negative plate were not present. That part of the orbit of each electron closest to the positive plate will be stretched, so the electron moves farther in that direction than it otherwise would (Figure 12-2).

The net effect is that the electrons within the dielectric are shifted slightly toward the positive plate, while the atoms of which they are a part are not. Since the atoms represent the positive charge of the dielectric, there is some net separation of the charges within the dielectric.

That face of the dielectric presented to the negative plate will appear to be slightly positively charged, since the center of the negative charge of the dielectric has been shifted away from that side. That face of the dielectric presented to the positive plate will appear to be slightly negatively charged, since the center of the negative charge of the dielectric has been shifted toward that side.

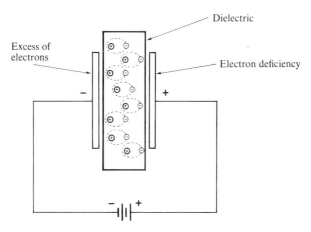

Figure 12-2   When a dielectric is placed between the plates of a capacitor, the electrons are repelled by the negative plate and attracted by the positive plate. Since the electrons are not free to move, their orbits become distorted—slightly compressed where the electron is closest to the negative plate and slightly stretched where the electron is closest to the positive plate.

The positive plate of the capacitor is thus more affected by the presence of the charge on the negative plate than otherwise, since both the charge on the negative plate and the induced charge on the dielectric facing it will tend to repel electrons from the positive plate to the positive terminal of the voltage source. Similarly, the negative plate can accumulate more electrons for a given source potential, since the electrons from the source will be attracted into the plate both by the positive charge on the opposite plate and by the slight excess positive charge induced in the dielectric on the side facing the negative capacitor plate.

The effect is as though the capacitor plates were brought closer together by the presence of the dielectric, through the induced charge on opposite dielectric faces. But bringing the plates closer together increases the capacitance of the capacitor, as we have seen.

DIELECTRIC CONSTANT (K_{ε}).   Just as a ferromagnetic core concentrates the flux lines of a magnetic field, so the dielectric concentrates the flux lines of the electric field existing between the plates of a charged capacitor. The ability of a ferromagnetic core to concentrate flux lines is measured by its relative permeability. The ability of a dielectric to concentrate flux lines is measured by its *relative permittivity*, with the symbol ε_r or K_{ε}.

Suppose that a given capacitor has a capacity C of 1 μF. That means that for a potential difference of 1 V between the plates, 1 μC of charge had to be transferred from the positive plate to the negative. If a material that can double the flux of the electric field is introduced between the plates, the force repelling electrons from the positive plate to the source, and attracting electrons into the negative plate from the source, is doubled. But by doubling the force on the electrons, twice as many will be moved from the positive plate through the voltage source to the negative plate. The charge transferred from the positive plate to the negative is now 2 μC, with the same source potential of 1 V and, consequently, with the same difference in potential between the plates. But the capacity is

$$C = \frac{Q}{E}$$

If Q is doubled while E remains the same, C must be doubled, and the capacity of the capacitor with the dielectric in place between the plates is now 2 μF (Figure 12-3).

Since, as we have seen, the presence of a dielectric increases the capacitance of a given capacitor in proportion to the relative permittivity of the dielectric, this becomes a convenient measure. It is called the *dielectric constant* of the material, and the product of the dielectric constant times the original capacitance of the capacitor with air or free space between the plates gives the capacitance with the dielectric present.

For a simple capacitor with parallel plates, the capacity is given by

$$C = K_\varepsilon \times \frac{A}{d} \times 8.85 \times 10^{-12} \text{ F}$$

where A is the plate area in square meters for either plate, and d is the distance in meters between the plates. K_ε is the relative permittivity, or dielectric constant, for the dielectric material between the plates, and 8.85×10^{-12} is the absolute permittivity of air or vacuum.

Figure 12-3   Capacity C of a given capacitor is increased by placing a dielectric between its plates. In this case, C is doubled.

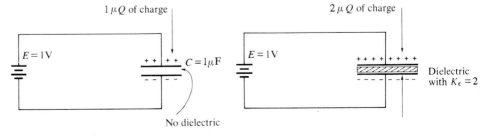

DIELECTRIC BREAKDOWN. If the electron orbits in the dielectric are stretched too far, the electrons may leave their parent atoms, and with free electrons thus created under the stress of the electric field, the material is no longer an insulator, but a conductor with high resistance. The charge difference between the plates cannot be maintained if the material between them permits direct transfer of charge from one plate to another, and instead of a capacitor the circuit element has become a resistor, with possible disastrous consequences for the remainder of the circuit. The closer together the plates, and the thinner the dielectric separating them, the greater the electrical stress due to the charge on the plates. The lower limit to the separation of plates and the thickness of the dielectric between them is determined by the potential difference in volts between the plates. The limit to which a given dielectric can be stressed—the *breakdown voltage*—is usually given in volts per mil (V/mil) of thickness.

PRACTICAL DIELECTRICS.   Practical dielectric materials are useful in terms of their dielectric constant and their breakdown voltage. Some materials widely used are listed in Table 12-1. The values given in this table are approximate, and will vary with different samples of similar materials. Barium–strontium titanate represents a different class of materials than the others listed. It is a ceramic and, as can be seen, has a very high dielectric constant. With this material, capacitors can be constructed with a high capacity in a small volume, though the breakdown voltage is low. This can be compensated for by making the material thicker than would otherwise need to be the case. A thickness of 4 mils, for example, would produce a capacitor with a breakdown voltage of 300 V, and the dielectric constant of this ceramic

TABLE 12-1   Dielectric Materials

Material	Dielectric Constant K_ε	Breakdown Voltage (V/mil)
Air or vacuum	1	20
Teflon	2	1,500
Glass	8	2,000
Oil	4	400
Porcelain	6	200
Mica	5	5,000
Barium–strontium titanate	7,500	75

is so high that the resulting capacitor would still occupy a relatively small volume.

Just as energy is lost in each cycle of magnetization and demagnetization of a ferromagnetic core, so energy is lost in each cycle of electrical stress on a dielectric. Some materials have a small energy loss, while some have considerable. Dielectric materials must also be classified according to the energy loss in each cycle of charge and discharge of a capacitor.

Each time the electric field reverses polarity when an alternating voltage is applied to a capacitor, the electrons in the dielectric material are strained first in one direction and then in the other. Energy must be used to displace these electrons from their normal paths. This energy can come only from the source of the alternating voltage, and represents a loss, which can become quite appreciable at high frequencies (Figure 12-4).

Air or vacuum has the lowest loss, since few or no electron orbits are being displaced. Mica and some ceramic materials have very low losses, and are thus suitable for high-frequency applications. Losses are higher in most other materials; impregnated paper capacitors have losses ten to fifty times as great as comparable mica capacitors.

ENERGY STORAGE IN CAPACITORS. Most of the energy stored in a capacitor is stored in the form of dielectric stress. If a capacitor is connected to a voltage source, charge is transferred from one plate of the capacitor to the other, and the electron orbits in the dielectric are stretched. If the capacitor is then disconnected from the voltage source, the charge and the stored energy will be retained for some time. If the insulation were perfect, the charge could theoretically be stored forever; but in practical capacitors charge can be stored for, at the most, a few days.

Figure 12-4   Alternating voltage applied to a capacitor causes electrons in the dielectric to strain in one direction, then in the opposite direction, repeatedly.

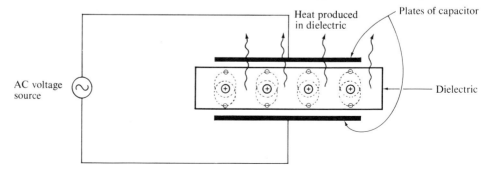

The amount of energy thus stored is determined by the capacitance of the capacitor and by the potential to which it is charged. This energy is measured in joules (J).

$$\text{Energy} = \mathscr{E} = \tfrac{1}{2}CE^2 \text{ J}$$

where C is the capacitance in farads, and E is the voltage to which the capacitor is charged. For example, a 10 μF capacitor charged to a potential of 100 V would have stored energy equal to

$$\mathscr{E} = \tfrac{1}{2}CE^2 = \tfrac{1}{2}(10^{-5})(100)^2 = 0.05 \text{ J}$$

This same capacitor charged to 400 V would have stored energy equal to

$$\mathscr{E} = \tfrac{1}{2}CE^2 = \tfrac{1}{2}(10^{-5})(400)^2 = 0.8 \text{ J}$$

Note that with four times the charging voltage, sixteen times as much energy is stored.

A capacitor containing stored energy can be a source of electrical shock. Since a capacitor may store energy for up to several days under some circumstances, even though the source of charging voltage is no longer connected, a "dead" circuit may present a hazard. If the stored energy is as much as 1 J, and the potential at which it is stored is sufficiently high to cause shock, then the stored energy may represent a serious shock hazard.

Problems

1. A capacitor consists of two parallel metal rectangular plates, 12 mils apart, with only a vacuum between them. The dimensions of each of the two plates are 9.1 cm × 9.46 cm. Calculate the capacitance and break-down voltage of this capacitor.

2. A capacitor consists of two circular metal plates, 15 mils apart, and a mica dielectric. The diameter of either capacitor plate is 3.1411 cm. Determine the capacitance and breakdown voltage of this capacitor.

3. A capacitor has a barium–strontium titanate dielectric between its plates. The area of either capacitor plate is 6.25 cm^2, and the distance between the plates is 20 mils. Calculate the capacitance and breakdown voltage of this capacitor.

4. A porcelain dielectric capacitor consists of plates 5 mils apart, each with a surface area of 4.783 cm^2. What are the capacitance and break-down voltage of this capacitor?

5. A glass dielectric capacitor consists of plates 18 mils apart, each with a surface area of 5 cm^2. Calculate the maximum charge that the capacitor can hold before breakdown.

   6.   What is the stored energy of a 120 μF capacitor charged to a potential
           of 300 V?

   7.   What is the stored energy of a 220 pF capacitor charged to a potential
           of 500 V? Of 1000 V?

   8.   What is the stored energy of a 0.75 μF capacitor charged to a potential
           of 250 V?

   9.   How much voltage is necessary to store 2 J of energy in a 0.0024 μF
           capacitor?

  10.   Suppose we want to design a 0.002 μF capacitor with a Teflon dielectric
           that is capable of storing a maximum of 0.0006 J of energy before
           voltage breakdown. Calculate the breakdown voltage of the capacitor,
           the distance between the capacitor plates, and the surface area of each
           plate.

12-3
Capacitive Circuits

CAPACITORS IN PARALLEL.   When capacitors are connected in parallel,
the effect is as though the plate area had been increased (Figure 12-5). Each
capacitor added to a parallel bank adds new plate area to be charged
proportional to its capacitance. The total capacitance is therefore the simple
sum of the individual capacitances.

$$C_t = C_1 + C_2 + C_3 \ldots$$

Thus, a 2 μF capacitor connected in parallel with a 3 μF capacitor will give
a total capacitance of 5 μF for the parallel combination. As with any parallel-

Figure 12-5   The effect of capacitors connected in parallel is as though
the plate area is increased.

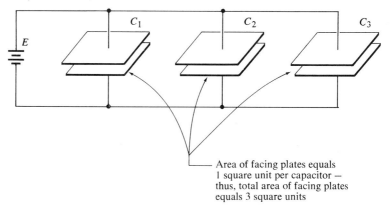

Area of facing plates equals
1 square unit per capacitor —
thus, total area of facing plates
equals 3 square units

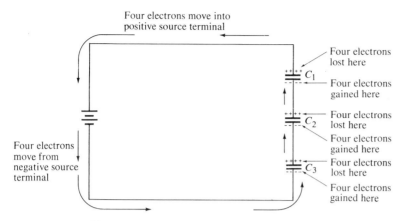

Figure 12-6 When capacitors are connected in series, the current through each at any given instant is the same.

connected circuit elements, the voltage is the same across each capacitor in a parallel bank.

CAPACITORS IN SERIES.   When any circuit elements are connected in series, the current must be the same through each at any instant, by Kirchhoff's current law. If the circuit elements are capacitors, the current is the current that exists during the time the charge is being transported from one plate to another. If that charging current is the same during each instant of the charging time, then the total charge transported must be the same for each capacitor, and equal to the total charge transported (Figure 12-6). Thus,

$$Q_t = Q_1 = Q_2 = Q_3 \ldots$$

And, by Kirchhoff's voltage law, the sum of the voltages across the circuit elements in any loop must equal the source voltage in that loop. Thus,

$$E = V_1 + V_2 + V_3 \ldots$$

But the voltage to which any capacitor is charged is a function of the charge transported and the capacity; thus,

$$V = \frac{Q}{C}$$

Therefore,

$$\frac{Q_t}{C_t} = \frac{Q_1}{C_1} + \frac{Q_2}{C_2} + \frac{Q_3}{C_3} \ldots$$

and, since the charge Q is equal for all, dividing each term by Q yields

$$\frac{1}{C_t} = \frac{1}{C_1} + \frac{1}{C_2} + \frac{1}{C_3} \cdots$$

Note that capacitors in series add in the same way as do resistors in parallel, and capacitors in parallel add the same way as do resistors in series. This is reasonable, since resistance represents an opposition, while capacitance represents an ability to accept charge.

Just as the total resistance of resistors in parallel is *less* than the value of any of the resistors, so the capacitance of a series string of capacitors is *less* than the capacity of any of the capacitors.

As we have seen, the voltage across a capacitor is a function of the charge and capacity ($V = Q/C$). Since for all capacitors in a series string the charge must be the same, the voltage across each must be inversely proportional to its capacitance. The smaller the capacitance in relation to the total for any capacitor, the greater the share of the total voltage that will appear across it.

The voltage across any capacitor of a series string is, therefore

$$V_1 = \frac{Q}{C_1}$$

But

$$Q = C_t V_t$$

therefore,

$$V_1 = \frac{C_t V_t}{C_1}$$

EXAMPLE   Given three capacitors in series—$C_1 = 10\ \mu F$, $C_2 = 2\ \mu F$, and $C_3 = 0.5\ \mu F$ (Figure 12-7)—find the total capacity, the charge on each capacitor, and the voltage across each if they have been connected to a 500 V source of potential for sufficient time to attain full charge.

Solution

Figure 12-7

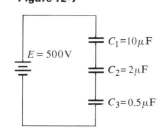

$$\frac{1}{C_t} = \frac{1}{C_1} + \frac{1}{C_2} + \frac{1}{C_3}$$

$$C_t = \frac{1}{\dfrac{1}{10} + \dfrac{1}{2} + \dfrac{1}{0.5}} = \frac{1}{0.1 + 0.5 + 2} = \frac{1}{2.6} = 0.385\ \mu F$$

and

$$Q = C_t V_t = (0.385 \times 10^{-6})(500) = 1.92 \times 10^{-4}\ C$$

The voltage across each capacitor is

$$V_1 = \frac{Q}{C_1} = \frac{1.92 \times 10^{-4}}{10 \times 10^{-6}} = 0.192 \times 10^2 = 19.2 \text{ V}$$

$$V_2 = \frac{Q}{C_2} = \frac{1.92 \times 10^{-4}}{2 \times 10^{-6}} = 0.96 \times 10^2 = 96 \text{ V}$$

$$V_3 = \frac{Q}{C_3} = \frac{1.92 \times 10^{-4}}{0.5 \times 10^{-6}} = 3.84 \times 10^2 = 384 \text{ V}$$

The sum of these voltages is 499.2 V, whereas Kirchhoff's voltage law says they ought to sum to 500 V, the source voltage. The difference between the two values is due to the fact that the calculations have been rounded off to three significant figures. If all calculations had been carried to four significant figures, the sum of the voltages would have been 499.98 V; and if the fraction $10/26 = 5/13$ had been used for C_t, then the results would have checked exactly. We are not actually justified in using three significant figures, since the capacities are given to only one significant figure and may not be considered precise.

1. Given two capacitors in parallel—$C_1 = 22 \ \mu\text{F}$, $C_2 = 3 \ \mu\text{F}$—determine   **Problems**
the total capacity, the total charge in the circuit, and the charge on each capacitor if they have been connected to a 350 V source.

2. For a circuit with four parallel capacitors—$C_1 = 1.5 \ \mu\text{F}$, $C_2 = 31 \ \mu\text{F}$, $C_3 = 12 \ \mu\text{F}$, $C_4 = 7.5 \ \mu\text{F}$—find the total capacity, the total charge in the circuit, and the charge on each capacitor if they have been connected to a 500 V source.

3. Given three capacitors in series—$C_1 = 2 \ \mu\text{F}$, $C_2 = 44 \ \mu\text{F}$, $C_3 = 0.6 \ \mu\text{F}$—determine the total capacity, the charge on each capacitor, and the voltage across each if they have been connected to a 400 V source.

4. Given a circuit with five capacitors in series—$C_1 = 2 \ \text{pF}$, $C_2 = 14 \ \text{pF}$, $C_3 = 45 \ \text{pF}$, $C_4 = 22 \ \text{pF}$, $C_5 = 5 \ \text{pF}$—determine the total capacity, the charge on each capacitor, and the voltage across each if they have been connected to a 750 V source.

5. Consider the following circuit with capacitors in a series–parallel combination, where $C_1 = 4\mu\text{F}$, $C_2 = 12\mu\text{F}$, $C_3 = 25\mu\text{F}$, $C_4 = 11\mu\text{F}$, and $C_5 = 20\mu\text{F}$. Find the total capacity, the charge on each capacitor, and the voltage across each if they are connected to a 100 V potential source.

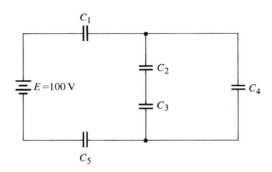

Circuit for Problem 5.

6. Consider the series–parallel capacitor combination shown, where
$C_1 = 12$ μF, $C_2 = 2$ μF, $C_3 = 20$ μF, $C_4 = 4$ μF, $C_5 = 16$ μF, and
$C_6 = 8\,\mu$F. Find the total capacity, the charge on each capacitor, and the
voltage across each if they are connected to a 400 V potential source.

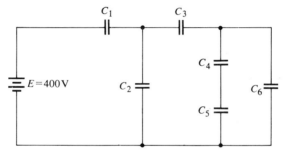

Circuit for Problem 6.

12-4
***RC* Circuits and**
Time Constants

THE SERIES *RC* CIRCUIT. A capacitor cannot charge in zero time. For a
capacitor to charge, some finite number of coulombs must be transferred
from one set of plates to the other. The average current for this charge
transfer is the number of coulombs per second (C/sec). Suppose 0.5 C of
charge must be transferred to charge a particular capacitor to a particular
voltage. If that charge is transferred in 1 sec, then the average current during
that second must be 0.5/1 C/sec, which is 0.5 A. If that charge were to be
transferred in 0.01 sec, then the average current during that time would be
0.5/0.01 = 50 A. If the charging time were to be as short as 1 μsec, the average
current during that time would have to be 500,000 A. Obviously, as the
charging time is shortened, the rate of current flow necessary to produce
the charge grows rapidly, and to have a charging time of zero seconds would

call for an impossible infinite current. Therefore, a capacitor cannot charge in zero time.

The voltage across an uncharged capacitor is zero. In an uncharged capacitor there is no dielectric stress, and there is no difference in charge between the two sets of plates. If there is no difference in charge between the two sets of plates, there can be no difference in potential between them. Therefore, the voltage across an uncharged capacitor is zero.

Now consider the circuit of Figure 12-8. A resistor, a capacitor, and a switch are connected in series with each other, and connected to a source of potential E. Assume the capacitor had no initial charge.

At the instant the switch is closed, the voltage across the capacitor is zero. Since it was uncharged, the voltage was zero immediately prior to the switch being closed; and since the capacitor cannot charge in zero time, the voltage must be zero at the instant the switch is closed to complete the circuit. At any instant, by Kirchhoff's voltage law,

$$E = V_R + V_C$$

where E is the source voltage, V_R the voltage across the resistor, and V_C the voltage across the capacitor. But at the initial instant, V_C is zero. Therefore, at this instant,

$$E = V_R = iR$$

where i is the value of the current at that instant. Thus,

$$i = \frac{E}{R}$$

The value of the current at the first instant after the switch is closed is the same as it would be with only the resistor in the circuit. At that instant the capacitor offers no opposition to the flow of current. If, of course, we did not insert a resistor in the circuit as a circuit element, then the resistance of the connecting wires, the internal resistance of the voltage source, and the internal resistance of the conducting materials of the capacitor plates would combine to act as a series circuit resistance, so the initial current i in that event would still not be infinite, though it could be large. For this reason, capacitors ought to be charged only through some series resistance.

Though the voltage across the capacitor was zero at the initial instant after the switch was closed, it will not stay zero. As current flows through the resistor, a charge difference accumulates between the plates of the capacitor. Since

$$V = \frac{Q}{C}$$

Figure 12-8 When the switch is closed, the source voltage E is applied to the series RC circuit.

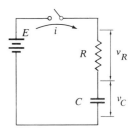

as Q increases, with C a constant, V must also increase. But in the circuit if V_C increases, V_R must decrease since their sum, E, is constant.

If the voltage across the resistor R decreases with passing time, then the current through it must also decrease. But the current through R is the total circuit current, and the charging current of the capacitor. If the charging current of the capacitor decreases with passing time, then the rate at which charge accumulates must decrease. The rate at which the voltage across the capacitor grows larger must also decrease. Figure 12-9 shows these changing rates.

TIME CONSTANTS.   Every day electronics uses more and more digital circuitry. It is typical of digital circuitry that a voltage waveform which consists of a rectangular pulse is fed into a circuit whose response is similar, at least in first approximation, to a simple series RC circuit. The rectangular pulse is little different from the rectangular voltage pulse produced by opening and closing the switch from the voltage source in our simple series RC circuit.

It is therefore more and more essential that the reaction of the simple RC circuit to rectangular voltage pulses be understood.

Figure 12-9   The rate at which charge accumulates varies with charging current, as does the voltage across the capacitor.

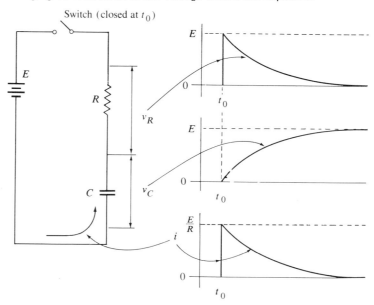

We know the initial current in a simple RC circuit is

$$i = \frac{E}{R}$$

Since the current I is defined as the rate of change of charge,

$$I = \frac{Q}{t}$$

where I is the average current for the time t. Hence,

$$Q = It$$

But

$$Q = CV$$

Therefore,

$$CV = Q = It = \frac{E}{R}t$$

This is on the assumption that the initial current i is the same as the average current I for the time t. On this assumption, from the above equation,

$$\frac{V}{t} = \frac{E}{RC}$$

and the dimensions of V/t are volts per second (V/sec). Since both sides of the equation must have the same dimensions, and since E is in volts, the product RC must have the dimensions of seconds. This product, RC, is the time constant of the circuit containing a series R and C. It is symbolized by the Greek letter τ (tau).

The time constant of an RC circuit is the time it would take for the voltage across the capacitor to rise to the source voltage if the capacitor voltage were to rise at a constant rate during the charging interval.

The capacitor voltage does *not* rise at a constant rate; instead it continually decreases as the charging current falls off. The time constant concept still gives us a very useful and simple tool. This is because, to a close approximation, the capacitor will charge to 63% of the source voltage E during one time constant, to 63% of the remaining 37% during the next time constant, and so on. For practical purposes, a capacitor is at essentially the source voltage five time constants after the switch is closed. The time constant concept also enables us to use a simple graphical method to calculate instantaneous values of the voltage across a charging capacitor for times less than five time constants.

EXAMPLE

Suppose a capacitor of $3\,\mu\text{F}$ is connected in series with a $2\,\text{M}\Omega$ resistor, and a source of potential of 150 V is connected to the series string, as in Figure 12-10. Find the initial charging current, the time for one time constant, and the approximate time required for the capacitor to charge to 150 V.

Solution.

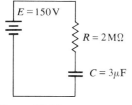

$E = 150\,\text{V}$

$R = 2\,\text{M}\Omega$

$C = 3\,\mu\text{F}$

Figure 12-10

$$i = E/R = \frac{150}{2 \times 10^6} = 75\,\mu\text{A} \qquad \text{(initial charging current)}$$

$$\tau = RC = (2 \times 10^6)(3 \times 10^{-6}) = 6\ \text{sec}$$

$$t = 5\,\tau = 5 \times 6 = 30\ \text{sec} \qquad \text{(to reach full charge)}$$

Note that in the product RC, the 10^6 for the number of megohms and the 10^{-6} for the number of microfarads cancel out. The time constant is thus easily calculated directly if R is in $\text{M}\Omega$ and C is in μF.

Figure 12-11 shows a *universal time constant graph*. The horizontal axis is calibrated in time constants, up to five time constants. The vertical axis is calibrated in percent of source voltage. Two curves are shown. The rising curve, (a), is the one which applies to the charging of a capacitor through a resistor.

Figure 12-11   Universal time constant graph.

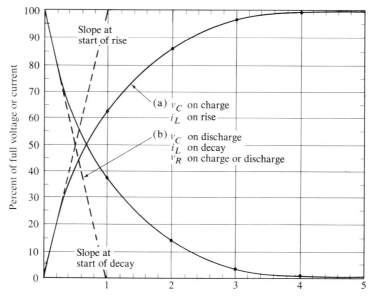

Time in RC or L/R time constants

EXAMPLE

A series RC circuit, where $R = 100$ kΩ and $C = 0.05$ μF, is connected to a 100 V source. How much time will elapse before the voltage across the capacitor equals 50 V?

Solution. The 50 V is 50% of the applied potential. From the time constant graph, 50% of the source potential corresponds to 0.7 time constants. The circuit time constant, τ, is

$$\tau = RC = 10^5 \times 5 \times 10^{-8} = 5 \times 10^{-3} = 5 \text{ msec}$$

$$t = 0.7\,\tau = 0.7 \times 5 \text{ msec} = 3.5 \text{ msec}$$

Thus, the voltage across the capacitor will rise from zero to 50 V 3.5 msec after the switch is closed.

Consider the circuit of Figure 12-12. It shows a circuit similar to the previous example, but with a switch arranged so that it can either connect the series resistor and capacitor combination to the voltage source, or disconnect the voltage source from the circuit and substitute in its place a short circuit. Note that it is so arranged that the voltage source itself is not shorted.

When the switch is closed, in position A, the capacitor charges as before. The graph of its voltage plotted against time would have the same shape as the rising curve of the universal time constant graph. This graph is called an *exponential curve*, from the mathematical form of the equation that describes it. The proper values of the time for the time base and the voltage for the vertical axis depend on the particular values of R and C and the voltage of the source E. The curve as shown applies where the time base is calibrated in time constants, and the vertical axis in percent of E for all values of R, C, and E.

The universal time constant graph has a descending curve as well as an ascending curve. The descending curve starts at 100% of the source potential and descends through five time constants to essentially zero. This descending curve describes the potential across the capacitor for five time constants after the switch is thrown to position B to initiate discharge.

Now let us suppose, after at least five time constants have elapsed and the capacitor is fully charged to the potential of E, that the switch is suddenly thrown to position B. The source is disconnected from the circuit and plays no further role.

The capacitor is fully charged at the instant the switch is thrown to its new position. Since the voltage across a capacitor cannot change in zero time, the voltage across the capacitor must still be E. But the resistor is connected directly across the capacitor when the switch is in position B. Therefore, the

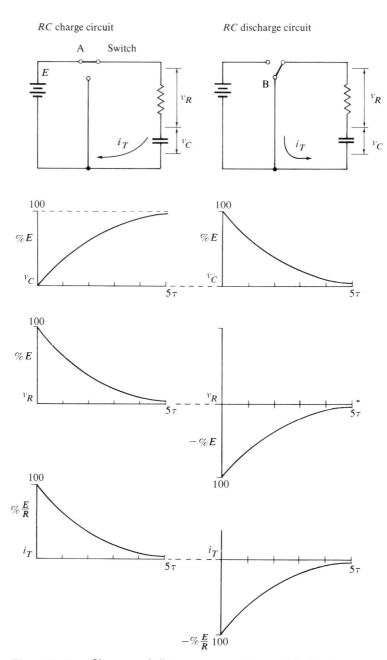

Figure 12-12   Charge and discharge curves for an *RC* circuit.

voltage $E = V_C$ at $t = 0$ must be across the resistor also. But if there is a voltage E across the resistor R, then by Ohm's law ($I = E/R$) there must be a current through the resistor at that instant.

This current is the discharge current of the capacitor. The voltage across the capacitor existed because of the charge difference between the two sets of plates. The excess electrons on the negative side flow through the resistor to the positive capacitor plates to make up the deficiency existing there.

So far as the resistor is concerned, the capacitor is now acting as a voltage source. The current through the resistor at the instant the switch is thrown to position B is the same value as the initial charging current. The current is, however, in the opposite direction. The polarity of the voltage developed across the resistor is also opposite to the polarity at the instant of initial charging current.

As the capacitor discharges through the resistor, the potential across the capacitor, and consequently the potential across the resistor, decreases. As this potential drops, the rate of current flow through the resistor also drops. This is the same phenomenon that occurred when the capacitor charged, only now it is occurring in reverse.

A 2 μF capacitor charged to 250 V is suddenly connected across a resistance   EXAMPLE
of 400 kΩ. How long will it take for the capacitor to discharge to 50 V?

Solution.   The time constant of the circuit is

$\tau = RC = (2)(0.4) = 0.8$ sec

$\% E = \dfrac{50}{250} \times 100 = 0.2 \times 100 = 20\%$

The number of time constants required for the voltage to decay to 20% of E is, from the descending curve on the universal time constant graph, 1.6 τ.

Since $\tau = 0.8$ sec, $1.6\,\tau = 1.6 \times 0.8$ sec, or $t = 1.28$ sec, the time required for the voltage across the capacitor to decay to 20% of the original value.

In the charging circuit shown in Figure 12-12, by Kirchhoff's voltage law the sum of the voltage across the resistor and the voltage across the capacitor must at all instants equal the source voltage E. That is,

$E = V_C + V_R$

As V_C rises toward E, V_R must be falling toward zero. The decay of the voltage across R as the capacitor charges is described by the descending curve of the universal time constant graph. Since with a resistor the voltage and current are directly proportional, this curve must also describe the circuit current, which is the same for both resistor and capacitor since they are connected in series.

When the capacitor discharges through the resistor, the voltage across the capacitor and, consequently, the voltage across the resistor is described by the descending curve. Again, this curve also describes the circuit current, which must be directly proportional to the voltage across the resistor.

Figure 12-12 shows the charge and discharge curves for V_C, V_R, and i_t, the total circuit current, for the situations just described. Note that the discharge circuit shows a voltage across the resistor opposite in polarity to the voltage in the charging circuit. Similarly, the direction of circuit current is opposite in the two situations. The precise value of voltage or current can be determined for any instant for any of the curves by using the universal time constant graph.

Consider the simple RC circuit of Figure 12-13. It is connected to a source of positive voltage pulses, which are presumed to go from zero volts to $E = 100$ V in essentially zero time, and at the end of some time t drop to zero

Figure 12-13   A simple RC circuit and resulting waveform of voltage taken across the capacitor when $\tau = RC = 1$ sec and pulse duration and time between pulses both equal 5τ.

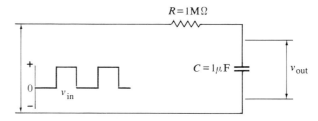

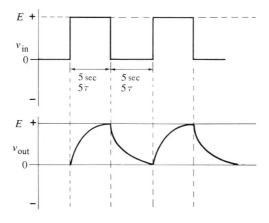

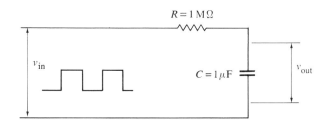

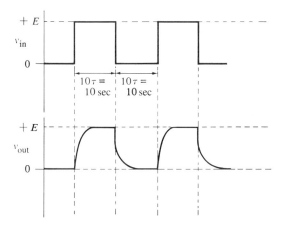

Figure 12-14 The circuit of Figure 12-13 and resulting waveform when pulse duration and time between pulses equal 10τ.

volts in essentially zero time. Let us also presume that the time duration of a single pulse is the same as the time between pulses, though it need not be. We must assume also that the voltage source has no significant internal resistance, so that during the interval between pulses the capacitor can discharge through the resistor as though the resistor were connected directly across the capacitor.

If we assume the pulse duration and time between pulses to be equal to 5τ, then the capacitor will just have time to reach full charge while the pulse is present, and just have time to fully discharge between pulses. The resulting waveform of the voltage across the capacitor is shown in Figure 12-13. The rectangular pulses of the input waveform have become rounded into a closely-spaced series of exponential curves on the output.

If the time constant τ of the circuit were shorter, or if the duration of the pulses were longer, so that the pulse width and space between pulses is equal to 10τ, as in Figure 12-14, then the output voltage waveform would have time to reach the source voltage E in half the duration of the pulse, and from then till the end of the pulse there would be no change in the voltage across the capacitor. At this point the capacitor is essentially fully charged. At the end of the pulse, when the source potential drops to zero, again the capacitor will discharge through the voltage source and the series resistor between them, and will reach essentially zero charge halfway through the time between pulses. The resulting voltage waveform across the capacitor will be a square wave with an exponentially rounded leading and trailing edge.

If we assume the time constant of the circuit still shorter in relation to the pulse duration, the shape of the output voltage waveform would be still nearer to the assumed perfect rectangular pulses of the input, though for any relationship between the time constant of the circuit and the pulse width, the leading and trailing edges of the output voltage waveforms must be exponential curves.

If we assume, as in Figure 12-15, that the pulse duration and the time between pulses are both short, on the order of $0.1\,\tau$, then the capacitor will never have time to either charge or discharge fully. At the arrival of the first pulse, the capacitor will be uncharged; as can be seen from the universal time

Figure 12-15   The circuit of Figure 12-13 and resulting wave-form when pulse duration and time between pulses equal $1/10\,\tau$.

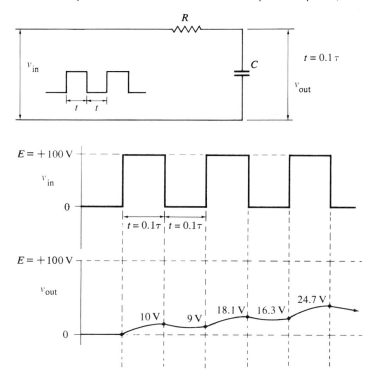

constant graph, during the first 0.1 τ the capacitor will charge to approximately 10 V, though this is not an exact figure.

At the end of this first pulse the capacitor potential is 10 V, which is 10% of E, and now the capacitor is to discharge at the same rate for 0.1 τ. At this rate it will lose 10% of its potential during this time interval. Ten percent of 10 V is 1 V, so the capacitor potential at the end of this interval will be $10 - 1 = 9$ V.

Thus, at the beginning of the second cycle, the capacitor already had a charge of 9 V, approximately, inherited from the first pulse. During the interval between pulses, this voltage decayed, but by the inexorable *laws of exponential decay*, it decayed by *10% of itself*, not to zero! Since 10% of 10 V is 1 V, the voltage at the end of this interval between pulses was 9 V.

Now the next positive pulse arrives, but the capacitor now has an initial charge of 9 V. The actual charging potential for the capacitor is the difference between its initial charge and the source potential. The charging potential is thus $100 - 9 = 91$ V, and the capacitor will store additional charge equal to 10% of this figure during the time the positive pulse is present. This additional charge is thus 9.1 V, which, added to the initial capacitor charge, gives a total capacitor charge of 18.1 V at the end of the second pulse.

During the interval between the second and third pulses, this voltage will decay, again by 10% *of itself*. The drop in capacitor charge during this interval is thus 1.81 V, and the charge on the capacitor at the end of this interval is $18.1 - 1.81 = 16.29$ V, which we may round off to 16.3 V.

At the instant of arrival of the third pulse, the capacitor now has an initial charge of 16.3 V. The actual charging potential across the capacitor is, again, the difference between the source potential and the capacitor's initial charge, which in this case will be 83.7 V. The change in charge on the capacitor during the third pulse will be 10% of this figure, or 8.37 V. This increase in charge, added to the initial charge 16.3 V at the beginning of this pulse, gives the capacitor a total charge of 24.7 V at the end of the third pulse.

Note that the increase in capacitor charge is less each pulse. The capacitor charge continues to increase, but each time by a smaller amount. The magnitude of the discharge between pulses also increases, so while the average charge on the capacitor increases, it does so at a slower rate each cycle.

It is apparent that the capacitor charge cannot increase without bound, since it cannot, in this circuit, exceed the charging potential E. Let us assume (incorrectly) that at the end of some pulse the capacitor had been charged to the potential E, and consider the voltages at the next cycle. During the interval between pulses the capacitor would lose 10% of that voltage, or 10 V, and at the end of the interval the capacitor charge would be 90 V. At the beginning of the next pulse the effective charging potential would again be the difference between the source voltage and the initial charge on the capacitor. This effective charging potential would in this case be only 10 V, and the increase in charge on the capacitor during the next pulse would be 10% of this figure, or 1 V. This increase in charge, added to the charge already on the capacitor at the beginning of the pulse, would give the capacitor a net charge of 91 V at the end of the pulse. Obviously, this is not a stable condition either; the capacitor cannot, during any following cycle, attain the source potential if it is assumed to have that potential at the end of any cycle.

It is reasonable to assume (and in this case correct as well—not always the same thing) that there will be some steady state, at which the loss in charge between pulses will be just balanced by the gain in charge during the pulses.

The loss in charge between pulses is the charge at the end of any pulse times the percent of that charge lost during the time interval between pulses. If the time interval between pulses is known, and the RC time constant τ for the circuit is known, then the percent of initial voltage lost during the interval between pulses can be determined from the universal time constant graph. Thus,

Loss in charge between pulses = Voltage at end of pulse $\times$ % change

where the percent change is indicated as a decimal fraction. For example, if the voltage at the end of any pulse is given as X, and the percent of change in voltage during a given time between pulses is determined from the table to be 25%, then the loss in voltage across the capacitor between pulses is $0.25X$. In the example we have been using, the circuit of Figure 12-15, the change in voltage between pulses is 10%. If we let X be the voltage at the end of any pulse, then the change is $0.1X$ volts.

The charge during the next pulse is the percent change during the time interval of the pulse, determined from the time constant graph, multiplied by the difference between the charging potential and the actual potential across the capacitor at the beginning of the charging pulse. The source potential is E. The initial charge on the capacitor at the beginning of the charging pulse is the value of the potential across the capacitor at the end of the previous charge pulse minus the discharge between pulses, or $X - \%$ change X. The difference between the source potential and the initial charge is, therefore,

$E - (X - \%$ change $X)$

Note that the percent change of X referred to is the percent change which occurs during discharge. Now the change in potential during charge may be written, since it is

% change during charge time $[E - (X - \%$ change during discharge $X)]$

Now the whole relationship, equating the change in potential during discharge to the change in potential during charge, and using 0.1 as the decimal fraction of change occurring during each interval, may be written.

$$0.1X = 0.1[E - (X - 0.1\,X)]$$

$$X = \frac{E}{1.9}$$

and where $E = 100$ V,

$$X = \frac{100}{1.9} = 52.63 \text{ V}$$

During the interval following the end of the pulse at which the capacitor is charged to this voltage, 10% of this voltage is lost, leaving $52.63 - 5.26 = 47.37$ V. This is the initial charge at the beginning of the next pulse. Since at the beginning of the next charging pulse, a potential of 100 V is applied to a capacitor which is already charged to 47.37 V, the effective charging potential is $100 - 47.37 = 52.63$ V. The charge gained by the capacitor during the

Figure 12-16   The 10% of voltage lost between pulses is regained with the next pulse.

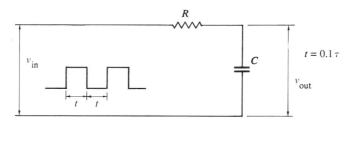

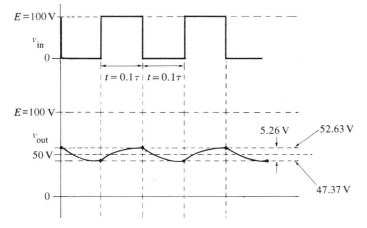

charge interval is 10% of this, or 5.26 V. This, added to the 47.37 V to which the capacitor was already charged, gives it a final charge at the end of the pulse of 52.63 V, which is what we started with (Figure 12-16). This method is general in its application and can be used with pulses of any width and any spacing.

The circuit of Figure 12-17 is similar to the one just considered, but the positions of the resistor and capacitor have been interchanged. The resistor and capacitor are still in series with each other, but output voltage V_{out} is taken across the resistor. This circuit is typical of the input circuit to most amplifiers.

Again, the circuit will have some time constant. If the input voltage consists of rectangular voltage pulses with a width equal to 5τ and a spacing between pulses of the same duration, then again, the capacitor will have just time to reach full charge during each pulse and to fully discharge between pulses.

This time, however, the output voltage is the resistor voltage, which is directly proportional to the circuit current, and the circuit current is the charge and discharge current of the capacitor.

At the beginning of the first input pulse, the capacitor is uncharged, and since no potential exists across it, the full source potential must appear across the resistor. The initial voltage at this instant in the output must be equal to E, the source voltage. As the capacitor charges, the voltage across the resistor must decrease, since the sum of the voltage across the resistor and the voltage across the capacitor must equal the source voltage E, which is constant during the pulse duration. The voltage across the resistor must decline to zero as the voltage across the capacitor rises to E.

At the end of the pulse the source voltage drops to zero. The capacitor at that instant had reached full charge, and must now discharge. The discharge path is through the source, which represents a low resistance. Resistor R is in series with the discharge path, and during the interval between pulses is effectively connected directly across the capacitor through the low internal resistance of the voltage source.

Therefore, the full voltage to which the capacitor had been charged will appear across the resistor at that instant, with the capacitor as the voltage source. The polarity of this voltage is the opposite to that of the original source voltage. If the original source voltage had consisted of a positive rectangular pulse, then the discharge voltage of the capacitor appearing across the resistor will be a *negative* voltage. This is shown in Figure 12-17.

As the capacitor discharges, the potential will decline exponentially, in accord with the declining curve in the universal time constant graph. At the end of 5τ, which we have assumed to be the interval between pulses, the

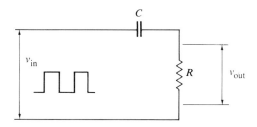

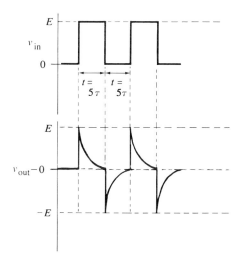

Figure 12-17   A simple *RC* circuit and resulting waveform of voltage taken across the resistor when $\tau = RC$ and pulse duration and time between pulses both equal 5τ.

capacitor will essentially have discharged to zero potential, and the potential across the resistor will also be zero.

Each succeeding repetition of the original source rectangular pulse will be identical, since there is no initial charge on the capacitor at the beginning of the pulse.

If the pulse width and the duration of the interval between pulses are long compared to the *RC* time constant of the circuit, then the output voltage waveform of Figure 12-18 will result. This is similar to the first case, but the time interval is such that the resistor voltage will have dropped to zero some time before the ending of the initial voltage pulse, and will remain zero for the duration of the pulse. The same thing is true for the interval between pulses; the resistor voltage will immediately rise to a negative peak equal to

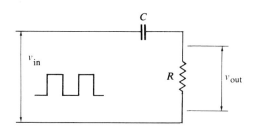

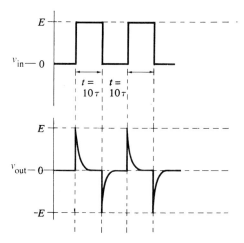

Figure 12-18   The circuit of Figure 12-17 and resulting waveform when pulse duration and time between pulses equal 10τ.

E, though opposite in polarity, then decay quickly to zero and remain there until the arrival of the next positive input pulse.

The output of this circuit is thus a series of positive and negative voltage spikes, with a steeply rising leading edge and exponentially decaying trailing edge, if the time constant of the RC circuit is short compared to the pulse duration. The shorter the time constant, the more sharply defined and narrow the resulting spikes.

If the time constant is long compared to the pulse duration, or (to put the same thing in another way) if the pulse duration is short compared to the circuit time constant, then there will not be time for the capacitor charge to either reach full charge when the pulse is present, or fully discharge during the interval between pulses. This situation is shown in Figure 12-19.

As the leading edge of the first pulse arrives, assuming the capacitor had no initial charge, the full source potential must appear across the resistor, and the output voltage measured across the resistor must be equal to E at that instant. Assume E is again 100 V, and assume again that the time for one pulse is 0.1 τ. Then, as before, the decay in potential during each interval will be 10% of the value of the voltage at that instant. Thus, during the first pulse the initial value of 100 V will decay according to the falling exponential curve of the universal time constant graph to a value of 90 V.

At the end of the first pulse the potential across the resistor is 90 V, but at the instant of the beginning of the interval between pulses, the source potential drops immediately to zero. The only potential in the circuit consisting of the capacitor and the resistor is now the charge on the capacitor, which is now 10 V. The potential across the resistor at this instant is -10 V, since this potential represents the discharge of the capacitor through the resistor.

Figure 12-19   The circuit of Figure 12-17 and resulting waveform when pulse duration and time between pulses equal $1/10\tau$.

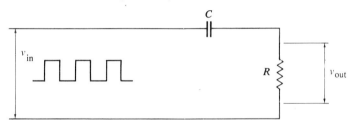

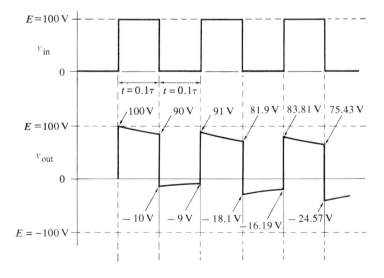

Note that as the input potential falls by 100 V, the output potential also falls by 100 V. Since the source potential changed by this amount and the potential across C cannot change in zero time, the whole change appears across R.

Now, at the beginning of the interval between pulses, the potential is -10 V. It decays toward zero, following the exponential curve of the universal time constant chart. It thus loses 10% of its value during this interval and, consequently, changes from -10 V to -9 V.

This represents the initial charge on the capacitor at the beginning of the second pulse. At the beginning of the second pulse, again the source potential changes by 100 V. Since, again, the potential across the capacitor cannot change in zero time, again the whole change in potential must appear across the resistor. Since the potential across the resistor at the instant before this change in source potential was -9 V, the instant after the change in source potential the voltage across the resistor must have risen by 100 V to equal 91 V.

Again, this voltage will decay by 10% of itself, to 81.9 V at the end of the pulse. Again, at the end of the pulse the source potential and, consequently, the potential across the resistor will drop by 100 V, to -18.1 V. This voltage will again decay by 10% of itself, to -16.19 V. At the beginning of the next pulse the potential will rise by 100 V, to $+83.81$ V.

As the sequence continues, the positive peaks become less positive, and the negative peaks become more negative. Since the amount by which the voltage peaks become less with each repetition of the input pulse is less each time, the output waveform will achieve some steady-state output level.

Let us assume that the output level after a large number of repetitions of the input waveform has reached a steady state, as shown in Figure 12-20. To be a steady state, it must satisfy the conditions that the positive and negative peaks are equal in amplitude, since they are equal in duration. Also, each time the potential at the source changes by E volts, at the beginning and at the end of each input pulse, the output voltage must instantaneously change by E volts.

Let us assume that at the instant of the start of a positive pulse, the value of the output voltage is X volts. Since this X volts was reached by an increase of E volts from the voltage at the previous instant, the voltage at that previous instant must have been $E - X$ volts. But this was the value at the end of the negative peak. If the waveform is symmetrical, the end of a negative peak and the end of a positive peak must have the same value, though opposite polarities. Thus, the end of the positive peak must have a value of $E - X$ volts. But this value is reached from X volts by a decay of 10% of X, or $0.1\ X$.

Therefore,

$$X - 0.1\ X = E - X$$

$$X = \frac{E}{1.9}$$

If the source potential E is 100 V

$$X = \frac{100}{1.9} = 52.63\ \text{V}$$

Thus, the positive peak is 52.63 V. It will decay by 10% of itself, or 5.26 V, to a value of 47.37 V. Then as the source potential drops by 100 V, it, too, will

Figure 12-20 The circuit of Figure 12-17 and a waveform indicating a steady state—equal amplitude of positive and negative peaks—has been reached.

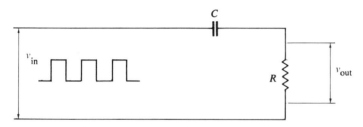

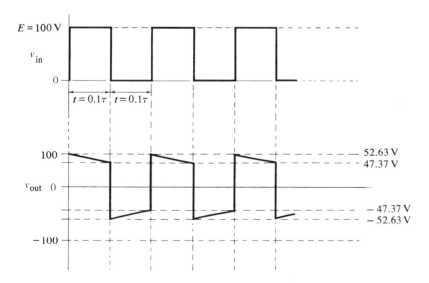

drop by 100 V, to a value of -52.63 V. Again, it will decay by 10% of itself, to a value of -47.37 V. Again, the source potential changes by 100 V, and again the output will rise by 100 V, from -47.37 to $+52.63$ V, which was the initial value at the start. Thus, this represents a stable situation, with each positive and negative pulse having the same value as the one preceding.

ALGEBRAIC SOLUTIONS TO *RC* EXPONENTIALS. The solutions presented so far have been based on the universal time constant graph. The results are limited by our ability to read the graph. There are algebraic solutions that provide accuracy limited only by the mathematical tables to which reference must be made, or by our ability to read a slide rule. If a small electronic calculator is available, results may be had to a high degree of accuracy.

Consider the simple series *RC* circuit of Figure 12-21. In order that Kirchhoff's voltage law be satisfied, the sum of the voltage drops in the circuit must equal the source voltage.

$$E = v_R + v_C$$

and since

$$v_R = iR$$

therefore,

$$E = iR + v_C$$

But the current i is the rate of change of charge.

$$i = \frac{dq}{dt}$$

and

$$q = Cv_C$$

Therefore, the current I is the rate of change of the product of the capacitance and the voltage across the capacitor. The capacitor value does not change: only the voltage v_C is subject to change. Therefore, the current i is the product of the capacity C times the rate of change of the voltage v_C. That is,

$$i = C\frac{dv_C}{dt}$$

Substituting this for i in the loop equation for the voltages,

$$E = RC\frac{dv_C}{dt} + v_C$$

This equation may not be solved by simple algebraic means, since it involves rates of change of quantities, not simply the quantities themselves. By using

Figure 12-21 A simple *RC* series circuit.

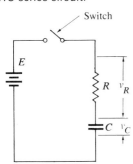

the methods of calculus, which are beyond the scope of this explanation, this equation may be reduced to the relatively simple algebraic expression

$$v_C = E(1 - \varepsilon^{-x})$$

where v_C is the value of the voltage across the capacitor at any instant t, E is the source voltage, $\varepsilon = 2.718\ldots$(the base of the system of natural logarithms), and x is actually the fraction,

$$x = \frac{t}{RC}$$

This expression is not as difficult to use as might be at first imagined. The value of ε^{-x} may be found from mathematical tables of exponentials. One is included in the appendix of this book.

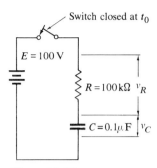

Figure 12-22

Suppose we have a series RC circuit, with $R = 100$ kΩ, $C = 0.1$ μF, and a source potential $E = 100$ V, as in Figure 12-22. Find the voltage v_C across the capacitor 0.003 sec after the circuit is completed.

EXAMPLE

Solution.   Elapsed time $t = 3 \times 10^{-3}$ sec.

$$RC = 10^5 \times 10^{-7} = 10^{-2} \text{ sec}$$

$$x = \frac{t}{RC} = \frac{3 \times 10^{-3}}{10^{-2}} = 3 \times 10^{-1} = 0.3$$

Therefore,

$$v_C = E(1 - \varepsilon^{-0.3})$$

From the tables

$$\varepsilon^{-0.3} = 0.740818$$

Substituting,

$$v_C = E(1 - 0.740818) = E(0.259182)$$

Since $E = 100$ V,

$$v_C = 100 \times 0.259182 = 25.9182 \text{ V}$$

This answer is expressed to more significant figures than are justified by the precision with which the original circuit constants are known; therefore, the result should be rounded off to 26 V.

Since

$$E = iR + v_C \quad \text{and} \quad v_C = E(1 - \varepsilon^{-x})$$

then by substitution,

$$E = iR + E(1 - \varepsilon^{-x})$$

Solving this equation for i,

$$i = \frac{E}{R}\varepsilon^{-x}$$

This equation gives the circuit current. Since i is the instantaneous value of the circuit current, and since resistor R is in series with the circuit, current i must also be the instantaneous value of the current through the resistor. From this, we can use Ohm's law to calculate the value of the voltage across the resistor at any instant.

$$i_R = \frac{e_R}{R}$$

Therefore,

$$\frac{e_R}{R} = \frac{E}{R}\varepsilon^{-x}$$

Multiplying both sides by R,

$$e_R = E\varepsilon^{-x}$$

This represents the instantaneous voltage across the resistor at t seconds after charge has started, where again, $x = t/RC$.

An examination of these equations, and a comparison of the results they give with the universal time constant graph, reveals that ε^{-x} represents a quantity that starts at 1 where x has the value 0, and as the value of x increases (with increasing t), the value of the quantity ε^{-x} decreases toward zero. The quantity $1 - \varepsilon^{-x}$ starts at zero and increases in value with increasing values of x, and finally approaches 1 as a limit. If this is kept in mind, then the problem of how to remember all the equations is greatly diminished. If you are dealing with a quantity that increases exponentially, then the initial value of the quantity times $1 - \varepsilon^{-x}$ will show how it increases, and give the value at any time t, if $x = t/RC$. If you are dealing with a quantity that decreases exponentially, then the proper multiplier for the initial value of that quantity is ε^{-x}.

Problems　　**1.** A 20 μF capacitor is connected in series with a 0.4 MΩ resistor and a 200 V potential source. Determine the initial charging current, the time for one time constant, and the approximate time required for the capacitor to charge to 200 V.

2. A 400 pF capacitor is connected in series with a 600 MΩ resistor and a 500 V potential source. Find the initial charging current, the time for one time constant, and the approximate time required for the capacitor to charge to 500 V.

3. A series RC circuit, where $R = 3\,\text{M}\Omega$ and $C = 0.002\,\mu\text{F}$, is connected to a 200 V source. Using the universal time constant graph, how much time will elapse before the voltage across the capacitor equals 50 V? equals 100 V? equals 150 V?

4. A series RC circuit, where $R = 400\,\text{k}\Omega$ and $C = 250\,\text{pF}$, is connected to a 500 V source. Using the universal time constant graph, determine the voltages across the capacitor after 0.05 msec, 0.2 msec, and 0.5 msec have elapsed.

5. A 40 μF capacitor, charged to 300 V, is suddenly connected across a resistance of 2 MΩ. How long will it take for the capacitor to discharge to 200 V? to 100 V? to 50 V?

6. The series RC circuit shown, where $R = 2\,\text{k}\Omega$ and $C = 8\,\mu\text{F}$, has a switch that connects to a 400 V potential source or to a short circuit across the source. Assume that the switch is initially connected to the voltage source. At the instant the capacitor has been charged to 300 V, the switch is suddenly connected to the short for 40 msec, and then switched back to the source for 24 msec. At this time the switch is opened but not connected to either terminal. Using the universal time constant graph, find the time elapsed at the first switching and the voltage across the capacitor at the times of the second and third switchings.

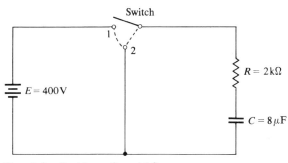

Circuit for Problems 6 and 13.

7. Consider the following series RC circuit with a pulsed voltage input signal (V_{in}), where $R = 20\,\text{M}\Omega$ and $C = 0.05\,\mu\text{F}$. Using the universal time constant graph, determine for the first four pulses the values of the voltages across R and C at the beginning and end of each pulse of the input signal. Make a drawing of the corresponding signals across R and C over the whole of this time period.

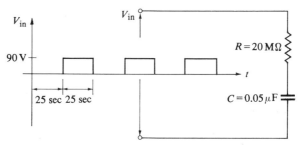

RC circuit for Problem 7.

8. Consider the series RC circuit with a pulsed input signal, where $R = 500$ kΩ and $C = 60$ μF. Using the universal time constant graph, determine the voltages across R and C at the beginning and end of each pulse of the input signal for the first four pulses and at steady state. Make a drawing of the corresponding signals across R and C over the time period of the first four pulses and when the circuit is in the steady-state condition.

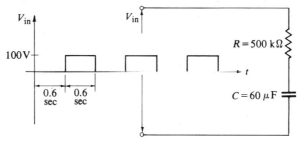

RC circuit for Problem 8.

9. Consider a series RC circuit with a pulsed input signal, where $R = 700$ kΩ and $C = 0.12$ μF. Using the universal time constant graph, determine the voltages across R and C at the beginning and end of each pulse of the input signal, for the first four pulses. Make a drawing of the corresponding signals across R and C over the whole of this time period.

RC circuit for Problem 9.

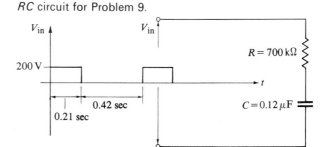

10. Consider a series *RC* circuit with a two-step pulsed input signal, where $R = 1.5$ MΩ and $C = 4$ μF. Using the universal time constant graph, make drawings of the resulting voltage output signals across *R* and *C* for the first four input pulses, giving the appropriate voltage values.

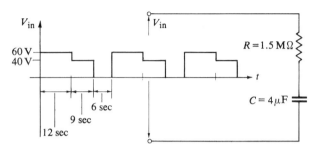

RC circuit for Problem 10.

11. Consider the series *RC* circuit and the input waveform illustrated, where $R = 5$ MΩ and $C = 0.01$ μF. Using the universal time constant graph, determine the voltages across *R* and *C* at every change of input voltage level during the first four cycles of the input signal and at steady state. Make drawings of the corresponding signals for both the initial period and at the steady-state condition.

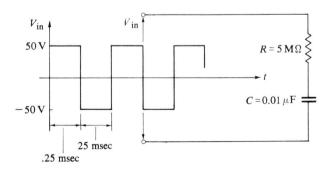

RC circuit for Problem 11.

12. A series *RC* circuit, where $R = 5.5$ MΩ and $C = 0.06$ μF, has the pulsed input voltage signal shown. Using algebraic methods, determine the voltages across *R* and *C*, and circuit current at the beginning and end of each input pulse, for the first four pulses. Draw the corresponding signals.

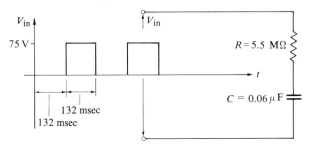

RC circuit for Problem 12.

13. Consider the series *RC* circuit with a two-way switch given in Problem 6. Using algebraic methods, determine the instantaneous value of the capacitor voltage, the resistor voltage, and the circuit current, at a time 3 msec after the switch is initially connected to the voltage source. Assume that the capacitor is initially uncharged. If also at that time the switch is then moved to the discharge position, calculate the voltages across *R* and *C*, and the circuit current, at a time 20 msec after this switching.

14. A 40 μF capacitor charged to 700 V is suddenly connected in series to a 600 kΩ resistor. Using algebraic means, calculate the instantaneous voltages across the capacitor and resistor, and the instantaneous circuit current at a time 29 sec after the connection is made.

12-5
Practical Capacitors

CAPACITOR TYPES. Capacitors may be fixed, adjustable, or variable. *Fixed capacitors* are usually tubular, though particularly in the smaller sizes they may be flattened rectangles. One common type is made as a small flat disk. Fixed capacitors are usually classified according to the dielectric used. The more common types are electrolytic, paper or mylar, mica, and ceramic.

ELECTROLYTIC CAPACITORS. Where high capacitance ratings are needed, leakage current is not significant, and the potential applied to the capacitor will always be the same polarity, *electrolytic capacitors* are usually used (Figure 12-23).

They consist of two metal electrodes, usually of aluminum, in an electrolytic solution of ammonia, boric acid, and water, though other materials may be used. During the process of manufacture, the capacitor is

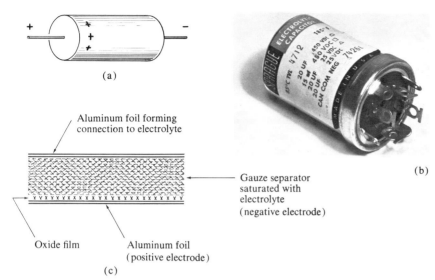

(a)

Aluminum foil forming
connection to electrolyte

Gauze separator
saturated with
electrolyte
(negative electrode)

(b)

Oxide film   Aluminum foil
(positive electrode)

(c)

Figure 12-23   Electrolytic capacitors. (a) A single electrolytic capacitor with axial leads. (b) A multiple-can type of electrolytic capacitor. (Courtesy Sprague Electric Co.) (c) A cross section of the internal construction of an electrolytic capacitor.

"formed" by passing a current through it. The electrolytic action on the surface of the aluminum electrode that is to form the positive plate of the capacitor results in the formation of an extremely thin layer of aluminum oxide.

This aluminum oxide is an insulator, and it is the dielectric of the finished capacitor. One plate is the aluminum electrode on which the oxide film is formed; the other plate of the capacitor is the electrolyte. The function of the other aluminum electrode is to provide the necessary connection to the electrolyte, so that the terminal connection may be brought out of the protective can in which the finished capacitor is encased.

Since the aluminum oxide layer which is the dielectric is so thin, high capacitance can be contained in a small space. Capacitors of 5 to 1000 μF are commonly electrolytics. Voltage ratings for these capacitors are usually below 500 V dc.

Electrolytic capacitors cannot be used on ac. The polarity of the applied voltage must always be such as to keep the electrode on which the aluminum oxide film is formed positive with respect to the electrolytic solution. If this electrode is permitted to become negative compared to the electrolyte, the chemical action which formed the film will be reversed, and the film will break down quickly. This results in the capacitor acting more like a resistor, and the heat due to current flow through it will cause the moisture in the electrolytic solution to turn to steam. This may develop sufficient pressure to rupture the case, producing a miniature boiler explosion. This is to be avoided. Electrolytic capacitors must always be connected with regard to polarity. The polarity for proper connections of the terminals is always marked on the case.

The thickness of the oxide film in electrolytic capacitors is determined at manufacture, but can be changed. Reverse connections will, as we have seen, result in the destruction of the film. Time, even without use, can result in a gradual reduction in the thickness of the film of oxide that is the necessary dielectric. With use, provided the voltage impressed across the dielectric is sufficient, the thickness of the film can be maintained for a considerable time. Therefore, electrolytic capacitors should be operated at near the design operating voltage in order to maintain the proper film thickness.

As electrolytic capacitors age, the electrolyte may tend to dry out. This increases the effective resistance of the capacitor terminals, and will usually result in a loss of capacity. This loss of capacity may be overshadowed by an apparent gain in capacity as the oxide film grows thinner. This thinning of the oxide film will result in an increase in resistive current, or leakage current, through the capacitor, increasing the heat loss in the electrolyte, and accelerating aging. Electrolytic capacitors are one of the most trouble-prone components in electronic circuitry, and in any equipment over ten years old are always suspect. Marginal functioning of electrolytic capacitors can be responsible for a bewildering array of minor malfunctions in the equipment of which they are a part.

PAPER AND PLASTIC FILM CAPACITORS. *Paper* and *plastic film capacitors* differ only in the nature of the dielectric. The usual construction employs thin sheets of aluminum foil separated by paper or plastic film insulation. The combination is rolled into tubular form, and separate connections made to each sheet of foil (Figure 12-24). The entire structure is then usually encapsulated in some insulating material, plastic being commonly used, though some may still be found with a wax-impregnated coating of paper. Leads may be either axial, as is most common with resistors, or radial.

In this rolled construction one of the two sheets of foil will, in the final turn, end up outside the other. This outside foil can serve as a shield surrounding the other, preventing the induced motion of electrons within the other foil due to the influence of external varying electric fields. This outer foil is usually marked, most often by a dark band around the body of the capacitor near the lead connecting to that foil. The capacitor should, for best shielding effect, be connected so the outer foil is nearest to ground potential in the circuit. Unlike the electrolytic capacitor, no damage will result from an incorrect connection, only a reduction in possible shielding effect.

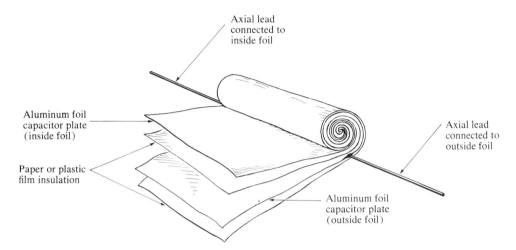

Figure 12-24   Construction of a paper or plastic film capacitor with axial leads.

If a plastic film is used as the dielectric, it is usually Mylar or Teflon. Both these materials have a very high insulation resistance, low losses, and long service life. They seem to be a real improvement over the tissue paper dielectric, long the most commonly used.

Both paper and plastic film capacitors are most commonly found in capacity ratings of from about 0.0001 μF to 1 μF, though a few are made with ratings outside these limits. Breakdown voltage ratings of the dielectric depend on thickness, but are usually from 200 V to 600 V.

In some larger units the paper dielectric is oil impregnated, and the finished capacitor is encapsulated in a metal case filled with insulating oil. This construction is usually reserved for capacitors of higher capacities, over 1 μF, and for voltage breakdown ratings of up to 5000 V. To a limited extent such a capacitor can be self-healing. A minor arc-through between plates that is of short duration will not cause the permanent damage that a similar puncturing of the dielectric film would in the case of a plastic film, since the oil with which the paper is impregnated can flow in to maintain the continuity of the dielectric film.

MICA CAPACITORS.   Mica is an extremely good insulator. It is a natural mineral material, and is found in a form that permits splitting into thin sheets. *Mica capacitors* have very low leakage losses, and what is more important for many applications, they lose little energy from losses comparable to hysteresis losses in each cycle of ac applied to the plates. They are, therefore, very useful in circuits where high frequencies are involved.

Mica is an intrinsically brittle material, and does not lend itself to the rolled construction suitable for paper or Mylar capacitors. In the usual construction, mica sheets are interleaved between sheets of conducting foil, with alternate sheets of the foil connected to each of the two terminals (Figure 12-25). The finished capacitor is usually encapsulated in Bakelite to make a small, flat, rectangular package, usually with axial leads. The customary range of values for mica capacitors is from 50 to 500 pF.

A *silvered-mica* capacitor is constructed by firing a thin layer of silver on each of the two sides of a thin sheet of mica, then attaching a lead to each layer of silver, and encapsulating the finished capacitor in plastic. This produces a capacitor of low capacitance, high stability, low leakage, low energy dissipation, and most important, consistent and repeatable variations in capacity with change in temperature. In many circuits, particularly those used in communications electronics, this is of extreme importance.

CERAMIC CAPACITORS.   The dielectric for *ceramic capacitors* is made of mineral materials fired under very high temperatures. The dielectric constant of some of these materials is extremely high, and they may be tailor-made to have desired changes in characteristics with change in temperature.

In one form a small disk of ceramic has silver fired onto both sides, with the leads connected to the thin silver plates, and the finished capacitor encapsulated by dipping into a plastic material. With this construction, capacities of up to 0.01 μF can be contained in very much less space than is required for a comparable paper or plastic film capacitor.

In another form a hollow tube of the ceramic is plated on the inside for one conductor, and on the outside for the other. This construction is most

Figure 12-25   A mica capacitor. (a) Interior construction. (b) The case. The color-coded dots on the case tell the value and rating.

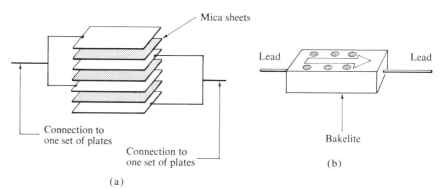

(a)   (b)

frequently used for units of small capacity, and where particular temperature variations of capacity are desired.

Ceramic capacitors have excellent stability, high insulation resistance, and low dissipation losses. They are suitable for high-voltage and high-frequency applications.

GLASS CAPACITORS. Though manufacturing techniques pose some difficulties, glass as a dielectric in small values of capacitance is becoming more common. Glass as a dielectric has extremely low losses, high stability, and reliability. A capacitor using glass as a dielectric, completely encapsulated in glass, and with gold-plated leads, is about as immune to deterioration from environmental factors as anything could be. Such capacitors are usually found in low values of capacitance, and are usually used in high-frequency applications.

VARIABLE CAPACITORS. *Variable capacitors* are usually air-spaced, which means there is nothing between the plates but air, or in some cases a vacuum, and the desired insulation between the plates is achieved by the space between them.

There are two sets of plates. In the most commonly encountered construction, one set of plates is mounted in a metal frame, from which it is insulated by porcelain, steatite, or micarta supports, while the other set of plates is attached to a shaft arranged so that it can rotate. The set of metal plates mounted in the frame is called the "fixed plates" or *stator*. The plates mounted on the rotatable shaft are called the "movable plates" or *rotor*. As the shaft is turned, the plates of the rotor move in or out of mesh with the stator. When the plates are meshed, or interleaved, the capacitance is maximum; when the plates are moved out of mesh, the capacitance is minimum.

Values of minimum capacitance are seldom lower than 10 pF, and maximum capacitance values with this construction are seldom above 500 pF, with the ratio between maximum and minimum capacitance for a particular unit seldom being more than about 40 to 1.

Sometimes, where the value of capacitance in more than one circuit at a time must be varied simultaneously, two or more sets of rotor plates are mounted on a single shaft, so they are mechanically locked in step with each other.

When you tune a radio, in the vast majority of cases you are turning the shaft of a variable capacitor with two sets of rotor plates. The two capacitors thus being varied work with inductors to vary the frequency to which the radio is tuned, and thus the stations which will be received.

Only three factors may be varied to change the value of a capacitance: the area of the plates, the spacing between plates, and the nature of the dielectric between the sets of plates. All three factors have been used to produce variable capacitors. In the capacitors just discussed, the capacitance is varied by varying the effective facing area of the plates, determined by the degree of mesh.

In one form, thin sheets of mica are interleaved between sets of plates which are arranged to spring apart if not constrained, but which have a screw through them to move them together against their springiness. When the screw is tightened, the capacitance is increased, and the capacitance may be decreased by loosening the screw. Such a capacitor is usually called *adjustable*, rather than variable. It is used for factory or maintenance adjustments of circuit constants, and is not meant for operator manipulation in the course of ordinary use of the device containing it.

The fine tuning of some TV sets is accomplished by rotating a spirally cut segment of Bakelite or a similar material between two metal plates which act as the plates of a capacitor. With the Bakelite segment rotated so that none of it is between the plates, the capacity between them is at a minimum, while the capacity is maximum with the Bakelite between the plates acting as a dielectric. In this way small changes in a low value of capacitance can be easily made. At the high frequencies at which TV tuners must operate, only such small changes are desired.

CAPACITOR COLOR CODES.   For capacitors of values above 1000 pF, the value of the capacitor and its voltage rating are almost invariably stamped on the outside of the case. If the capacitor is electrolytic, the proper polarity of connection will also be indicated. If it is of rolled foil construction, a band will mark the end to which the outer foil is connected.

For capacitors below 1000 pF in value, and for most mica and tubular ceramic capacitors, the value in pF is usually indicated by a *color code*. The numbers in the color code are the same as the numbers for the resistor color code system. Color coding systems for capacitors have been less standardized than for resistors. The marking systems most commonly encountered are detailed in the Appendix.

12-6
Capacitor Defects

OPENS AND SHORTS.   The internal connection of the leads to the plates of a capacitor may fail due to corrosion, or sometimes due to undue flexing of the lead itself. If this occurs, the capacitance of the unit will be reduced nearly to zero, though there will still be some residual capacitance. The capacitor will fail to function as designed, but there will be little likelihood of damage to other components because of this sort of failure. The capacitor in which this occurs is said to be *open* and must be replaced.

A *shorted* capacitor is one in which there is a low resistance connection between plates. This is usually the result of too high a voltage applied, even for a fraction of a second, though some units may fail for no apparent cause. If this defect occurs, there can be high current through the capacitor, and other components in series with the capacitor and the source of potential may be damaged. Where such a defect has occurred, it is always wise to suspect the possibility of such secondary damage. In particular, resistors in series with a shorted capacitor may become open, or have their resistance increase, and may need to be replaced themselves to restore the circuit to proper functioning.

In some instances, particularly with paper capacitors, the shorted condition may exist only when the voltage across the capacitor exceeds a certain value. If there is a rupture of the dielectric film that does not involve actual contact between the opposite sets of plates, arcing may occur only at the peaks of the applied voltage. As arcing continues to occur over a period of time, the chemical nature of the dielectric may break down. If it is a paper or plastic film dielectric, one of the breakdown materials formed is carbon, which is a conductor. This will cause leakage current, and the voltage at which the breakdown occurs gradually becomes less. In the early stages this condition can be difficult to diagnose, especially since it may occur only occasionally.

A capacitor may be checked roughly with an ohmmeter. A shorted condition will reveal itself by a low resistance reading between the capacitor terminals. It is, of course, necessary to be sure there are no parallel current paths which could be responsible for the low resistance reading. If the capacitor is connected in a circuit, one terminal may need to be disconnected before the ohmmeter reading can be made. For the protection of the ohmmeter, the capacitor must be discharged before the reading is attempted.

Capacitors of large value which have been subjected to high dc voltages for any length of time, particularly electrolytic capacitors, may seem to regain their charge after they have been discharged, and without being connected to any source of potential. This may be seen if an electrolytic capacitor in good condition is connected to a dc source, with the correct polarity, and charged to the source potential through some suitable current-limiting resistor. When the dc voltage source is disconnected, and the capacitor discharged, again through a suitable current-limiting resistor, the voltage across the capacitor can be shown—by connecting a voltmeter across it—to be zero at that instant. If the discharge circuit is then opened, while the voltmeter remains connected across the capacitor, the capacitor voltage will be seen to rise, perhaps to several tens of volts. If the capacitor is again discharged to zero, and the discharge circuit immediately broken, the same phenomenon may again occur, though this time with the capacitor regaining a smaller charge. This occurs because some of the energy stored in the dielectric is in the form of mechanical stress or short-term chemical stress, and is returned to a charge difference between the plates quite slowly. Such a capacitor may need to be discharged for several minutes before ohmmeter readings across it will have any validity. If there is any charge existing on a capacitor to which an ohmmeter is connected, the reading obtained may well indicate a resistance higher than infinity or less than zero, depending on the polarity of charge. Both readings are manifestly useless as indications of any condition of the capacitor except that it retains some charge.

Assuming the capacitor is uncharged, an ohmmeter can indicate opens, shorts, and to an extent, leakage. A shorted capacitor will show a low resistance. A good capacitor, checked on a high range of the ohmmeter, will show an initial deflection of the pointer as the capacitor charges. The pointer should climb immediately following this initial deflection to a reading of infinity, or near infinity. The initial deflection may not be observable with capacitors having only a few picofarads of capacity. Capacitors having a large capacity will show a large deflection, and a slow climb toward infinity.

Electrolytic capacitors will show a high leakage current and, consequently, a low apparent resistance. The leakage current will be much greater if the ohmmeter is connected with a polarity opposite to the marked polarity of the capacitor. If the reading is to be meaningful, care should be taken to ensure correct polarity of connections.

Care must also be taken to ensure that the body of the person holding the ohmmeter leads does not become a parallel current path, particularly when testing low-capacity capacitors on a high resistance range. If you are accidentally reading your own body resistance, you will gain no knowledge of the capacitor you are attempting to check.

Commercial capacitor checkers do a better job than the simple ohmmeter. They will measure capacity, leakage current, and insulation resistance, and the leakage current measurements will be made at the rated working voltage of the capacitor. This can show up defects that the low voltage of the ohmmeter cannot. Many of the commercial capacitor checkers can also measure the capacitor losses due to such factors as internal resistance and dielectric hysteresis. Again, at least one terminal of the capacitor must be disconnected from the circuit before such tests can be made.

Key Words

breakdown voltage   the limit to which a dielectric can be stressed without destroying its insulating properties, usually expressed in V/mil

capacitor   any two-terminal circuit element in which the current is directly proportional to the rate of change of voltage between the terminals

ceramic capacitor   a type of capacitor in which the dielectric is composed of mineral materials and fired at very high temperatures, giving it a high dielectric constant

dielectric   any insulating material (including a vacuum) between two conductors

dielectric constant (K_ε)   a measure of the ability of a given dielectric to concentrate flux lines of the field existing between the plates of a charged capacitor

electrolytic capacitor   a capacitor consisting of two metal electrodes (usually aluminum) in an electrolytic solution of ammonia, boric acid, and water, suitable only for use with dc

farad (F)   the unit of capacity. Practical measurements are usually given in microfarads (μF) or picofarads (pF). $1\ \mu\mathrm{F} = 10^{-6}\ \mathrm{F}$ and $1\ \mathrm{pF} = 10^{-12}\ \mathrm{F}$.

glass capacitor   a capacitor whose dielectric is glass, which resists deterioration. Glass capacitors are used in high-frequency applications.

mica capacitor   a capacitor whose dielectric is the mineral mica; used in high-frequency applications

open   a capacitor defect in which the internal connection of the leads to the plates fails

paper or plastic film capacitor   capacitor in which thin sheets of aluminum separated by paper or plastic film insulation are rolled into tubular form and encased in insulating material, usually plastic

relative permittivity   permittivity compared to the absolute permittivity of free space

short   a capacitor defect in which there is a low resistance connection between plates, usually the result of too high voltage

variable capacitor   a capacitor with two sets of plates, one set fixed and the other set rotating, and used where variable capacity is necessary as in a radio tuner

1. A two-terminal circuit which fits the definition of a capacitor will function as a capacitor in any circuit to which it is connected.   **Summary of Concepts**

2. In a simple capacitor, charge depends on the source potential and the innate capacity of the plates to store charge.

3. The capacity of the plates to store charge depends on the area of the plates, the distance between them, and the nature of the material between them.

4. If an insulator is placed between the plates of a charged capacitor, the electrons of the insulator will experience a force impelling them away from the negative plate and toward the positive plate.

5. In a charged capacitor the face of the dielectric toward the negative plate will be positively charged, while the face toward the positive plate will be slightly negatively charged. This is so because the electrons of the dielectric are shifted slightly toward the positive plate, but the atoms to which the electrons belong are not.

6. A dielectric concentrates the flux lines of the electric field existing between the plates of a charged capacitor.

7. Most of the energy stored in a capacitor is in the form of dielectric stress.

8. A capacitor containing stored energy can be a source of electric shock.

9. When capacitors are connected in parallel, the effect is the same as if the plate area were increased.

10. The capacitance of a series string of capacitors is less than the capacitance of any of the capacitors in the string.

11. A capacitor cannot charge in zero time.

12. The voltage across an uncharged capacitor is zero since there is no dielectric stress, no difference in charge between the plates, and therefore no difference in potential between them.

13. The time constant of an *RC* circuit is the time it would take for the voltage across the capacitor to rise to the source voltage if the capacitor voltage were to rise at a constant rate during the charging interval.

14. An ohmmeter can indicate shorts, opens, and, to an extent, leakage in an uncharged capacitor.

15. The time constant makes it possible to use a simple graphic method to calculate instantaneous values of the voltage across a charging capacitor for times less than five time constants.

16. For practical purposes, a capacitor essentially reaches source voltage five time constants after the switch is closed.

On a separate sheet of paper, fill in the blanks or answer the questions below. The number following each question refers to the section in the chapter where the correct answer can be found.

To Help You Review

1. What is the current in a capacitor directly proportional to? (12-1)

2. Charging a capacitor depends on _____ and _____? (12-1)

3. What is the basic unit of capacity? What two compound units are usually more practical in electronics? (12-1)

4. How does the dielectric in a capacitor work? (12-2)

5. What is the operating similarity between a dielectric and a ferromagnetic core? (12-2)

6. Explain dielectric breakdown. (12-2)

7. In what two ways are practical dielectric materials measured? (12-2)

8. What dielectric has the lowest energy loss? (12-2)

9. Energy is stored in a capacitor in the form of _____. (12-2)

10. How can the energy stored in a capacitor be hazardous? (12-2)

11. When capacitors are connected in parallel, the effect is the same as if _____. (12-3)

12. For capacitors connected in parallel, total capacitance is the sum of _____. (12-3)

13. Capacitors in series add the same way as _____. (12-3)

14. Why can't a capacitor charge in zero time? (12-4)

15. Why is the voltage across an uncharged capacitor zero? (12-4)

16. What is the time constant of an *RC* circuit? (12-4)

17. What use do we make of the time constant in calculations? (12-4)

18. The graph of voltage plotted against time is a _____. (12-4)

19. At what point is a capacitor considered to be fully charged? (12-4)

20. What happens to voltage between pulses? What is this called? (12-4)

21. Write an equation that describes your answer to Question 20. (12-4)

22. The full voltage to which a capacitor has been charged will appear across _____. The polarity of this voltage is _____. (12-4)

23. Name three capacitor types and mention at least one good or bad point of each. (12-5)

24. What is unique about variable capacitors? (12-5)

25. What three factors change the value of a capacitor? (12-5)

26. Describe two capacitor defects. (12-6)

27. How can an ohmmeter be used to indicate capacitor defects? (12-6)

THIRTEEN

INDUCTANCE AND INACTORS

INDUCTANCE DEFINED. An *inductance* is a companion circuit element to the capacitor. Though the two perform many functions separately, they also work together to form what has been perhaps the most important team in communications electronics.

The capacitor was defined in terms of current and voltage, as a two-terminal device in which the circuit current was proportional to the rate of change of voltage.

The inductor is the dual of the capacitor. We may define an inductor as follows:

An inductor is a two-terminal circuit element in which the voltage between terminals of the element is proportional to the rate of change of current through the inductor.

Note that the magnitude of the current does not enter into this definition. The current may be large or small, but if it is not changing, there will be no voltage between the terminals. If the

13-1
Inductance

415

current is changing, then the voltage will be present. The magnitude of the voltage is completely independent of the amount of current, and completely dependent on the rate of change of current. The polarity of the voltage is determined by whether the current is increasing or decreasing.

THE SIMPLE INDUCTOR.   Suppose a conductor is wound into a coil. If it is connected to a source of potential, with a series switch and a resistor, then current will start to flow through the coil when the switch is closed (Figure 13-1).

As the current starts to flow, the magnetic field due to the current must increase. As this magnetic field expands, it cuts across the turns of the coil. As the magnetic field due to the current flow in any one turn of the coil cuts across adjacent turns of the same coil, it induces a potential in them.

By Lenz's law this potential must be in opposition to the potential that produced the original current. Since this potential appears as the result of the relative motion between the expanding or contracting magnetic field and the turns of the coil through which it moves, it can occur only when the current that produces the magnetic field is changing. If the current is steady, the magnetic field associated with it is neither expanding nor contracting, and there can be no relative motion between it and the turns of the coil.

At the instant the switch is closed, the current is zero. At some later time, the current will have risen to its maximum value, limited only by the series resistance in the circuit. Between those two times, the current must obviously change.

Figure 13-1   A simple circuit, in which current flowing from the source through the coil induces an opposing potential in the coil.

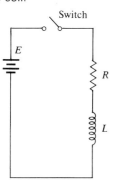

INDUCTANCE.   Consider the following statement from the definition of the inductor:

The voltage at any instant is proportional to the rate of change of current. And now, the same statement in mathematical symbols:

$$e_L = L \frac{di}{dt}$$

where e_L is the instantaneous value of the voltage between the terminals of the inductor, di/dt is the rate of change of current at that instant measured in amperes/second (A/sec), and L is the proportionality factor necessary if e_L is to be in volts.

This proportionality factor L is called the *inductance* and is as characteristic of a particular coil as the resistance in ohms is of a particular resistor, or the capacity in farads is of a particular capacitor. The unit of inductance is the *henry* (H).

Given a coil of 0.1 H inductance, if the current is changing at some instant at the rate of 4 A/sec, what will be the voltage between the coil terminals?   EXAMPLE

Solution. $L = 0.1$ H, and $di/dt = 4$ A/sec. Therefore,

   $e_L = (0.1)(4) = 0.4$ V at that instant

It is observed that when the current through a coil is changing at the rate of 100 A/sec, the voltage across the coil is 2 V at the same instant. What is the inductance of the coil?   EXAMPLE

Solution. $e_L = 2$ V, and $di/dt = 100$ A/sec. Therefore,

$$L = \frac{e_L}{di/dt} = \frac{2}{100} = 0.02 \text{ H} = 20 \text{ mH}$$

As with all the other units, henrys are expressed in the number of thousandths of a henry, or *millihenrys* (mH), and in the number of millionths, or *microhenrys* (μH). Nearly all the inductance values encountered in electronics are between the values of 100 H and a few μH.

The actual inductance of a given coil depends on its physical construction. The following factors determine the inductance.

1.   The number of turns (N) affects the inductance, because each turn is cut by the magnetic field of every other turn. Thus, doubling the number of turns doubles the amount of flux cutting each turn and, consequently, doubles the potential developed in each turn. The total coil potential e_L is the sum of the potentials developed in each turn. Doubling the number of turns *and* doubling the potential in each turn will *quadruple* the total coil potential. Thus, the inductance is proportional to the square of the number of turns (N^2).
2.   Increasing the area A for each turn increases the inductance, because each portion of a turn will be more affected by those portions of another turn immediately adjacent to it, and less by those portions of turns opposite to it, on the other side of the coil.
3.   The inductance is affected by the permeability of the core. The more permeable the core, the more it concentrates the flux. Doubling the core permeability doubles the flux and, therefore, the inductance.
4.   For a given number of turns, a long coil will have less inductance than a short one, since with the short coil the flux is more concentrated.

The inductance is therefore *inversely* proportional to the length l of a coil.

From the consideration of the above factors, the equation relating them nearly writes itself. It is

$$L = \frac{N^2 A \mu_a \mu_r}{l}$$

where N is the number of turns, A is the area in square meters of each turn, μ_a is the absolute permeability of air or vacuum in MKS units, μ_r is the relative permeability of any core material other than air, and l is the length of the coil in meters. This is correct only for a long coil, where the length is at least ten times the diameter, since it assumes parallel lines of force which are approached only with a long coil.

EXAMPLE   Calculate the inductance of a coil of 250 turns if the coil is 2 cm in diameter and 25 cm long, with an air core.

Solution. $N = 250 = 2.5 \times 10^2$ and $A = 2\pi r^2$, where $r = 2$ cm $= 0.02$ m. Therefore, $A = 2\pi \times 0.002$. $l = 0.25$ m, and $\mu_a = 1.26 \times 10^{-6}$. Thus,

$$L - \frac{[2.5 \times 10^2]^2 [2\pi(0.02^2)](1.26 \times 10^{-6})}{0.25}$$

$$= 252 \times 10^{-6} \text{ H} \cong 250 \ \mu\text{H}$$

Problems   **1.**   Given a coil of 25 mH, if at some instant of time the current is changing at a rate of 50 A/sec, what will be the voltage between the coil terminals?

2.   Given a coil of 0.6 H, if at some instant of time the current is changing at a rate of 3 A/sec, what will be the voltage between the coil terminals?

3.   If at a certain point in time the voltage across a coil of 2 μH is 12.4 mV, what is the rate of change of the current at that instant?

4.   At the instant the current through a coil is changing at a rate of 350 A/sec, the voltage across the coil's terminals is measured at 10.5 V. What is the inductance of the coil?

5.   Calculate the inductance of a coil of 450 turns if the coil is 3.5 cm in diameter and 40 cm long, with an air core.

6.   Calculate the inductance of a coil of 1500 turns if the coil is 3 cm in diameter, 35 cm long, and wrapped around a ferromagnetic core with with a relative permeability of 22,000.

7. A 3.6 H coil is wrapped around a ferromagnetic core with a relative permeability of 50,000. The coil has a diameter of 2 cm and is 22 cm long. How many turns are there in the coil?

8. A coil of 300 turns, having a diameter of 3 cm, is wrapped around a ferromagnetic core with a relative permeability of 45,000. If the inductance of the coil is 10 H, what is its length?

SERIES INDUCTORS. If two inductors are in series with each other, as in Figure 13-2, but the magnetic fields of either do not cut through the turns of the other, then the inductance of the combination will be the simple sum of the separate inductances. That is,

13-2
Inductance in Series
and Parallel

$$L_t = L_1 + L_2$$

And for more than two inductors,

$$L_t = L_1 + L_2 + L_3 \ldots$$

This is true only if *none* of the inductors is affected by the magnetic field of *any* of the others.

PARALLEL INDUCTORS. If inductors are connected in parallel, and if *none* of the inductors is affected by the magnetic field of *any* of the others, as in Figure 13-3, the total inductance is calculated the same as for resistors in parallel. That is,

$$\frac{1}{L_t} = \frac{1}{L_1} + \frac{1}{L_2} + \frac{1}{L_3} \ldots$$

Figure 13-2 If inductors are connected in series and if the magnetic field of neither one cuts through the turns of the other inductor, then the total inductance is the simple sum of the separate inductances.

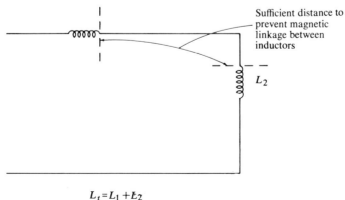

Sufficient distance to prevent magnetic linkage between inductors

L_2

$L_t = L_1 + L_2$

If there are only two inductors, then by the same mathematical manipulation as for the case of two resistors in parallel,

$$L_t = \frac{L_1 L_2}{L_1 + L_2}$$

EXAMPLE Given two inductors connected in parallel, so that neither is affected by the magnetic field of the other, if $L_1 = 6$ H and $L_2 = 3$ H, what is the total inductance of the combination?

Solution.

$$L_t = \frac{L_1 L_2}{L_1 + L_2} = \frac{(6)(3)}{6 + 3} = \frac{18}{9} = 2 \text{ H}$$

MUTUAL INDUCTANCE. If two or more coils are connected so that each *is* affected by the magnetic field of the other, they are said to have *mutual inductance*. The total inductance of the combination, assuming the coils are series-connected, depends on the amount of mutual inductance and on whether the coils are connected *series-aiding* or *series-opposing* (Figure 13-4). If they are series-aiding, the magnetic fields of the two coils are in the same direction; if they are series-opposing, the magnetic fields are of opposite polarity and partially cancel each other.

For series inductances where there is significant mutual inductance,

$$L_t = L_1 + L_2 \pm 2L_M$$

Figure 13-3 If two inductors are connected in parallel and if neither inductor is affected by the magnetic field of the other, then total inductance is calculated as for resistors in parallel.

where L_M is the mutual inductance. It will be positive if the two coils are connected series-aiding, and negative when they are series-opposing.

The mutual inductance depends on the amount of *flux linkage* between the two coils. Coils are said to be *tightly coupled* if all or nearly all of the flux of one coil also cuts through the other coil, and *loosely coupled* if only a small part of the flux of one links the other.

This is expressed numerically by the *coefficient of coupling*, k, which is the ratio between the flux linkages between the coils and the flux of one coil. That is,

$$k = \frac{\text{Flux linkages}}{\text{Flux of a single coil}}$$

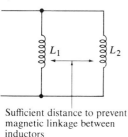

Sufficient distance to prevent magnetic linkage between inductors

$$L_t = \frac{1}{\frac{1}{L_1} + \frac{1}{L_2}}$$

There are no units for k, since it is a ratio between two quantities expressed in the same units. If $k = 1$, the two coils are completely coupled, and all of the flux produced by a coil links it to the other coil. If $k = 0$, there is no mutual coupling between coils.

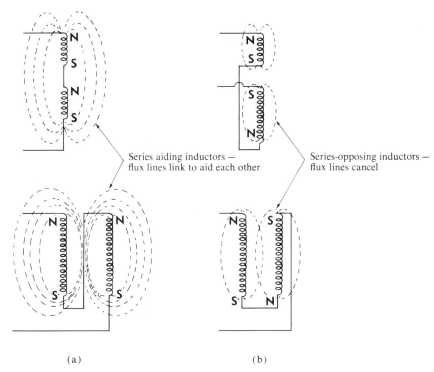

Series aiding inductors —
flux lines link to aid each other

Series-opposing inductors —
flux lines cancel

(a)(b)

Figure 13-4 Mutual inductance. (a) Coils are series-aiding, and the magnetic fields have the same polarity. The flux lines link to aid each other. (b) Coils are series-opposing, and the fields have opposing polarity and partially cancel one another.

Mutual inductance L_M is related to the coefficient of coupling k by the following equation:

$$L_M = k \sqrt{L_1 L_2}$$

In practice, the coefficient of coupling is seldom known. If it is, of course, then the mutual inductance can be calculated, knowing the inductance of the two coils.

In the more common case, the inductance of two coils may be measured separately, and the total inductance with both series-aiding and series-opposing connections measured. If this can be done, both L_M and k can be calculated.

Since the total inductance L_{t_a} of two coils in series-aiding is

$$L_{t_a} = L_1 + L_2 + 2L_M$$

and the total inductance L_{t_o} of two coils in series-opposing is

$$L_{t_o} = L_1 + L_2 - 2L_M$$

the difference between the two values of total inductance must be

$$L_{t_a} - L_{t_o} = (L_1 + L_2 + 2L_M) - (L_1 + L_2 - 2L_M) = 4L_M$$

and

$$L_M = \frac{L_{t_a} - L_{t_o}}{4}$$

It is not necessary to know ahead of time which connection is series-aiding, and which is series-opposing. The larger of the two values of total inductance *must* be the series-aiding connection.

Where the mutual inductance L_M can be thus experimentally derived, and the value of the inductance of the two individual inductors can be determined, the coefficient of coupling k can be readily calculated from

$$L_M = k \sqrt{L_1 L_2}$$

Therefore,

$$k = \frac{L_M}{\sqrt{L_1 L_2}}$$

EXAMPLE   Two coils are known to be 0.008 H and 0.006 H, respectively. When they are connected in series and the total inductance is measured, it is found to be 0.018 H. The leads to one of the two coils are then reversed, and the total inductance found to be 0.010 H. What is the mutual inductance, and what is the coefficient of coupling k? Was the first connection series-aiding or series-opposing?

Solution. The first connection must have been series-aiding, since it produced the greatest value of total inductance. Thus, $L_{t_a} = 0.018$ H and $L_{t_o} = 0.010$ H.

$$L_M = \frac{L_{t_a} - L_{t_o}}{4} = \frac{0.018 - 0.010}{4} = 0.002 \text{ H}$$

and

$$k = \frac{L_M}{\sqrt{L_1 L_2}} = \frac{0.002}{\sqrt{0.018 \times 0.010}} = \frac{0.002}{1.34 \times 10^{-2}} = 0.149$$

1. Consider three inductors connected in series, where $L_1 = 2$ mH, $L_2 = 44$ mH, and $L_3 = 14$ mH. Calculate the total inductance, assuming that none of the inductors is affected by the magnetic field of any of the others.

2. Consider five inductors connected in series, where $L_1 = 20$ mH, $L_2 = 410$ mH, $L_3 = 1.1$ H, $L_4 = 720$ mH, and $L_5 = 61$ mH. Calculate the total inductance, assuming that none of the inductors is affected by the magnetic field of any of the others.

3. Consider three inductors connected in parallel, where $L_1 = 2$ μH, $L_2 = 13\,\mu$H, and $L_3 = 7.4\,\mu$H. Calculate the total inductance, assuming that there is no mutual magnetic interaction between them.

4. Consider five inductors connected in parallel, where $L_1 = 1.5$ H, $L_2 = 12$ H, $L_3 = 4$ H, $L_4 = 7$ H, and $L_5 = 20$ H. Calculate the total inductance, assuming that there is no mutual magnetic interaction between them.

5. Calculate the total inductance of the series–parallel combination of inductors shown, where $L_1 = 0.03$ H, $L_2 = 0.75$ H, $L_3 = 1$ H, $L_4 = 0.04$ H, $L_5 = 0.17$ H, $L_6 = 0.06$ H and $L_7 = 0.08$ H. Assume that there is no magnetic interaction between the inductors.

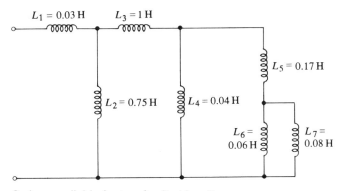

Series–parallel inductors for Problem 5.

6. Calculate the total inductance of the series–parallel combination of inductors shown, where $L_1 = 6$ H, $L_2 = 1$ H, $L_3 = 20$ H, $L_4 = 14$ H, $L_5 = 7$ H, $L_6 = 8$ H, $L_7 = 2$ H, $L_8 = 30$ H, $L_9 = 3$ H, and $L_{10} = 9$ H. Assume that there is no magnetic interaction between the inductors.

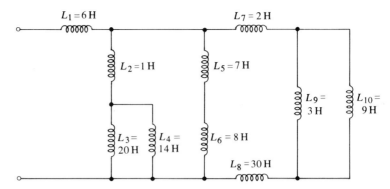

Series–parallel inductors for Problem 6.

7. Consider two inductors connected in series, where $L_1 = 2$ mH, $L_2 = 5$ mH, and a coefficient of coupling $k = 0.472$. Calculate the mutual inductance.

8. Consider two inductors connected in series, where $L_1 = 0.03$ H, $L_2 = 0.15$ H, and a coefficient of coupling $k = 0.98$. Calculate the mutual inductance, and the total inductance when the two inductors are in a series-aiding combination.

9. Consider two inductors connected in series, where $L_1 = 0.002$ H and $L_2 = 0.007$ H. When the inductance is first measured, it is found to be 0.0075 H. When the leads of one of the coils are reversed, the total inductance is found to be 0.013 H. What is the mutual inductance, and what is the coefficient of coupling k? Was the first connection series-aiding or series-opposing?

10. Consider two inductors connected in series, where $L_1 = 32$ μH and $L_2 = 44$ μH. When the total inductance is first measured, it is found to be 93 μH. When the leads of one of the coils are reversed, the total inductance is found to be 53 μH. What is the mutual inductance, and what is the coefficient of coupling k? Was the first connection series-aiding or series-opposing?

11. Two inductors are combined in a series-opposing combination, where $L_1 = 4$ H, $L_2 = 18$ H, and the mutual inductance is 6.4 H. What are the coefficient of coupling k and the total inductance? If the connections of one of the coils are reversed so as to make the inductors series-aiding, what would be the new total inductance?

12. Consider four inductors connected in series, as shown, where $L_1 = 0.2$ H, $L_2 = 0.5$ H, $L_3 = 0.9$ H, and $L_4 = 0.75$ H. The magnetic fields of L_1 and L_2 affect each other, and the fields of L_3 and L_4 affect each other. However, the fields between any other pair do not interact. When the total inductance of the circuit is initially measured, it is found to be 3.43 H. After the connecting leads between coils L_3 and L_4 are reversed, the total inductance is found to be 1.83 H. The connections between coils L_1 and L_2 are then reversed and the total inductance is now found to be 1.27 H. The connections between L_3 and L_4 are reversed again and the total inductance is measured at 2.87 H. Calculate the mutual inductances and coefficients of coupling for both inductance pairs (L_1 and L_2, and L_3 and L_4).

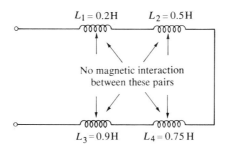

$$L_1 = 0.2\text{H} \qquad L_2 = 0.5\text{H}$$

No magnetic interaction between these pairs

$$L_3 = 0.9\text{H} \qquad L_4 = 0.75\text{H}$$

Series-connected inductors for Problem 12.

THE SERIES *LR* CIRCUIT.   The current through an inductor cannot change in zero time. An inductor has been defined as a two-terminal component in which the terminal voltage is proportional to the rate of change of current through the component. If the current through an inductor were to change in zero time, then the rate of change of current would at that instant be infinite, and, consequently, the terminal voltage would also have to be infinite. This is not possible; therefore, the current through an inductor cannot change in zero time.

Consider the circuit of Figure 13-5. It is a simple series circuit, with a voltage source E, a resistance R, and an inductance L, with a switch. With the switch open, there is no current through either component, and no voltage across them. There is no magnetic field associated with the inductor L, and no energy stored in it.

At the instant after the switch is closed, the circuit current must be zero. This is because the current through the inductor cannot change in zero time. The current through the resistor must, therefore, at that instant be zero, and the voltage across the resistor will, consequently, be zero.

13-3
LR Circuits and Time Constants

Figure 13-5   A   simple series *RL* circuit.

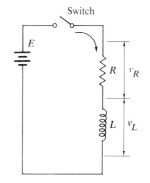

By Kirchhoff's voltage law the circuit voltages at any instant must sum to zero. Therefore,

$$E = v_R + v_L$$

where E is the source voltage, v_R is the instantaneous value of the voltage across the resistor, and v_L is the instantaneous value of the voltage across the inductor. But at the initial instant after the switch is closed, the voltage v_R across the resistor is zero. Therefore, at that instant,

$$v_L = E$$

Thus, at the initial instant the full source voltage will appear across the inductor. But the only condition under which there can be a voltage across the terminals of an inductor, from our definition, is if the current is changing, since the voltage is proportional to the rate of change of current.

It is not a contradiction to say the current is zero, but is at that instant changing. Imagine that a gun is fired straight up. At the instant the bullet leaves the barrel its altitude is zero, but it is at that instant changing. In the same way, the current at the initial instant after the switch is closed is zero, but is increasing rapidly.

Thus, though the circuit current is zero at the initial instant after the switch is closed, it will not stay zero. But as current starts to flow, it must flow through the resistor, too, and there must, therefore, be some voltage across the resistor. Since the sum of the voltage across the resistor and the voltage across the inductor must be a constant and equal to the circuit source potential, the voltage across the inductor must decrease as the current increases and the consequent resistor voltage rises.

The inductor voltage is directly proportional to the rate of change of current, since

$$v_L = L\frac{di}{dt}$$

and L is a constant. If v_L changes, then di/dt, which is the rate of change of current, must also be changing.

Therefore, as the circuit current rises, and the voltage across the resistor increases and the voltage across the inductor decreases, the rate at which the current increases must continually grow less.

Figure 13-6 shows the way in which the circuit current, the voltage across the resistor, and the voltage across the inductor change with time. Compare this with Figure 12-12 for the *RC* circuit.

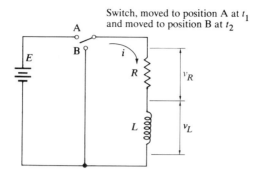

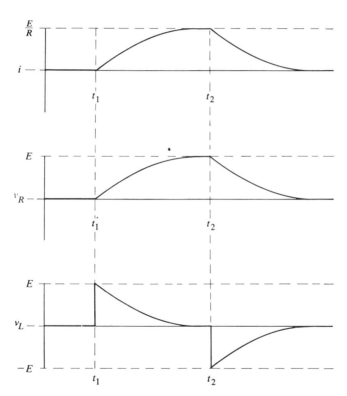

Figure 13-6　Curves showing change in current, voltage across the resistor, and voltage across the inductor with change in time for a simple *RL* series circuit.

TIME CONSTANTS. The universal time constant graph also applies to series RL circuits. At the instant the circuit switch is closed, voltage v_R across the resistor is zero, the circuit current is zero, and voltage v_L across the inductor is equal to the source potential. After the switch has been closed for five or more time constants, inductor voltage v_L closely approaches zero, while the circuit current has risen to a value limited only by the series resistor. The voltage across the series resistor is very nearly equal to the source voltage.

In the interval between the instant the switch is closed and the time five time constants later when the limiting values for voltage and current have been reached, both voltages and currents behave exponentially. During one time constant the circuit current will have risen to 63% of its final value. The voltage across the resistor will also have risen to 63% of its final value, while the voltage across the inductor will have decayed to 37% of its original value, which was equal to the source potential.

The time constant for an RL circuit is

$$\tau = \frac{L}{R}$$

where τ is the time constant in seconds, L the inductance in henrys, and R the series resistance in ohms.

This is of the same form as the time constant for capacitive series circuits, except that C for capacitance appeared in the denominator of the fraction, while L for inductance appears in the numerator. This is not surprising, if we consider that capacitances in series and parallel combine like conductances, while inductances in series and parallel combine like resistances. Since conductance and resistance are reciprocal functions, we might expect that capacitance and inductance might appear in reciprocal positions in at least some equations. This is *not* to say that capacitance and inductance are reciprocals of each other; they are not. They appear in reciprocal positions because inductance represents an opposition, while capacitance represents an acceptance. Therefore, L/R is a time constant with the dimension of seconds, just as $1/RC$ was a time constant with the dimension of seconds.

Using this time constant, calculations of voltage and current in LR circuits may be done exactly as was the case with RC circuits.

EXAMPLE   Calculate the time constant for a series RL circuit with a 1 mH inductor and a 1000 Ω resistor.

Solution.

$$\tau = \frac{L}{R} = \frac{10^{-3}}{10^3} = 10^{-6} \text{ sec}$$

Calculate the time constant for a series *RL* circuit with a 1 H inductor   EXAMPLE
and a 1000 Ω resistor.

Solution.

$$\tau = \frac{L}{R} = \frac{1}{10^3} = 10^{-3} \text{ sec}$$

Calculate the time constant for a series *RL* circuit with a 1 mH inductor   EXAMPLE
and a 1 Ω resistor.

Solution.

$$\tau = \frac{L}{R} = \frac{10^{-3}}{1} = 10^{-3} \text{ sec}$$

As can be seen from the above examples, the time constant increases
for increasing values of the inductance and for decreasing values of the
resistance. Once the time constant is known, calculation of voltage or
current anywhere in the circuit can be done by using the universal time
constant graph of Figure 12-11, repeated here for the sake of convenience
as Figure 13-7.

Figure 13-7   Universal time constant graph.

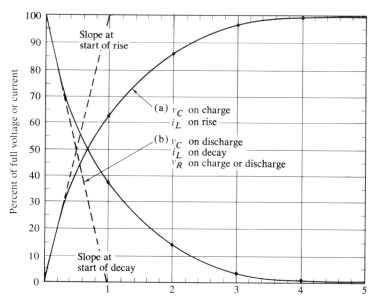

Time in *RC* or *L/R* time constants

EXAMPLE   Consider an *RL* circuit with a 5 kΩ resistor in series with a 2 mH inductor. The voltage source is 10 V. Calculate the voltage across the resistor 0.5 μsec after the switch is closed.

Solution.

$$\tau = \frac{L}{R} = \frac{2 \times 10^{-3}}{5 \times 10^3} = 0.4\ \mu\text{sec}$$

The number of time constants is

$$\frac{T}{\tau} = \frac{0.5}{0.4} = 1.25\ \text{time constants}$$

From the universal time constant graph, the voltage across the resistor will rise to about 72% of its final value in 1.25 time constants. That final value is $E = 10$ V. Therefore, the voltage across the resistor 0.5 μsec after the switch is thrown will be

$$v_R = 0.72 \times 10 = 7.2\ \text{V}$$

CURRENT DECAY IN INDUCTIVE CIRCUITS.   When the switch in an inductive circuit is opened, the flow of current must stop. It cannot stop in zero time, since the current through an inductor cannot change in zero time.

The voltage across the inductor is a function of the rate of change of current through the inductor. When the switch is opened, the rate of change of current from the circuit maximum to zero is very fast indeed. Consequently, by

$$e_L = L\frac{di}{dt}$$

inductor voltage e_L must be very high at that instant.

There is no way the circuit can be broken in zero time. If we wish to imagine a switch which can be opened in zero time, separating the conductors by a centimeter in zero microseconds in spite of the inertia of the moving mechanical parts, then we would be forced to conclude that the voltage across the inductor and, consequently, the voltage across the switch, must be infinite. But this is ridiculous. A voltage a good deal less than infinite could jump the centimeter gap of the switch. An arc or spark across the gap opened in the circuit by the switch would mean, during the instant it existed, that the circuit had not actually been broken, even though the switch had been mechanically opened.

We can break a circuit containing an inductance in a very short time. We can easily break the circuit in a fraction of the time required for the current to build up when the switch was originally closed.

The resistance in the circuit plays a role in determining the time constant of the *RL* circuit. The higher the resistance, the shorter the time constant. As the switch is opened, the initial gap becomes effectively part of the circuit resistance, and since its own resistance is quite high, the total circuit resistance is very considerably increased.

Though the voltage across the inductor may be very much higher than the source voltage, this represents no violation of the law of the conservation of energy. The total energy stored in the inductor was stored through the relatively low series resistance *R*, for a comparatively long time equal to five time constants of the original circuit. When the circuit is broken, that energy must be dissipated in the form of reverse current flow, as the magnetic field in which it was stored collapses. It is simply a question of the energy being stored for a long time at a low rate, and being released for a short time at a high rate. The total quantity of energy is the same in both cases, except for the inevitable losses due to circuit resistance.

It is a common practice to check the continuity of windings of an inductor with an ohmmeter. The ohmmeter is a current source, and in the low resistance ranges may cause a current of several hundred milliamps to flow through the inductor. If the inductance is large, on the order of henrys, the voltage induced across its terminals when the ohmmeter connection is broken may be considerable; several hundred volts is not unlikely. If the individual making the resistance measurement on the inductor should happen to be himself in contact with the inductor terminals at the instant the circuit is broken, he will forever after harbor not the slightest doubt that the voltage at that instant is higher than the source voltage. Such a shock is not likely to cause serious damage, since its duration is so brief, but no shock should ever be deliberately sought. Avoid them all; this is not the way to check your heart for soundness.

This extremely high voltage developed across the terminals of an inductance as the circuit is broken is the basis for the spark production in the ignition system of most automobiles. As the contact points are closed, current builds up in the inductor, which is the spark coil. As the contact points open and that current is interrupted, the resulting rapid collapse of the magnetic field produces a very high voltage at the terminals of the spark coil. The voltage is sufficiently high to produce an arc between the terminals of a spark plug, igniting the fuel–air mixture.

ALGEBRAIC SOLUTIONS TO *RL* EXPONENTIALS.   Just as the *RC* circuit response to a square wave may be solved algebraically, so the response of the *RL* circuit may be found to a high degree of accuracy.

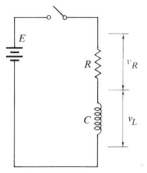

Figure 13-8

Consider the circuit of Figure 13-8. In order that Kirchhoff's voltage law be satisfied, at any instant,

$$E = v_R + v_L$$

But

$$v_R = iR \quad \text{and} \quad v_L = L\frac{di}{dt}$$

Therefore,

$$E = iR + L\frac{di}{dt}$$

This is not a simple algebraic equation, since it involves rates of change. It may be solved by the methods of calculus, which are beyond the scope of this presentation. The result is

$$i = I(1 - \varepsilon^{-x})$$

where i is the circuit current at any instant, I is the final circuit current, and is equal to E/R, $\varepsilon = 2.718\ldots$ (the base of the system of natural logarithms), and x is the fraction

$$x = \frac{RT}{L}$$

where R is the series resistance, L the inductance, and T the time in seconds for i to reach the specified value.

This equation represents the *rise* in the value of i for any time T after the switch is closed. Remember, if the equation contains $(1 - \varepsilon^{-x})$, it represents a rising exponential. If the exponential is decaying, the equation representing it will contain only ε^{-x}.

When the switch is closed in an RL circuit, the circuit current is a rising exponential. The resistor voltage is also a rising exponential, and is represented by the equation

$$v_R = E(1 - \varepsilon^{-x})$$

At the instant the switch is closed the full source voltage appears across L, and then decays exponentially toward zero. The equation representing this is

$$v_L = E\varepsilon^{-x}$$

After five or so time constants have elapsed, the circuit current and the voltage across the resistor have risen to the maximum value, and the voltage across the inductor has dropped to zero. If now the switch is opened, the current must decay to zero according to

$$i = I\varepsilon^{-x}$$

where

$$x = \frac{RT}{L}$$

and R is the resistance for the current path between the inductor terminals *after the switch is opened*. This will *not* ordinarily be the same as the series circuit resistance was when the switch was closed.

The voltage across the inductor at that instant must be IR, where I is the inductor current the instant *before* the switch was opened and R the circuit resistance *after* the switch is opened. This is because the current through the inductor cannot change in zero time; thus, when the switch is opened, the inductor current must continue to flow for the initial instant through the new circuit resistance.

The voltage during the exponential decay of current following the opening of the switch must therefore be

$$v_L = IR\varepsilon^{-x}$$

where I is the inductor current the instant before the switch is opened, R the resistance after the switch is opened, and, as before,

$$x = \frac{RT}{L}$$

where, again, R is the resistance after the switch is opened.

Problems

1. Calculate the time constant for a series RL circuit with a 4.4 H inductor and a 2.2 kΩ resistor.

2. Calculate the time constant for a series RL circuit with a 35 μH inductor and a 400 Ω resistor.

3. Calculate the time constant for a series RL circuit with a 12 H inductor and a 30 Ω resistor.

4. A 2 Ω resistor and an inductor are in series with a 50 V source and a switch. Exactly 55 msec after the switch is closed the voltage across the resistor is measured at 31.5 V. What are the time constant of the circuit and the value of the inductance?

5. Consider an RL circuit with a 400 Ω resistor in series with an 18 mH inductor and a 60 V source. Calculate the voltage across the resistor 32 μsec after the switch is closed, using the universal time constant graph.

6. Consider an *RL* circuit with a 23 Ω resistor in series with a 0.4 H inductor and a 150 V source. Calculate the voltage across the resistor and the inductor, and the current in the circuit, 22 msec after the switch is closed, using the universal time constant graph.

7. Consider an *RL* circuit with a 3 kΩ resistor in series with a 75 H inductor and a 300 V source. How long will it take, after the switch is closed, for the current in the circuit to reach a value of 82 mA?

8. Consider an *RL* series circuit with a two-way switch, where $R = 750\,\Omega$, $L = 2$ mH, and the voltage source is 200 V. Assume the switch starts in position A, and current in the circuit is at steady state. If the switch is moved to position B, calculate the voltages across *L* and *R*, and circuit current *i* after 1.3 μsec has elapsed. If at this time the switch is moved back to A, how long will it take before the voltage across *R* reaches a value of 160 V? Calculate the voltage across *L* and the circuit current at this time. If the switch is again moved to position B, how much time will elapse before *i* has dropped to 22% of its original steady-state value? Calculate *i* and the voltages across *R* and *L* at this time. Use the universal time constant graph in all calculations.

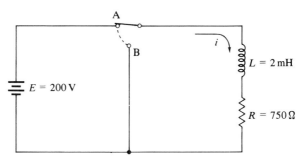

Circuit for Problems 8 and 12.

9. Consider the *RL* series circuit shown, where $R = 4\,\Omega$, $L = 50$ H, and the source potential is 90 V. Using algebraic means, calculate the voltages across *R* and *L* and the circuit current at a time 8.4 sec after the switch is closed.

10. Consider the *RL* circuit in Problem 9, where $R = 70\,\Omega$, $L = 35$ mH, and the source potential is 30 V. Using algebraic means, calculate the voltages across *R* and *L* and the circuit current at a time 0.76 msec after the switch is closed.

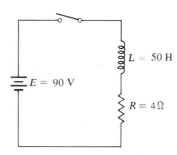

Circuit for Problems 9–11.

11. Consider the *RL* series circuit in Problem 9, where $R = 170$ Ω, $L = 0.22$ H, and the source potential is 180 V. Using algebraic means, calculate the time it will take the current to reach 20% of its steady-state value. 50% of its steady-state value. 85% of its steady-state value. Calculate the values of the voltages across *R* and *L* at these times.

12. Consider the *RL* series circuit in Problem 8, where $R = 4.0$ Ω, $L = 0.16$ H, and the source potential is 75 V. Assume that the switch starts in position A and that the current is at a steady state. The switch is then moved to position B for 25 msec, moved back to A for another 10 msec, and then moved back again to B until the current is 10% of its steady-state value. At this time the switch is finally moved back to A. Using algebraic means, calculate the values of the voltages across *R* and *L* and the circuit current at the time of each switching, and calculate the time of the last switching to A.

INDUCTOR WINDINGS. So far, we have considered inductors as though the wire with which they were wound had no resistance. This is not true for any practical inductor. A high inductance requires many turns of wire, and often the wire is of small diameter. Consequently, the resistance of the inductor may be considerable. An inductor of 8 H designed for use in a power supply as a "choke" may have a resistance of several hundred ohms. This resistance acts as a series resistance in calculations of the maximum current any source can cause to flow through the inductor. Inductors of lower values, wound with less wire or with a larger-diameter wire, often have very low resistance.

The wire needs to be insulated. Consider an inductor with 100 turns of wire, in which the rate of change of current, *di/dt*, is such that for that instant the voltage across the inductor terminals is 100 V. That

13-4

Practical Inductors

voltage is 1 V per turn of wire, which means that for adjacent wires there will be a potential difference of 1 V. If they are not insulated from each other, current will flow directly between them, and that single turn of the coil will be ineffective in producing output voltage.

Consider a *multilayer coil,* in which a great many turns of wire are necessary to provide the required inductance. Since it is usually not practical to make a coil with a large number of turns as a single-layer coil, it may be necessary to use several layers one over the other. If the windings extend the length of the coil core, and then back again to form the second layer, the two terminals of the inductor are at the same end of the core. If the potential between the two inductor terminals is at some instant 100 V, that 100 V appears between the first and last turns of the coil, which are separated from each other only by the thin layer of varnish with which the wire is coated. In such a situation, the insulation may arc through. It is sometimes necessary to use layers of insulating material between the layers of such a coil.

Sometimes, where a coil must be multilayer, it is made short and with a large number of layers, rather than a longer coil with fewer layers.

INDUCTOR CORES.   The cores of inductors depend on the inductance required and on the rate of change of current expected through the inductor. For low values of inductance the coil is usually wound on a nonferromagnetic core, which acts only as a mechanical support. For higher values of inductance the core may be ferromagnetic, or a ferrite ceramic, depending on whether the current is expected to have a high rate of change. In some inductors the core is movable, and the inductance of the coil may be adjusted by moving the core in or out. This method is used primarily for low-inductance coils designed for use at low frequencies.

INDUCTOR TROUBLES—OPENS.   The resistance of an inductor ought to be less than infinite. Some inductors may have a resistance of several thousand ohms, if they are made of many turns of fine wire, but most inductors will show a low resistance with an ohmmeter. If the ohmmeter test indicates an infinite resistance, which would mean an open-circuit condition between the inductor terminals, it usually means the inductor must be replaced. Rarely, the defect may be accessible to repair, but this is not the rule.

INDUCTOR TROUBLES—SHORTS.   Unless the proper value of resistance for a particular inductor is known, the ohmmeter check will usually fail to reveal a shorted condition. If a shorted condition exists, the resistance between the inductor terminals will be *less* than it would otherwise be, but it will probably not be zero. The shorted condition will most frequently involve only a few turns, and the consequent reduction in the resistance of the whole winding may be only a small percent.

coefficient of coupling (k)   the ratio of the flux linkages between the coils   **Key Words**
   to the flux of one coil

henry (H)   The basic unit of inductance. In electronics, values are often expressed in two compound units, millihenrys (mH) and microhenrys (μH).

inductor   a two-terminal circuit element in which the voltage between the terminals of the element is proportional to the rate of change of current through the element

multilayer coil   a coil consisting of two or more layers of turns. A multilayer coil is used where a single-layer coil that provides the required inductance would require too much space.

mutual inductance   the condition where two or more coils are connected so that each is affected by the magnetic field of the other

1.   Inductance is determined by (1) the number of turns in a coil, (2) the   **Summary** area of each turn, (3) the permeability of the core, and (4) the length   **of Concepts** of the coil.

2.   If two or more inductors are in series with each other, but the magnetic field of any one coil does not cut through the turns of any other coil, then the inductance of the series is the simple sum of the separate inductances. Thus,

$$L_t = L_1 + L_2 + L_3 \ldots$$

3.   If inductors are connected in parallel and if none is affected by the magnetic field of any other, then the total inductance is calculated as for resistors in parallel. Thus,

$$\frac{1}{L_t} = \frac{1}{L_1} + \frac{1}{L_2} + \frac{1}{L_3} \ldots$$

4.   The current through an inductor cannot change in zero time.

5. The time constant for an RL circuit is $\tau = L/R$, where τ is the time constant in seconds, L is the inductance in henrys, and R is the series resistance in ohms.

6. Inductances in series and parallel combine like resistances.

7. When the switch in an inductive circuit is opened, the flow of current must stop. Since the current through an inductor cannot change in zero time, the flow of current cannot stop in zero time.

8. Just as the RC circuit response to a square wave can be solved algebraically, so can the response of the RL circuit be found to a high degree of accuracy.

9. A high inductance requires many turns of wire, so the resistance may be considerable.

10. The core of an inductor is selected to fit a specific application. For low inductance values, the coil is usually wound on a nonferromagnetic core which acts merely as a mechanical support. For higher inductance values, the core is usually ferromagnetic or ferrite ceramic.

11. Infinite resistance indicated by an ohmmeter indicates that an open circuit condition exists between indicator terminals.

12. If a shorted condition exists in an inductor, the resistance between the inductor terminals will be less than it would otherwise be, but not zero.

To Help You Review *On a separate sheet of paper, fill in the blanks or answer the questions below. The number following each question refers to the section in the chapter where the correct answer can be found.*

1. Define an inductor. (13-1)

2. The inductor is a companion to what other circuit element? (13-1)

3. In an inductor what is the voltage proportional to? (13-1)

4. List three factors that determine inductance. (13-1)

5. Under what circumstance is each of the following equations used? (13-2)

(a) $L_t = L_1 + L_2 + L_3 \ldots$ (b) $\dfrac{1}{L_t} = \dfrac{1}{L_1} + \dfrac{1}{L_2} + \dfrac{1}{L_3} \cdots$

6. What is mutual inductance, and what does it mainly depend on? (13-2)

7. Explain the following statement: The current flowing through an inductor cannot change in zero time. (13-2)

8. How does the universal time constant graph apply to series RL circuits? (13-3)

9. Is it correct to say that capacitance and inductance are reciprocals? If not, what is their relationship? (13-3)

10. How is inductor winding related to resistance? (13-4)

11. What is the reason for using various materials as inductor cores? (13-4)

12. What is the purpose of a movable core in an inductor? (13-4)

13. Explain two inductor defects. (13-4)

FOURTEEN
TRANSFORMERS

This chapter will help you understand

☐ mutual induction in transformers
☐ transformer voltage and turns ratio
☐ impedance transformation
☐ autotransformers and multiple-winding transformers
☐ transformer limitations and defects

14-1
Transformer Action

MUTUAL INDUCTION.   We have already seen that in the case of two inductors in series, the total inductance may be increased or decreased by mutual induction. But it is not necessary that the two inductors be electrically connected. All that is necessary is that the magnetic field of one inductor cut through the turns of the other. Consider two inductors wound on the same iron core, so that *all* of the flux lines of the changing magnetic field of one inductor caused by a sinusoidal current through it also cut across the turns of the other inductor. This is shown in Figure 14-1. L_1 is connected to a source of alternating current, and L_2 is connected to a load resistor. Note that there is no electrical connection between the two coils; they are linked only by the overlapping magnetic flux.

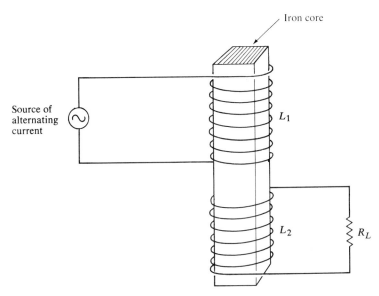

Figure 14-1   Inductors need not be connected electrically for mutual inductance to occur. All that is necessary is that the magnetic field of one inductor cut through the turns of the other.

The changing current produces a changing magnetic field which cuts across the turns of L_1 and induces a voltage in each turn. The total voltage across the terminals of L_1 must, by Kirchhoff's voltage law, be equal to the source voltage. If, at some instant, the source potential is 100 V, and there are 100 turns in L_1, then at that instant the voltage across each turn caused by the varying magnetic flux must be 1 V.

But every line of flux that cuts across the turns of L_1 also cuts across the turns of L_2. If 1 V is induced in each turn of L_1 at some instant, then 1 V must be induced in each turn of L_2 at the same instant. The total voltage across the terminals of L_2 must be the product of the number of volts per turn times the number of turns. If there is an induced voltage of 1 V per turn, and there are 100 turns in L_2, then the terminal voltage of L_2 must be 100 V. This terminal voltage will appear across the load resistor R and will cause current to flow through it in accordance with Ohm's law.

If a varying current in L_1 can, because of the flux linking it to L_2, produce current in L_2, then a varying current in L_2 can, through the flux linking the two coils, produce current in L_1. Current in *either* coil will induce a voltage in the other. Thus, the inductance is mutual, and not only will changes in the input circuit affect the output, but changes in the output, such as a change in load resistance, will be reflected in changes in the input voltage and current.

If two or more coils are wound on the same core, or physically placed so close to each other that there is significant coupling between them, then this combination of coils together with their core is called a *transformer*. The purpose of a transformer is to transfer power from the primary winding, which is connected to a power source producing a varying current, to the other winding or windings, which are called secondary windings. They are connected to loads, to which they transfer power from the primary.

If a transformer has a ferromagnetic core, all the flux lines from the primary winding will cut through each turn of each of the secondary windings. This is another way of saying that the ferromagnetic core transformer has *unity coupling*, or $k = 1$. If this is true for a particular transformer, then, as we have seen, the same *voltage per turn* will be present at any instant for *all* windings, both primary and secondary. The voltage at the terminals of any secondary winding can be calculated if the primary voltage is known, and the number of turns in the secondary compared to the number of turns in the primary.

14-2	**TURNS RATIOS.** The *turns ratio* of a simple transformer with a single
Transformer Ratios	primary and a single secondary is simply the number of turns in the

TURNS RATIOS. The *turns ratio* of a simple transformer with a single primary and a single secondary is simply the number of turns in the secondary divided by the number of turns in the primary, thus:

$$\text{Turns ratio} = \frac{\text{Total secondary turns}}{\text{Total primary turns}} = \frac{N_s}{N_p}$$

If, in a particular transformer, there are 100 turns in the primary winding and 300 turns in the secondary winding, then the turns ratio is $300/100 = 3:1$. This may be given as $3:1$ (read this as 3 to 1) or it may simply be given as 3, with the 1 as an implied denominator.

VOLTAGE RATIO. With unity coupling, the same number of volts will be induced in each turn of both primary and secondary at any instant. Therefore, the ratio between the total voltage across any one winding and any other winding will be the same as the turns ratio between the two windings. Therefore,

$$\frac{E_s}{E_p} = \frac{N_s}{N_p}$$

where E_s is the voltage at the terminals of the secondary winding and E_p the voltage at the terminals of the primary. N_s/N_p is the turns ratio.

If there are more turns in the secondary than in the primary, then the secondary voltage must be higher than the primary voltage. A transformer of which this was true would be called a *step-up transformer*. If there are fewer turns in the secondary than in the primary, then the secondary voltage must be less than the primary voltage. A transformer of which this was true would be called a *step-down transformer*. Note that this applies only to transformers with unity coupling, which in practice means transformers with a ferromagnetic core.

If there is more than one secondary, as in a *multiple-winding transformer*, then the voltage at any secondary depends only on the ratio between its turns and the number of primary turns, regardless of the other secondary windings that may be present. (This assumes the transformer is to be operated within its design limitations, and is not defective.)

Consider a transformer with 250 primary turns and 1000 turns on a single   EXAMPLE
secondary. If the primary voltage is 120 V rms, what is the turns ratio of the transformer, and what secondary voltage should be expected?

Solution. The turns ratio is $N_s/N_p = 1000/250 = 4$. The ratio between primary voltage and secondary voltage is the same as the turns ratio; therefore,

$$E_s = \frac{N_s}{N_p} \times E_p = 4 \times 120 = 480 \text{ V rms}$$

Given a transformer with 250 primary turns and 50 secondary turns,   EXAMPLE
what secondary voltage should be expected if the primary voltage is 120 V rms?

Solution. $N_p = 250$, $N_s = 50$, and $E_p = 120$. Therefore,

$$E_s = \frac{N_s}{N_p} \times E_p = \frac{50}{250} \times 120 = 24 \text{ V rms}$$

Given a transformer with 100 turns in the primary and with two secondary   EXAMPLE
windings, one with 250 turns and one with 8 turns. Find the voltage at the terminals of each secondary winding if the primary voltage is 120 V.

Solution. For the 250-turn secondary,

$$E_s = \frac{N_s}{N_p} \times E_p = \frac{250}{100} \times 120 = 300 \text{ V}$$

and for the 8-turn secondary,

$$E_s = \frac{N_s}{N_p} \times E_p = \frac{8}{100} \times 120 = 9.6 \text{ V}$$

CURRENT RATIO.   When current is delivered to a load, power is expended in that load. By the law of conservation of energy, that power must come from somewhere, and the source of the power delivered by the secondary winding is the primary winding. The primary winding, in turn, derives its power from the generator.

If the secondary winding is not connected to a load, so that no current flows, there is no magnetic field due to secondary current. The only magnetic flux cutting the primary windings is due to the primary current in this case. If the core of the transformer is ferromagnetic, this primary current may be very slight. Thus, the power drawn by the primary winding from a source of alternating current with no load connected to the secondary is sufficiently low that it is often considered zero.

If the secondary winding is connected to a load, load current flows. This means that there will be a current in the secondary winding, and this varying current will produce its own varying magnetic field. But this varying magnetic field caused by the secondary current must, by Lenz's law, oppose the magnetic field produced by the primary current.

There must be sufficient varying flux to produce a voltage across the primary terminals equal to the source voltage, by Kirchhoff's voltage law, since the primary is connected directly to the generator. If the magnetic field caused by the primary current is being opposed by the magnetic field associated with the secondary current, then to produce sufficient net field to produce the necessary primary voltage to satisfy Kirchhoff's law, *more* primary current must flow. In short, the more secondary current we draw, the more primary current must flow.

If we assume no losses of any sort, then the power expended in the load must all come from the source. That is,

$$P_{\text{load}} = P_{\text{source}} \qquad \text{or} \qquad P_{\text{primary}} = P_{\text{secondary}}$$

Therefore,

$$E_p I_p = E_s I_s \qquad \text{and} \qquad \frac{I_p}{I_s} = \frac{E_s}{E_p}$$

Note that the *current ratio* is the *inverse* of the voltage ratio and, consequently, of the turns ratio as well. If the secondary voltage is less than the primary voltage, then the secondary current must be more than the primary current.

A transformer with a 1:20 voltage step-down ratio is connected to a 3 Ω   EXAMPLE
load. If 120 V is applied to the primary, what is the primary current?

Solution.

$$\frac{E_s}{E_p} = \frac{1}{20}$$

$$E_s = 120 \times \frac{1}{20} = 6 \text{ V} \qquad \text{(secondary voltage)}$$

$$I_s = \frac{e_s}{R_s} = \frac{6}{3} = 2 \text{ A} \qquad \text{(secondary current)}$$

$$I_p = \frac{E_s}{E_p} \times I_s = \frac{1}{20} \times 2 = 0.1 \text{ A} \qquad \text{(primary current)}$$

If a transformer has more than one secondary winding, the total
primary current is the sum of the primary currents due to the secondary
current in each winding. Also, the power expended in the primary is the
sum of the powers expended in the loads.

A transformer has three secondary windings. The primary is to be connected   EXAMPLE
across the 120 V power line. One secondary is rated at 180 V and is to be
connected to a 9 kΩ load. Another secondary is rated at 12.6 V and is
to be connected to a load that will draw 600 mA. The third secondary
is to be connected to a load that will draw 2 A at 5 V. What is the total
primary current?

Solution. The solution may be quickly arrived at by noting that the
primary power is equal to the sum of the powers expended in the
loads. Thus,

$$P_p = P_1 + P_2 + P_3$$

$$= \frac{180^2}{9000} + (12.6)(0.6) + (2)(5)$$

$$= 3.6 + 7.56 + 10$$

$$= 21.16 \text{ W} \qquad \text{(primary power expended)}$$

$$I_p = \frac{P}{E} = \frac{21.16}{120} = 0.176 \text{ A} \qquad \text{(primary current)}$$

This same figure could have been arrived at by calculating the primary
current due to the current in each secondary, and then summing the
contributions to the total primary current.

Problems

1. What is the turns ratio of a transformer with 700 turns in the primary winding and 4200 turns in the secondary winding?

2. A transformer with a 550 turn primary winding has three secondary windings with the respective turns ratios of 4:1, 2:5, and 3:2. Calculate the number of turns in each secondary winding.

3. Consider a transformer with 600 primary turns and a secondary coil with 4000 turns. If the primary voltage is 220 V rms, what are the turns ratio and the voltage across the secondary winding?

4. Consider a transformer with 2200 turns and 550 turns on a single secondary. If the primary voltage is 110 V rms, what are the turns ratio and the secondary voltage?

5. A transformer with 200 turns in the primary has three secondary windings with 500 turns, 800 turns, and 50 turns. Find the voltage at the terminals of each secondary winding if the primary voltage is 120 V rms.

6. Consider a transformer with two secondary windings, one with 200 turns, the other with 1000 turns. If the voltage output of the first secondary is 88 V rms and the primary voltage is 220 V rms, calculate the number of turns in the primary winding and the voltage across the other secondary.

7. A transformer with a 2:15 voltage step-up ratio is connected to an 8 Ω load. If 240 V rms is applied to the primary, what are the primary current and the power expended in the primary?

8. A transformer with a 600 turn primary and a 3600 turn secondary is connected to a 400 Ω load. If 120 V rms is applied to the primary, what are the primary current, the power expended in the primary, and the voltage across the secondary?

9. A transformer with a 250 turn primary has two secondary windings. One secondary has 1000 turns and is connected to a 5 kΩ load. The other secondary winding has 50 turns and is connected to a 60 Ω load. If the primary is connected to a 110 V rms source, what is the total primary current?

10. A transformer has four secondary windings. One secondary is rated at 440 V rms and is connected to a 1.4 kΩ load. Another secondary is connected to a load that will draw 1.4 mA at 4 V. A third winding is rated at 16 V and is connected to a load that will draw 0.4 A.

The fourth secondary is rated at 55 V and is connected to a 200 Ω load. If the primary is connected to a 110 V rms source, calculate the total primary current. If the fourth secondary has 200 turns, calculate the number of turns in the other three secondaries and in the primary winding. Also, calculate the contributions to the total primary current of each of the secondaries.

MAXIMUM POWER TRANSFER. Suppose we have an ac generator with an internal resistance of 100 Ω, and we wish to connect to it some load such that the maximum possible amount of power will be expended in the load (Figure 14-2).

14-3
Impedance
Transformation

If the load resistance is made very high, approaching infinity, then the load voltage will be approximately equal to the source voltage; but the load current will be vanishingly small, and the power, which is the product of the two, must approach zero.

If the load resistance is made very low, approaching zero, then the load current will be limited by the internal resistance of the source while the load voltage will be very small, approaching zero. This is because nearly all the source voltage will be dropped across its own internal resistance. This time, too, the power expended in the load will approach zero.

Figure 14-2   The power produced by a generator is affected by the internal resistance.

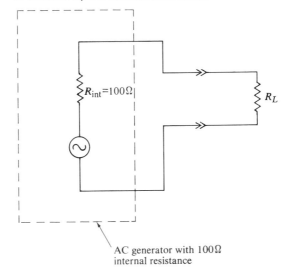

AC generator with 100Ω
internal resistance

TABLE 14-1 Load Power

R_L	R_t	I_t	P_L
1	101	0.99	0.98
50	150	0.67	2.22
90	190	0.53	2.49
100	200	0.50	2.50
110	210	0.48	2.49
150	250	0.40	2.40
200	300	0.33	2.22
1000	1100	0.09	0.83

But if zero power is expended in the load for the two extreme conditions of both zero and infinite load resistance, then there must be some intermediate value of load resistance for which the power expended will be a maximum.

Suppose we connect loads of different value to our ac generator with an internal resistance of 100 Ω, calculate the power expended in each load, and tabulate the results. This has been done in Table 14-1.

The greatest amount of power was expended in this example when the value of the load resistor was 100 Ω. See the graph of Figure 14-3, based on the data of Table 14-1. It is not a coincidence that this is also the value of the internal resistance of the source. It can be demonstrated mathematically that this will always be so—that the greatest power will be expended in the load when its resistance is the same as the internal resistance of the source. This is often stated as the *maximum power transfer theorem. The maximum power is expended in the load when the load opposition matches the internal opposition of the source.*

In the case just examined, the load and the internal opposition of the source were entirely resistive. If inductance or capacitance is involved, the statement as it stands is still correct, but will require further interpreting.

We don't always want to transfer the maximum power to the load. Sometimes we want the maximum voltage across the load; if this is the case, then the load resistance should be made as high as possible. If we want maximum current in the load, then the load resistance should be as low as possible.

A simple calculation will show that when the conditions of the maximum power transfer theorem are met, half the total power expended is expended

Figure 14-3   Graph of the load power data of Table 14-1.

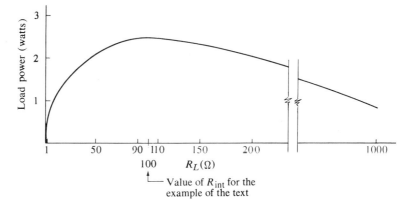

in the load, and half in the internal resistance of the source. Obviously, we would not want this to occur when we plug our electric razor into the wall socket, since the other end of that wall socket goes to the power utility generator, with a very low internal resistance, and a power capability of perhaps a million kilowatts.

If, however, we are attempting to transfer the ac voltage whose variations in amplitude represent information from the output of our hi-fi amplifier to a speaker, we will wish to transfer the maximum possible power to the speaker. There are many such situations in electronics. Let us consider a simplified example.

Suppose that the part of a circuit in which originates an ac voltage representing the desired signal can be simplified into a Thevenin equivalent circuit consisting of a perfect voltage source with a voltage $E = 100$ V, in series with a 1 kΩ resistor. Let us suppose that this is to be connected to a load with an internal resistance of 10 Ω. This is shown in Figure 14-4.

If the connection is made directly, the total circuit resistance is 1010 Ω, and the circuit current is

$$I_t = \frac{E}{R} = \frac{100}{1010} \cong 99.01 \text{ mA}$$

This is the current through the load, and the power expended in the load is thus

$$P = I^2 R = (99.01 \times 10^{-3})^2(10) = 0.098 \text{ W}$$

This is nearly 100 mW, and the total power expended in the source is very nearly 10 W, a hundred times as much. The voltage that would appear across the load is likewise quite small, approximately 1 V. If this load were a speaker, the volume of sound would not be deafening.

Figure 14-4   A Thevenin equivalent circuit connected to a load with a small internal resistance.

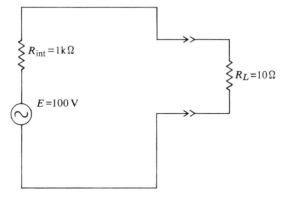

Our voltage source with an internal resistance of 1000 Ω can transfer maximum power to a 1000 Ω load. The current through such a 1000 Ω load would be

$$I = \frac{E}{R_t} = \frac{100}{2000} = 50 \text{ mA}$$

and the power dissipated in such a load would be

$$P = I^2 R = (5 \times 10^{-2})^2 (1000) = 2.5 \text{ W}$$

This is not much power, but it is 25 times as much as was dissipated in the 10 Ω load.

To get this same power of 2.5 W dissipated in the 10 Ω load would require a load current of

$$I = \sqrt{\frac{P}{R}} = \sqrt{\frac{2.5}{10}} = \sqrt{\frac{1}{4}} = \frac{1}{2} \text{ A}$$

What is needed is a source current of 0.05 A, while the load current must be simultaneously 0.5 A. If this can be done, 2.5 W will be dissipated in the source, and 2.5 W will be dissipated in the load, thus meeting the conditions of the maximum power transfer theorem.

A transformer can be used to step up the current to the load, while simultaneously stepping down the voltage. Since the desired load current is ten times the desired source current, a transformer with a 1:10 turns ratio can be used. With this transformer the load voltage will be 1/10 the primary voltage, and the load current will be ten times the primary current. This is shown in Figure 14-5.

Figure 14-5   A transformer can be used to increase current and decrease voltage.

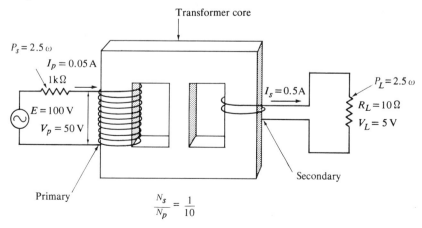

Now the desired conditions have been met. The source is supplying 0.05 A to a load at a voltage of 50 V, so to the source it appears to be a load with a resistance of 1000 Ω. It is not actually a 1000 Ω load, of course, but the voltage source does not know that. All it knows is that its two terminals are connected to something that responds just like a 1000 Ω load, and it will quite cheerfully transfer 2.5 W of power to it.

The load is just as happily receiving the 2.5 W, assuming the transformer charges no interest in the form of power dissipated as heat. To the load, it seems, to be connected to a voltage source that delivers 0.5 A at 5 V. If we assume the two terminals from the secondary of the transformer to be a voltage source for that load, and attempt to find the Thevenin equivalent for it, we could find the open-circuit voltage and the short-circuit current and from that, by Ohm's law, we could deduce the equivalent Thevenin resistance.

The open-circuit voltage would be 10 V. This can be seen from the fact that with the secondary not connected to a load, the primary would draw no significant current; thus, the full source voltage of 100 V would appear across it since none would be dropped across the internal resistance of the source.

The short-circuit current would be 1 A. This can be seen from the fact that with the secondary terminals shorted, the primary current would be limited to 0.1 A by the 1000 Ω resistance of the source. Since the current of 0.1 A in the primary is stepped up by a factor of 10 in the secondary, the secondary short-circuit current is 1 A.

If the two secondary terminals are considered as a "black box" source, we can from the data find the Thevenin equivalent. The Thevenin resistance is

$$R_{Th} = \frac{E_{Th}}{I_N} = \frac{10}{1} = 10 \, \Omega$$

Therefore, to the load, the transformer secondary looks like a 10 V source with 10 Ω of internal resistance. But this is only because of what is connected to the transformer primary. The load sees the voltage source of 100 V with its internal resistance of 1000 Ω through the transformer as a 10 V source with an internal resistance of 10 Ω. The voltage source of 100 V with its 1000 Ω internal impedance meanwhile sees the load, through the transformer, as a 1000 Ω load.

We have been using the resistance of the load and source, but ordinary resistance is not the only kind of opposition encountered by ac. Both inductance and capacitance offer a kind of opposition known as reactance (X, measured in ohms), which is the subject of the next chapter. The combination of resistance and reactance is the total opposition to the flow of an alternating current, and the term to express this total opposition is *impedance* (*Z*, measured in ohms).

What we have just done is use a transformer to match the internal impedance of the voltage source to the impedance of the load. Note that the ratio of the two impedances to be matched was

$$\frac{Z_{\text{source}}}{Z_{\text{load}}} = \frac{1000}{10} = 100$$

and the *impedance-matching transformer* ratio required to properly match these two different impedances was 10, which is the *square root of the impedance ratio*. This is true in general. Thus,

$$\frac{N_p}{N_s} = \sqrt{\frac{Z_{\text{in}}}{Z_{\text{out}}}}$$

EXAMPLE   Suppose it is desired to match a voltage source having an internal impedance of 6400 Ω to a load with an impedance of 16 Ω, in order to transfer the maximum power to the load. What turns ratio should be chosen for the transformer to be used?

Solution.

$$\text{Turns ratio} = \frac{N_p}{N_s} = \sqrt{\frac{Z_{\text{in}}}{Z_{\text{out}}}} = \sqrt{\frac{6400}{16}} = 20$$

Problems   1.   A 120 V rms ac generator with an internal resistance of 250 Ω is connected to a load resistor. Calculate the circuit current and power dissipated in the load for load resistors with values of 1 Ω, 50 Ω, 100 Ω, 150 Ω, 200 Ω, 220 Ω, 240 Ω, 250 Ω, 260 Ω, 280 Ω, 300 Ω, 500 Ω, and 1000 Ω. Draw a graph of the power dissipated versus the load resistance. What value of the load resistance gives the maximum power expended in the load? If we wish to expend this power across a 10 Ω load resistor, what should be the turns ratio of a transformer employed to match the impedance of the voltage source with that of the load?

2.   A 220 V rms ac generator with an internal resistance of 350 Ω is connected to a load resistor. What turns ratio should be chosen for a transformer used to match the voltage source with a load of 105 kΩ in order to insure maximum power transfer to the load? Calculate the primary and the secondary currents and the power expended in the load.

3.   Consider a 110 V rms ac generator with an internal resistance of 120 Ω connected to a transformer with a turns ratio of 5:2. What value of the load resistance would give maximum power transfer to the load?

4. Suppose we wish to match a voltage source with an internal impedance of 8100 Ω to a load with an impedance of 9 Ω, in order to transfer the maximum power to the load. What turns ratio should be chosen for the transformer to be used?

5. Suppose we wish to match a voltage source with an internal impedance of 7200 Ω with three different loads having impedances of 8 Ω, 72 Ω, and 1600 Ω, in order to transfer the maximum power to each load. What turns ratio should be chosen for the transformer with three secondary windings to be used for matching the impedances? Calculate the total primary current, the secondary currents, and the power dissipated at each load and at the source. Assume $E_s = 30$ V.

AUTOTRANSFORMERS. An *autotransformer* uses a single continuous winding, with one or more connections, or *taps,* made to it at some point or points intermediate between its ends (Figure 14-6). Again, just as with a multiple-winding transformer, since all the turns are cut by the same flux, the number of volts per turn is the same throughout the coil. Suppose an autotransformer with a coil of 500 turns has a tap 100 turns from one end. If an ac voltage of 100 V is connected across the entire coil, then there will be $\frac{1}{5}$ V per turn. Between the end of the coil and the tap there are 100 turns; therefore, the voltage between the end of the coil and the tap must be $\frac{1}{5} \times 100 = 20$ V.

Suppose, as in Figure 14-6, the source of potential is connected between the tap and the end of the coil. If we assume that a 10 V source is

**14-4
Practical
Transformers**

Figure 14-6   An autotransformer.

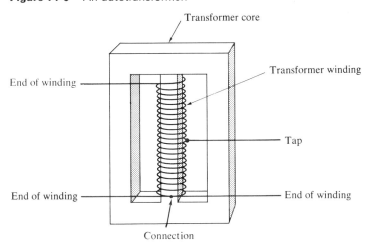

connected between the tap and the end of the coil, then for those turns the number of volts per turn is $10/100 = 0.1$ V per turn. But this number of volts must be the same for all turns in the coil. If a load is connected between the two ends of the coil, with 500 turns between, then the voltage at the load must be $0.1 \times 500 = 50$ V. Thus, the autotransformer can be used as either a step-up or step-down transformer.

An important difference between an autotransformer and a regular transformer with multiple windings is that the autotransformer has a direct electrical connection between the input and the output, whereas in the multiple-winding transformer these are isolated from each other, with only the common magnetic field linking them. This direct connection between the input and the output permits the possibility of electrical shock of a kind that cannot occur between coils connected only by a magnetic field.

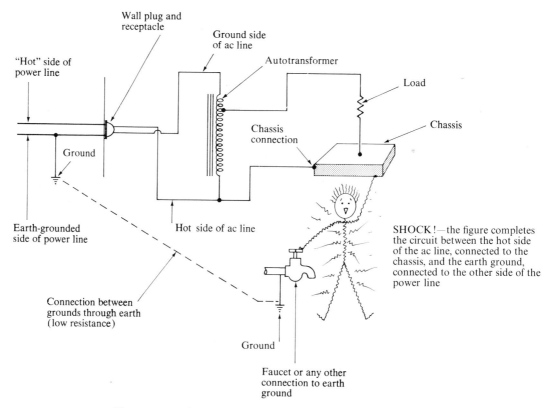

Figure 14-7 In an autotransformer, the direct electrical connection between input and output can be fatal.

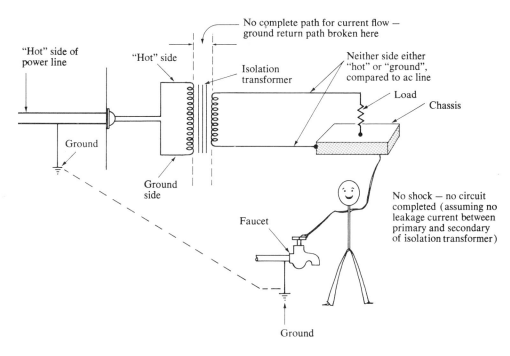

Figure 14-8 This transformer has separate primary and secondary windings, and—fortunately for this person—the gap between the windings acts like an open switch to break the circuit.

Suppose an autotransformer is used to supply power to some item of electrical or electronic equipment. One side of the power line is grounded to an earth ground by the public utility company furnishing the power. It is also common practice, for a variety of reasons, to connect one side of the power transformer to the chassis of the equipment to which it furnishes power. It is also possible in most cases to plug the equipment into the wall socket with either of the two possible polarities. The results of the worst case, which has a 50–50 chance of occurring, are shown in Figure 14-7.

If the plug is inserted in the wall socket with this polarity, the chassis will be connected directly to the "hot" side of the power line. If a human body should chance to complete a path for current flow from the chassis to any ground, such as a water or gas pipe or a damp concrete floor, then current will flow through that body. This has proved lethal in many cases.

Figure 14-8 shows the same situation except that a transformer with separate primary and secondary windings is shown in place of the auto-transformer. Note that the circuit is broken by the gap between the primary and secondary. This acts like an open switch to the flow of current that could otherwise provide a lethal shock. In some situations a special transformer, called an *isolation transformer,* is used with a 1:1 ratio to provide this electrical separation of the load circuit from the power lines with their inevitable ground. This is almost essential to the technician who must work on equipment where the chassis may be connected directly to one side of the power line. Touching the chassis of such equipment without the protection of an isolation transformer is exactly the same as sticking a finger into the wall socket!

MULTIPLE-WINDING TRANSFORMERS. Often, two or more secondary windings will be found on a single transformer. For use in vacuum tube equipment, transformers are designed with secondary windings providing 5 V, 6.3 V, or 12.6 V and a special *center-tapped winding* to provide a high voltage ranging from 150 to 600 V, approximately. For use with transistor circuits, transformers with lower secondary voltages are commonly used. These secondaries may or may not be center tapped. A center-tapped winding is the equivalent to two windings connected together at the tap, so that the output voltages add together. Measured from the center tap, the two end terminals of the coil will at any instant have opposite polarities to each other. If they are both drawn as sine waves, they will be 180° out of phase with each other (Figure 14-9).

Sometimes, when a transformer is designed to operate from the power lines, several taps may be brought out near one end of the primary. By connecting to one of these taps instead of the end of the winding, the turns ratio between primary and secondary is increased. This can be used to compensate for line voltages that are slightly too high or low.

Often a transformer is designed to operate from either 120 V or 240 V ac rms from the power lines. Such a transformer is usually supplied with two primary windings, each designed for 120 V. They are connected in parallel for 120 V operation, and in series for 240 V operation.

TRANSFORMER LIMITATIONS. Any given transformer is limited in its applications by a number of factors. These include input voltage and waveform, dc component of input voltage, ac frequency of input voltage, power drawn by load, and type of load.

Transformers designed to operate from the power line, or some other

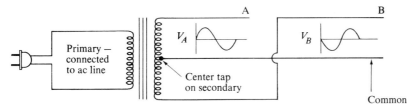

Figure 14-9 A center-tapped secondary winding. Note the opposing polarities of the end terminals.

source of ac power, are usually rated in terms of input voltage and frequency, and the output voltage and maximum allowable current drain for each secondary. As an example, a transformer might be rated as having a 120 V 50–60 Hz primary, and secondary windings rated at 5 V at 3 A, 6.3 V at 4 A, and 350–0–350 V at 80 mA. The last winding is a center-tapped high-voltage winding, in which each end of the winding has an output voltage of 350 V rms compared to the center tap. Since the two opposite ends of the coil are 180° out of phase with each other, the total rms voltage between the two opposite ends of this winding would be 700 V. Each secondary winding has a current rating, which is the maximum load current that is safe for that winding to carry. The 80 mA rating on the high-voltage winding indicates that it is wound with very fine wire, since it can carry little current. The load current must also flow through the wires of the winding attached to the load; thus, the heat energy that will be dissipated in the winding is the product of the load current squared times the internal resistance of the winding.

The total input power, excluding losses in the transformer, is the same as the total output power. The primary winding of the transformer will necessarily have a current rating that will enable it to deliver the stated maximum load currents to each of the secondary loads.

The *frequency rating* of the transformer is a function of the amount of core and the kind of material composing it. The lower the frequency, the more ferromagnetic material there must be in the core. This is because the maximum value of the rate of change of current is a function of the frequency; the lower the frequency, the slower the rate of change of current in the primary at any instant. Therefore, to get the same number of lines of flux *per second* cutting the windings, there must be more total lines— which, in turn, means more ferromagnetic material in the core.

But the higher the frequency, the less ferromagnetic material there must be in the core. This is because the hysteresis losses and losses due to eddy currents are greatly magnified as the frequency increases.

Power transformers are designed for use at either a single frequency or a narrow range of frequencies. Attempts to use a power transformer at a frequency for which it was not designed can be disastrous, either in terms of lost efficiency, or in terms of excessive primary current resulting in overheating and consequent "burnout" of the transformer.

Transformers designed for impedance matching have normally the function of transferring from a source of one impedance a wide range of frequencies of "signal" to a load of a different impedance. If such a transformer is to function well at low frequencies, it must have a relatively large amount of ferromagnetic material in the core; and if it is to function well at high frequencies, it must have as few losses as possible from eddy currents and hysteresis. This means the core materials and the thickness of the core laminations must receive special care by the designer. Impedance-matching transformers capable of transferring large amounts of power from a source to a load over a wide range of frequencies are expensive, as well as heavy.

TRANSFORMER DEFECTS.   Any single winding of a transformer is subject to all of the defects any inductor is subject to. Any set of windings, either primary or secondary, may have shorted turns or an open condition. Open conditions are revealed by the ohmmeter or a voltmeter. If a voltage, which may be less than the normal operating voltage, is applied to any winding, then the proper proportionate value of voltage ought to be present at each of the other windings. If it is absent at only one winding, then that winding is open. If the proper voltage is absent at all other windings of a multiple-winding transformer, then the winding to which the test voltage is applied is open.

Shorted turns reveal themselves in practice by severe overheating of the transformer, excessive primary current, and reduced secondary voltage. This is because any shorted turn forms a current loop of low resistance, but with a voltage driving the current through the loop that is equal to the number of volts per turn for any winding. If the transformer has 0.1 V per turn, and a turn is shorted so the resistance for the current loop thus formed is 0.001 Ω, then the current in that loop would be 100 A. The power involved in that current loop is $EI = 0.1 \times 100 = 10$ W. This is power drawn from the primary which does not appear in the secondary, but is dissipated in the form of heat in the body of the transformer.

A transformer may also have a short between windings. This is a condition which can be readily revealed by an ohmmeter test, since the resistance between windings ,ought to be very nearly infinite. A short between the primary and secondary windings of a power transformer may have no effect on the operation of a circuit, for example, except to subject the technician and operator of the equipment to exactly the same shock hazard as was discussed with respect to the autotransformer.

Transformer defects are usually easily located but are usually remedied only by removing and replacing the transformer. It is possible to rewind a transformer, but except in a few special cases, it is seldom either practical or economical.

Key Words

autotransformer   a transformer that uses a single continuous winding with one or more connections (taps) made to it at some point (or points) between the ends of the winding

center-tapped windings   the equivalent of two windings connected together at the tap so that the output voltages add together

impedance (Z)   the total opposition to the flow of an ac current; the combination of resistance and reactance, measured in ohms

reactance (X)   an opposition to an ac current flow offered by both inductance and capacitance (discussed fully in Chapter 15)

step-down transformer   a transformer which has fewer turns in the secondary winding than in the primary, and thus secondary voltage must be less than primary. A *step-up transformer* has more turns in the secondary winding than in the primary.

transformer   two or more coils wound around the same core, whose purpose is to transfer power from the primary winding to the secondary winding and then to a load or loads

turns ratio   the number of turns in the secondary winding divided by the number of turns in the primary winding, N_s/N_p

Summary of Concepts

1. If two or more inductors are connected in series so that the magnetic field of one cuts through the turns of the other, the total inductance may be increased or decreased by mutual induction.

2. If a transformer has a ferromagnetic core, then all the flux lines from the primary winding will cut through each turn of each of the secondary windings. This is unity coupling, or $k = 1$.

3. In a ferromagnetic core transformer the same voltage per turn is present at any instant for all windings, both primary and secondary.

4. The ratio between the total voltage across any one winding and any other winding is the same as the turns ratio between the two windings, $E_s/E_p = N_s/N_p$.

5. Power drawn by the primary winding from a source of alternating current with no load connected to the secondary is so low that it is often considered zero.

6. The more secondary current drawn, the more primary current that must flow. If we assume no losses, then $P_{\text{load}} = P_{\text{source}}$.

7. In a transformer, current ratio is the inverse of voltage ratio and, thus, of turns ratio. If secondary voltage is less than primary voltage, secondary current must be greater than primary current.

8. The maximum power transfer theorem states that maximum power is expended in the load when the load opposition matches the internal opposition of the source.

9. It can be shown by simple calculation that when the conditions of the maximum power transfer theorem are met, half the total power expended is expended in the load and half is expended in the internal resistance of the source.

10. A transformer can be used to step up the current to the load while simultaneously stepping down the voltage.

11. The transformer ratio required to match two different impedances is the square root of the impedance ratio, $N_p/N_s = \sqrt{Z_{\text{in}}/Z_{\text{out}}}$.

12. An autotransformer differs from a regular transformer with multiple windings in that in the autotransformer there is a direct electrical connection between the input and the output, whereas in the regular transformer they are isolated from each other, with only a common magnetic field linking them.

13. Any transformer is limited in its applications by a number of factors, including input voltage and waveform, dc component of input voltage, ac frequency of input voltage, type of load, and power drawn by the load.

14. The frequency rating of a transformer is the function of the amount of core and the material of which the core is composed.

15. Transformers designed for impedance matching normally have the function of transferring from a source of one impedance a wide range of frequencies of "signal" to a load of different impedance.

16. Any single winding of a transformer is subject to all the defects that any inductor is subject to.

17. A voltage applied to any winding of a transformer should be present at every other winding. If the voltage is absent at one other winding, then that winding is open.

18. Shorted turns cause severe overheating of the transformer, excessive primary current, and reduced secondary voltage.

On a separate sheet of paper, fill in the blanks or answer the questions below. **To Help You Review**
The number following each question refers to the section in the chapter where the correct answer can be found.

1. Total inductance can be increased or decreased with no electrical connection. All that is necessary is _____ . (14-1)

2. Define a transformer. (14-1)

3. What does N_s/N_p represent? (14-1)

4. What are transformers with ferromagnetic cores called? Why? (14-1)

5. What do we know about the primary current of a transformer with a ferromagnetic core? (14-2)

6. If secondary voltage is less than primary voltage, then secondary current must be _____ than primary current. (14-2)

7. What does the maximum power transfer theorem state? (14-3)

8. When the conditions of the maximum power transfer theorem are met, what can you say about how power is expended? Give an application in which this condition is *not* desirable. (14-3)

9. A transformer can step up the _____ to the load while stepping down the _____ at the same time. (14-3)

10. Explain reactance and impedance. (14-3)

11. What is one very important difference between the autotransformer and the multiple-winding transformer? (14-4)

12. What is a center-tapped winding? (14-4)

13. List three factors that limit the application of transformers. Explain one of these factors in detail. (14-4)

14. What determines the frequency rating of a transformer? (14-4)

15. The higher the frequency, the less ferromagnetic material there must be in the core. Why is this? (14-4)

16. Explain in detail two transformer defects. (14-4)

17. A voltage is applied to one winding of a multiple-winding transformer. This voltage is absent from all other windings. What does this absence indicate? (14-4)

☐ how to calculate capacitive and inductive reactance
☐ *RC* and *RL* circuits in series and parallel
☐ power in reactive circuits

FIFTEEN
REACTANCE AND REACTIVE CIRCUITS

CAPACITOR CURRENT. Suppose a capacitor is connected through a resistor to a source of sinusoidal alternating voltage, as shown in Figure 15-1. Suppose also that the value of the resistance is sufficiently low that it will have no significant effect on the capacitor voltage or current, but is just sufficient so that an oscilloscope connected across it will show the waveform of the current through it.

A capacitor has already been defined as a two-terminal circuit component in which the current is proportional to the rate of change of voltage across the terminals. Whenever the voltage across the capacitor terminals is increasing, the capacitor is charging; and when the voltage is decreasing, the capacitor is discharging.

The graph of a sinusoidal waveform shows that the voltage is increasing from $0°$ to $90°$, decreasing from $90°$ to $270°$, and increasing again from $270°$ to $360°$. The rate at which the voltage

**15-1
Capacitive
Reactance**

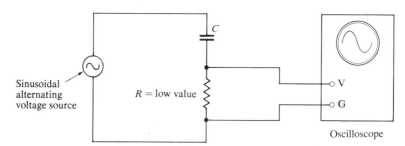

Figure 15-1 The oscilloscope shows the waveform of the current through the resistor.

is increasing at any instant is measured in volts per second. Since the time base may be calibrated in seconds, and the vertical axis calibrated in volts, the change in voltage indicated by the graph for any two points along the horizontal axis is the average rate of change of voltage per second during that interval.

Consider some short interval, such as the time between 0° and 1°. The actual time for one degree along the horizontal axis depends, of course, on the frequency and, consequently, the period. If the waveform is 60 Hz, then 360° is 1/60 sec, and 1° is 1/360 of 1/60, or approximately 46.3 μsec. This is shown in Figure 15-2. If the peak value of the voltage was 100 V, then the voltage at 1° is given by

$$e = E_{max} \sin \theta = 100 \sin 1 = 100(0.01745) = 1.745 \text{ V}$$

Figure 15-2 Graph of a sinusoidal waveform of 60 Hz, used to determine the rate of change of voltage in the time interval between 0° and 1°.

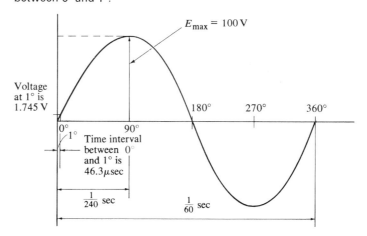

During the interval of 46.3 μsec between 0° and 1°, the voltage changed from zero to 1.745 V. This is an average rate of change of

$$\text{Rate of change}_{\text{av}} = \frac{\text{Volts}}{\text{Seconds}} = \frac{1.745}{46.3 \times 10^{-6}} = 3.77 \times 10^4 \text{ V/sec}$$

This is a high rate of change, some 37,700 V/sec, but the duration of this rate is short.

Now let us consider another short interval, the time between 89° and 90°. This is 1° and is the same 46.3 μsec in time duration. The change in voltage during this time is the difference between the voltage at 89° and the voltage at 90° (Figure 15-3). At 89° the voltage is

$$e = E_{\text{max}} \sin \theta = 100 \sin 89 = 100(0.99985) = 99.985 \text{ V}$$

At 90° the voltage is

$$e = E_{\text{max}} \sin \theta = 100 \sin 90 = 100(1.00000) = 100 \text{ V}$$

and the difference is

$$100 - 99.985 = 0.015 \text{ V}$$

Since this change in voltage occurs in 46.3 μsec, the rate of change of voltage is

$$\text{Rate of change}_{\text{av}} = \frac{\text{Volts}}{\text{Seconds}} = \frac{0.015}{46.3 \times 10^{-6}} = 324 \text{ V/sec}$$

Figure 15-3   Graph of a 60 Hz sinusoidal waveform, used to determine the rate of change of voltage in the time interval between 89° and 90°.

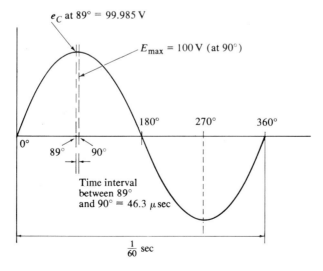

though this may seem a high rate of change of voltage, it is less than 1/100 the average rate of change of voltage during the interval between 0° and 1°.

Now suppose we had taken as the last interval the time between 89° and 91°. A little calculation will show that the voltage has the same value at both instants. The change in average voltage during that time would be zero. Consider the interval between 89.9° and 90.1°; again, the average change during that interval is zero, since the voltage is the same both times. Suppose, finally, that we take some very short interval whose center is 90°, extending an infinitesimal time both before and after the time the voltage is at a maximum. If the time interval is so short as to approximate what we mean by an instant, it can be seen that at the instant the voltage waveform is at 90°, the rate of change of voltage is zero. If we were to do the same thing for other portions of the waveform representing the sinusoidal voltage, we would find that the variations in the rate of change of voltage, plotted against the time when they occur, would also graph as a sine wave. Such a graph is shown in Figure 15-4.

It can be seen from this graph that the rate of change of voltage is zero when the voltage itself is a maximum, and maximum when the voltage is zero.

But the current in the capacitor is given by the relationship

$$i_C = C\frac{dv_C}{dt}$$

where C is the capacitance in farads, and dv_C/dt is the value of the rate of change of voltage at that instant.

At the instant when the voltage is 100 V, the rate of change of voltage is zero, and the current for any value of capacitance is

$$i_C = C\frac{dv_C}{dt} = C(0) = 0$$

At the instant when the voltage is zero, the rate of change of voltage is 37,700 V/sec, approximately. Suppose we calculate the current flow this would cause through a 1 μF capacitor.

$$i_C = C\frac{dv_C}{dt} = (10^{-6})(3.77 \times 10^4) = 37.7 \text{ mA}$$

Though the rate of change of voltage in volts per second may have seemed high a moment ago, it does not produce any great current in the capacitor, since practical values of capacitance are very small measured in farads.

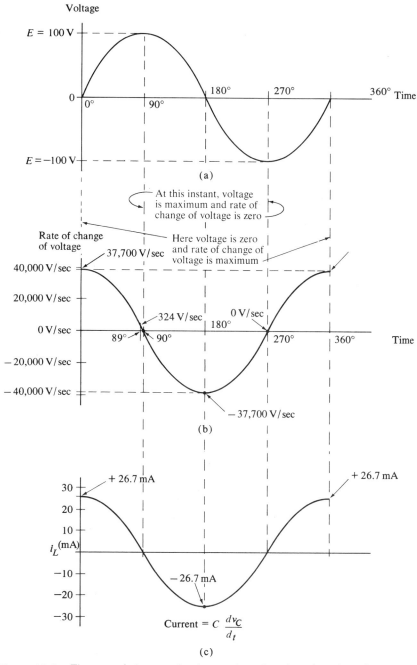

Figure 15-4 The rate of change of voltage, plotted against time, is a sine wave. Graphs show (a) voltage, (b) rate of change of voltage, and (c) current as sinusoidal waveforms.

This is a peak value of current. Expressed in rms, it would be approximately 26.7 mA. The same voltage we assumed across the capacitor of 100 V peak value, which is 70.7 V rms, would cause this value of current through a resistor of

$$R = \frac{E}{I} = \frac{70.7}{26.7 \times 10^{-3}} = 2.65 \times 10^3 \, \Omega$$

In other words, so far as the magnitude of the current flow through this capacitor of 1 μF at 60 Hz is concerned, it acts very much like a 2650 Ω resistor.

But this is true *only* so far as the magnitude is concerned. Precisely the same current would flow through a 2650 Ω resistor, but if such a resistor were to be put in place of the capacitor, the current peaks through the resistor would coincide with the voltage peaks. When the capacitor is in the circuit, the current peaks do not coincide with the voltage peaks, but are displaced by a quarter cycle, or 90°, since the current is proportional to the rate of change of voltage, and *not* to the voltage itself.

Thus, the capacitor offers an opposition to the flow of current; this opposition is measured in ohms, like resistance, but it is not resistance, since the phase relationship between voltage and current is not the same as it would be if the capacitor were to be replaced by a resistor. The kind of opposition offered by a capacitor is called *reactance,* with the symbol X. Since the opposition in this case is that offered by a capacitor, the subscript C is used with the symbol for reactance to designate this, as X_C. It is characteristic of reactance that the phase relationship between voltage and current is shifted by 90°. Where the reactance is due to a capacitance, the current will lead the voltage by 90°.

Suppose we had used a different frequency in our calculation of the current flow through this capacitance. If the frequency had been higher, the period for one cycle would have been shorter, and the time for 1° of rotation also shorter. At a frequency of 1000 Hz, the time for 1° is 1/360,000 sec, or 2.78 μsec. If the peak voltage of the sine wave is still 100 V, then the rate of change of voltage must be much greater than it was with the frequency 60 Hz, since the voltage must change by the same amount in much less time.

But the current at any instant is the product of two things, the capacity and the rate of change of voltage.

If the capacitance stays the same, but the rate of change of voltage is higher for higher frequencies, then the current must increase with higher frequencies. It is also apparent from the equation that increasing the capacity will increase the current, even if the rate of change of voltage does not increase.

If higher frequencies and more capacity both mean higher current, it is apparent that the opposition, or *capacitive reactance* (X_C), must decrease with frequency and capacity. The way X_C is related to frequency for any capacitor is shown in the graph of Figure 15-5. Capacitive reactance never reaches zero as the frequency increases, but it may reach a very low value. As the frequency decreases, X_C increases; and as the frequency approaches zero, which is dc, the apparent opposition approaches infinity. Aside from the initial charging current that occurs for the first five time constants, dc can produce no continual current flow through a capacitor; thus, the opposition a capacitor offers to dc is infinite.

Capacitive reactance X_C, capacitance C, and frequency f are all related by the equation

$$X_C = \frac{1}{2\pi f C}$$

where the factor 2π comes from the circular motion from which a sine wave is derived. *This equation applies only to sine waves.* If a waveform other than a sine wave is applied to a capacitor, this equation cannot be used directly to indicate the capacitive reactance. It *can* be used indirectly; if the waveform can be considered to be made up of combinations of sine waves of different amplitudes and phase, but all the same frequency or

Figure 15-5   Graph of the relationship of capacitive reactance to frequency.

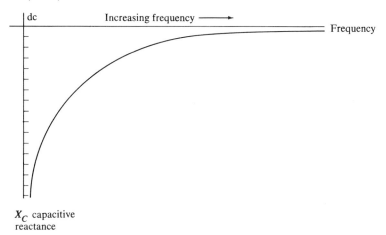

multiples of the fundamental frequency, then the equation can be applied to each of the sine waves individually, and the results summed. We will apply it only to sine waves.

EXAMPLE   Calculate the capacitive reactance of a 1 microfarad capacitor at a frequency of 60 Hz.

Solution.

$$X_C = \frac{1}{2\pi f C} = \frac{15.9 \times 10^{-2}}{6 \times 10^{-5}} = 2.65 \times 10^3$$

Note that this is precisely the opposition we had calculated before, by the method of finding the rate of change of voltage (approximately) at the instant when it was the greatest, and from this calculating the current and thus the opposition offered by the capacitor. Use of the equation is much simpler. Note also that the factor 2π, appearing in the denominator, was rewritten as 15.9×10^{-2} in the numerator. They are equivalent, since $2\pi \cong 6.28$, and 6.28 goes into 1 approximately 0.159 times. This is a convenience to those using a slide rule, but not necessary if an electronic calculator with the ability to calculate reciprocals is used.

Problems   1. Calculate the capacitive reactance of a 30 μF capacitor at a frequency of 700 kHz.

2. Calculate the capacitive reactance of a 70 pF capacitor at a frequency of 40 MHz.

3. Calculate the capacitive reactance of a 0.4 μF capacitor at a frequency of 30 Hz.

4. A capacitor has a reactance of 3.858 Ω at a frequency of 750 Hz. What is its capacitance?

5. A capacitor has a reactance of 26.5 Ω at a frequency of 24 Hz. What is its capacitance?

6. A 14 μF capacitor has a reactance of 18.9 Ω. What is the frequency of the sinusoidal voltage signal across the capacitor?

15-2
Inductive Reactance   INDUCTOR CURRENT.   Suppose a source of 60 Hz ac is connected to an inductor, as shown in Figure 15-6. Let us assume that the peak value of the current is 1 A, for the sake of convenience.

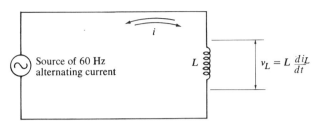

Figure 15-6   A simple inductance circuit.

An inductor has been defined as a two-terminal component in which the voltage is directly proportional to the rate of flow of current at any instant. This is defined more precisely by the equation

$$v_L = L \frac{di_L}{dt}$$

where v_L is the voltage across the inductance at any instant, L is the inductance in henrys, and di_L/dt is the rate of change of current through the inductor at that instant.

The waveform for an alternating current is the same as for an alternating voltage; it is a sine wave. As was the case with the alternating voltage applied to the capacitor, the maximum rate of change of current occurs when the value of the current is zero. At $0°$ and $360°$ the current is increasing at its maximum rate, and at $180°$ the current is decreasing at its maximum rate. At $90°$ and $270°$, the rate of change of current is zero, though the current has its maximum values at those instants.

We can, as before, calculate approximately the maximum value of the rate of change of current by noting the value of the current at $0°$ and its value at $1°$. The value is zero at $0°$ since this is the point at which the sine curve representing it crosses the horizontal axis. The value of current at $1°$ is

$$i = I_{max} \sin \theta = 1 \sin 1 = 0.01745 \text{ A}$$

This is the change in current during one degree of the cycle, measured from $0°$ to $1°$. The time required for this change, if the frequency of the current is 60 Hz, is, as we have seen, 46.3×10^{-6} sec. The average rate of change during this interval is

$$\text{Rate of change}_{av} = \frac{\text{Change in current}}{\text{Time}} = \frac{0.01745}{46.3 \times 10^{-6}} = 377 \text{ A/sec}$$

This is approximately the maximum rate of change of current. The voltage across the terminals of a 1 H inductor when the rate of change is 377 A/sec is

$$e_L = L\frac{di_L}{dt} = (1)(377) = 377 \text{ V}$$

Thus, at the instant the rate of change of current is 377 A/sec through the 1 H inductor, the voltage across its terminals is 377 V. Note that at this instant the *magnitude* of the current is zero.

If we were to plot the voltage for each instant, using this same technique, we would get the graph shown in Figure 15-7. The voltage waveform is sinusoidal, but the voltage peak occurs 90° ahead of the current peak. When the current is zero, the voltage is a maximum; when the current is maximum, the voltage is zero.

The rms value of the current with a peak value of 1 A is 0.707 A, and the rms value of the voltage with a peak value of 377 V is 0.707×377. The value of resistance through which this current would flow with this voltage applied is

$$R = \frac{E}{I} = \frac{(377 \times 0.707)}{0.707} = 377 \text{ }\Omega$$

Thus, so far as the magnitudes of current and voltage are concerned, the 1 H inductor acts like a 377 Ω resistor to a frequency of 60 Hz. With a resistor, the current and voltage are in phase with each other. With the inductor, as we have seen, the voltage leads the current by 90°.

In both the cases of the capacitor and the inductor, the voltage and current are out of phase with each other by 90°. In the case of the capacitor, the current leads the voltage; in the case of the inductor, the voltage leads the current. The opposition offered by an inductor and by a capacitor are both measured in ohms, and are called reactance, but we must distinguish between them since they have the *opposite* effect on the phase angle between voltage and current. This is why we appended the subscript C on the X_C for capacitive reactance, and why we must append the subscript L on the X_L for *inductive reactance*.

As the frequency of the applied sinusoidal current increases, the rate of change of current in the interval between 0° and 1° must also increase, since the same change in current must take place in less time. For a given inductor, this means that the voltage across it at that instant must also increase. But if for a given inductor the voltage across it is greater for the same current when the frequency is increased, its apparent opposition must increase with frequency.

It is also evident, from the fact that the current is equal to the inductance

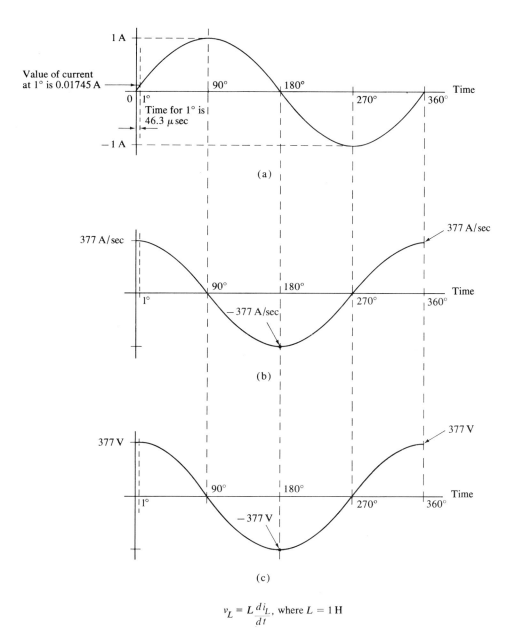

$$v_L = L\frac{di_L}{dt}, \text{ where } L = 1\text{ H}$$

Figure 15-7   Graphs of (a) 60 Hz alternating current, (b) rate of change of current, and (c) inductor voltage for the circuit of Figure 15-6.

times the rate of change of voltage, that if the value of the inductance increases, the voltage for a given current must also increase, and, consequently, the opposition offered by any inductance is directly proportional to the value of the inductance. If a 1 H inductor offers an opposition of 377 Ω to a frequency of 60 Hz, then a 2 H inductor would offer an opposition of 754 Ω to the same frequency.

A graph showing the way in which X_L changes with frequency is given in Figure 15-8. Each line on the graph represents the opposition offered by a given inductance. Note that they all increase with frequency at a constant rate, and that they all indicate zero opposition at a frequency of 0 Hz, which is dc.

Inductive reactance X_L, inductance L, and frequency f are all related to each other by the equation

$$X_L = 2\pi f L$$

where f is in hertz and L is in henrys.

EXAMPLE   Calculate the inductive reactance of a 1 H inductor to a frequency of 60 Hz.

Solution.

$$X_L = 2\pi f L = (2\pi)(60)(1) = 377\,\Omega$$

This is, as it should be, the same result we got by quite different considerations. Again, this is a very much simpler method to use.

Figure 15-8   Graph showing the change of X_L with frequency.

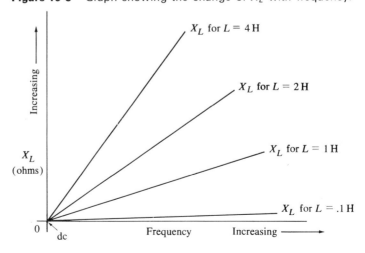

There are several points to remember. First, reactance refers *only* to sinusoidal waveforms. Second, most students find it difficult at first to remember the proper phase relationships. A simple memory aid is "*ELI* the *ICE* man." The *L* in *ELI* refers to inductance, and the *E* precedes the *I*; thus reminding the student that in an inductive circuit the voltage leads the current. The *C* in *ICE* refers to capacitance, and the *I* precedes the *E*, thus reminding the student that in a capacitive circuit the current leads the voltage.

Third, it is important to remember that a capacitor *blocks* dc and offers *decreasing* opposition to increasing frequencies, while an inductor *passes* dc unopposed and offers *increasing* opposition to increasing frequencies.

1. Calculate the inductance reactance of a 3.2 H inductor at a frequency of 75 Hz.   **Problems**

2. Calculate the inductance reactance of a 7 mH inductor at a frequency of 800 Hz.

3. An inductor has a reactance of 1.429 Ω at a frequency of 6.5 kHz. What is the value of its inductance?

4. An inductor has a reactance of 0.0236 Ω at a frequency of 15 Hz. What is the value of its inductance?

5. An 18 H inductor has a reactance of 192 kΩ. What is the frequency of the voltage signal across it?

6. A 0.03 H inductor has a reactance of 122 Ω. What is the frequency of the voltage signal across it?

THE SERIES *RC* CIRCUIT.   Suppose a resistor and a capacitor are connected in series with each other and a source of alternating voltage. If they are in series with each other, then by Kirchhoff's current law, the current must at any instant be the same in each. This current is plotted in the graph of Figure 15-9(a).   **15-3**
Series *RC* and *RL*
Circuits

Now suppose the value of the resistor is chosen so that the opposition it offers to the flow of current is the same as is offered for the particular capacitor used at the frequency of the generator. Let us suppose they each offer an opposition of 1000 Ω—resistance *R* for the resistor, and capacitive reactance X_C for the capacitor. If the generator voltage is adjusted so the

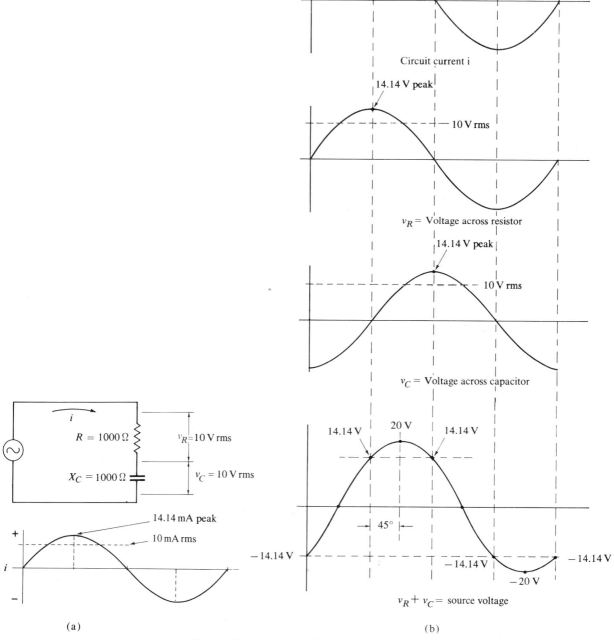

(a)

(b)

Figure 15-9   A series *RC* circuit and associated waveforms.

voltage across the resistor is 10 V rms, then the value of the current through the resistor is

$$I = \frac{e}{R} = \frac{10}{1000} = 0.010 = 10 \text{ mA}$$

Since the resistor and capacitor are in series, this must be the value of the capacitor current. The capacitor voltage must be

$$E = IX_C = (0.010)(1000) = 10 \text{ V}$$

Note that the relationship between voltage, current, and reactance is handled the same way as though it were resistance. This is because reactance represents an opposition in ohms.

Now the voltage across the resistor and capacitor are both known, and are both equal to 10 V. These voltages are plotted on the graphs of Figure 15-9(b). Note that the voltage across the resistor is in phase with the circuit current, but the voltage across the capacitor *lags* (remember *ELI* the *ICE* man) the current by 90°.

The generator voltage is, by Kirchhoff's voltage law, the sum of the voltage across the resistor and the voltage across the capacitor. This is one time that ten and ten *do not* make twenty. If we look at the graphs of Figure 15-9(b), we see that the peak voltage across the resistor occurs at an instant when the voltage across the capacitor is zero, and the peak voltage across the capacitor occurs when the voltage across the resistor is zero. In our original statement of Kirchhoff's laws we added the magic phrase "at any instant," and we must now invoke this phrase.

We can, laboriously, plot the sum of these two voltages by calculating their values at several instants during one complete current cycle, and then connecting the points thus obtained in a continuous curve. We can do the same thing, less accurately but less laboriously, by measuring the height of each of the waveforms at corresponding points on the time axis, and using these measurements to plot a new curve. The new curve will use the same time axis, and the height of this curve at any point on the time axis will be the *algebraic* sum of the heights of the other two voltage curves. We must remember that the other two curves represent voltages of 10 V rms, and they must be plotted, therefore, as voltages having an $E_{\max}$ of 14.14 V. This new curve is shown in the graphs of Figure 15-9(b).

This new curve has an $E_{\max}$ of 20 V, but the peak voltage occurs at 135°. Since the maximum value of the voltage representing the sum of the two original voltages is 20 V, its rms value is 14.14 V. Now we can write an equation for the sum of the two original voltages where the two original values and the sum are all expressed in rms values; thus,

10 V rms + 10 V rms = 14.14 V rms

This obviously calls for an unusual kind of arithmetic. To see just what kind, it is necessary to represent these ac voltages not as sine waves, but as *phasors*. Figure 15-10 shows the two original voltages in phasor representation. The voltage across the resistor is shown as an arrow pointing to the *right*. This is the reference position, and represents 0° of rotation. The phasor representing the voltage across the capacitor is drawn as an arrow pointing *straight down*. Recall that in a capacitor, the voltage *lags* the current by 90° (*ICE* again). The voltage across the resistor is in step with the current; therefore, the current arrow, if drawn, would be drawn in the same direction as the voltage arrow for the resistance. Thus, the capacitor phasor is shown 90° behind the reference; and since the direction of phasor rotation is counterclockwise, it is drawn straight down.

These voltage phasors can be thought of as forces acting on the electrons, and these two forces are acting at right angles to each other. The single force equivalent to two forces acting at a single point but at an angle with each other can be found graphically by drawing two lines from a single point, each having a length proportional to the magnitude of the force, and in the direction in which the force is acting, then completing the parallelogram and drawing the diagonal.

We can do this with our phasors. The arrow representing the voltage across the resistor can be drawn as a phasor pointing to the right, and with a length of 10 cm to represent its magnitude of 10 V rms. (Note that we are *not* saying it is a phasor with a magnitude $E_{max} = 10$ V. We are simply using 1 cm/V rms as a convenient scale for the drawing.) The arrow representing the 10 V rms across the capacitor is similarly drawn as a phasor 10 cm long, pointing straight down. The sum of the two can now be drawn by completing the parallelogram of which they form two sides, and drawing the diagonal. The length of the diagonal, if carefully drawn and measured, will be found to be very close to 14.14 cm long. This length is, by our scale, proportional to a voltage of 14.14 V rms.

This phasor, which represents the sum of the two original voltages, makes an angle to the horizontal, or reference, axis that, if measured, is seen to be very close to 45°. Since it is below the axis, it represents a lagging phase angle, or an angle of $-45°$.

Suppose we were to do as we did when we first introduced phasors, and compare them to the sinusoidal representation of alternating voltages and currents. We might imagine this phasor, with a length of 14.14 V, starting with a phase angle of $-45°$, is projected on a screen, so that only the arrowhead casts a shadow. If the screen is moved to the left by some appropriate distance equal to the desired time base, while the phasor rotates through 360° to its original initial position of 45° below the

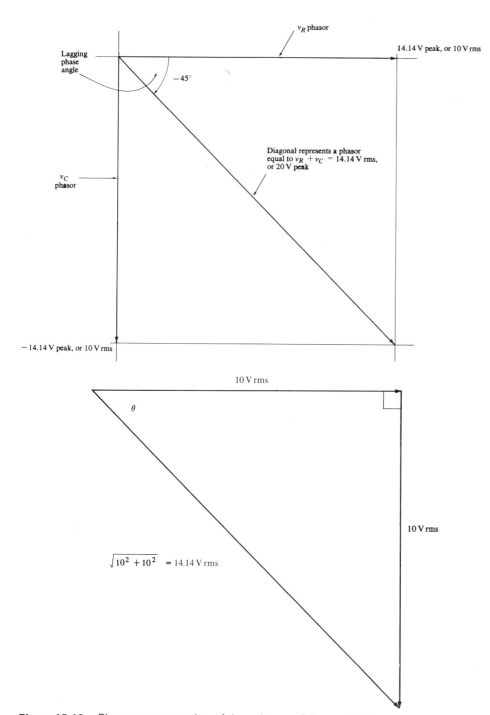

Figure 15-10   Phasor representation of the voltages of Figure 15-9.

horizontal axis, the shadow on the screen will trace out exactly the last graph we plotted in Figure 15-9(b). This phasor is, therefore, an equivalent to the sum of the two voltages, added instant by instant. The phasor representation provides us with a simple and convenient means of performing the necessary addition.

Algebraically, this phasor arithmetic is performed by either of two methods. If the phasors are represented in the polar coordinate system, the voltage across the resistor is $10 \angle 0°$, and the voltage across the capacitor is $10 \angle -90°$. The two phasors form the two sides of a triangle whose hypotenuse is the length of their sum. This is shown in Figure 15-10.

The *Pythagorean theorem* tells us *the length of the hypotenuse of a right triangle is equal to the square root of the sum of the squares of the lengths of the other two sides.* Thus,

$$v_t = \sqrt{v_R{}^2 + v_C{}^2}$$

For the case just considered, where the rms values of the two voltages to be summed both happen to be equal to 10 V, this gives

$$v_t = \sqrt{10^2 + 10^2} = \sqrt{100 + 100} = \sqrt{200} = 14.14 \text{ V rms}$$

which is in agreement with the result obtained from the graph; but the method is obviously capable of greater precision than graphical methods.

The phase angle can be easily obtained from the observation that

$$\tan \theta = v_C v_R$$

Thus,

$$\tan \theta = \frac{10}{10} = 1$$

and from the tables of trigonometric functions, $\theta = 45°$.

Expressed in polar coordinates, the sum of the two original voltages is

$$v_t = 10 \angle 0° + 10 \angle -90° = 14.14 \angle -45°$$

The calculation may also be done readily by using rectangular coordinates where the reactive components are represented by imaginary quantities, and the resistive components by real quantities. The two quatities to be summed are

$$v_R = 10 \qquad \text{and} \qquad v_C = -10j$$

and their sum is simply

$$v_t = 10 - 10j$$

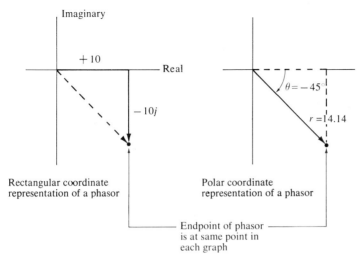

Figure 15-11   Relationship between polar and rectangular co-ordinate systems.

This is the final answer in the rectangular coordinate system, but to be useful it must be converted to the polar coordinate system, since meters do not read the rectangular coordinates of a voltage, but only the length of the phasor in polar coordinates. Figure 15-11 shows the relationship between the polar and rectangular coordinate systems. From the figure,

$$r = \sqrt{Real^2 + Imaginary^2}$$

and

$$\theta = Arctan \frac{Imaginary}{Real}$$

Therefore, to convert the rectangular coordinate quantity $10 - 10j$ to the corresponding polar quantity in the form $r \angle \theta$,

$$r = \quad 10^2 + (-10)^2 = 14.14$$

$$\theta = \arctan \frac{-10}{10} = -45°$$

Therefore,

$$v_t = 10 - 10j = 14.14 \angle -45°$$

We have now gotten exactly the same result by four methods, two graphical and two algebraic. The algebraic methods are much preferred, since they are quicker and more precise, but they should *always* be accompanied by a sketch showing the phasor relationship, to avoid gross errors.

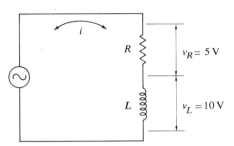

Figure 15-12 A series *RL* circuit.

THE SERIES *RL* CIRCUIT. An inductor and a capacitor are alike in that there is a phase angle of 90° between the voltage across and current through them, for sinusoidal ac, but they differ in the direction of the phase angle.

Suppose we have a series *RL* circuit such as the circuit of Figure 15-12. Let us assume the value of the resistance is chosen so that the voltage across it will be 5 V, and the value of the inductor and the frequency of the source ac are chosen such that the voltage across the inductor is 10 V.

The current through the two components must, at any instant, be the same since they are in series. Therefore, the current will be the common reference. The resistor voltage is in phase with the current through it; thus, the resistor voltage is in phase with the common reference. The voltage across the inductor is *not* in phase with the current through it. The voltage across an inductor *leads* (remember *ELI* the *ICE* man) the current by 90°. Therefore, the phasor representing the inductor voltage must be drawn 90° ahead of the zero reference. This is shown in Figure 15-13.

The sum is obtained precisely as was the case with the series *RC* circuit. The total voltage and, consequently, the source voltage, is

$$v_t = \sqrt{v_R{}^2 + v_L{}^2} = \sqrt{5^2 + 10^2} = \sqrt{25 + 100} = \sqrt{125} = 11.18 \text{ V}$$

and the phase angle of this total voltage is

$$\theta = \arctan \frac{v_L}{v_R} = \frac{10}{5} = \arctan 2 = 63° \, 26'$$

The generator voltage is thus 11.18 V, and it leads the generator current by a phase angle of 63° 26′.

SERIES IMPEDANCE. As we have seen, the sum

$$v_t = v_R + v_C \qquad \text{(summed as phasors)}$$

or

$$v_t = v_R + v_L \qquad \text{(summed as phasors)}$$

Figure 15-13 Phasor representation of inductor voltage.

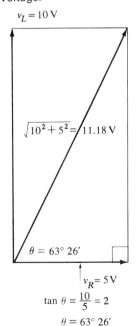

$v_L = 10 \text{ V}$

$\sqrt{10^2 + 5^2} = 11.18 \text{ V}$

$\theta = 63° \, 26'$

$v_R = 5 \text{ V}$

$\tan \theta = \frac{10}{5} = 2$

$\theta = 63° \, 26'$

must be obtained by adding the voltages as phasors. It is evident that it is necessary to consider these voltages as *directed* quantities, having both magnitude and direction.

By Ohm's law ($E = IR$),

$$IZ = IR + IX_C \quad \text{and} \quad IZ = IR + IX_L \quad \text{(summed as phasors)}$$

where Z is the total impedance of the circuit. Since this is a series circuit, the current in each component must be the same, and equal to the source current. Therefore, dividing each term in both of the above equations by I,

$$Z = R + X_C \quad \text{and} \quad Z = R + X_L \quad \text{(summed as phasors)}$$

If v_R, v_C, and v_L can be considered to have both magnitude and direction, and if they are respectively equal to IR, IX_C, and IX_L, then these products must have direction and magnitude, and must be phasors themselves. Since the current is identical in all these terms, it cannot be responsible for the fact that the phasors representing v_R, v_C, and v_L all point in different directions. The vector quantity must, therefore, be inherent in R, X_C, and X_L, and these quantities must be summed as phasors (Figure 15-14).

$$Z = \sqrt{R^2 + X^2}$$

where X can be capacitive, inductive, or the result of a combination of the two.

Suppose a capacitor with $X_C = 10 \ \Omega$ is in series with a resistor $R = 5 \ \Omega$.   EXAMPLE
Calculate the impedance.

Figure 15-14   Phasor representation of R, X_C, and X_L.

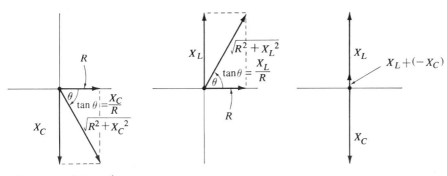

Phasor sum of R and X_L

Solution.

$$Z = \sqrt{R^2 + X_C^2} = \sqrt{5^2 + 10^2} = \sqrt{25 + 100} = \sqrt{125} = 11.18\,\Omega$$

EXAMPLE   Suppose a resistor with $100\,\Omega$ resistance is in series with an inductance $X_L = 100\,\Omega$. Calculate the impedance.

Solution.

$$Z = \sqrt{R^2 + X_L^2} = \sqrt{10^2 + 10^2} = 141.4\,\Omega$$

PHASE ANGLE CALCULATIONS.   Since the voltage leads the current in inductive circuits and the voltage lags the current in capacitive circuits, X_L must be a phasor *leading* by $90°$ the reference phasor R, which is in step with the current as the reference in series circuits, while X_C must be a phasor *lagging* by $90°$ the reference phasor R.

The phase angle between the source voltage and the series circuit current has already been defined as

$$\theta = \arctan\frac{v_X}{v_R}$$

where v_X is the voltage across the reactive component of the series circuit, and v_R is the voltage across the resistive component. Since, by Ohm's law, $v_R = IR$, and $v_X = IX$,

$$\theta = \arctan\frac{IX}{IR} = \arctan\frac{X}{R}$$

where X may be either inductive or capacitive reactance. If X represents inductive reactance X_L, then it is positive, and the resultant phase angle is between $0°$ and $90°$. If X represents capacitive reactance X_C, then it is negative, and the ratio X_C/R is also negative. The phase angle in this case is between $0°$ and $-90°$.

EXAMPLE   Given a series circuit with an inductive reactance of $3\,\Omega$ and a resistance of $4\,\Omega$. Find the impedance and the phase angle.

Solution.

$$Z = \sqrt{R^2 + X^2} = \sqrt{3^2 + 4^2} = 5\,\Omega$$

$$\theta = \arctan\frac{X}{R} = \arctan\frac{3}{4} = 36°\,52'$$

EXAMPLE   Given a series circuit with a capacitive reactance of $12\,\Omega$ and a resistance of $5\,\Omega$, calculate the impedance and the phase angle.

Solution.

$$Z = \sqrt{R^2 + X^2} = \sqrt{5^2 + 12^2} = 13\,\Omega$$

$$\theta = \arctan\frac{X}{R} = \arctan\frac{-12}{5} = -67°\,23'$$

Note that in the last example the phase angle is negative, as it should be from a capacitive circuit.

1. Consider a series *RC* circuit connected to an ac voltage source. The **Problems** rms voltage across the resistor is 85 V and the rms voltage across the capacitor is 122 V. Calculate the magnitude and phase angle of the source voltage.

2. Consider a series *RC* circuit connected to an ac voltage source, where the rms voltage across the resistor is 13 V and the rms voltage across the capacitor is 7.5 V. Calculate the magnitude and phase angle of the source voltage.

3. Consider a series *RC* circuit connected to an ac voltage source, where the rms voltage across the resistor is 1.8 V and the voltage across the capacitor is 0.42 V. Calculate the magnitude and phase angle of the source voltage. Express first in rectangular coordinates and then in polar coordinates.

4. Consider a series *RC* circuit connected to an ac source generating a voltage of 150 V $\angle\,0°$ rms, where the voltage across the resistor is measured at 100 V. Calculate the magnitude and the phase angle (using the source voltage as the reference) of the voltage across the capacitor, and the phase angle of the voltage across the resistor.

5. Consider a series *RL* circuit connected to an ac voltage source, where the rms voltage across the resistor is 10 V and the rms voltage across the inductor is 15 V. Calculate the magnitude and phase angle of the source voltage.

6. Consider a series *RL* circuit connected to an ac voltage source where the rms voltage across the resistor is 115 V and the rms voltage across the inductor is 72 V. Calculate the magnitude and phase angle of the source voltage.

7. Consider a series *RL* circuit connected to an ac source generating a voltage of 22 V $\angle\,0°$ rms, where the voltage across the inductor is measured at 11 V rms. Calculate the magnitude and phase angle (using the source voltage as the reference) of the voltage across the resistor. What is the phase angle of the voltage signal across the capacitor?

8. A capacitor with $X_C = 2500\,\Omega$ is in series with a $750\,\Omega$ resistor. Calculate the total impedance.

9. A capacitor with $X_C = 14\,\Omega$ is in series with a $3\,\Omega$ resistor. Calculate the total impedance.

10. An inductor with $X_L = 200\,\Omega$ is in series with a $550\,\Omega$ resistor. Calculate the total impedance.

11. An inductor with $X_L = 4\,\Omega$ is in series with an $11\,\Omega$ resistor. Calculate the total impedance.

12. A capacitor with a capacitive reactance of $900\,\Omega$ is in series with a resistor of 1.3 kΩ. Calculate the impedance and phase angle.

13. An inductor with an inductance reactance of $23\,\Omega$ is connected in series with a resistor of $105\,\Omega$. Calculate the impedance and phase angle.

14. A 3 μF capacitor is connected in series with a $700\,\Omega$ resistor and a 100 Hz ac voltage source. Calculate the impedance and phase angle of the *RC* combination.

15. A 0.4 H inductor is connected in series with a 2.2 kΩ resistor and a 1.5 kHz ac voltage source. Calculate the impedance and phase angle of the *RC* combination.

16. An inductor with a reactance of $750\,\Omega$ is connected in series with a $240\,\Omega$ resistor and a capacitor with a capacitive reactance of $630\,\Omega$. Calculate the impedance and phase angle.

15-4
Parallel *RC* and *RL*
Circuits

THE PARALLEL *RL* CIRCUIT. In the circuit of Figure 15-15 a resistance and an inductance are connected in parallel with each other, and the parallel bank is connected to a source of alternating current. By Kirchhoff's voltage law, the voltage across each component must be the same at any instant.

Since the voltage across the inductor and the resistor must be the same at any instant, this voltage is the common reference. The current through the resistor is in phase with the voltage, but the current through the inductor is 90° *behind* the voltage (*ELI* the *ICE* man). Therefore, the inductor current *lags* the resistor current by 90°.

The source current is the sum of the currents in the parallel branches. Since we are adding two currents that are 90° out of phase with each other, they must be added as phasors. Therefore,

$$I_t = \sqrt{I_R^2 + I_L^2}$$

These currents are shown in the phasor diagram of Figure 15-16. The angle the resultant makes with the reference phasor, which in this case is the voltage, is

$$\theta = \arctan \frac{I_L}{I_R}$$

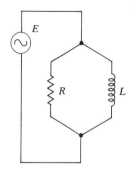

Figure 15-15   A parallel *RL* circuit.

EXAMPLE

Given a parallel *LR* circuit in which the current in the inductive branch is 8 mA while the current in the resistive branch is 6 mA, find the total current and the phase angle it makes with the source voltage.

Solution.

$$I_t = \sqrt{I_R^2 + I_L^2} = \sqrt{6^2 + 8^2} = 10 \text{ mA}$$

$$\theta = \arctan \frac{I_L}{I_R} = \arctan = \frac{-8}{6} = \arctan -1.333 = -53°8'$$

Note that the phase angle is given as negative, and this is an inductive circuit. The reason is that the reference is different from that of the series circuit. In the series circuit the current is common to each element and is, therefore, the reference. In the parallel circuit the voltage is common to each element and is, therefore, the reference.

If we compare the series and parallel circuits, *using the same reference*, the distinction disappears. If the voltage is used as a reference in the series inductive circuit, then instead of saying, as we did, that *the voltage leads the current* by the number of degrees in the phase angle, we would say *the current lags the voltage* by that same phase angle. That is precisely the situation we now have. The calculation for the last example showed the current *lagging* the voltage, and this was expressed as a negative phase angle. We could equally say the voltage *leads* the current by precisely the same angle.

THE PARALLEL *RC* CIRCUIT.   In the circuit of Figure 15-17 a resistance and a capacitance are connected in parallel with each other, and the parallel bank is connected to a source of alternating current. By Kirchhoff's voltage law the voltage across each component must be the same at any instant.

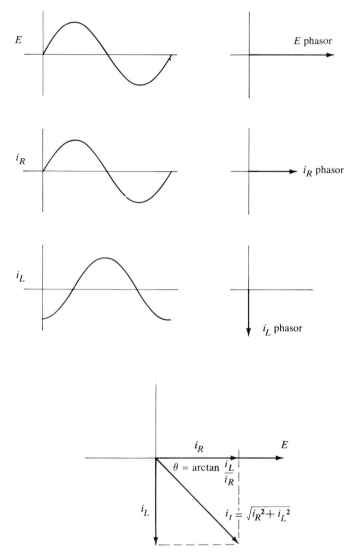

Figure 15-16 Phasor diagram of the currents for the circuit of Figure 15-15.

Since the voltage across the capacitor and the resistor must be the same at any instant, this voltage is the common reference. The current through the resistor is in phase with the voltage, but the current through the capacitor is 90° *ahead* of the voltage (*ELI* the *ICE* man). Therefore, the capacitor current *leads* the resistor current by 90°.

The source current is the sum of the currents in the parallel branches. Since we are adding two currents that are 90° out of phase with each other, they must be added as phasors. Therefore,

$$I_t = \sqrt{I_R^2 + I_C^2}$$

These currents are shown in the phasor diagram of Figure 15-18. The angle the resultant makes with the reference phasor, which in this case is the voltage, is

$$\theta = \arctan\frac{I_C}{I_R}$$

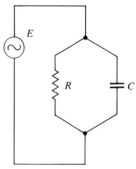

Figure 15-17   A parallel *RC* circuit.

Figure 15-18   Phasor diagram of the currents for the circuit of Figure 15-17.

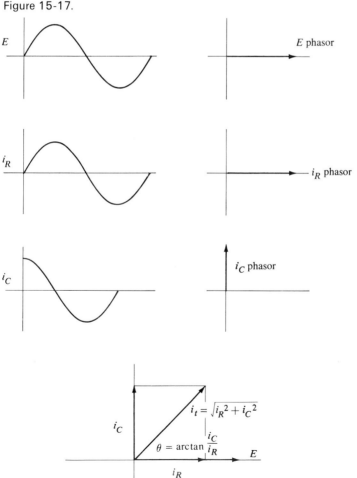

EXAMPLE   Consider a parallel *RC* circuit in which the current in the capacitive branch is 20 mA while the current in the resistive branch is 15 mA. Find the total current and the phase angle it makes with the source voltage.

Solution.

$$I_t = \sqrt{I_R^2 + I_C^2} = \sqrt{15^2 + 20^2} = \sqrt{225 + 400} = \sqrt{625} = 25 \text{ mA}$$

$$\theta = \arctan \frac{I_C}{I_R} = \arctan \frac{20}{15} = \arctan 1.333 = 57° \, 8'$$

Again, the phase angle is opposite in sign to the phase angle calculated for a series capacitive circuit. This only appears to be the case, since the voltage is taken as a reference here in the parallel circuit, and the current is given with reference to the voltage. In the series circuit, the current was given as a reference, and the phase angle of the voltage given with reference to the current.

Whether the circuit is inductive or capacitive, and whether it is series or parallel, the phase relationship between voltage and current will have the same sign if the reference is the same.

If the circuit is inductive, the phase angle will be positive if the current is the reference. If the circuit is capacitive, the phase angle will be negative if the current is the reference. If the voltage is the reference, the sign of the phase angle will be reversed.

Figure 15-19   Phasor representation of total current in a parallel circuit.

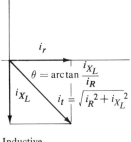

Inductive

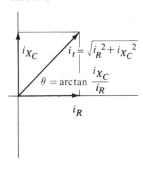

Capacitive

IMPEDANCE IN PARALLEL REACTIVE CIRCUITS.   The total current in a parallel circuit is the phasor sum of the individual branch currents (Figure 15-19). Thus,

$$I_t = I_R + I_X \qquad \text{(summed as phasors)}$$

where I_R is the current in the resistive branch, and I_X is the current in the reactive branch, whether it is inductive or capacitive. By Ohm's law,

$$I = \frac{E}{R}, \qquad I = \frac{E}{X}, \qquad \text{and} \qquad I = \frac{E}{Z}$$

Substituting in the equation for the sum of the currents,

$$\frac{E}{Z} = \frac{E}{R} + \frac{E}{X} \qquad \text{(summed as phasors)}$$

Since the voltage is the same across each component in a parallel circuit, and is equal to the source voltage, each term in the above equation may be divided by *E*, and the result is

$$\frac{1}{Z} = \frac{1}{R} + \frac{1}{X} \qquad \text{(summed as phasors)}$$

Since the original current equation from which this is derived is a phasor equation, in which the current through the two branches must be summed as phasor quantities, in this equation, too, the quantities must be treated as phasors. Algebraically, this equation may be solved for any of the unknowns without regard for the fact that they represent phasor quantities; thus,

$$Z = \frac{RX}{R+X} \qquad \text{(using phasor arithmetic)}$$

The solution of the equation for Z, once values have been substituted for R and X, involves multiplication and division, as well as addition. The addition is performed as before.

To illustrate, let us assume a $4\,\Omega$ resistance in parallel with a $3\,\Omega$ inductive reactance. Then

$$X = 3\angle +90° \qquad \text{and} \qquad R = 4\angle 0°$$

therefore,

$$R + X = \sqrt{R^2 + X^2}\,\angle \arctan\frac{X}{R}$$

$$= \sqrt{3^2 + 4^2}\,\angle \arctan\frac{3}{4}$$

$$= 5\angle 36°52'$$

This is the value of $R + X$, using phasor arithmetic, which is the denominator of the impedance equation for the parallel circuit of the example. The numerator is the product RX. Multiplication using phasors is, in the polar coordinate system, the product of the numerical values of the phasors, and the angle of the resultant is the sum of the two phase angles of the factors. Therefore,

$$(a\angle \theta)(b\angle \phi) = ab\angle (\theta + \phi)$$

and for our product RX,

$$RX = (4\angle 0°)(3\angle 90°) = (4)(3)\angle (0° + 90°) = 12\angle 90°$$

This is the numerator of our phasor equation, which is the product RX divided by the sum $R + X$. The impedance is, therefore,

$$Z = \frac{12\angle 90°}{5\angle 36°52'}$$

The division of phasor quantities expressed in polar notation is the inverse of multiplication. The resultant is the quotient of the numerical values of the phasors, at the phase angle which is the difference between the phase angles of the numerator and the denominator.

$$\frac{a \angle \theta}{b \angle \phi} = \frac{a}{b} \angle (\theta - \phi)$$

Therefore, in our calculation of parallel impedance,

$$Z = \frac{12}{5} \angle (90° - 36° 52') = 2.4 \angle 53° 8'$$

Exactly the same result could be obtained by using the rectangular coordinate system. Using the same figures, $R = 4$ and $X = 3j$, and the same relationship,

$$Z = \frac{RX}{R + X}$$

then

$$Z = \frac{(4)(3j)}{4 + 3j}$$

Multiplying the numerator,

$$Z = \frac{12j}{4 + 3j}$$

Now numerator and denominator are to be multiplied by the complex conjugate of the denominator, formed by changing the sign of the imaginary term of the denominator. Thus,

$$Z = \frac{12j(4 - 3j)}{(4 + 3j)(4 - 3j)}$$

The multiplication is now carried out, with regard for the fact that $j^2 = -1$. Thus,

$$Z = \frac{48j - (36)(-1)}{16 - 12j + 12j - (9)(-1)}$$

$$= \frac{36 + 48j}{25}$$

$$= \frac{36}{25} + \frac{48}{25}j = 1.44 + 1.92j$$

This is the impedance, expressed as a complex number, in the rectangular coordinate system. To be useful, this result must be changed to the polar coordinate system.

The length of the phasor in the polar system is

$$r = \sqrt{1.44^2 + 1.92^2} = 2.4$$

Phase angle θ is

$$\theta = \arctan \frac{\text{Imaginary}}{\text{Real}} = \arctan \frac{1.92}{1.44} = \arctan 1.3\overline{333}$$

$$\theta = 53° \, 8'$$

Therefore, the result as calculated by using rectangular coordinates, and expressed in polar coordinates, is

$$Z = 2.4 \angle 53° 8'$$

This agrees precisely with the result obtained by making all the calculations in the polar coordinate system. Since the results are precisely the same, either method may be used.

1. Consider a parallel RL circuit in which the current in the inductive branch is 30 mA and the current in the resistive branch is 40 mA. Determine the total current and the phase angle it makes with the voltage source.   **Problems**

2. Consider a parallel RL circuit in which the current in the inductive branch is 1.3 A and the current through the resistor is 0.8 A. Find the total current and the phase angle that it makes with the source voltage.

3. Suppose in a parallel RL circuit, where $R = 400 \, \Omega$ and $L = 0.2$ H, the total current is found to be 35.35 mA. If the source voltage is 10 V $\angle 0°$ rms, what are the currents (magnitudes and phase angles) in the resistive and inductive branches, and what is the phase angle that the total current makes with the source voltage?

4. A parallel RC circuit has 0.4 A in its resistive branch and 0.65 A in its capacitive branch. Calculate the total current and the phase angle that it makes with the source voltage.

5. Suppose a parallel RC circuit has 0.17 mA in its capacitive branch and 0.32 mA going through the resistor. Calculate the total current and the phase angle that it makes with the source voltage.

6. Consider a parallel RC circuit where $R = 250 \, \Omega$, $C = 220 \, \mu$F, the source voltage is 75 V $\angle 0°$ rms, and the total current is found to be 0.25 A. Calculate the currents through the resistor and capacitor, their phase angles relative to the source voltage, and the phase angle that the total circuit current makes with the source voltage.

7. An 840 Ω resistor is in parallel with an inductor that has an inductive reactance of 330 Ω. Calculate the impedance and phase angle, using polar coordinates.

8. A 13 Ω resistor is in parallel with a capacitor that has a capacitive reactance of 8 Ω. Calculate the impedance and phase angle, using polar coordinates.

9. A 2 kΩ resistor is in parallel with an inductor that has an inductive reactance of 650 Ω. Calculate the impedance and phase angle, using rectangular coordinates.

10. A 5 Ω resistor is in parallel with a capacitor that has a capacitive reactance of 16.5 Ω. Calculate the impedance and phase angle, using rectangular coordinates.

11. A 75 Ω resistor is in parallel with a capacitor with a 22 Ω capacitive reactance, and an inductor with a 152 Ω inductive reactance. Calculate the total impedance and phase angle.

12. Suppose a 400 Ω resistor is connected in parallel with a 1.86 H inductor and a 60 Hz, 12 V $\angle 0°$ rms ac voltage source. Calculate the total current and the phase angle it makes with the source.

15-5
Power in Reactive
Circuits

REACTIVE POWER. Figure 15-20 shows the voltage and current waveforms for a capacitor. The current leads the voltage by 90°. The power drawn from the source at any instant by the capacitor is the product of the voltage and current at that instant.

During the first quarter-cycle both voltage and current are positive, and the power, which is the product of the two, is therefore also positive. During the second quarter-cycle, the voltage is still positive, but the current is now negative. The power during this quarter-cycle, being the product of a positive and a negative quantity, is now negative.

A negative power is the opposite of a positive power. If the positive sign on the power during the first quarter-cycle indicates that the capacitor is drawing power from the source, the negative sign for the power during the second quarter-cycle indicates the capacitor is delivering power back into the circuit.

During the third and fourth quarter-cycles the same phenomenon is repeated. During the third quarter-cycle both the voltage and current are negative, and their product is, consequently, positive. During the fourth and final quarter the voltage is negative while the current is positive. Consequently, the power during this quarter-cycle is negative.

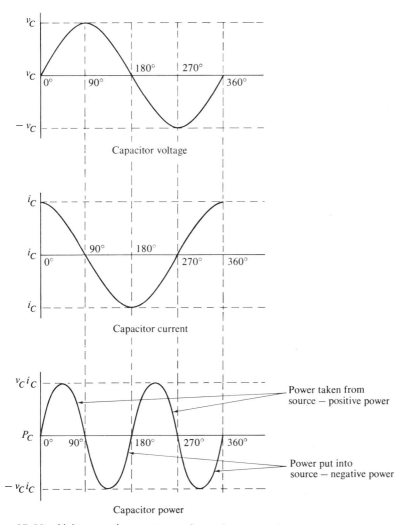

Figure 15-20   Voltage and current waveforms for a capacitor.

The power thus goes through two complete cycles during one cycle of the voltage and current. The average power during any half-cycle of the voltage or current is zero, since the power is negative for exactly as long as it is positive during that time, and by the same amount. During any quarter of a cycle the capacitor is either drawing power from the circuit source, or is in the process of discharging, putting the power back into the circuit. Therefore, over any period of time longer than a single half-cycle, the total power consumed by a capacitor is zero.

The voltage and current are similarly 90° out of phase with each other in an inductor (Figure 15-21). During the first quarter-cycle, using the voltage as the reference, the voltage is positive, while the current is negative. The power during this half-cycle is therefore negative. During the second quarter-cycle, both voltage and current are positive, and the power is therefore positive. Again, the second half-cycle is a repeat of the first, so far as power is concerned.

Figure 15-21   Voltage and current waveforms for an inductor.

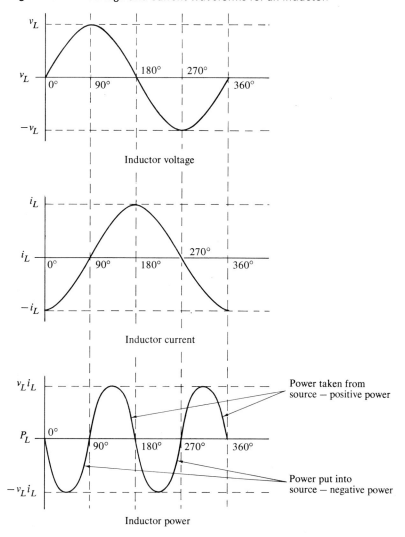

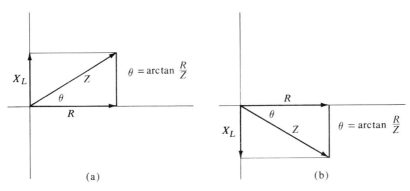

Figure 15-22 Impedance triangles show the relationship between reactance and resistance for (a) inductors and (b) capacitors.

Since the inductor absorbs power from the source during the time the magnetic field is building up, and returns that same power to the source during the time the magnetic field is collapsing, the net power drawn from the circuit is zero during any half-cycle.

Therefore, for a pure reactance, either inductive or capacitive, the power drawn from the source is zero.

Assume the source is delivering power to a load which consists of both reactive and resistive circuit elements. Since the reactive circuit elements draw no power from the source, all the power delivered to the load by the source must be dissipated in the resistance.

The *impedance triangle* shown in Figure 15-22 indicates the relationship between the impedance and the resistance. The phase angle between the voltage and current is the same as the phase angle between the impedance and the resistance. For a given impedance, the phase angle of which is known, the resistance can be calculated as follows:

$$\frac{R}{Z} = \cos \theta$$

Therefore,

$$R = Z \cos \theta$$

Any complex load may be reduced to a single resistor either in series or in parallel with a single reactive component, and, in a fashion similar to the conversion from series to parallel source seen in the Thevenin and Norton equivalent sources, either may be converted into an equivalent to the other circuit. That is, the series load may be converted into an

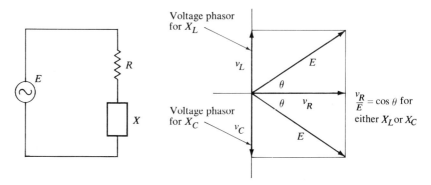

Figure 15-23   Voltage phasor diagram for a series load.

equivalent parallel load, and the parallel load may be converted into an equivalent series load. Therefore, we will consider both the series and parallel loads.

In the series load, with the voltage phasor diagram shown in Figure 15-23, the current is the same for each component. The voltage across the resistor is

$$v_R = E \cos \theta$$

The power expended is

$$P_t = P_R + P_X$$

but the power expended in the reactive component is zero. Therefore,

$$P_t = P_R$$

and the power expended in the resistor is

$$P = v_R I$$

but

$$v_R = E \cos \theta$$

Therefore,

$$P_t = EI \cos \theta$$

In the parallel load, with the current phasor diagram shown in Figure 15-24, the voltage is the same for each component. The current through the resistor is

$$i_R = I \cos \theta$$

The power expended is

$$P_t = P_R + P_X$$

but the power expended in the reactive component is zero. Therefore,

$$P_t = P_R$$

and the power expended in the resistor is

$$P = Ei_R$$

But

$$i_R = I \cos \theta$$

therefore,

$$P_t = EI \cos \theta$$

This is the real power expended in the load. As we have seen, it is the same regardless of whether the load is series RX or parallel RX.

POWER FACTOR.   The *power factor* is, by definition, $\cos \theta$. For a series circuit it is

$$\text{Power factor} = \cos \theta = \frac{E_R}{E_t}$$

and for a parallel circuit it is

$$\text{Power factor} = \cos \theta = \frac{I_R}{I_t}$$

Figure 15-24   Current phasor diagram for a parallel load.

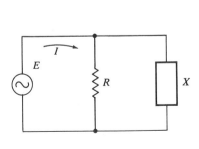
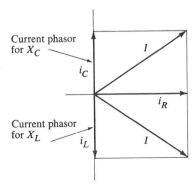

and for either series or parallel circuits it is

$$\text{Power factor} = \cos \theta = \frac{R}{Z}$$

The product *EI* is called the *apparent power*. For a circuit containing only resistance the power factor is 1, and the real power and the apparent power are the same. For a circuit containing only reactance the power factor is zero, and the real power is zero regardless of how high the apparent power is.

For the efficient operation of power distribution circuits by utility companies, the phase angle between the voltage and current should be as close to zero as possible. If the phase angle is too great, then current will flow and voltage will be present, but the power delivered to the load may be very low. In order to have the current in the distribution system at a minimum value for the real power consumed, it is sometimes necessary to correct the power factor of the load. Usually, the load is inductive, as in the case of electric motors. The leading inductive voltage can be corrected by connecting a capacitor of sufficient capacity and voltage rating in parallel with the load on a utility pole. The value of the capacitor is calculated to shift the phase angle of the source voltage as close as practical to zero. Note that no real power is drawn by this capacitor—only reactive power, which is zero. Its only effect is to correct the phase angle between voltage and current as far as the generator is concerned.

Problems　　**1.** Given a series *RC* circuit where the voltage across the resistor is 10 V and the voltage across the capacitor is 20 V, calculate the power factor.

2. Given a parallel *RL* circuit where the current through the resistor is 1.2 A and the current through the inductor is 1 A, calculate the power factor.

3. Calculate the power factor in a parallel *RC* circuit where the capacitive reactance is 73 Ω and the resistor is 95 Ω.

4. Given a series *RL* circuit where the inductive reactance is equal to 650 Ω and the resistor is 450 Ω, calculate the power factor.

5. Suppose a 3000 Ω resistor is connected in series with a capacitor and an ac source generating a voltage of 100 V $\angle 0°$ rms. If the capacitive reactance is 1700 Ω, calculate the total power expended in the circuit.

6. Suppose an inductor with an inductive reactance of 7.5 Ω is connected in series with a 9 Ω resistor and an ac source generating a voltage of 20 V $\angle\,^\circ$ rms. Calculate the total power expended in the circuit.

7. Suppose a capacitor with a capacitive reactance of 120 Ω is connected in parallel with a 270 Ω resistor and an ac source generating a voltage of 17 V $\angle\,0°$ rms. Calculate the total power expended in the circuit and the power factor.

8. Suppose an inductor with an inductive reactance of 35 Ω is connected in parallel with a 14 Ω resistor and an ac source generating a voltage of 110 V $\angle\,0°$ rms. Calculate the total power expended in the circuit and the power factor.

9. Consider a parallel *RC* circuit with an ac source voltage of 110 V $\angle\,0°$ rms. If the resistor has a value of 120 Ω and the power factor is 0.47, calculate the total impedance and the total power expended in the circuit.

10. Consider a series *RL* circuit with an ac source voltage of 18 V $\angle\,0°$ rms. If the resistor has a value of 11 Ω and the power factor is 0.88, calculate the total circuit impedance, the inductive reactance, and the total power expended in the circuit.

11. Consider a series *RC* circuit with an ac source voltage of 90 V $\angle\,0°$. If the resistor has a value of 35 Ω and the power factor is 0.23, calculate the total circuit impedance, the capacitive reactance, and the total power expended in the circuit.

apparent power   the product EI **Key Words**
impedance triangle   graphic representation of the relationship between impedance and resistance
power factor (cos θ)   for a series circuit, E_R/E_t. For a parallel circuit, I_R/I_t. For either series or parallel circuits, R/Z.
Pythagorean theorem   says that the length of the hypotenuse (the side opposite the right angle) equals the square root of the sum of the squares of the other two sides

1. When a capacitor is in a circuit, the current peaks do not coincide   **Summary** with the voltage peaks, but are displaced by a quarter-cycle, or 90°,   **of Concepts** since the current is proportional to the rate of change of voltage, and not to the voltage itself.

2. If the capacitance stays the same but the rate of change of voltage is higher for higher frequencies, then the current must increase with higher frequencies.

3. Capacitive reactance, while reaching very low values, never reaches zero, regardless of the increase in frequency.

4. *For sine waves only,* capacitive reactance X_C, capacitance C, and frequency f are related by the following equation: $X_C = 1/(2\pi fC)$, where 2π comes from the circular motion from which a sine wave is derived.

5. In both the capacitor and inductor the voltage and current are out of phase with each other by $90°$.

6. As the frequency of an applied sinusoidal current increases, the rate of change of current in the interval between $0°$ and $1°$ must also increase, and in the case of a given inductor so will the voltage across it at that instant.

7. Reactance refers only to sinusoidal waveforms.

8. A capacitor *blocks* dc and offers *decreasing* opposition to increasing frequencies, while an inductor *passes* dc unopposed and offers *increasing* opposition to increasing frequencies.

9. An inductor and a capacitor, while alike as to $90°$ phase angle between voltage across and current through them for sinusoidal ac, differ in the *direction* of the phase angle. In a capacitor, current leads voltage. In an inductor, voltage leads current.

10. When a resistance and an inductance are connected in parallel, the inductor current lags the resistor current by $90°$.

11. In a series circuit, current is common to each element and is, therefore, the reference; in a parallel circuit, voltage is the reference.

12. Whether a current is inductive or capacitive, in series or in parallel, the phase relationship between voltage and current will have the same sign if the reference is the same.

13. The power drawn from the source at any instant by the capacitor is the product of the voltage and the current at that instant.

14. A negative power is the opposite of a positive power—if the positive sign on the power during the first quarter-cycle indicates that the capacitor is drawing power from the source, the negative sign for the

power during the second quarter-cycle indicates that the capacitor is delivering power back into the circuit.

15. Power goes through two complete cycles during one cycle of voltage and current. Therefore, total power consumed by a capacitor during more than a single half-cycle is zero.

16. For a circuit containing only resistance the power factor is 1, and real and apparent power are the same. For a circuit containing only reactance the power factor is zero, and the real power is zero regardless of how high the apparent power is.

On a separate sheet of paper, fill in the blanks or answer the questions below. The number following each question refers to the section in the chapter where the correct answer can be found.   **To Help You Review**

1. Define reactance. (15-1)

2. Capacitive reactance is measured in ohms but is not considered resistance. Why? (15-1)

3. If capacitance stays the same, what happens to (a) rate of change of voltage and (b) current? (15-1)

4. For what kind of waveform is the equation $X_C = 1/(2\pi fC)$ applicable? (15-1)

5. In capacitors and inductors _____ and _____ are out of phase with each other by 90°. (15-2)

6. As the frequency of an applied sinusoidal current increases, the rate of change of current _____ and voltage _____ . (15-2)

7. In terms of dc, a capacitor offers _____ opposition to increasing frequencies, while an inductor offers _____ opposition to increasing frequencies. (15-2)

8. Explain the Pythagorean theorem. (15-3)

9. An inductor and a capacitor both have a phase angle between voltage and current. How do they differ in this respect? (15-3)

10. Explain reference, with respect to voltage and current in series and in parallel. (15-3) and (15-4)

11. What is the power drawn from a source by a capacitor equal to? (15-5)

12. Explain the following: A negative power is the opposite of a positive power. (15-5)

13. Over any period of time longer than _____ , the total power consumed by a capacitor is zero. (15-5)

14. What is an impedance triangle? (15-5)

15. What does each of the following represent, and for what kind of circuit: (a) $\cos \theta = E_R/E_t$ (b) $\cos \theta = R/Z$. (15-5)

16. Compare real and apparent power with respect to (a) resistance and (b) reactance. (15-5)

SIXTEEN
AC NETWORKS

NETWORK ARITHMETIC.   Mathematics can be used to solve network problems involving reactive as well as resistive circuit elements. It is necessary to be able to add, subtract, multiply, and divide quantities which have both magnitude and direction.

In this chapter the emphasis will be on solutions using the rectangular coordinate system. Any of the problems can also be solved by using the polar coordinate system, as well as by several other means. In the interest of clarity, economy of space and effort, and simplicity, other approaches will be used only where they are clearly more useful than the rectangular coordinate system.

Note that network problems where reactive circuit elements are involved are solved in the same way as are purely resistive networks. Indeed, this is why this book contains two chapters on resistive networks. All of the techniques learned there still apply. It is only necessary to include the relatively minor complications caused by out-of-phase voltages and currents.

16-1
Superposition

SUPERPOSITION.   The method of superposition as shown in the chapter on resistive networks is applied to ac reactive networks in exactly the same way. This is usually the simplest method where there are two or more generators; and now any or all the generators may be sinusoidal ac generators, or they may be dc sources, as well. If the generators are dc sources, then capacitors will appear as open circuits while inductors will appear as short circuits.

The circuit of Figure 16-1(a) contains two ac generators, an inductor, a capacitor, and a resistor. As is usual with the method of superposition, the circuit has been redrawn into two separate circuits, each with one generator and with the other shorted. The arrangement of components is otherwise unchanged.

Figure 16-1   (a) An ac circuit with two generators, an inductor, a capacitor, and a resistor. (b) Redrawn with one generator shorted and the inductor and resistor in parallel. (c) Redrawn with the other generator shorted and the capacitor and resistor in parallel.

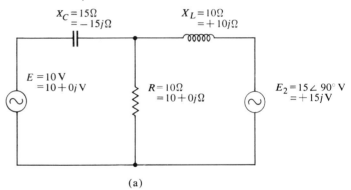

(a)

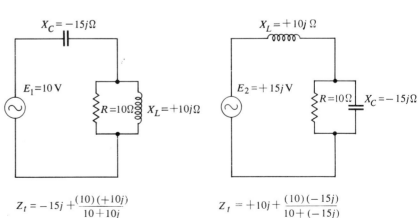

$$Z_t = -15j + \frac{(10)(+10j)}{10+10j}$$

(b)

$$Z_t = +10j + \frac{(10)(-15j)}{10+(-15j)}$$

(c)

In Figure 16-1(b) the only voltage source is E_1, with E_2 replaced by a short circuit. The inductor and resistor are in parallel with each other, and the capacitor is in series with the combination. The 10 Ω inductive reactance is, in rectangular coordinates, an impedance of $+10j$ Ω, while the 15 Ω of capacitive reactance becomes $-15j$ Ω. The resistance of 10 Ω is still simply 10 Ω in the rectangular coordinate system.

The impedances can now be combined and expressed in the rectangular coordinate system as complex numbers, *exactly as though they were ordinary resistances but with the $+j$ or $-j$ handled like any algebraic literal factor, except that $j^2 = -1$.*

The impedance of the parallel bank is

$$\text{Parallel impedance} = \frac{(10)(+10j)}{10 + (+10j)}$$

This impedance is in series with the capacitor, which has an impedance of $-15j$ Ω. The total impedance is therefore the sum of the impedance of the parallel bank and the impedance of the capacitor.

$$Z_t = -15j + \frac{(10)(+10j)}{10 + (+10j)} = -15j + 5 + 5j = (5 - 10j)\ \Omega$$

With the total impedance and the source voltage known, the total current can be found. The voltage of source E_1 is given as $10 \angle 0°$, which in rectangular coordinate notation is simply $10 + 0j$. The imaginary part of the complex number is not written since it is equal to zero. By Ohm's law,

$$I = \frac{E}{Z}$$

$$I_t = \frac{10}{5 - 10j} = \left(\frac{2}{5} + \frac{4}{5}j\right) A = (0.4 + 0.8j)\ A$$

The voltage drop across the capacitor is IX_C, not IR, and is equal to

$$V_C = IX = \left(\frac{2}{5} + \frac{4}{5}j\right)(-15j) = (12 - 6j)\ V$$

The voltage across the parallel bank is the difference between the voltage drop across the capacitor and the source voltage.

$$V_{\text{bank}} = E_1 - V_C = 10 - (12 - 6j) = (-2 + 6j)\ V$$

This is the voltage across both the resistor and the inductor. The current flow through the resistor is

$$I_R = \frac{V_R}{R} = \frac{-2 + 6j}{10} = \left(-\frac{2}{5} + \frac{3}{5}j\right) A = (-0.2 + 0.6j)\ A$$

The current through the inductor is

$$I_L = \frac{V_L}{X_L} = \frac{-2 + 6j}{+10j} = \left(\frac{3}{5} + \frac{1}{5}j\right) A = (0.6 + 0.2j)\, A$$

As a partial check, the current through the inductor plus the current through the resistor should equal the total current.

$$I_t = I_R + I_L = \left(-\frac{2}{5} + \frac{3}{5}j\right) + \left(\frac{3}{5} + \frac{1}{5}j\right) = \left(\frac{2}{5} + \frac{4}{5}j\right) A$$

which agrees with the previous calculation.

Now the magnitude and direction of current for each component due to E_1 are known and are shown in Figure 16-2(a). In a similar fashion, all the current due to E_2 may be calculated. The drawing of Figure 16-1(c) shows the components in their proper relationship, with E_1 replaced by a short circuit.

Figure 16-2 The circuits of Figure 16-1, showing magnitude and direction of current for each component.

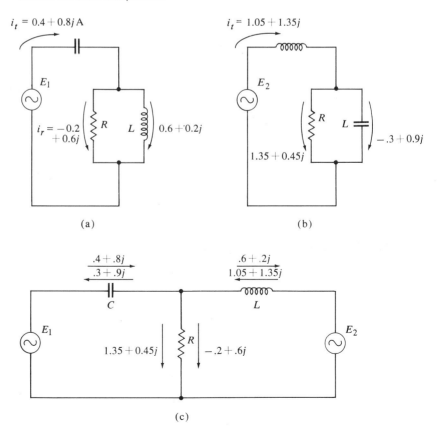

(a)

(b)

(c)

The circuit impedance is

$$Z = +10j + \frac{(10)(-15j)}{10 + (-15j)} = \frac{90}{13} + \frac{70}{13}j$$

The total circuit current is then

$$I_t = \frac{E_t}{Z_t} = \frac{15j}{\dfrac{90}{13} + \dfrac{70}{13}j} = (1.05 + 1.35j)\,\text{A}$$

The voltage drop across the inductor is

$$V_L = IX_L = (10j)(1.05 + 1.35j) = (-13.5 + 10.5j)\,\text{V}$$

The voltage across the parallel bank is this voltage subtracted from the source voltage.

$$V_{\text{bank}} = E_2 - V_L = 15j - (-13.5 + 10.5j) = (13.5 + 4.5j)\,\text{V}$$

This is the voltage across both the capacitor and the resistor. The current flow through the resistor is

$$I_R = \frac{V_R}{R} = \frac{13.5 + 4.5j}{10} = (1.35 + 0.45j)\,\text{A}$$

The current through the capacitor is

$$I_C = \frac{V_L}{X_C} = \frac{13.5 + 4.5j}{-15j} = (-0.3 + 0.9j)\,\text{A}$$

These currents are plotted on Figure 16-2(b).

As another check, the current through the capacitor plus the current through the resistor should equal the total current.

$$I_t = I_C + I_R = (-0.3 + 0.9j) + (1.35 + 0.45j) = (1.05 + 1.35j)\,\text{A}$$

which agrees with the previous calculation for I_t.

Now the current through each component caused by each of the two sources is known. If these currents are plotted on the original circuit, as in Figure 16-2(c), it is apparent that the final current is the sum of the two currents contributed by the two sources for the resistor, since these currents are in the same direction. For the two reactive components, the final current is the difference between the two currents, since these currents are opposed. Accordingly, for the resistor the total current is

$$I_R = 1.35 + 0.45j + (-0.2 + 0.6j) = 1.15 + 1.05j$$

The total current through the capacitor is

$$I_C = (0.4 + 0.8j) - (-0.3 + 0.9j) = 0.7 - 0.1j$$

The total current through the inductor is

$$I_L = 1.05 + 1.35j - (0.6 + 0.2j) = 0.45 + 1.15j$$

With the current through each component known, the voltage across each is easily calculated. Thus, the voltage across the capacitor is

$$E_C = I_C X_C = (0.7 - 0.1j)(-15j) = -1.5 - 10.5j$$

The voltage across the resistor is

$$E_R = I_R R = (1.15 + 1.05j)(10) = 11.5 + 10.5j$$

The voltage across the inductor is

$$E_L = I_L X_L = (0.45 + 1.15j)(10j) = -11.5 + 4.5j$$

We have now calculated the current through each component and the voltage across each. The source current for E_1 is, of course, the same as the current through the capacitor since they are in series with each other; and the source current for E_2 is the same as the inductor current for the same reason.

Since errors can occur in a calculation involving this much arithmetic, it is wise to make a relatively independent check on the validity of the results. Observation of the circuit makes it apparent that if Kirchhoff's laws are not to be violated, the currents entering the junction of the resistor, capacitor, and inductor must sum to zero. Therefore, for the junction

$$I_R = I_L + I_C = 0.45 + 1.15j + (0.7 - 0.1j) = 1.15 + 1.05j$$

This is in agreement with the figure already calculated for the resistor current, so Kirchhoff's current law is not violated by our solution.

It is desirable to check also to see that Kirchhoff's voltage law is not violated. Therefore, the sum of the voltage drops in any complete loop about the circuit must equal the source voltage in that loop. Checking first the loop involving E_1, the capacitor, and the resistor, we sum the voltages.

$$E_1 = V_C + V_R = (-1.5 - 10.5j) + (11.5 + 10.5j) = 10$$

This is the correct value for E_1. Therefore, Kirchhoff's voltage law is not violated for this loop. For the loop involving E_2, the inductor, and the resistor,

$$E_2 = E_L + E_R = (-11.5 + 4.5j) + (11.5 + 10.5j) = +15j$$

which is the correct value for E_2. Therefore, Kirchhoff's voltage law is not violated for this loop.

Knowing the source voltage and current for each source, it is also simple to calculate the impedance "seen" by each source. For E_1 the impedance is

$$Z_1 = \frac{E_1}{I_1} = \frac{10}{0.7 - 0.1j} = 3.5 + 0.5j$$

This impedance is the load on E_1, including the other source E_2, and could be duplicated by a 3.5 Ω resistor in series with an inductance having a reactance of 0.5 Ω. The load "seen" by E_2 may be similarly calculated.

The voltages and currents have been given in rectangular coordinates. They may be easily converted to the corresponding polar notation. This is left as an exercise for the student.

1. Completely solve the circuit shown. Check your answers by using Kirchhoff's laws.

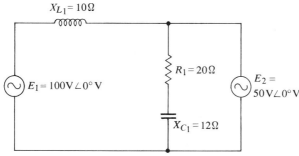

Circuit for Problem 1.

2. Completely solve the circuit shown. Check your answers by using Kirchhoff's laws.

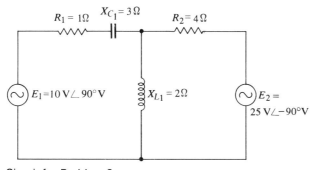

Circuit for Problem 2.

3. Completely solve the circuit shown. Use Kirchhoff's laws to check your answers.

Circuit for Problem 3.

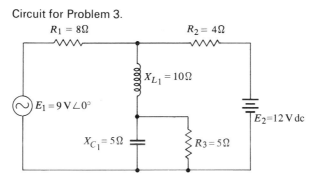

4. Completely solve the circuit shown. Check your answers by using Kirchhoff's laws.

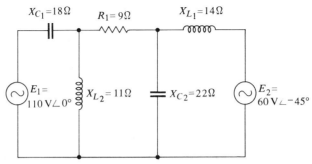

Circuit for Problem 4.

5. Completely solve the circuit shown. Check your answers by using Kirchhoff's laws.

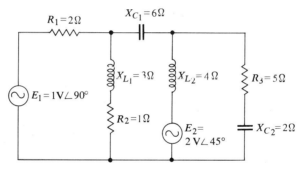

Circuit for Problem 5.

6. Completely solve the circuit shown. Use Kirchhoff's laws to check your answers.

Circuit for Problem 6.

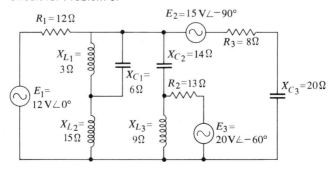

THEVENIN'S THEOREM RESTATED. A more inclusive statement of Thevenin's theorem is as follows:

**16-2
Thevenin's Theorem**

Any two-terminal network can be replaced by an equivalent circuit consisting of a perfect voltage source E_{Th}, with a voltage equal in magnitude, frequency, and phase to the open-circuit voltage of the original circuit with the load impedance removed, in series with an impedance Z_{Th}, equal to the impedance measured back into the original network with the load removed and all internal sources in the network removed and replaced with their equivalent internal impedances.

This sounds more difficult than it really is. Let us consider a relatively simple example.

The circuit of Figure 16-3(a) is a simple series–parallel circuit, which can be simply calculated by other means but which will serve as an illustration of the method of application of Thevenin's theorem to reactive circuits.

If the open-circuit voltage is calculated with the load impedance removed, the circuit that remains is a simple series circuit as in Figure 16-3(b). The impedance of this series circuit is

$$Z = R + X_C = 10 + (-10j) = 10 - 10j$$

Figure 16-3   A simple series–parallel reactive circuit.

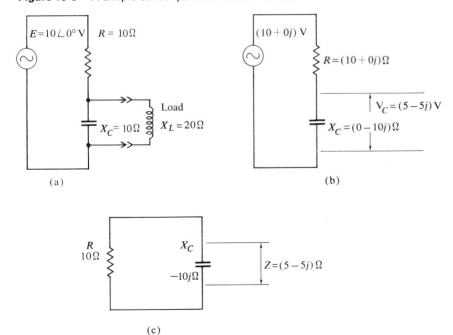

(a)

(b)

(c)

The current through this series circuit and, consequently, the current through the capacitor is

$$I = \frac{E}{Z} = \frac{10}{10 - 10j} = 0.5 + 0.5j$$

and the voltage across the capacitor is

$$V_C = I_C X_C = (0.5 + 0.5j)(-10j) = 5 - 5j$$

This is also the voltage across the load terminals with the load impedance removed, and is therefore the E_{Th} for the Thevenin equivalent circuit.

The Z_{Th} is similarly calculated. With the load impedance removed and the internal voltage source shorted, the impedance that would be measured back into the circuit is the impedance of the resistor and capacitor seen in parallel, as in Figure 16-3(c). This is

$$Z_{Th} = \frac{RX_C}{R + X_C} = \frac{(10)(-10j)}{10 - 10j} = 5 - 5j$$

This is the equivalent of a 5 Ω resistor in series with a capacitor having a reactance of 5 Ω. The Thevenin equivalent circuit to the original circuit is shown in Figure 16-4(a). It consists of a voltage source of $(5 - 5j)$ V and an impedance of $(5 - 5j)$ Ω in series with it.

If the original load, which was an inductor with a reactance of 20 Ω $(+20j)$ is now connected to this equivalent circuit, as in Figure 16-4(b), the current through and voltage across the load are easily calculated. The total impedance of the new circuit, consisting of the Thevenin equivalent and the load, is

$$Z_t = (5 - 5j) + (20j) = 5 + 15j$$

The current through the inductor is the total current since the equivalent circuit is a simple series circuit. This current is

$$I_t = \frac{E_{Th}}{Z_t} = \frac{5 - 5j}{5 + 15j} = -0.2 - 0.4j$$

This is the current through the inductive load. The voltage across this load is

$$E_L = I_L X_L = (-0.2 - 0.4j)(20j) = 8 - 4j$$

We have now calculated both the current through and the voltage across the load. Both may be represented in the polar coordinate system. The voltage is

$$r = \sqrt{8^2 + 4^2} = \sqrt{64 + 16} = \sqrt{80} = 8.944 \text{ V}$$

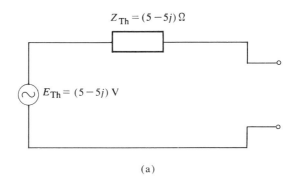

(a)

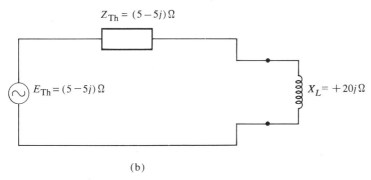

(b)

Figure 16-4   The Thevenin equivalent circuit for the circuit of Figure 16-3.

and the phase angle this voltage makes with the reference is

$$\theta = \arctan \frac{\text{Imaginary}}{\text{Real}} = \arctan -\frac{4}{8} = -26° \, 34'$$

The inductor current in the polar coordinate system is

$$r = \sqrt{0.2^2 + 0.4^2} = \sqrt{0.04 + 0.16} = \sqrt{0.2} = 0.447 \text{ A}$$

and the phase angle this current makes with the reference is

$$\theta = \arctan \frac{\text{Imaginary}}{\text{Real}} = \arctan \frac{-0.4}{-0.2}$$

Since both the real and imaginary parts of the complex number representing this phasor in the rectangular coordinate system are negative, the phasor must be in the third quadrant. It may be expressed as either the positive angle $180° + \theta$, or the negative angle $\theta - 180°$. Since the voltage has already been

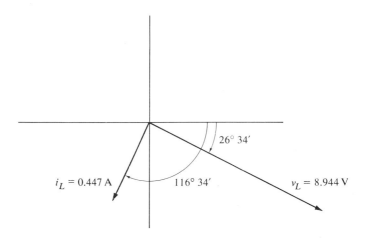

Figure 16-5 Phasor diagram of the voltage and current of the circuit of Figure 16-3.

expressed with a negative phase angle, the current will be treated the same way. Therefore,

$$\theta = 63° 26'$$

and since the whole phase angle is

$$\phi = 180° - \theta = 180° - 63° 26' = -116° 34'$$

Thus, the voltage across the inductor is $8.944 \angle -26° 34'$ V, and the current through the inductor is $0.447 \angle -116° 34'$ A. The phasors are drawn in the diagram of Figure 16-5. It may be seen that the current is lagging the voltage by 90°, as it must for an inductor.

Note that both current and voltage through the load have been given with phase angles, using the generator voltage as a reference. The load voltage is lagging the generator voltage by 26° 34'. With the voltages and currents expressed in the polar coordinate system, it is simple to change references. We may, if we wish, simply add 26° 34' to the load voltage and current as well as the source voltage, and express them each with reference to the load. If the load is changed, however, the results will not be valid for any new load.

Problems **1.** Find the Thevenin equivalent of the circuit shown, looking back from points A and B.

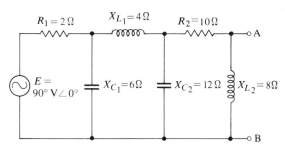

Circuit for Problem 1.

2. Find the Thevenin equivalent of the circuit shown, looking back from points A and B.

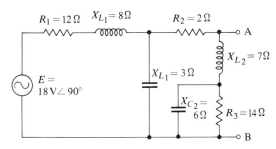

Circuit for Problem 2.

3. Using Thevenin's theorem with the circuit shown, determine the current through the load and the voltage across each load component.

Circuit for Problem 3.

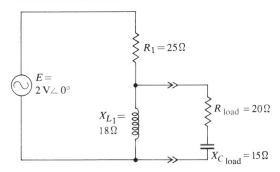

4. Using Thevenin's theorem with the circuit shown, determine the load current and voltage.

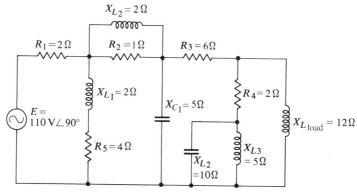

Circuit for Problem 4.

5. Using Thevenin's theorem with the circuit shown, determine the current and voltage between points A and B.

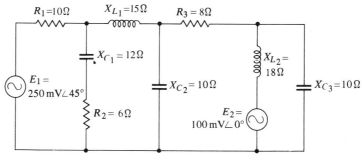

Circuit for Problem 5.

6. Using Thevenin's theorem with the circuit shown, determine the load current and load voltage.

Circuit for Problem 6.

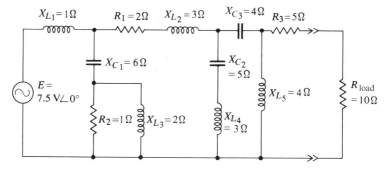

NORTON'S THEOREM RESTATED.   A more inclusive statement of Norton's theorem is as follows:

Any two-terminal network can be replaced by an equivalent circuit consisting of a constant current source I_N, with a current equal in magnitude, frequency, and phase to the short-circuit current of the original circuit with the load impedance removed, in parallel with an impedance Z_{Th}, equal to the impedance measured back into the original network with the load removed and all internal sources in the network removed and replaced with their equivalent internal impedances.

Again, the application is simpler than the statement of the theorem. For the sake of convenience, we will use the same circuit for the demonstration of Norton's theorem as was used to demonstrate Thevenin's theorem. It is shown repeated in Figure 16-6(a).

The short-circuit current is the current that would flow through an ammeter (imaginary, since we wish it to read in ractangular coordinates) connected between the load terminals, as in Figure 16-6(b). This imaginary ammeter is assumed to have zero internal impedance. The capacitor is thus shorted and can have no potential across it. Consequently, the only circuit element in series with the ammeter and the source is the resistor, and the ammeter current will be

$$I_N = \frac{E}{R} = \frac{10}{10} = 1\,A$$

The parallel impedance is calculated the same way for the Norton equivalent circuit, and has the same value, as the series impedance used for the Thevenin equivalent circuit. It has been already calculated for this circuit when we used it as the model to illustrate Thevenin's theorem, and we will use the same result, though the circuit is shown in Figure 16-6(c). The impedance for the equivalent circuit is thus

$$R_{Th} = R_N = (5 - 5j)\,\Omega$$

Now we may construct the Norton equivalent circuit. It consists of a 1 A constant current generator with an impedance of $(5 - 5j)\,\Omega$ in parallel with it. The Norton equivalent circuit is shown in Figure 16-7(a).

In the original calculation of the load current in the Norton equivalent circuit, using only resistive circuit elements, in Chapter 7, we developed a relationship for calculating the load current directly. It is

$$I_{load} = \frac{I_N R_{Th}}{R_{load} + R_{Th}}$$

Since we are now dealing with impedances rather than simple resistance, the

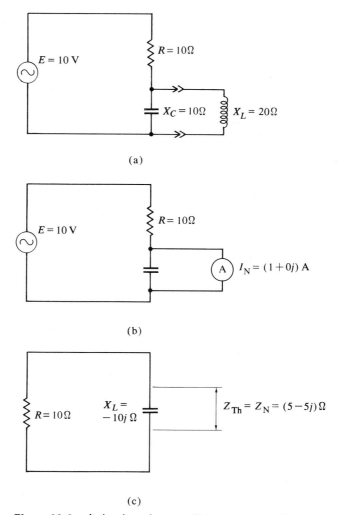

(a)

(b)

(c)

Figure 16-6   A simple series–parallel reactive circuit.

same relationship may be used with impedances expressed in rectangular coordinates in the place of the corresponding resistances. Therefore,

$$I_{\text{load}} = \frac{I_N Z_{\text{Th}}}{Z_{\text{load}} + Z_{\text{Th}}}$$

Substituting the proper values for this problem in the equation,

$$I_{\text{load}} = \frac{(1)(5-5j)}{(20j)+(5-5j)} = -0.2 - 0.4j$$

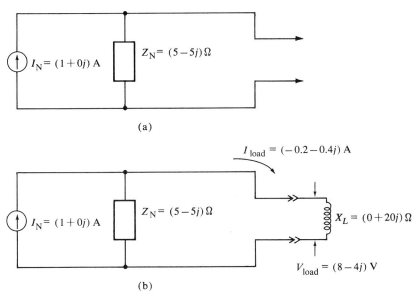

(a)

(b)

Figure 16-7   The Norton equivalent circuit for the circuit of Figure 16-6.

This is the same as the result for this circuit obtained by the use of Thevenin's theorem, as it must be. With the load current and the load impedance known, the voltage across the load may be calculated by using Ohm's law [see Figure 16-7(b)].

$$E_{load} = I_{load} Z_{load} = (-0.2 - 0.4j)(20j) = 8 - 4j$$

which also agrees with the previous result.

The same relationship exists between the open-circuit voltage E_{Th}, the short-circuit current I_N, and the impedance measured back into the original circuit, as was noted in Chapter 7, with the difference that impedance is substituted for resistance. Thus,

$$E_{Th} = I_N R_{Th}$$

and for the circuit just discussed,

$$E_{Th} = (1)(5 - 5j) = 5 - 5j$$

which is in agreement with the previous result.

1.   Find the Norton equivalent of the circuit shown, looking back from   **Problems**
points A and B.

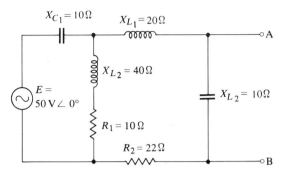

Circuit for Problem 1.

2. Find the Norton equivalent of the circuit shown, looking back from points A and B.

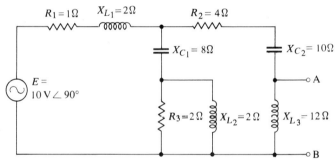

Circuit for Problem 2.

3. Using Norton's theorem with the circuit shown, determine the load current and load voltage.

Circuit for Problem 3.

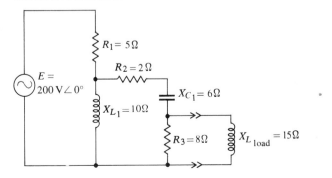

4. Using Norton's theorem with the circuit shown, determine the load current and load voltage.

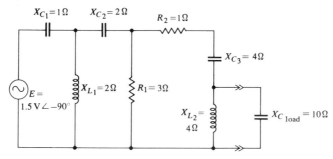

Circuit for Problem 4.

5. Using Norton's theorem with the circuit shown, determine the load current and load voltage.

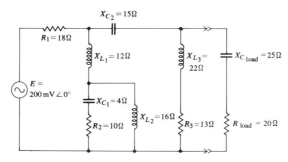

Circuit for Problem 5.

6. Using Norton's theorem with the circuit shown, determine the branch current between points A and B, and the voltage across the components in that branch.

Circuit for Problem 6.

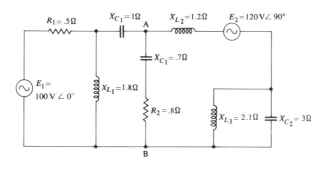

16-4
Maximum Power
Transfer

IMPEDANCE MATCHING.   We said earlier that the maximum power was transferred to a load when the load impedance *matched* the source impedance. It would be easy to assume that the word "matched" is synonymous with "equaled," but it is not, as can be easily demonstrated.

Consider the circuit of Figure 16-8. It is a series circuit consisting of a generator of ac with its internal impedance, connected to a load with some internal impedance.

The power transferred to the load is transferred entirely as real power to the resistive part of the load. There is no real power transferred to the reactive component of the load. The real power to the load is, therefore,

$$P_{\text{load}} = I^2 R_{\text{load}}$$

The current in this series circuit is

$$I = \frac{E}{Z_t} = \frac{E}{Z_{\text{int}} + Z_{\text{load}}}$$

If the impedances are expressed in rectangular notation, then the final impedance is the square root of the square of the sum of the resistive parts plus the square of the sum of the reactive parts. Thus,

$$I = \frac{E}{\sqrt{(R_{\text{int}} + R_{\text{load}})^2 + (X_{\text{int}} + X_{\text{load}})^2}}$$

and

$$I^2 = \frac{e^2}{(R_{\text{int}} + R_{\text{load}})^2 + (X_{\text{int}} + X_{\text{load}})^2}$$

Figure 16-8   A series ac circuit with both generator and load having internal impedance.

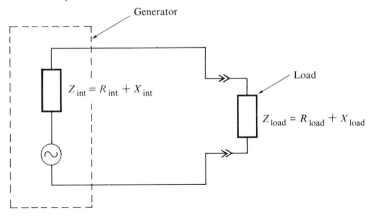

Thus, the power to the load is

$$P_{\text{load}} = \frac{e^2 R_{\text{load}}}{(R_{\text{int}} + R_{\text{load}})^2 + (X_{\text{int}} + X_{\text{load}})^2}$$

For the power to be a maximum, the denominator of this fraction must be at its minimum value. R_{int} and X_{int} are fixed quantities, but R_{load} and X_{load} can change. It is apparent from the mathematical form of the expression for the load power that any value other than zero for the sum of the reactive components of the generator and load will result in less load power than a zero sum.

This sum can be zero since these are phasor quantities; and if one is inductive, the other can be made capacitive. We can select a value of load reactance that is equal in magnitude to the internal reactance of the source, but opposite in sign. If the generator has a capacitive internal impedance, we select an inductive load reactance such that the sum of the reactances is zero. Once this is done, the load resistance may be matched to the internal resistance of the generator, and maximum power will be transferred to the load.

Now we can see what is meant by "matching" the load impedance to the source impedance. Instead of making them equal, we make the load impedance the *complex conjugate* of the source impedance. If, expressed in the rectangular coordinate system, the internal impedance of the source is $(23 + 48j)\ \Omega$, the impedance of the load should be made $(23 - 48j)\ \Omega$. The value of the real part of the load impedance and source impedance will be the same since this represents the resistance of each. The value of the imaginary part of the load and source impedance will have the same magnitude but be opposite in sign since this represents the reactive part of the opposition of each.

RULE   *Maximum power transfer occurs when the load impedance is the complex conjugate of the internal impedance of the source.*

When we talked about the power factor in an ac line, this is exactly what we were talking about. With the appropriate load, the phase angle between voltage and current for the generator, considered as a perfect source, will be zero.

Thevenin's theorem simplifies the procedure involved in finding the appropriate reactive and resistive components to form the load for a voltage source which is itself a network. The internal impedance of the source is exactly the same as the Thevenin resistance R_{Th} of the source.

Figure 16-9(a) shows a simple network, consisting of a generator with internal resistance, inductance, and capacitance, to which is to be attached a load. So far as the generator is concerned, the load is in parallel with the capacitor, and the resistor and inductor are in series with the parallel combination.

First, let us Theveninize the circuit. With the load impedance removed, the impedance looking back into the circuit is

$$R_{Th} = \frac{(-5j)(10+20j)}{-5j+(10+20j)}$$

since to the load, the series combination of resistance and inductance is seen in parallel with the capacitor, as in Figure 16-9(b). Thus,

$$R_{Th} = \frac{10}{13} - \frac{80}{13}j$$

Figure 16-9 A simple ac network.

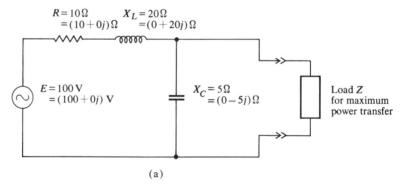

(a)

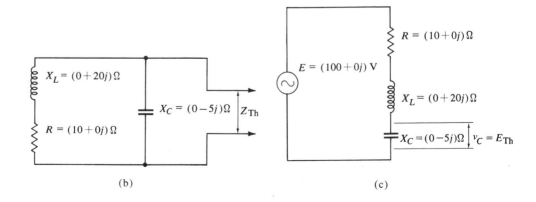

(b)   (c)

The open-circuit voltage is the voltage across the capacitor with the load impedance removed, as in Figure 16-9(c). By Ohm's law this is

$$E_C = I_C X_C$$

and the current I_C through the capacitor is

$$I_C = \frac{E}{X_C + R + X_L}$$

since the capacitor, resistor, and inductor all are in series with the internal voltage source E. Therefore,

$$E_{Th} = E_C = \frac{E X_C}{X_C + R + X_L} = \frac{(100)(-5j)}{-5j + 10 + 20j} = -\frac{300}{13} - \frac{200}{13}j$$

With both E_{Th} and R_{Th} determined, the Thevenin equivalent circuit can be drawn. It is shown in Figure 16-10. It consists of a voltage source with a voltage of the value calculated for E_{Th}, in series with the impedance R_{Th}, which could consist of a capacitor with a reactance of 80/13 Ω in series with a resistor of 10/13 Ω. The load required by the maximum power transfer theorem is also shown. It consists of a resistance of 10/13 Ω in series with an inductance with a reactance of 80/13 Ω.

The power dissipated in this load may be easily calculated. The circuit current is also the current through the load resistance since this is a series circuit. Note that the only power that is dissipated in the load is in the load resistance. No power is dissipated in the load inductance, since it is a reactive circuit element, and its voltage and current are 90° out of phase with each other. The current through the load resistance is

$$I = \frac{E}{Z}$$

Figure 16-10 The Thevenin equivalent circuit for the network of Figure 16-9.

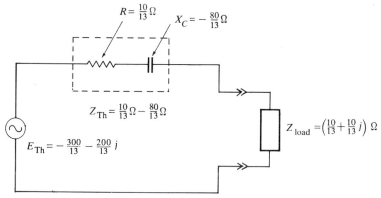

$$I_{\text{load}} = \cfrac{-\dfrac{300}{13} - \dfrac{200}{13}j}{-\dfrac{80}{13}j + \dfrac{10}{13} + \dfrac{10}{13} + \dfrac{80}{13}j} = (-15 - 10j)\,\text{A}$$

Note that the apparent phase angle for this current is exactly the same as the phase angle for the voltage. The voltage has an imaginary component only because it is compared with the original circuit voltage as a reference.

The current through the load resistance and the voltage across it must be in phase with each other, since this is the definition of a resistive circuit element. Since they are in phase, the power dissipated in the resistor is the product of the value of voltage and current, without regard to such phase angle as they may both have with respect to the voltage source in the original circuit. We may also, for the sake of convenience, calculate the power dissipated as I^2R without regard to the phase angle with respect to the original voltage. To do this, I is converted from rectangular coordinates to polar coordinates.

$$I = \sqrt{15^2 + 10^2} = \sqrt{325}\,\text{A}$$

This gives the peak value of I in polar coordinates. To find the power, we want I^2.

$$I^2 = (\sqrt{325})^2 = 325\,\text{A}^2$$

The power expended in the load is

$$P = I^2R = (325)\left(\frac{10}{13}\right) = 250\,\text{W}$$

We may also calculate the power expended in the internal impedance of the generator. If the maximum power transfer theorem is satisfied, the power expended in the internal impedance of the generator must be the same as the power expended in the load. This power must all be expended in the resistive circuit elements of this internal impedance, since no real power is expended in a reactance.

Since the total circuit current must flow through this resistance, the product of the circuit current squared times the resistance is the power expended in the internal impedance of the generator. The total circuit impedance is

$$Z_t = 10 + 20j + \cfrac{(-5j)\left(\dfrac{10}{13} + \dfrac{80}{13}j\right)}{(-5j) + \left(\dfrac{10}{13} + \dfrac{80}{13}j\right)} = 10 + 20j + \cfrac{(-5j)(10 + 80j)}{-65j + 10 + 80j}$$

$$= 10 + 20j + \frac{80 - 10j}{2 + 3j} = 10 + 20j + \frac{(80 - 10j)(2 - 3j)}{13}$$

$$= 10 + 20j + \frac{130 - 260j}{13} = 10 + 20j + 10 - 20j = 20\,\Omega$$

With a source voltage of 100 V and a total circuit impedance of 20 Ω, the total circuit current is

$$I_t = \frac{E_t}{Z_t} = \frac{100}{20} = 5\,\text{A}$$

and the power dissipated by this current through the 10 Ω resistor is

$$P = I^2 R = (5^2)(10) = 250\,\text{W}$$

Thus, the power dissipated in the internal impedance of the generator is the same as the power dissipated in the load. This is a necessary consequence of the fulfillment of the conditions of the maximum power transfer theorem.

1. Given the circuit shown, determine the load impedance that will allow the maximum transfer of power to the load. Calculate the power expended in both the internal impedance and the load.

Problems

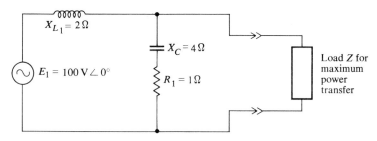

Circuit for Problem 1.

2. Given the circuit shown, determine the load impedance that will allow maximum transfer of power to the load. Calculate the power expended in both the internal impedance and the load.

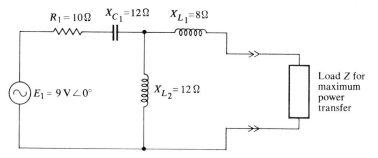

Circuit for Problem 2.

3. Determine the load impedance that will allow the maximum transfer of power to the load in the circuit shown. Calculate the power expended in both the internal impedance and the load.

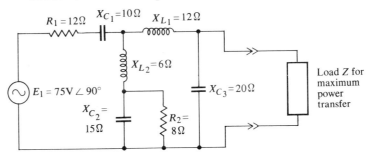

Circuit for Problem 3.

4. Given the circuit shown, determine the load impedance that will allow the maximum transfer of power to the load. Calculate the power expended in both the internal impedance and the load.

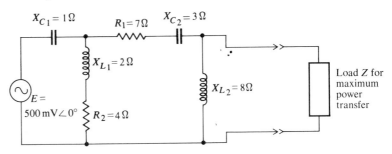

Circuit for Problem 4.

5. Determine the load impedance that will allow the maximum transfer of power to the load in the circuit shown. Calculate the power expended in both the internal impedance and the load.

Circuit for Problem 5.

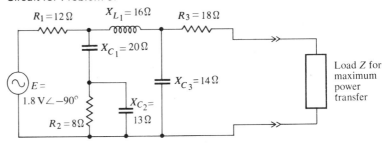

6. Given the circuit shown, determine the value of R_{L_1} and X_{L_5} in the load that will allow the maximum power transfer to the load. Calculate the power expended in both the load and the internal impedance.

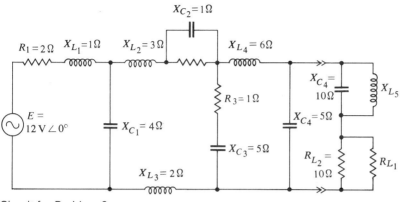

Circuit for Problem 6.

LOOP EQUATIONS.   Network problems may be solved using Kirchhoff's   **16-5**
voltage and current laws, where simultaneous equations based on these laws   **Kirchhoff's**
are solved for unknown currents or voltages. If the voltage sources are   **Solutions**
sinusoidal ac, and the reactances and resistances are expressed in rectangular
coordinates, the procedure for the solution of networks is exactly the same
as it was when pure resistances were the only circuit elements.

As an illustration, we will apply the method of loop analysis to the same
circuit as in the previous section. This circuit is shown again in Figure 16-11.

Two loop currents, I_1 and I_2, are assigned. For the sake of convenience
and consistency, they are both drawn clockwise. The rule for writing loop
equations with resistive circuits will still apply to these reactive circuits. Each
loop equation is the loop current times the sum of the impedances in that

Figure 16-11   The network of Figure 16-9, redrawn for loop analysis.

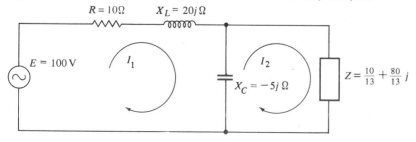

loop, minus the product of any adjacent loop current times such impedances as are common to both loops, set equal to the voltage sources in the loop. Following this rule, with all impedances expressed in rectangular coordinates, the first loop equation is

$$[10 + 20j + (-5j)]I_1 - (-5j)I_2 = 100$$

The second loop equation, written for I_2, is

$$\left[\frac{80}{13}j + \frac{10}{13} + (-5j)\right]I_2 - (-5j)I_1 = 0$$

Now these equations may be simplified and put in the appropriate order of the unknown currents.

$$10 + 15j)I_1 + \qquad\qquad (5j)I_2 = 100$$

$$(5j)I_1 + \left(\frac{10}{13} + \frac{15}{13}j\right)I_2 = 0$$

From this the determinant for I_1 may be written in the usual form, as follows:

$$I_1 - \frac{\begin{vmatrix} 100 & 5j \\ 0 & \left(\frac{10}{13} + \frac{15}{13}j\right) \end{vmatrix}}{\begin{vmatrix} (10 + 15j) & 5j \\ 5j & \left(\frac{10}{13} + \frac{15}{13}j\right) \end{vmatrix}}$$

and solved in the same way as for real numbers, but using the algebra of complex numbers,

$$I_1 = \frac{(100)\left(\frac{10}{13} + \frac{15}{13}j\right) - 0}{(10 + 15j)\left(\frac{10}{13} + \frac{15}{13}j\right) - (5j)(5j)}$$

$$= \frac{\dfrac{1000}{13} + \dfrac{1500}{13}j}{\dfrac{100}{13} + \dfrac{150}{13}j + \dfrac{150}{13}j - \dfrac{225}{13} + \dfrac{325}{13}} = \frac{\dfrac{1000 + 1500j}{13}}{\dfrac{200 + 300j}{13}}$$

$$= \frac{1000 + 1500j}{200 + 300j} = \frac{500(2 + 3j)}{100(2 + 3j)} = 5\,\text{A}$$

Similarly, the current I_2 may be found from its determinant.

$$I_2 = \frac{\begin{vmatrix} 10 + 15j & 100 \\ 5j & 0 \end{vmatrix}}{\dfrac{200 + 300}{13}j}$$

$$= (-15 - 10j)\,\text{A}$$

With both loop currents known, the current through the capacitor can be found since it is the difference between the two loop currents through it.

$$I_C = I_1 - I_2$$
$$= (5) - (-15 - 10j) = 20 + 10j\,\text{A}$$

Since the only current through the 10 Ω resistor and the $20j$ Ω inductor is I_1, and the only current through the $(80/13)j$ Ω inductor and the 10/13 Ω resistor is I_2, all circuit component currents are now known. Since the current through each component is now known, as well as the component's impedance, the voltage across each may be easily calculated, using Ohm's law.

Problems

1.   Solve the circuit shown, using loop equations.

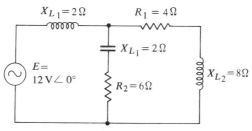

Circuit for Problem 1.

2.   Solve the circuit shown, using loop equations.

Circuit for Problem 2.

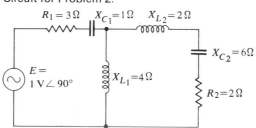

3. Use loop equations to solve the circuit shown.

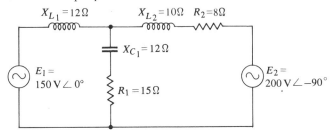

Circuit for Problem 3.

4. Solve the circuit shown, using loop equations.

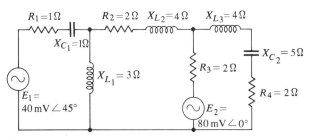

Circuit for Problem 4.

Summary of Concepts

1. Thevenin's theorem is more fully stated as follows: Any two-terminal network can be replaced by an equivalent circuit consisting of a perfect voltage source E_{Th}, with a voltage equal in magnitude, frequency, and phase to the open-circuit voltage of the original circuit with the load impedance removed, in series with an impedance Z_{Th}, equal to the impedance measured back into the original network with the load removed and all internal sources in the network removed and replaced with their equivalent internal impedances.

2. Norton's theorem is more fully stated as follows: Any two-terminal network can be replaced by an equivalent circuit consisting of a constant current source I_N, with a current equal in magnitude, frequency, and phase to the short-circuit current of the original circuit with the load impedance removed, in parallel with an impedance Z_{Th}, equal to the impedance measured back into the original network with the load removed and all internal sources in the network removed and replaced with their equivalent internal impedances.

3. For the Norton equivalent circuit, parallel impedance is calculated the same way and has the same value as series impedance for the Thevenin equivalent circuit.

4. Maximum power is transferred to a load when the load impedance matches (but does not necessarily equal) the source impedance. Maximum power transfer occurs when the load impedance is the complex conjugate of the internal impedance of the source.

5. From the mathematical form of the expression for the load power, it is apparent that any value other than zero for the sum of the reactive components of a generator and load will result in less load power than a zero sum.

6. The power dissipated in the internal impedance of a generator is the same as the power dissipated in the load. This is a necessary consequence of the fulfillment of the conditions of the maximum power transfer theorem.

7. Network problems may be solved by using Kirchhoff's voltage and current laws, where simultaneous equations based on these laws are solved for unknown currents or voltages.

On a separate sheet of paper, fill in the blanks or answer the questions below. The number following each question refers to the section in the chapter where the correct answer can be found. **To Help You Review**

1. In an ac reactive network, if Kirchhoff's laws are not to be violated, the currents entering a junction must sum to _____. (16-1)

2. Compare Thevenin's theorem as stated in Section 7-2 and in this chapter. Explain the differences you find in terms of calculating impedance. (16-2)

3. Compare Norton's theorem as stated in Section 7-3 and in this chapter. Explain the differences you find in terms of calculating I_N and Z_{Th}. (16-3)

4. What aspect of both the Norton and Thevenin equivalent circuits is calculated the same way? (16-3)

5. Explain the word "matches" in the following statement. Maximum power is transferred to a load when the load impedance matches the source impedance. (16-4)

6. Complete this statement: Maximum power transfer occurs when _____. (16-4)

7. What is a complex conjugate? (16-4)

SEVENTEEN
RESONANCE

This chapter will help you understand

- [ ] resonance in series and parallel resonant circuits
- [ ] series and parallel resonant circuit impedance
- [ ] inductor resistance in resonant circuits
- [ ] quality factors in resonant circuits
- [ ] series and parallel Q (quality) magnification—tuning

17-1
Resonance

RESONANCE DEFINED. A *resonant circuit* is one in which the opposing effects of inductive and capacitive reactances cancel each other out. Since they are precisely opposite in their effect, they can cancel each other only if they are of equal magnitude, that is, if

$$X_L = X_C$$

For any inductor, X_L increases with increasing frequency; and for any capacitor, X_C decreases with increasing frequency. Figure 17-1 shows how each changes with frequency.

Vertical lines from the frequency axis to the curves give the relative value of X_L and X_C for any frequency. At the point marked f_1, which is a relatively low frequency, the arrow showing the magnitude of X_C is longer than that for X_L; therefore, for that frequency, X_C is greater than X_L.

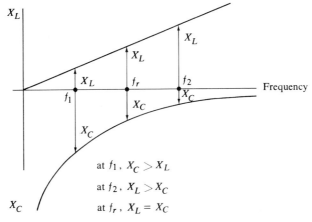

Figure 17-1   Resonance—the combination of the opposing effects of inductive and capacitive reactance.

At the point marked f_2, which is a relatively high frequency, the arrow showing the magnitude of X_L is longer than that for X_C; therefore, for that frequency, X_L is greater than X_C.

Obviously, from the figure, it is possible to find a point on the frequency axis at which the two vertical lines will be equal. That point has been designated on the graph as f_r, the *resonant frequency*. Though this is not the only possible definition, the resonant frequency may be defined as that frequency at which $X_L = X_C$.

THE RESONANT FREQUENCY.   The frequency at which resonance occurs for any combination of inductive reactance and capacitive reactance may be found simply. Since

$$X_L = 2\pi f L$$

and

$$X_C = \frac{1}{2\pi f C}$$

and the condition $X_L = X_C$ is required for resonance,

$$2\pi f L = \frac{1}{2\pi f C}$$

This equation may be solved for f_r since the equality is based on the condition of resonance. Thus,

$$f_r^2 = \frac{1}{4\pi^2 LC}$$

and

$$f_r = \frac{1}{2\pi\sqrt{LC}}$$

For the resonant frequency to be in hertz, L is in henrys and C is in farads. This is a defining equation of resonance, since it is based on the original requirement that the inductive and capacitive reactances be equal.

EXAMPLE   Find the resonant frequency of a combination of an inductance of 1 H and a capacitor of 1 μF.

Solution. $L = 1$ H and $C = 10^{-6}$ F.

$$f_r = \frac{1}{2\pi\sqrt{LC}} = \frac{1}{2\pi\sqrt{1 \times 10^{-6}}}$$

$$= \frac{0.159}{10^{-3}} = 159 \text{ Hz}$$

EXAMPLE   Find the resonant frequency of a combination of an inductance of 0.1 mH and a capacitor of 47 pF.

Solution. $L = 10^{-4}$ H   and $C = 47 \times 10^{-12}$ F

$$f_r = \frac{1}{2\pi\sqrt{LC}} = \frac{1}{2\pi\sqrt{10^{-4} \times 47 \times 10^{-12}}}$$

$$= \frac{0.159}{\sqrt{47 \times 10^{-8}}} = \frac{0.159}{6.86} \times 10^8 = \frac{15.9}{6.86} \times 10^6$$

$$= 2.32 \times 10^6 \text{ Hz} = 2.32 \text{ MHz}$$

As can be seen from the two examples, the smaller the values of inductance and capacitance, the higher the resonant frequency.

Problems   **1.**   Find the resonant frequency of an inductor–capacitor combination where $C = 3 \mu$F and $L = 30$ mH.

2.   Find the resonant frequency of an inductor–capacitor combination where $C = 12$ pF and $L = 0.03$ H.

3. Find the resonant frequency of an inductor–capacitor combination where $C = 0.5\ \mu F$ and $L = 2.5$ H.

4. Find the resonant frequency of an inductor–capacitor combination where $C = 400$ pF and $L = 0.016$ H.

5. The inductive reactance of an inductor in combination with a 36 μF capacitor is 8.33 Ω at resonance. Calculate the resonant frequency and the value of the inductance.

6. The capacitive reactance of a capacitor in combination with a 10 mH inductor is 8333 Ω at resonance. Calculate the resonant frequency and the value of the capacitance.

**17-2
Series Resonance**

SERIES RESONANT IMPEDANCE.   The impedance of a series resonant circuit can be easily calculated by using rectangular coordinates. Consider the circuit of Figure 17-2, which shows a series inductor and capacitor, with $X_C = X_L$ at the generator frequency. The total impedance of the circuit is the simple sum of the individual impedances.

$$Z = X_C + X_L$$

Let us assume both X_C and X_L are 10 Ω reactances. Then

$$Z = (-10j) + (+10j) = 0\ \Omega$$

This, of course, is assuming no circuit resistance at all. On this assumption, which is never correct in a practical circuit, we can say that *the impedance of a resonant circuit at the resonant frequency is zero.*

Now let us assume some circuit resistance. This may be no more than the resistance of the wiring of the inductor, but it will not be zero, and will act as a series resistance. Thus,

$$Z = X_L + X_C + R$$

and if $X_L = X_C$,

$$Z = (+X_L\,j) + (-X_C\,j) + R = R$$

Therefore, at the resonant frequency, the opposition of a series resonant circuit is a minimum, and equal to the circuit resistance. This can be very small.

Figure 17-3 shows a series *LCR* circuit. The generator is a constant voltage 1000 kHz source, with a voltage $E = 1$ mV. The inductor is 159 μH, the capacitor is 159 pF, and the resistor is 1 Ω. At a generator frequency

Figure 17-2   A simple series resonant circuit.

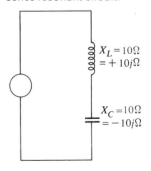

$X_L = 10\Omega$
$= +10j\Omega$

$X_C = 10\Omega$
$= -10j\Omega$

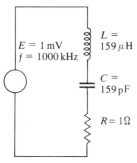

Figure 17-3   A series *LCR* circuit.

of 1000 kHz, the reactance of the inductor is

$$X_L = 2\pi f L = 2\pi(10^6)(159 \times 10^{-6}) = 1000 \ \Omega$$

At the same frequency the reactance of the capacitor is

$$X_C = \frac{1}{2\pi f C} = \frac{1}{2\pi(10^6)(159 \times 10^{-12})} = 1000 \ \Omega$$

The total circuit impedance is the sum of these two reactances plus the resistance of the resistor. This impedance is

$$Z_t = 1000j + (-1000j) + 1 = 1 \ \Omega$$

The total circuit current is

$$I_t = \frac{E}{Z_t} = \frac{1 \ \text{mV}}{1 \ \Omega} = 1 \ \text{mA}$$

This total circuit current must flow through each component in this series circuit. Knowing this current, we can find the voltage across each of the two reactive components. The voltage across the inductor is

$$E_L = IX_L = (0.001)(1000) = 1 \ \text{V}$$

The voltage across the capacitor is

$$E_C = IX_C = (0.001)(1000) = 1 \ \text{V}$$

It may seem at first glance as though Kirchhoff's voltage law has been violated. The voltage across the capacitor and the voltage across the inductor are both a thousand times the source voltage in this circuit. The voltages are real, and they can be easily measured with standard instruments.

The voltage across the inductor leads the current by 90°, while the voltage across the capacitor lags the current by the same amount (*ELI* the *ICE* man). Therefore, the two voltages are 180° out of phase with each other. At the instant the voltage across the inductor is positive, the voltage across the capacitor will be negative by an equal amount. Each voltage will therefore cancel the other at every instant, and the only voltage remaining will be the voltage across the resistor.

Expressed in rectangular coordinates, the voltage across the inductor is

$$E_L = +1j \ \text{V}$$

and the voltage across the capacitor is

$$E_C = -1j \ \text{V}$$

If these values are substituted in the mathematical statement that the source voltage is at any instant equal to the sum of the voltage drops across the components of this series circuit, the result is

$$E_t = E_L + E_C + E_R = 1j + (-1j) + 0.001 = 0.001 \text{ V}$$

which is the correct source voltage. Therefore, Kirchhoff's voltage laws are not violated.

This rise in voltage across the inductor and capacitor is called the resonant rise in voltage, and as we have seen from this example, the voltage across either of these two components can be considerably greater than the source voltage. The lower the series resistance of the circuit, the greater this voltage will be. Conversely, the greater the resistance, the less this resonant rise in voltage will be. If the total circuit resistance had been 10 Ω, the voltage across the inductor or capacitor at resonance would have been 0.10 V; and if the circuit resistance had been 1000 Ω, the voltage across either reactive component would have been only 0.001 V, the same as the source voltage.

Suppose we can change the generator frequency to some convenient frequencies above and below the resonant frequency. If the generator frequency is above the resonant frequency, the inductive reactance X_L will increase, and the capacitive reactance X_C will decrease. The total reactance will increase since it is made up of both the resistance of the circuit and the *difference* between the two reactances. Only a slight change in frequency will make this difference large compared to the resistance, assuming a small resistance.

Consider the result when the generator frequency is changed from the resonant frequency of 1000 kHz to 900 kHz. At this new frequency the inductive reactance is less, since it is a lower frequency, and the capacitive reactance is more. X_L now is 900 Ω, and X_C has risen to 1110 Ω, approximately. The difference between the two reactances is now 210 Ω, and the total impedance Z_t is the phasor sum of this net reactance and the resistance. Thus,

$$Z_t = \sqrt{210^2 + 1^2} \cong 210\,\Omega$$

Since the reactance is so great compared to the resistance, the resistance makes no significant difference in the final result. As a rule of thumb, when one of the quantities to be summed as phasors is greater than ten times the other, the smaller of the two may be disregarded, and the sum considered to be simply equal to the value of the larger quantity.

With the total circuit impedance known, the total circuit current may be easily calculated from

$$I = \frac{E}{Z_t} = \frac{0.001 \text{ V}}{210 \ \Omega} = 4.76 \ \mu\text{A}$$

This current is very much smaller than the current at resonance, which is to be expected since the total circuit impedance is very much greater than at resonance. It is this smaller current which must flow through the two reactances and produce the voltage which appears across them.

The reactance of the inductor is 900 Ω at this lower frequency, and the reactance of the capacitor has increased to approximately 1110 Ω. The voltage across each of them due to this smaller current is

$$V_L = IX_L \qquad\qquad\qquad V_C = IX_C$$
$$= (4.76 \times 10^{-6})(900) \qquad = (4.76 \times 10^{-6})(1110)$$
$$= 4.29\,\text{mV} \qquad\qquad = 5.24\,\text{mV}$$

These voltages are both very much less than the 1 V observed across both the inductor and the capacitor at resonance.

Table 17-1 shows the appropriate circuit impedances, currents, and voltages at resonance, and for three frequencies above and three frequencies below resonance. Since the tabulation alone may not give as clear a picture as does a graph, the pertinent quantities have been graphed in Figure 17-4.

TABLE 17-1   Resonance Impedances, Currents, and Voltages for Circuit of Figure 17-4

Freq. (kHz)	X_L (Ω)	X_C (Ω)	$X_L + X_C$ (Ω)	Z_t (Ω)	I_t (μA)	V_L (mV)	V_C (mV)
700	700	1430	730 (X_C)	730	1.37	0.96	1.96
800	800	1250	450 (X_C)	450	2.22	1.77	2.87
900	900	1110	210 (X_C)	210	4.76	4.29	5.24
1000 (f_r)	1000	1000	0	1	1000	1000	1000
1100	1100	910	190 (X_L)	190	5.26	5.79	4.78
1200	1200	833	367 (X_L)	367	2.72	3.26	2.26
1300	1300	770	530 (X_L)	530	1.89	2.46	1.45

It is apparent, both from the tabulation and from the graph, that total circuit impedance Z_t is a minimum at resonance and rises sharply on both sides of the resonant frequency. The impedance is capacitive below resonance and inductive above, while exactly at resonance the circuit appears as a resistive load.

The circuit current is a reciprocal function of the impedance, and it rises at resonance as sharply as the impedance dips. The current below resonance is capacitive, with a leading phase compared to the source voltage, while the current at frequencies above resonance is inductive, with a lagging phase angle.

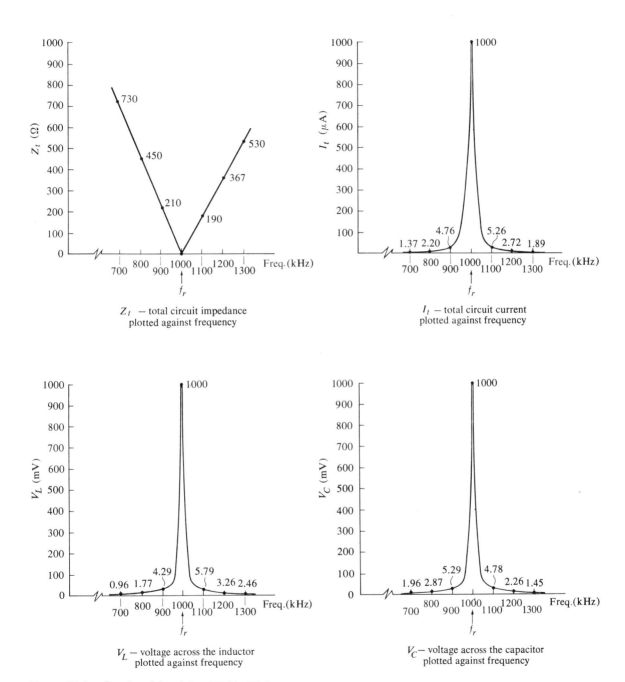

Figure 17-4   Graphs of the data of Table 17-1.

Both the voltage across the capacitor and the voltage across the inductor rise sharply to a peak 1000 times as high as the source voltage at resonance. Usually, the voltage across the capacitor is used as the output voltage of the circuit.

The resonant circuit, which we have so far seen only as the series resonant circuit, is a frequency-selective circuit. Communications electronics, as we know it today, could not exist without frequency-selective circuits. Every time a radio is tuned, it is a frequency-selective circuit that does the tuning and selects the desired frequency from the thousands on the air.

Problems

1. Consider an LCR series circuit with $L = 4$ H, $C = 0.16\ \mu$F, $R = 250\ \Omega$, and a 100 mV ac voltage generator. Calculate the voltages across the inductor and capacitor when the generator is at the resonant frequency.

2. Consider an LCR series circuit with $L = 0.32$ H, $C = 4.5\ \mu$F, $R = 50\ \Omega$, and a 110 V ac voltage generator. Calculate the voltages across the inductor and capacitor when the generator is at the resonant frequency.

3. Consider an LCR series circuit where $L = 20$ mH, $C = 8$ pF, and $R = 2000\ \Omega$, with a 25 V ac voltage generator. Calculate the voltages across the inductor and capacitor when the generator is at the resonant frequency; when the frequency of the generator signal is 10 Hz greater than the resonant frequency; when it is 100 Hz greater than the resonant frequency.

4. Consider an LCR series circuit where $L = 0.052$ H, $C = 1.3\ \mu$F, and $R = 2.5\ \Omega$, with a 10 V ac voltage generator. Calculate the voltages across the capacitor and inductor and the total circuit impedance at the resonant frequency and at 1 Hz, 10 Hz, 20 Hz, 50 Hz, 100 Hz, and 200 Hz above and below resonance. Using these calculations, plot the curves of V_C, V_L, and Z_t versus the frequency.

5. Consider an LCR circuit where $R = 100\ \Omega$ and the source is a 100 mV $\angle\ 0°$ ac generator. When the frequency of the generator is 200 Hz, the voltage across the capacitor is found to be $-297.912 - 134.178j$ mV, and the voltage across the inductor is found to be $381.052 + 171.64j$ mV. Determine the resonant frequency of this circuit and the voltages across the capacitor and the inductor at the resonant frequency.

6. Consider an LCR circuit where $R = 10\ \Omega$ and the source is a 100 V ac generator. At a frequency 10 Hz less than the resonant frequency the voltage across the capacitor is found to be $423.964 - 15.587j$ V, and the

voltage across the inductor is found to be $-324.1 + 11.88j$ V. At resonance the voltage across the capacitor is found to be 10,000 V. What are the resonant frequency and the values of L and C?

PARALLEL RESONANT CIRCUIT IMPEDANCE.   Suppose we have a parallel resonant circuit, such as the circuit of Figure 17-5, without any resistance. The total impedance of this circuit can be easily calculated by using rectangular coordinates.

17-3
Parallel Resonance

The total circuit impedance is

$$Z_t = \frac{X_L X_C}{X_L + X_C}$$

At the resonant frequency, X_L and X_C are equal. Let us assume that the inductor is 159 μH, and the frequency of the generator is 1000 kHz. Then for this inductor the reactance X_L must be 1000 Ω. If the capacitor is 159 pF, then at the same frequency the reactance X_C will be 1000 Ω. In the rectangular coordinate system these values are

$$X_L = +1000j \qquad X_C = -1000j$$

These values may be used to find the total impedance.

$$Z_t = \frac{(1000j)(-1000j)}{(1000j) + (-1000j)} = \frac{1,000,000}{0}$$

This is an impossible figure. Division by zero is not a legitimate mathematical operation. If we wish to discover the behavior of the circuit at resonance, we must choose some different means. If we assume that we are arbitrarily near resonance, so that X_L and X_C are very nearly but not quite equal, then their phasor sum will not be zero, and we will not be faced with a mathematical impossibility.

Figure 17-5   A parallel resonant circuit with no resistance.

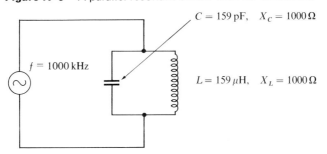

$C = 159\,\text{pF}, \quad X_C = 1000\,\Omega$

$f = 1000\,\text{kHz}$

$L = 159\,\mu\text{H}, \quad X_L = 1000\,\Omega$

Let us assume the difference between the two reactances is 1 Ω at some frequency near resonance. This will affect their product only slightly, since 999.5 times 1000.5 is only a quarter of an ohm less than the original product of 1,000,000 Ω. With this assumption,

$$Z_t = \frac{1,000,000}{1} = 1,000,000 \ \Omega$$

It is evident that the total impedance of the parallel circuit at resonance is going to be very high. If we had decided to make the difference between X_L and X_C arbitrarily as low as 0.1 Ω, the result for Z_t would have been 10,000,000 Ω, and reducing the difference between the reactances still more would have resulted in a still greater figure for Z_t. We may therefore say that as the difference between the two reactances approaches zero, the total impedance approaches infinity.

This is on the assumption that there is no significant circuit resistance. If we are using real circuit components, made of real materials, and not the imaginary components we make with ink on a page or chalk on a blackboard, there will be some resistance; and in this case, as with the series resonant circuit, it will be of significance.

To see the significance of this resistance, let us consider the circuit of Figure 17-6, which shows the same circuit as before, but with the addition of 1 Ω resistance in the branch of the parallel circuit containing the inductance. This is rather a low figure for a practical inductor, but not an impossible figure. It is shown only for the inductor, since the resistance of any practical inductor is almost certain to be considerably greater than the resistance of the leads of a comparable capacitor.

Figure 17-6 The circuit of Figure 17-5 with 1 Ω resistance.

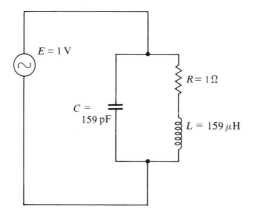

The total circuit impedance is not as simply calculated as for a series circuit. Still, the calculation is not difficult, since this is a simple series–parallel circuit. The total impedance of the branch containing the inductor and the resistor is

$$Z_t = X_L + R$$

The total impedance of the parallel circuit is

$$Z_t = \frac{(-X_C j)(X_L + R)}{-X_C + X_L + R} = \frac{(-1000j)(1000j + 1)}{-1000j + 1000j + 1} = 1,000,000 - 1000j$$

This is the impedance in rectangular coordinates. If we wish the impedance in polar coordinates, the result is

$$Z_t = \sqrt{1,000,000^2 + 1000^2} \cong 1\,000\,000.5\ \Omega$$

The phase angle to be associated with this impedance is

$$\theta = \arctan \frac{1000}{1,000,000} = \arctan 0.001 \cong 0°\,3.5'$$

This phase angle is so slight that, for all practical purposes, the impedance might be considered purely resistive. With this low resistance the total impedance of the circuit is quite high at resonance.

Suppose the resistance had been much higher, perhaps as high as 1000 Ω. Then the total impedance, based on the definition of resonance as the frequency at which the inductive reactance and capacitive reactance are equal, would be much higher. Also, with the parallel circuit at resonance, the voltage and current are not exactly in phase when resonance is based on the equality of the two reactances.

At a frequency above resonance the current through the capacitive branch of the parallel circuit will exceed the current through the inductive branch, and the total impedance will appear to be capacitive. At a frequency below resonance, the current through the inductive branch will be the greater of the two, and the total impedance will appear to be inductive. There must obviously be some frequency between these two extremes at which the impedance will appear to be purely resistive. It is also obvious that we will not find it based on the definition of resonance as the condition that the reactances be equal. This was sufficient for the series resonant circuit, but it is not sufficient for the parallel resonant circuit.

For the parallel resonant circuit the most suitable definition of resonance is that frequency at which the total impedance of the circuit is purely resistive. This is also the frequency at which the circuit impedance is maximum, and the total current drawn from the source is a minimum. For most practical circuits it differs only slightly from the frequency given by the original definition. The defining equation for parallel circuits with a series resistor in the inductive leg is

$$f_r = \frac{1}{2\pi\sqrt{LC}}\sqrt{1 - \frac{R^2C}{L}}$$

This differs from the equation for finding the frequency of series resonance by only the factor

$$\sqrt{1 - \frac{R^2C}{L}}$$

where R is the series resistance in the inductive leg, C the capacity in farads, and L the inductance in henrys. If the ratio R^2C/L is small, then this factor is very close to unity, and the parallel resonant frequency does not differ significantly from the series resonant frequency for the same inductance and capacitance.

Ordinarily, this factor will be small. Usually, the capacity is expressed in pF, and the inductance in μH; if this is the case, then the ratio C/L will contain the factor 10^{-6}, since a picofarad is 10^{-12} farads while a microhenry is 10^{-6} henrys.

The circuit constants in the circuit of Figure 17-6 may be used with this equation.

$$f_{r(p)} = \frac{1}{2\pi\sqrt{LC}}\sqrt{1 - \frac{R^2C}{L}}$$

$$= \frac{1}{2\pi\sqrt{(159 \times 10^{-6})(159 \times 10^{-12})}}\sqrt{1 - \frac{1^2(159 \times 10^{-12})}{159 \times 10^{-6}}}$$

$$= 1{,}000{,}000\sqrt{1 - 0.000\,001} = 1{,}000{,}000\sqrt{0.999\,999}$$

$$\cong 1{,}000{,}000$$

The answer is approximate. The correct figure is less than one cycle below the previously calculated series resonant frequency of 1 MHz, and the difference is very much less than the possible error in our knowledge of the value of the circuit constants themselves. For most practical purposes, the frequencies of series resonance and parallel resonance are considered to be the same.

If, however, precision is both required and justified by our knowledge of the circuit constants, or if R^2C/L is greater than 0.01, then it may be necessary to use the corrected equation for the true parallel resonant frequency. Note that the parallel resonant frequency must always be slightly less than the series resonant frequency for the same components, but seldom more than a fraction of 1%.

The behavior of a parallel resonant circuit at frequencies above and below resonance makes clear its frequency-selective qualities. A series of calculations have been made for the circuit of Figure 17-6, giving current through each branch of the parallel bank, and the total impedance of the circuit, at frequencies both above and below the resonant frequency, as well as at the resonant frequency itself. The calculation for a frequency of 700 kHz is shown; all others are similar.

First, the inductive and capacitive reactances for the two reactive components are calculated by formula.

$$X_C = \frac{1}{2\pi f C}$$

$$X_L = 2\pi f L$$
$$= 2\pi(700 \times 10^5)(159 \times 10^{-6})$$

$$= \frac{1}{2\pi(7 \times 10^5)(159 \times 10^{-12})}$$

$$= 699.3 \ \Omega$$

$$= 1430 \ \Omega$$

If the generator voltage and the total current are both known, the circuit impedance can be easily calculated, since

$$Z_t = \frac{E_t}{I_t}$$

The total current is the sum of the currents in the two branches of the parallel bank.

$$I_t = I_C + I_L$$

These currents must, of course, be summed with due regard for the fact that they are phasors, and are not in phase with each other; consequently, vector algebra must be used. The currents themselves may be easily found, once the impedance of each branch of the parallel bank is known, from the relations

$$I_C = \frac{E_t}{Z_C} \qquad \text{and} \qquad I_L = \frac{E_t}{Z_L}$$

Since there is no resistance in the capacitive branch of the parallel bank, its reactance and its impedance are the same, and may be expressed easily in either rectangular or polar coordinates. Since the operation to immediately follow will be division, polar coordinates seem simpler; thus,

$$I_C = \frac{E_t}{X_C} = \frac{1}{1430 \angle -90°} = 6.99 \times 10^{-4} \angle 90° \ \text{A} = 0.7 \angle 90° \ \text{mA}$$

Since it has both a resistive and a reactive component, the current through the inductive branch is not quite as easily calculated, but the calculation is not difficult. The impedance in this branch is the vector sum of the resistance and the reactance.

$$Z_L = X_L + R = 699.3j + 1$$

Expressed in polar coordinates, this becomes

$$Z_L = 699.3 \angle 89.92°$$

The current through the inductive branch is thus

$$I_L = \frac{E_t}{Z_L} = \frac{1}{699.3 \angle 89.92°} = 1.43 \angle -89.92° \text{ mA}$$

The total current is the sum of the two branch currents.

$$I_t = I_C + I_L = 0.70 \angle 90° + 1.43 \angle -89.92° = 0.73 \angle -89.84° \text{ mA}$$

The total impedance of the circuit at this frequency is found by

$$Z_t = \frac{E_t}{I_t} = \frac{1}{0.73 \angle -89.84°} = 1.37 \angle 89.84°$$

The calculation has been repeated for other frequencies both above and below the resonant frequency, and the results entered in Table 17-2. Since, as before, it is easier to read a picture, the results have also been graphed in Figure 17-7.

Clearly, the total circuit impedance at resonance is much higher than it is for any frequency off resonance, either above or below f_r. Consequently, the current drawn from the source is a minimum at resonance. At resonance the current through the capacitor and the current through the inductor are both much higher than the current drawn by the circuit from the source.

Again, this does not represent a violation of Kirchhoff's current law. The current through the inductive branch and the current through the capacitive branch of the circuit are 180° out of phase with each other, and both are 90° out of phase with the generator current.

The parallel resonant circuit is often called a *tank circuit*. To see why, let us consider the action of the electron flow within the circuit during one full cycle, starting at an instant when the capacitor is fully charged. At this instant the capacitor must begin to discharge through the inductor. As the discharge current flows through the inductor, the magnetic field of the inductor must expand; but as it does, it cuts through the turns of the inductor, so that the voltage generated in the inductor by this discharge current opposes the capacitor voltage. As the capacitor charge reaches zero, after some time

TABLE 17-2   Resonance Impedances and Currents for Circuit of Figure 17-7

Freq. (kHz)	$X_C(\Omega)$	$X_L(\Omega)$	$Z_C(\Omega)$	$Z_L(\Omega)$	I_C(mA)	I_L(mA)	I_t(mA)	Z_t(kΩ)
700	1430	700	$1430\angle-90°$	$700\angle89.91°$	$0.70\angle90°$	$1.43\angle-89.9°$	$0.73\angle-89.9°$	$1.37\angle+89.7°$
800	1250	800	$1250\angle-90°$	$800\angle89.93°$	$0.80\angle90°$	$1.25\angle-89.93°$	$0.45\angle-89.8°$	$2.22\angle+89.8°$
900	1110	900	$1110\angle-90°$	$900\angle89.94°$	$0.90\angle90°$	$1.11\angle-89.94°$	$0.21\angle-89.6°$	$4.76\angle+89.6°$
950	1050	950	$1050\angle-90°$	$949\angle89.94°$	$0.949\angle90°$	$1.05\angle-89.94°$	$0.10\angle-89.4°$	$9.62\angle+89.4°$
980	1020	980	$1020\angle-90°$	$979\angle89.94°$	$0.979\angle90°$	$1.02\angle-89.94°$	$0.04\angle-88.5°$	$23.58\angle+88.5°$
990	1010	990	$1010\angle-90°$	$989\angle89.94°$	$0.989\angle90°$	$1.01\angle-89.94°$	$0.02\angle-87.2°$	$45.40\angle+87.2°$
995	1006	995	$1006\angle-90°$	$994\angle89.94°$	$0.994\angle90°$	$1.006\angle-89.94°$	$0.012\angle-85.0°$	$83.33\angle+85.0°$
998	1003	998	$1003\angle-90°$	$997\angle89.94°$	$0.997\angle90°$	$1.003\angle-89.94°$	$0.006\angle-80.0°$	$164.72\angle+80.0°$
1000	1000	1000	$1000\angle-90°$	$1000\angle89.94°$	$1.00\angle90°$	$1.00\angle-89.94°$	$0.001\angle+0.03°$	$1000\angle-0.03°$
1002	999	1002	$999\angle-90°$	$1001\angle89.94°$	$1.001\angle90°$	$0.999\angle-89.94°$	$0.003\angle+62.7°$	$438.82\angle-62.7°$
1005	996	1005	$996\angle-90°$	$1004\angle89.94°$	$1.004\angle90°$	$0.996\angle-89.94°$	$0.008\angle+82.5°$	$123.85\angle-82.5°$
1010	991	1010	$991\angle-90°$	$1009\angle89.94°$	$1.009\angle90°$	$0.991\angle-89.94°$	$0.018\angle+86.7°$	$55.66\angle-86.7°$
1020	981	1020	$981\angle-90°$	$1019\angle89.94°$	$1.019\angle90°$	$0.98\angle-89.94°$	$0.04\angle+88.4°$	$26.54\angle-88.4°$
1050	953	1050	$953\angle-90°$	$1049\angle89.94°$	$1.049\angle90°$	$0.95\angle-89.94°$	$0.10\angle+89.4°$	$10.45\angle-89.4°$
1100	910	1100	$910\angle-90°$	$1100\angle89.95°$	$1.10\angle90°$	$0.91\angle-89.95°$	$0.19\angle+89.8°$	$5.26\angle-89.8°$
1200	833	1200	$833\angle-90°$	$1200\angle89.95°$	$1.20\angle90°$	$0.83\angle-89.95°$	$0.37\angle+89.9°$	$2.70\angle-89.9°$
1300	770	1300	$770\angle-90°$	$1300\angle89.96°$	$1.30\angle90°$	$0.77\angle-89.96°$	$0.53\angle+89.9°$	$1.89\angle-89.9°$

determined by the capacity of the capacitor and the inductance of the inductor, all of the energy that was stored in the capacitor in the form of charge is now stored in the magnetic field of the inductor.

With the capacitor completely discharged, the magnetic field of the inductor must collapse; but as it does so, it must cut across the turns of the inductor. It will generate a voltage across the terminals of the inductor as it does so, and by Lenz's law this voltage must be in opposition to the change that caused it. The change that caused this voltage was the cessation of the discharge current of the capacitor, so the voltage developed across the inductor terminals at the end of the capacitor charge must be such as to charge the capacitor with the opposite polarity. Thus, as the magnetic field of the inductor collapses to zero, the resulting voltage will charge the capacitor with a polarity opposite to the original, but equal to it in magnitude if there are no losses in any circuit resistance.

With the capacitor charged to the original value, though with opposite polarity, and the magnetic field of the inductor again at zero, the action must

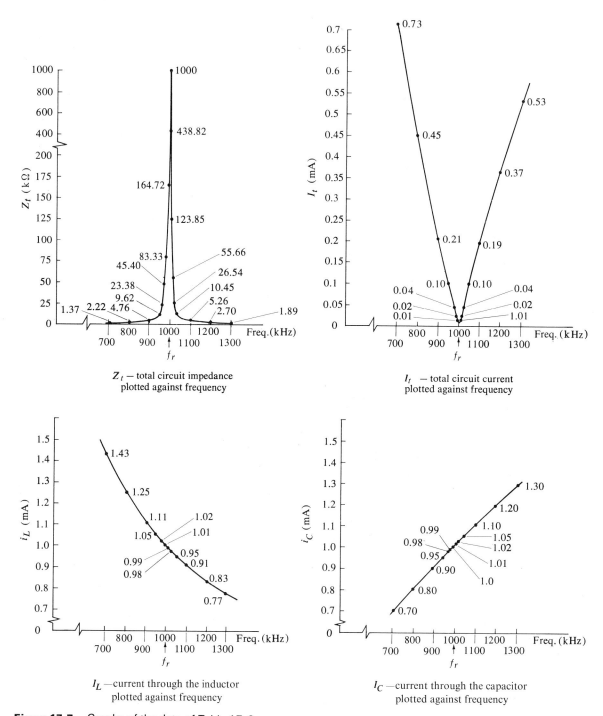

Figure 17-7 Graphs of the data of Table 17-2.

repeat itself in reverse. Again, the capacitor must discharge through the inductor; and again, the energy of the charge in the capacitor must appear as energy stored in the magnetic field of the inductor. As the capacitor charge reaches zero, the magnetic field of the inductor is at a maximum; and as the inductor field collapses, the capacitor again will charge to the original polarity, and to the original value if there are no circuit losses in resistance.

It is the function of the generator to restore to the circulating current in the tank circuit the energy lost in the circuit resistance in each cycle. If the resistance in the circuit is low, the energy required from the source is slight; but if the resistance is high, the energy required from the source will be greater.

The source voltage *need not be sinusoidal*. All that is required is that the source supply energy at the right time. Thus, the frequency of the source energy must be the same as the natural period of oscillation of the combination of inductance and capacitance. If the circuit can be supplied with an initial source of energy, so that the capacitor can be charged for an instant, the circuit will oscillate, with the electrons surging back and forth from one side of the capacitor to the other, through the inductance, at the period of oscillation determined by the circuit constants, and with a sinusoidal waveform for the inductor current and capacitor voltage. This effect has been called the *flywheel effect,* and has also been likened to water surging back and forth in a bathtub or a tank. It may be this that has resulted in the name "tank circuit" for the parallel resonant configuration.

If there were no resistance in a tank circuit, it would continue to oscillate forever once an initial stimulus had been applied. It is not possible to have such a circuit, since real components must always have some resistance. If enough energy to overcome the circuit losses is continually supplied by the source, then the circuit will continue to oscillate.

Problems

1. Find the resonant frequency of a parallel *LC* circuit with a 0.5 Ω resistance in the inductive branch, where $L = 40$ mH and $C = 900$ μF.

2. Find the resonant frequency of a parallel *LC* circuit with a 12 Ω resistance in the inductive branch, where $L = 1.8$ mH and $C = 162$ pF.

3. Consider a parallel *LC* circuit with a 50 Ω resistance in the inductive branch, where $L = 250$ mH, $C = 0.01$ μF, and the source is a 12 V ac voltage generator. Calculate the total circuit impedance, and the current through each branch of the circuit, at the resonant frequency.

4. Consider a parallel LC circuit with a 1 Ω resistance in the inductive branch, where $L = 0.004$ mH, $C = 0.81$ μF, and the source is a 120 V ac voltage generator. Calculate the total circuit impedance, the current through each branch of the circuit, and the voltage across R at the resonant frequency.

5. A parallel LC circuit with a resistance R in the inductive branch is connected to a 500 mV ac voltage generator. If $L = 500$ mH and $C = 0.005$ μF, calculate the resonant frequency, the currents through both branches, the total current, and the total impedance, at the resonant frequency, for the following values of R: 10 Ω, 100 Ω, 500 Ω, and 1000 Ω.

6. A parallel LC circuit with a resistor R in the inductive branch is connected to a 30 V ac voltage generator. If $L = 300$ mH, $C = 0.147$ μF, and $R = 7$ Ω, calculate the currents through both branches, the total current, and the total impedance at the resonant frequency; at 1 Hz below and above resonance; at 10 Hz below and above resonance; at 100 Hz below and above resonance. Plot the calculated values versus frequency.

17-4
Inductor Resistance

INDUCTOR RESISTANCE.   In nearly all cases the only significant resistance in either a series or a parallel resonant circuit is in the resistance of the inductor itself. This resistance acts as though it were in series with the inductor so far as circuit calculations are concerned, but it is not something separate from the inductor so far as physical measurements on the circuit are concerned.

In a circuit diagram this resistance is shown adjacent to the inductor. In the diagram of a series circuit it may be shown anywhere, but in the diagram of a parallel circuit it must be shown in the branch containing the inductor, and in series with the inductor.

SKIN EFFECT.   The resistance of an inductor as measured with an ohmmeter will always be less than the actual dc resistance of the inductor with an alternating current flowing through the inductor. The reason is two-fold.

With an alternating current flowing through the conductors of the inductor, each conductor has a rapidly varying magnetic field about it. This field is expanding and contracting about the centerline of the conductor, as shown in Figure 17-8. If we consider a point in the interior of the conductor, near the center, and a point on the surface of the conductor, it is clear that during one half-cycle of expansion and contraction of the magnetic field of

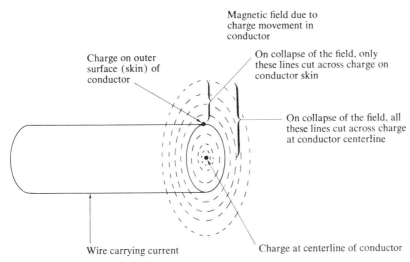

Magnetic field due to
charge movement in
conductor

Charge on outer
surface (skin) of
conductor

On collapse of the field, only
these lines cut across charge on
conductor skin

On collapse of the field, all
these lines cut across charge
at conductor centerline

Wire carrying current

Charge at centerline of conductor

Figure 17-8 An alternating current flowing through a conductor has many more lines of flux in its rapidly changing magnetic field that cut across a point in the interior of the conductor than those that cut across a point on the exterior.

the ac current flowing in the conductor many more lines of flux must cut across the point in the interior of the conductor than will cut across the point on the conductor surface.

Thus, the voltage opposing the current will be greater in the interior of the conductor than it will be on its surface. The greatest current will flow where the opposition is least; therefore, most of the current flow will be on the surface, or skin, of the conductor when the current through it is varying rapidly, as with a high-frequency alternating current.

This *skin effect* applies to all conductors, and to the conductors within an inductor, since in terms of length they are almost invariably the longest in either a series or parallel resonant circuit.

We are accustomed to thinking of the resistance of a conductor as being inversely proportional to its cross-sectional area, but with most of the current flowing on the surface skin of a conductor, its surface area becomes more important. For this reason, inductors for high-frequency operation are usually made of large-diameter wire. Sometimes hollow tubing is used since the interior will have little to do with carrying current anyway. Because the surface layers are the main conductors, sometimes the conductors are silver plated to increase their effective conductivity.

Since the effective cross-sectional area of a conductor that is useful in carrying current is decreased by the skin effect at high frequencies, the effective dc resistance to high-frequency currents is significantly higher than the resistance as measured by an ohmmeter. The effective high-frequency resistance can be several times the dc resistance.

Another factor that increases the effective high-frequency resistance is the *core losses,* if the inductor has a core. These losses can be quite significant, and for this reason such inductors usually are air wound. Even with no core but air, there are some slight losses, and this contributes to the overall effective dc resistance of the inductor.

Thus, the effective dc resistance of any practical inductor is greater at high frequencies than at dc, and will tend to reduce the effectiveness of the resonant circuit of which it is a part.

17-5
Circuit Q

DEFINITION OF Q. The Q of a circuit is sometimes called its *quality factor,* or figure of merit, since it relates to the efficiency and sharpness of tuning of a resonant circuit. It is a simple ratio, and is usually defined as the ratio between reactance and resistance in a resonant circuit. Thus,

$$Q = \frac{X_L}{R}$$

In a series circuit $X_L - X_C$; but in a parallel resonant circuit they are not, as we have seen, precisely equal. This disparity is usually insignificant; nevertheless, as a question of mathematical purity if nothing else, we usually limit the definition of Q to its relationship to the resistance and inductive reactance.

Q is a relationship between two quantities both expressed in ohms. As a ratio it has no units, but is a pure number.

SERIES Q-MAGNIFICATION. Consider the simple series resonant circuit of Figure 17-9. At resonance the voltage across the resistance is precisely the generator voltage, while the voltage across either reactance is very much higher, being the product of the circuit current times the value of the reactance. Since

Figure 17-9 A simple series resonant circuit.

$$Q = \frac{X_L}{R}$$

then

$$Q = \frac{IX_L}{IR} = \frac{v_L}{v_R}$$

or

$$v_L = v_C = Qv_r$$

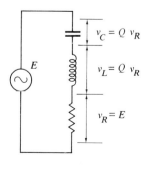

Thus, the voltage across either the inductor or the capacitor in a series resonant circuit at resonance is Q times the circuit source voltage.

In practical terms the actual ac resistance of the coil at the operating frequency is not usually known. Rather than calculate Q from the ratio between the reactance and resistance, it is more practical to calculate Q from the ratio between the generator voltage and the voltage across either reactive component at resonance. With Q known, the actual ac resistance of the coil can be calculated.

Suppose we have a 1 mH coil and a 1000 pF capacitor in series, as in Figure 17-10. At the resonant frequency the voltage across the coil is observed to be 100 times the source voltage. Calculate the Q of the circuit, and find the resistance of the coil at the operating frequency.

EXAMPLE

Solution. The Q is simply found from the ratio between the generator voltage and the voltage across either reactive component. Since this ratio is given as 100 in the statement of the problem, this is the Q, and

$$Q = 100$$

To find the ac resistance of the inductor, it is necessary to find the reactance. Before this can be found, it is necessary to know the resonant frequency, which is

$$f_r = \frac{1}{2\pi\sqrt{LC}} = \frac{1}{2\pi\sqrt{10^{-3} \times 10^{-9}}} = 159 \text{ kHz}$$

With the resonant frequency known, the reactance of the inductor can be calculated.

$$X_L = 2\pi fL = 2\pi(159 \times 10^3)(10^{-3}) = 1000 \ \Omega$$

Now the ac resistance can be calculated. Since

$$Q = \frac{X_L}{R}$$

then

$$R = \frac{X_L}{Q} = \frac{1000}{100} = 10 \ \Omega$$

Figure 17-10

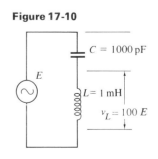

The ac resistance of this inductor is 10 Ω at the operating frequency. At a higher frequency it might be more. If it were measured with an ohmmeter at dc, it might very well be less than 5 Ω.

PARALLEL Q-MAGNIFICATION.   In a parallel resonant circuit at resonance the line current dips to a minimum value, and the impedance rises to a maximum. For a circuit where the Q is greater than 10, the impedance at resonance is Q times the inductive reactance at the resonant frequency. For the circuit just discussed, Figure 17-10, the Q is 1000, and at resonance, X_L is 1000. Therefore,

$$Z_t = QX_L = (1000)(1000) = 1,000,000 \; \Omega$$

At resonance the line current dips to a minimum value, and is less than the circulating current in the tank circuit. The circulating current is Q times the line current; thus,

$$I_C = I_L = QI_s$$

where I_C is the current in the capacitor, I_L is the current through the inductor, and I_s is the current drawn from the source.

In the circuit of Figure 17-10 the generator voltage was 1 V. Since the total circuit impedance Z_t was 1 MΩ at resonance, the current drawn from the generator would be

$$I_t = \frac{E}{Z_t} = \frac{1}{10^6} = 10^{-6} = 0.000\,001 \text{ A}$$

Since the current through the inductor and capacitor is Q times the generator current, the value of this circulating current is

$$I_C = I_L = QI_s = (1000)(0.000\,001) = 0.001 \text{ A} = 1 \text{ mA}$$

Since the source voltage appears across the capacitor and inductor both, the current through each may also be calculated from Ohm's law when their reactance is known. At the resonant frequency the reactance of each is 1000 Ω. Therefore,

$$I_C = I_L = \frac{E}{X} = \frac{1}{1000} = 0.001 \text{ A} = 1 \text{ mA}$$

BANDWIDTH.   As can be seen from the graphs of Figures 17-4 and 17-7, the increased impedance of a parallel resonant circuit, and the increased current of a series resonant circuit, are not phenomena that occur only at a single frequency with no effect at nearby frequencies. Figure 17-11 is a graph showing the variations occurring in the current in a series resonant circuit at frequencies near resonance.

The points marked f_1 and f_2 on the slope of the curve are called the *half-power points,* and the frequency between them is called the *bandwidth* (BW) of the resonant circuit. Other points could have been chosen to define the bandwidth, of course; but, by agreement, bandwidth is defined in terms of the half-power points.

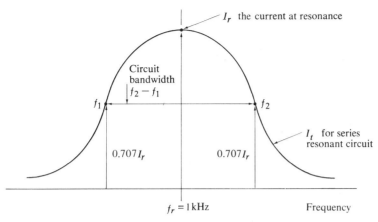

Figure 17-11　Graph of the current in a series resonant circuit at frequencies near resonance.

All of the power from the generator is dissipated in the resistance, and none in the reactance. At the points marked f_1 and f_2 the net reactance of the series circuit is not zero, as it is at resonance, but is equal to the resistance. The total impedance at this point is the phasor sum of the resistance and reactance.

$$Z_t = \sqrt{X^2 + R^2} = \sqrt{2R^2} = R\sqrt{2}$$

The current is

$$I = \frac{E}{Z_t} = R\sqrt{2}$$

But E/R is the current at resonance for the series resonant circuit. Therefore,

$$I_{f_1} = I_r\left(\frac{1}{\sqrt{2}}\right) = 0.707\, I_r$$

Thus, the current is 0.707 times the peak current occurring at resonance at the frequencies above and below resonance where the net reactance is equal to the series resistance.

The power at resonance is

$$P_r = I_r^2 \times R$$

The power at f_1 and f_2 is

$$P_{f_1} = P_{f_2} = I_f^2 \times R = (0.707\, I_r)^2\, R = 0.5\, I_r^2 \times R$$

Thus, the power at f_1 and f_2 is half the power at resonance.

The bandwidth, which is the total frequency between f_1 and f_2, is given by

$$BW = f_2 - f_1 = \frac{f_r}{Q}$$

For the problem of Figure 17-3, the resonant frequency was 1 MHz, and the Q was 1000. The bandwidth was, therefore,

$$BW = \frac{1,000,000}{1000} = 1000 \text{ Hz}$$

This bandwidth is the total frequency range between f_1 and f_2. Therefore, f_1 is half that frequency range below the resonant frequency, and is at a frequency of

$$f_1 = f_r - \frac{BW}{2} = 1,000,000 - \frac{1000}{2} = 999,500 \text{ Hz}$$

Similarly, f_2 is half the bandwidth above the resonant frequency and is at a frequency of

$$f_2 = f_r + \frac{BW}{2} = 1,000,000 + \frac{1000}{2} = 1,000,500 \text{ Hz}$$

The higher the Q of a resonant circuit, the less its bandwidth, and the more it will select a narrow range of frequencies. A low-Q circuit has a broader bandwidth, with a lower peak current for a series circuit, or a lower peak impedance for a parallel circuit.

The bandwidth of a parallel resonant circuit with a Q of more than ten may be calculated in exactly the same way as was done for a series circuit.

EXAMPLE Given a parallel resonant circuit with a Q of 200 and a resonant frequency of 600 kHz. Find the bandwidth, and the frequencies of f_1 and f_2.

Solution. The bandwidth is

$$BW = \frac{f_r}{Q} = \frac{600,000}{200} = 3000 = 3 \text{ kHz}$$

Therefore,

$$f_1 = f_r - \frac{BW}{2} \qquad \text{and} \qquad f_2 = f_r + \frac{BW}{2}$$

$$= 600 - \frac{3}{2} \qquad\qquad\qquad = 600 + \frac{3}{2}$$

$$= 598.5 \text{ kHz} \qquad\qquad\qquad = 601.5 \text{ kHz}$$

TUNING AND MISTUNING. In a series resonant circuit above resonance, the inductive reactance is greater than the capacitive reactance, and to the source the circuit looks like a net inductance. The source current lags the source voltage.

In a parallel resonant circuit above resonance, the current through the capacitive branch is greater than the current through the inductive branch. Therefore, the net source current is capacitive, and the source current leads the source voltage.

The voltages across both the capacitor and the inductor are at a maximum at resonance for a series circuit. Since the internal resistance of the capacitor is invariably less than the internal resistance of the inductor, the output voltage of the series-tuned circuit is usually taken across the capacitor. This is shown in Figure 17-12.

If several frequencies are applied to such a series resonant circuit simultaneously, one being at the resonant frequency while the others are above or below resonance, only the frequency to which the circuit is tuned will produce the Q-magnification of voltage; consequently, the output voltage at that frequency will be much greater than the voltage produced across the capacitor for the other frequencies. This is shown in Figure 17-13. Note that any load connected to the output can affect the capacitance if it has any reactive component; if it has any resistive component, such a load can affect the circuit Q. For this reason, the output load should appear as a resistance and draw minimum current.

The internal circulating current in a parallel resonant circuit is maximum at resonance. The output of this circuit is usually taken as shown in Figure 17-14. A separate coil is physically close to the inductor of the tuned circuit,

Figure 17-12 Output voltage of a series-tuned circuit is taken across the capacitor.

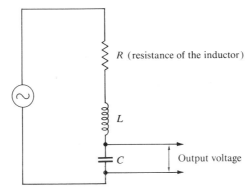

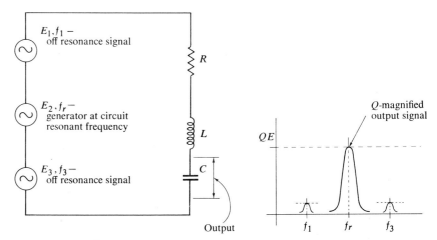

Figure 17-13   Only the frequency to which a circuit is tuned will produce the Q-magnification of voltage.

and the rapidly varying magnetic field caused by the circulating tank current produces a voltage in this second coil. This provides the opportunity to match the internal impedance of the tank circuit, considered as a source, to whatever the load may be. If the load is a vacuum tube, its input impedance will be high, and a large number of turns may be used in the second coil. If the load is a transistor, its impedance will be low, and fewer turns will be used in the second coil.

Figure 17-15 shows a parallel-tuned circuit with three generators in series, each supplying an ac voltage at a slightly different frequency to the tuned circuit. The capacitor of the tuned circuit is shown as a variable capacitor, indicated by the diagonal arrow drawn through the symbol for the capacitor.

Three possible outputs are shown. In Figure 17-15(b) the variable capacitor has been adjusted so that the resonant frequency of the circuit coincides with the frequency of generator 2. Therefore, the circulating current produced in the tank circuit by that generator is very much greater than the

Figure 17-14   Output voltage of a parallel resonant circuit is taken across a second coil placed close to the inductor of the tuned circuit.

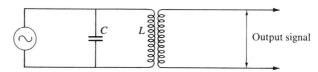

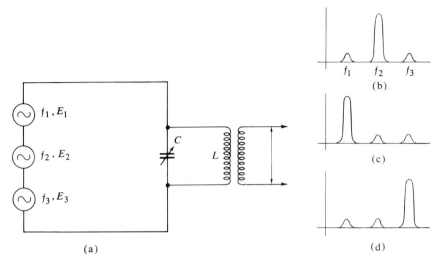

Figure 17-15 (a) A parallel-tuned circuit with variable capacitance. (b), (c), and (d) Graphs of the current produced when the capacitor of the circuit is tuned to generators 2, 1, and 3, respectively.

currents produced in the resonant circuit by the other generators. The output is a function of the tank circuit current, and will be, therefore, significantly greater at the frequency of this generator than for the others.

In Figure 17-15(c) the capacitor has been retuned, and now the resonant frequency of the circuit coincides with the output frequency of generator 1. Now the output of this generator appears as an output signal of considerable amplitude, while the output of the other two generators is very much less. If the capacitor is again retuned, this time to the frequency of generator 3, the output will appear as in Figure 17-15(d). Now the output is high at the frequency of generator 3, and very much lower for the other two generators.

In this way, both series and parallel resonant circuits may be used as frequency-selective circuits, and by adjusting either the value of capacitance or the value of inductance, may be made to select the desired frequency out of a number of different signals presented to them. Without these frequency-selective circuits, communications electronics as we have known it during this century could not have existed.

Problems

1. A 25 mH coil and a 62.5 μF capacitor are connected in series with a 1 V ac voltage source. At the resonant frequency the voltage across the coil is observed to be 250 times the source voltage. Calculate the Q of the circuit and the resistance of the coil at the operating frequency.

2. A 150 mH coil and a 150 pF capacitor are connected in series with a 25 V ac voltage source. If the voltage across the capacitor at the resonant frequency is measured at 1375 V, what are the Q of the circuit and the resistance of the coil?

3. A 3.6 H coil and a 7.2 pF capacitor are connected in series with a 500 mV ac voltage source. If the Q of the circuit is 15, find the voltage across the capacitor at the resonant frequency, and the resistance of the coil.

4. Consider a parallel resonant circuit, where $L = 1.5$ H, $C = 0.0267\ \mu$F, and $R = 150\ \Omega$. Calculate the Q of the circuit.

5. Consider a parallel resonant circuit with a resonant frequency of 796 Hz, where $R = 0.8\ \Omega$. If $Q = 25$, calculate the capacitance and inductance. Determine the total circuit impedance, applying Q magnification.

6. Consider a parallel resonant circuit, where $L = 100$ mH, $C = 3.6\ \mu$F, and $R = 4.167\ \Omega$, connected to a 150 mV ac voltage source. If $Q = 40$, calculate the source current and the currents through the capacitive and inductive branches, when the source frequency is set equal to the resonant frequency of the circuit.

7. Consider a parallel resonant circuit, where $L = 0.072$ H, $C = 0.096\ \mu$F, and $R = 12\ \Omega$, connected to a 110 V ac voltage source. If the current through the inductor is 72 times the source current, with the circuit at resonance, calculate the Q of the circuit and the value of the currents in all parts of the circuit.

8. Consider a series resonant circuit, where $L = 0.024$ mH, $C = 6$ pF, and $R = 80\ \Omega$, connected to a 5 V ac voltage source. Find the Q of the circuit and then calculate all the currents in the circuit and the total circuit impedance at resonance.

9. Given a parallel resonant circuit with a Q of 550 and a resonant frequency of 750 kHz, find the bandwidth, and the frequencies at both half-power points.

10. Given a parallel resonant circuit with a Q of 22 and a resonant frequency of 1.5 MHz, find the bandwidth, and the frequencies at both half-power points.

11. Consider a parallel resonant circuit, where $C = 1.2$ pF, $L = 0.48$ mH, and $R = 250\ \Omega$, connected to a 500 mV ac voltage source. If the frequency at one half-power point is known to be 6,590,014.8 Hz, calculate the Q of the circuit, the other half-power frequency, and the bandwidth.

12. A series resonant circuit, where $C = 0.016$ μF, $L = 0.25$ mH, and $R = 5 \Omega$, is connected to a 2 V ac voltage source. First, calculate the Q of the circuit and then the bandwidth and half-power frequencies. Also, calculate the power dissipated in the circuit at resonance and at the half-power frequencies.

13. The series resonant circuit shown is connected to three ac voltage generators, operating at different frequencies, where $L = 0.96$ mH, $R = 300$ Ω, $E_1 = 100$ mV at $f_1 = 1500$ Hz, $E_2 = 500$ mV at $f_2 = 95,000$ Hz, and $E_3 = 250$ mV at $f_3 = 36,500$ Hz. The value of C is adjusted until the series circuit resonant frequency is equal to f_1, then to f_2, and finally to f_3. For each case calculate C, the voltage across C due to each source, and the Q of the circuit.

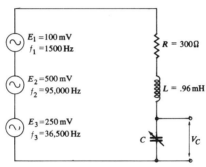

Circuit for Problem 13.

14. The parallel resonant circuit shown is connected to three ac voltage generators operating at different frequencies, where $L = 0.072$ H, $R = 40 \Omega$, $E_1 = 25$ V at $f_1 = 180$ Hz, $E_2 = 110$ V at $f_2 = 2500$ Hz, and $E_3 = 75$ V at $f_3 = 60,000$ Hz. The value of C is adjusted until the parallel circuit resonant frequency is equal to f_1, then to f_2, and finally to f_3. For each case calculate C and the current through L due to each source.

Circuit for Problem 14.

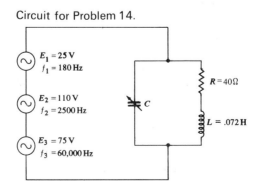

Key Words   **bandwidth**   the frequency that lies between specified half-power points

core losses   a factor that increases the effective high-frequency resistance of an inductor

half-power points   the two frequencies at which the output power is half that at resonance. They define the bandwidth.

Q (quality factor) Q represents the efficiency and sharpness of tuning of a resonant circuit. This quality is also called figure of merit. Mathematically, $Q = X_L/R$.

Q-magnification   in a series circuit, the product of Q times the source voltage, giving the voltage across the reactive components; in a parallel circuit, the product of Q times the source current, giving the current through each of the reactive components

resonant circuit   one in which the opposing effects of inductive and capacitive reactances cancel each other out

resonant frequency   in a circuit, that frequency where $X_L = X_C$

skin effect   refers to the fact that the area of greatest current flow in a conductor is at the surface, or "skin," especially when the current varies rapidly, as in high-frequency ac. This is due to the expanding and contracting magnetic fields, which makes resistance greater toward the center of the conductor.

tank circuit   another name for a parallel resonant circuit

Summary of Concepts

1.   At the resonant frequency the opposition of a series resonant circuit is at a minimum, and equal to the circuit resistance.

2.   Due to resonant rises in voltage, the voltage across either the inductor or capacitor in a series circuit can be considerably greater than the source voltage.

3.   As a rule of thumb, when one of the quantities to be summed as phasors is greater than ten times the other, the smaller of the two may be disregarded and the sum may simply be considered equal to the value of the larger quantity.

4.   Circuit current is a reciprocal function of impedance and rises at resonance as sharply as impedance drops.

5.   The resonant circuit is a frequency-selective circuit.

6.   In a parallel circuit, as the difference between two reactances approaches zero, the total impedance approaches infinity.

7. In a parallel resonant circuit, resonance is best defined as that frequency at which the total impedance of the circuit is purely resistive.

8. The only significant resistance in either a series or parallel resonant circuit is, in nearly all cases, in the resistance of the inductor itself.

9. Measured with an ohmmeter, the resistance of an inductor is always less than the actual dc resistance of the inductor with an ac flowing through it.

10. Rather than calculate Q from the ratio of reactance to resistance, it is more practical to calculate Q from the ratio between the generator voltage and the voltage across either reactive component at resonance.

11. If several frequencies are applied to a series resonant circuit simultaneously, only the frequency to which the circuit is tuned will produce the Q-magnification of voltage.

12. The voltage across either the inductor or the capacitor in a series resonant circuit is Q times the circuit source voltage. The current through either the inductor or capacitor is Q times the generator current.

13. Both series and parallel circuits may be used as frequency-selective circuits, and by adjusting the value of either the capacitance or inductance, the circuits may be made to select the desired frequency out of a number of different signals.

On a separate sheet of paper, answer the questions or fill in the blanks below. The number following each section refers to the section in the chapter where the correct answer can be found. **To Help You Review**

1. Define a resonant circuit. (17-1)

2. The frequency at which $X_L = X_C$ is the _____ frequency. (17-1)

3. At resonant frequency, the opposition of a series resonant circuit is equal to the _____ . (17-2)

4. What is resonant rise in voltage, and how is it affected by series resonance? (17-2)

5. When reactance is ten or more times resistance, what rule of thumb can you follow in summing phasors? (17-2)

6. Circuit current is a reciprocal function of impedance. As impedance drops sharply at resonance, what happens to the circuit current? (17-2)

7. Why are resonant circuits so vital to communications electronics? (17-2)

8. What is the most suitable definition of resonance in a parallel resonant circuit? (17-3)

9. What is another name for parallel resonant circuit? Why is it so named? (17-3)

10. Explain the "flywheel" effect. (17-3)

11. Where does the real resistance in a series or parallel resonant circuit come from? (17-4)

12. What is the "skin" effect? (17-4)

13. What does the following statement define? It is a simple ratio and is usually defined as the ratio between reactance and resistance in a resonant circuit. (17-5)

14. The voltage across either the inductor or capacitor in a series resonant circuit is _____ times the circuit source voltage. (17-5)

15. What is parallel Q-magnification? (17-5)

16. Explain the terms *bandwidth* and *half-power point*. (17-5)

17. What happens if several frequencies are applied simultaneously to a series reasonant circuit? (17-5)

18. How can series and parallel resonant circuits each be used as frequency-selective circuits? (17-5)

Carbon resistors rated at 2 W or less, and many of the similar values of mica, disc, and tubular ceramic capacitors, are color coded for value, tolerance, and, in some cases, operating characteristics according to the values listed in Table A-1.

TABLE A-1   Color values for resistor and capacitor codes

Color Figure	Significant Figure	Decimal Multiplier	Tolerance* (%)	Voltage Rating*
Black	0	1	20	
Brown	1	10	1	100
Red	2	10^2	2	200
Orange	3	10^3	3	300
Yellow	4	10^4	4	400
Green	5	10^5	5	500
Blue	6	10^6	6	600
Violet	7	10^7	7	700
Gray	8	10^8	8	800
White	9	10^9	9	900
Gold		0.1	5	1000
Silver		0.01	10	2000
No color			20	500

* Tolerance colors other than red, gold, and silver and the voltage-rating colors are used for capacitors only.

Figure A-1

The majority of carbon resistors now manufactured have four color bands, which are arranged as shown in Figure A-1. Some carbon resistors may have only three bands. If so, the indication for tolerance is the one that is lacking, and the tolerance can be assumed to be 20%. Some resistors in military use have a fifth band to indicate reliability in terms of failure rate, as indicated below:

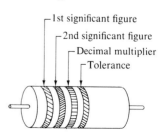

Brown   1.0 percent per 100 hours

Red   0.1 percent per 100 hours

Orange	0.01 percent per 100 hours
Yellow	0.001 percent per 100 hours

The majority of mica capacitors now in use are either coded with the present six-dot code or have the value printed on them. The present six-dot code may start with white (EIA), black (MIL), or silver (paper capacitor in the AWS code). In all three cases, the value in picofarads is read from the next three dots. If the first dot has a color, this indicates the old EIA code, and the first four dots are used for the capacitor value. The characteristics indicated by the last dot on the new EIA code specify classes according to temperature coefficient and other factors.

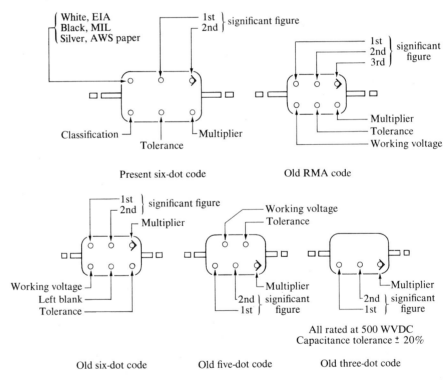

Figure A-2

Ceramic capacitors have dots or stripes with three, five, or six colors. If there are only three colors, they indicate the value of the capacitor in picofarads. If five colors are shown, the first indicates temperature coefficient, the last is tolerance, and the middle three give the value in picofarads. If a sixth color is shown, it indicates voltage rating.

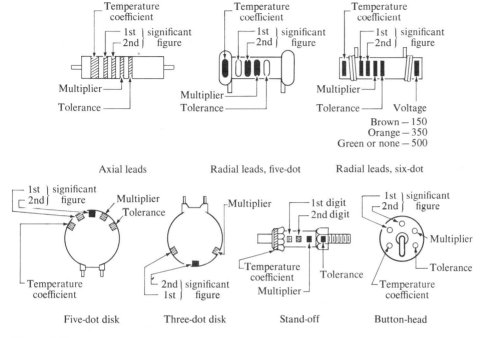

Figure A-3

TABLE A-2   Color code for ceramic capacitors

Color	Decimal Multiplier	Tolerance		Temperature Coefficient (ppm °C)
		Above 10 pF (%)	Below 10 pF (pF)	
Black	1	20	2.0	0
Brown	10	1		−30
Red	100	2		−80
Orange	1000			−150
Yellow				−220
Green		5	0.5	−330
Blue				−470
Violet				−750
Gray	0.01		0.25	30
White	0.1	10	1.0	500

Table A-3 gives preferred values for resistors and capacitors. The two numbers given in the table are the two significant figures to be followed by any decimal multiplier. Thus 15 in the table could, with the appropriate third color, represent 0.15 or 1,500,000 Ω or pF, depending on the component. The numbers were chosen so that the downward variation permissible for any value overlaps the permissible upward tolerance of the value below it.

TABLE A-3   Preferred values for resistors and capacitors

20% Tolerance	10% Tolerance	5% Tolerance
10	10	10
		11
	12	12
		13
15	15	15
		16
	18	18
		20
22	22	22
		24
	27	27
		30
33	33	33
		36
	39	39
		43
47	47	47
		51
	56	56
		62
68	68	68
		75
	82	82
		91

APPENDIX B
TABLES

n	0	1	2	3	4	5	6	7	8	9
1.0	.0000	.0043	.0086	.0128	.0170	.0212	.0253	.0294	.0334	.0374
1.1	.0414	.0453	.0492	.0531	.0569	.0607	.0645	.0682	.0719	.0755
1.2	.0792	.0828	.0864	.0899	.0934	.0969	.1004	.1038	.1072	.1106
1.3	.1139	.1173	.1206	.1239	.1271	.1303	.1335	.1367	.1399	.1430
1.4	.1461	.1492	.1523	.1553	.1584	.1614	.1644	.1673	.1703	.1732
1.5	.1761	.1790	.1818	.1847	.1875	.1903	.1931	.1959	.1987	.2014
1.6	.2041	.2068	.2095	.2122	.2148	.2175	.2201	.2227	.2253	.2279
1.7	.2304	.2330	.2355	.2380	.2405	.2430	.2455	.2480	.2504	.2529
1.8	.2553	.2577	.2601	.2625	.2648	.2672	.2695	.2718	.2742	.2765
1.9	.2788	.2810	.2833	.2856	.2878	.2900	.2923	.2945	.2967	.2989
2.0	.3010	.3032	.3054	.3075	.3096	.3118	.3139	.3160	.3181	.3201
2.1	.3222	.3243	.3263	.3284	.3304	.3324	.3345	.3365	.3385	.3404
2.2	.3424	.3444	.3464	.3483	.3502	.3522	.3541	.3560	.3579	.3598
2.3	.3617	.3636	.3655	.3674	.3692	.3711	.3729	.3747	.3766	.3784
2.4	.3802	.3820	.3838	.3856	.3874	.3892	.3909	.3927	.3945	.3962
2.5	.3979	.3997	.4014	.4031	.4048	.4065	.4082	.4099	.4116	.4133
2.6	.4150	.4166	.4183	.4200	.4216	.4232	.4249	.4265	.4281	.4298
2.7	.4314	.4330	.4346	.4362	.4378	.4393	.4409	.4425	.4440	.4456
2.8	.4472	.4487	.4502	.4518	.4533	.4548	.4564	.4579	.4594	.4609
2.9	.4624	.4639	.4654	.4669	.4683	.4698	.4713	.4728	.4742	.4757
3.0	.4771	.4786	.4800	.481́4	.4829	.4843	.4857	.4871	.4886	.4900
3.1	.4914	.4928	.4942	.4955	.4969	.4983	.4997	.5011	.5024	.5038
3.2	.5051	.5065	.5079	.5092	.5105	.5119	.5132	.5145	.5159	.5172
3.3	.5185	.5198	.5211	.5224	.5237	.5250	.5263	.5276	.5289	.5302
3.4	.5315	.5328	.5340	.5353	.5366	.5378	.5391	.5403	.5416	.5428
3.5	.5441	.5453	.5465	.5478	.5490	.5502	.5514	.5527	.5539	.5551
3.6	.5563	.5575	.5587	.5599	.5611	.5623	.5635	.5647	.5658	.5670
3.7	.5682	.5694	.5705	.5717	.5729	.5740	.5752	.5763	.5775	.5786
3.8	.5798	.5809	.5821	.5832	.5843	.5855	.5866	.5877	.5888	.5899
3.9	.5911	.5922	.5933	.5944	.5955	.5966	.5977	.5988	.5999	.6010
4.0	.6021	.6031	.6042	.6053	.6064	.6075	.6085	.6096	.6107	.6117
4.1	.6128	.6138	.6149	.6160	.6170	.6180	.6191	.6201	.6212	.6222
4.2	.6232	.6243	.6253	.6263	.6274	.6284	.6294	.6304	.6314	.6325
4.3	.6335	.6345	.6355	.6365	.6375	.6385	.6395	.6405	.6415	.6425
4.4	.6435	.6444	.6454	.6464	.6474	.6484	.6493	.6503	.6513	.6522
4.5	.6532	.6542	.6551	.6561	.6571	.6580	.6590	.6599	.6609	.6618
4.6	.6628	.6637	.6646	.6656	.6665	.6675	.6684	.6693	.6702	.6712
4.7	.6721	.6730	.6739	.6749	.6758	.6767	.6776	.6785	.6794	.6803
4.8	.6812	.6821	.6830	.6839	.6848	.6857	.6866	.6875	.6884	.6893
4.9	.6902	.6911	.6920	.6928	.6937	.6946	.6955	.6964	.6972	.6981
5.0	.6990	.6998	.7007	.7016	.7024	.7033	.7042	.7050	.7059	.7067
5.1	.7076	.7084	.7093	.7101	.7110	.7118	.7126	.7135	.7143	.7152
5.2	.7160	.7168	.7177	.7185	.7193	.7202	.7210	.7218	.7226	.7235
5.3	.7243	.7251	.7259	.7267	.7275	.7284	.7292	.7300	.7308	.7316
5.4	.7324	.7332	.7340	.7348	.7356	.7364	.7372	.7380	.7388	.7396

TABLE B-1   Four-Place Logarithms of Numbers

n	0	1	2	3	4	5	6	7	8	9
5.5	.7404	.7412	.7419	.7427	.7435	.7443	.7451	.7459	.7466	.7474
5.6	.7482	.7490	.7497	.7505	.7513	.7520	.7528	.7536	.7543	.7551
5.7	.7559	.7566	.7574	.7582	.7589	.7597	.7604	.7612	.7619	.7627
5.8	.7634	.7642	.7649	.7657	.7664	.7672	.7679	.7686	.7694	.7701
5.9	.7709	.7716	.7723	.7731	.7738	.7745	.7752	.7760	.7767	.7774
6.0	.7782	.7789	.7796	.7803	.7810	.7818	.7825	.7832	.7839	.7846
6.1	.7853	.7860	.7868	.7875	.7882	.7889	.7896	.7903	.7910	.7917
6.2	.7924	.7931	.7938	.7945	.7952	.7959	.7966	.7973	.7980	.7987
6.3	.7993	.8000	.8007	.8014	.8021	.8028	.8035	.8041	.8048	.8055
6.4	.8062	.8069	.8075	.8082	.8089	.8096	.8102	.8109	.8116	.8122
6.5	.8129	.8136	.8142	.8149	.8156	.8162	.8169	.8176	.8182	.8189
6.6	.8195	.8202	.8209	.8215	.8222	.8228	.8235	.8241	.8248	.8254
6.7	.8261	.8267	.8274	.8280	.8287	.8293	.8299	.8306	.8312	.8319
6.8	.8325	.8331	.8338	.8344	.8351	.8357	.8363	.8370	.8376	.8382
6.9	.8388	.8395	.8401	.8407	.8414	.8420	.8426	.8432	.8439	.8445
7.0	.8451	.8457	.8463	.8470	.8476	.8482	.8488	.8494	.8500	.8506
7.1	.8513	.8519	.8525	.8531	.8537	.8543	.8549	.8555	.8561	.8567
7.2	.8573	.8579	.8585	.8591	.8597	.8603	.8609	.8615	.8621	.8627
7.3	.8633	.8639	.8645	.8651	.8657	.8663	.8669	.8675	.8681	.8686
7.4	.8692	.8698	.8704	.8710	.8716	.8722	.8727	.8733	.8739	.8745
7.5	.8751	.8756	.8762	.8768	.8774	.8779	.8785	.8791	.8797	.8802
7.6	.8808	.8814	.8820	.8825	.8831	.8837	.8842	.8848	.8854	.8859
7.7	.8865	.8871	.8876	.8882	.8887	.8893	.8899	.8904	.8910	.8915
7.8	.8921	.8927	.8932	.8932	.8943	.8949	.8954	.8960	.8965	.8971
7.9	.8976	.8982	.8987	.8993	.8998	.9004	.9009	.9015	.9020	.9025
8.0	.9031	.9036	.9042	.9047	.9053	.9058	.9063	.9069	.9074	.9079
8.1	.9085	.9090	.9096	.9101	.9106	.9112	.9117	.9122	.9128	.9133
8.2	.9138	.9143	.9149	.9154	.9159	.9165	.9170	.9175	.9180	.9186
8.3	.9191	.9196	.9201	.9206	.9212	.9217	.9222	.9227	.9232	.9238
8.4	.9243	.9248	.9253	.9258	.9263	.9269	.9274	.9279	.9284	.9289
8.5	.9294	.9299	.9304	.9309	.9315	.9320	.9325	.9330	.9335	.9340
8.6	.9345	.9350	.9355	.9360	.9365	.9370	.9375	.9380	.9385	.9390
8.7	.9395	.9400	.9405	.9410	.9415	.9420	.9425	.9430	.9435	.9440
8.8	.9445	.9450	.9455	.9460	.9465	.9469	.9474	.9479	.9484	.9489
8.9	.9494	.9499	.9504	.9509	.9513	.9518	.9523	.9528	.9533	.9538
9.0	.9542	.9547	.9552	.9557	.9562	.9566	.9571	.9576	.9581	.9586
9.1	.9590	.9595	.9600	.9605	.9609	.9614	.9619	.9624	.9628	.9633
9.2	.9638	.9643	.9647	.9652	.9657	.9661	.9666	.9671	.9675	.9680
9.3	.9685	.9689	.9694	.9699	.9703	.9708	.9713	.9717	.9722	.9727
9.4	.9731	.9736	.9741	.9745	.9750	.9754	.9759	.9763	.9768	.9773
9.5	.9777	.9782	.9786	.9791	.9795	.9800	.9805	.9809	.9814	.9818
9.6	.9823	.9827	.9832	.9836	.9841	.9845	.9850	.9854	.9859	.9863
9.7	.9868	.9872	.9877	.9881	.9886	.9890	.9894	.9899	.9903	.9908
9.8	.9912	.9917	.9921	.9926	.9930	.9934	.9939	.9943	.9948	.9952
9.9	.9956	.9961	.9965	.9969	.9974	.9978	.9983	.9987	.9991	.9996

TABLE B-1   Four-Place Logarithms of Numbers (cont.)

x	e^x	e^{-x}	x	e^x	e^{-x}	x	e^x	e^{-x}
0.00	1.0000	1.0000	1.00	2.7183	0.3679	3.50	33.115	0.0302
0.02	1.0202	0.9802	1.05	2.8577	.3499	3.55	34.813	.0287
0.04	1.0408	.9608	1.10	3.0042	.3329	3.60	36.598	.0273
0.06	1.0618	.9418	1.15	3.1582	.3166	3.65	38.475	.0260
0.08	1.0833	.9231	1.20	3.3201	.3012	3.70	40.447	.0247
0.10	1.1052	0.9048	1.25	3.4903	0.2865	3.75	42.521	0.0235
0.12	1.1275	.8869	1.30	3.6693	.2725	3.80	44.701	.0224
0.14	1.1503	.8694	1.35	3.8574	.2592	3.85	46.993	.0213
0.16	1.1735	.8521	1.40	4.0552	.2466	3.90	49.402	.0202
0.18	1.1972	.8353	1.45	4.2631	.2346	3.95	51.935	.0193
0.20	1.2214	0.8187	1.50	4.4817	0.2231	4.00	54.598	0.0183
0.22	1.2461	.8025	1.55	4.7115	.2122	4.05	57.397	.0174
0.24	1.2712	.7866	1.60	4.9530	.2019	4.10	60.340	.0166
0.26	1.2969	.7711	1.65	5.2070	.1920	4.15	63.434	.0158
0.28	1.3231	.7558	1.70	5.4739	.1827	4.20	66.686	.0150
0.30	1.3499	0.7408	1.75	5.7546	0.1738	4.25	70.105	0.0143
0.32	1.3771	.7261	1.80	6.0496	.1653	4.30	73.700	.0136
0.34	1.4049	.7118	1.85	6.3598	.1572	4.35	77.478	.0129
0.36	1.4333	.6977	1.90	6.6859	.1496	4.40	81.451	.0123
0.38	1.4623	.6839	1.95	7.0287	.1423	4.45	85.627	.0117
0.40	1.4918	0.6703	2.00	7.3891	0.1353	4.50	90.017	0.0111
0.42	1.5220	.6570	2.05	7.7679	.1287	4.55	94.632	.0106
0.44	1.5527	.6440	2.10	8.1662	.1225	4.60	99.484	.0101
0.46	1.5841	.6313	2.15	8.5849	.1165	4.65	104.58	.0096
0.48	1.6161	.6188	2.20	9.0250	.1108	4.70	109.95	.0091
0.50	1.6487	0.6065	2.25	9.4877	0.1054	4.75	115.58	0.0087
0.52	1.6820	.5945	2.30	9.9742	.1003	4.80	121.51	.0082
0.54	1.7160	.5827	2.35	10.486	.0954	4.85	127.74	.0078
0.56	1.7507	.5712	2.40	11.023	.0907	4.90	134.29	.0074
0.58	1.7860	.5599	2.45	11.588	.0863	4.95	141.17	.0071
0.60	1.8221	0.5488	2.50	12.182	0.0821	5.00	148.41	0.0067
0.62	1.8589	.5379	2.55	12.807	.0781	5.05	156.02	.0064
0.64	1.8965	.5273	2.60	13.464	.0743	5.10	164.02	.0061
0.66	1.9348	.5169	2.65	14.154	.0707	5.15	172.43	.0058
0.68	1.9739	.5066	2.70	14.880	.0672	5.20	181.27	.0055
0.70	2.0138	0.4966	2.75	15.643	0.0639	5.25	190.57	0.0052
0.72	2.0544	.4868	2.80	16.445	.0608	5.30	200.34	.0050
0.74	2.0959	.4771	2.85	17.288	.0578	5.35	210.61	.0047
0.76	2.1383	.4677	2.90	18.174	.0550	5.40	221.41	.0045
0.78	2.1815	.4584	2.95	19.106	.0523	5.45	232.76	.0043
0.80	2.2255	0.4493	3.00	20.086	0.0498	5.5	244.69	0.0041
0.82	2.2705	.4404	3.05	21.115	.0474	6.0	403.43	.0025
0.84	2.3164	.4317	3.10	22.198	.0450	6.5	665.14	.0015
0.86	2.3632	.4232	3.15	23.336	.0429	7.0	1096.6	.0009
0.88	2.4109	.4148	3.20	24.533	.0408	7.5	1808.0	.0006
0.90	2.4596	0.4066	3.25	25.790	0.0388	8.0	2981.0	0.0003
0.92	2.5093	.3985	3.30	27.113	.0369	8.5	4914.8	.0002
0.94	2.5600	.3906	3.35	28.503	.0351	9.0	8103.1	.0001
0.96	2.6117	.3829	3.40	29.964	.0334	9.5	13360	.00007
0.98	2.6645	.3753	3.45	31.500	.0317	10	22026	.00005
x	e^x	e^{-x}	x	e^x	e^{-x}	x	e^x	e^{-x}

TABLE B-2 Exponential Functions

TABLE B-3 Four-Place Values of Functions

x	sin x	cos x	tan x	cot x	sec x	cosec x	x
0° 0'	.00000	1.0000	.00000		1.0000		90° 0'
0°10'	.00291	1.0000	.00291	343.77	1.0000	343.78	89°50'
0°20'	.00582	1.0000	.00582	171.88	1.0000	171.89	89°40'
0°30'	.00873	1.0000	.00873	114.59	1.0000	114.59	89°30'
0°40'	.01164	.9999	.01164	85.940	1.0001	85.946	89°20'
0°50'	.01455	.9999	.01455	68.750	1.0001	68.757	89°10'
1° 0'	.01745	.9998	.01746	57.290	1.0002	57.299	89° 0'
1°10'	.02036	.9998	.02036	49.104	1.0002	49.114	88°50'
1°20'	.02327	.9997	.02328	42.964	1.0003	42.976	88°40'
1°30'	.02618	.9997	.02619	38.188	1.0003	38.202	88°30'
1°40'	.02908	.9996	.02910	34.368	1.0004	34.382	88°20'
1°50'	.03199	.9995	.03201	31.242	1.0005	31.258	88°10'
2° 0'	.03490	.9994	.03492	28.636	1.0006	28.654	88° 0'
2°10'	.03781	.9993	.03783	26.432	1.0007	26.451	87°50'
2°20'	.04071	.9992	.04075	24.542	1.0008	24.562	87°40'
2°30'	.04362	.9990	.04366	22.904	1.0010	22.926	87°30'
2°40'	.04653	.9989	.04658	21.470	1.0011	21.494	87°20'
2°50'	.04943	.9988	.04949	20.206	1.0012	20.230	87°10'
3° 0'	.05234	.9986	.05241	19.0811	1.0014	19.107	87° 0'
3°10'	.05524	.9985	.05533	18.0750	1.0015	18.103	86°50'
3°20'	.05814	.9983	.05824	17.1693	1.0017	17.198	86°40'
3°30'	.06105	.9981	.06116	16.3499	1.0019	16.380	86°30'
3°40'	.06395	.9980	.06408	15.6048	1.0021	15.637	86°20'
3°50'	.06685	.9978	.06700	14.9244	1.0022	14.958	86°10'
4° 0'	.06976	.9976	.06993	14.3007	1.0024	14.336	86° 0'
4°10'	.07266	.9974	.07285	13.7267	1.0027	13.763	85°50'
4°20'	.07556	.9971	.07578	13.1969	1.0029	13.235	85°40'
4°30'	.07846	.9969	.07870	12.7062	1.0031	12.746	85°30'
4°40'	.08136	.9967	.08163	12.2505	1.0033	12.291	85°20'
4°50'	.08426	.9964	.08456	11.8262	1.0036	11.868	85°10'
5° 0'	.08716	.9962	.08749	11.4301	1.0038	11.474	85° 0'
5°10'	.09005	.9959	.09042	11.0594	1.0041	11.105	84°50'
5°20'	.09295	.9957	.09335	10.7119	1.0044	10.758	84°40'
5°30'	.09585	.9954	.09629	10.3854	1.0046	10.433	84°30'
5°40'	.09874	.9951	.09923	10.0780	1.0049	10.128	84°20'
5°50'	.10164	.9948	.10216	9.7882	1.0052	9.839	84°10'
6° 0'	.10453	.9945	.10510	9.5144	1.0055	9.5668	84° 0'
6°10'	.10742	.9942	.10805	9.2553	1.0058	9.3092	83°50'
6°20'	.11031	.9939	.11099	9.0098	1.0061	9.0652	83°40'
6°30'	.11320	.9936	.11394	8.7769	1.0065	8.8337	83°30'
6°40'	.11609	.9932	.11688	8.5555	1.0068	8.6138	83°20'
6°50'	.11898	.9929	.11983	8.3450	1.0072	8.4647	83°10'
7° 0'	.12187	.9925	.12278	8.1443	1.0075	8.2055	83° 0'
7°10'	.12476	.9922	.12574	7.9530	1.0079	8.0157	82°50'
7°20'	.12764	.9918	.12869	7.7704	1.0083	7.8344	82°40'
7°30'	.13053	.9914	.13165	7.5958	1.0086	7.6613	82°30'

(Bottom labels, reading complements: cos x | sin x | cot x | tan x | cosec x | sec x *)*

x	sin x	cos x	tan x	cot x	sec x	cosec x	x
7°30'	.1305	.9914	.1317	7.5958	1.0086	7.6613	82°30'
7°40'	.1334	.9911	.1346	7.4287	1.0090	7.4957	82°20'
7°50'	.1363	.9907	.1376	7.2687	1.0094	7.3372	82°10'
8° 0'	.1392	.9903	.1405	7.1154	1.0098	7.1853	82° 0'
8°10'	.1421	.9899	.1435	6.9682	1.0102	7.0396	81°50'
8°20'	.1449	.9894	.1465	6.8269	1.0107	6.8998	81°40'
8°30'	.1478	.9890	.1495	6.6912	1.0111	6.7655	81°30'
8°40'	.1507	.9886	.1524	6.5606	1.0116	6.6363	81°20'
8°50'	.1536	.9881	.1554	6.4348	1.0120	6.5121	81°10'
9° 0'	.1564	.9877	.1584	6.3138	1.0125	6.3925	81° 0'
9°10'	.1593	.9872	.1614	6.1970	1.0129	6.2772	80°50'
9°20'	.1622	.9868	.1644	6.0844	1.0134	6.1661	80°40'
9°30'	.1650	.9863	.1673	5.9758	1.0139	6.0589	80°30'
9°40'	.1679	.9858	.1703	5.8708	1.0144	5.9554	80°20'
9°50'	.1708	.9853	.1733	5.7694	1.0149	5.8554	80°10'
10° 0'	.1736	.9848	.1763	5.6713	1.0154	5.7588	80° 0'
10°10'	.1765	.9843	.1793	5.5764	1.0160	5.6653	79°50'
10°20'	.1794	.9838	.1823	5.4845	1.0165	5.5749	79°40'
10°30'	.1822	.9833	.1853	5.3955	1.0170	5.4874	79°30'
10°40'	.1851	.9827	.1883	5.3093	1.0176	5.4026	79°20'
10°50'	.1880	.9822	.1914	5.2257	1.0182	5.3205	79°10'
11° 0'	.1908	.9816	.1944	5.1446	1.0187	5.2408	79° 0'
11°10'	.1937	.9811	.1974	5.0658	1.0193	5.1636	78°50'
11°20'	.1965	.9805	.2004	4.9894	1.0199	5.0886	78°40'
11°30'	.1994	.9799	.2035	4.9152	1.0205	5.0159	78°30'
11°40'	.2022	.9793	.2065	4.8430	1.0211	4.9452	78°20'
11°50'	.2051	.9787	.2095	4.7729	1.0217	4.8765	78°10'
12° 0'	.2079	.9781	.2126	4.7046	1.0223	4.8097	78° 0'
12°10'	.2108	.9775	.2156	4.6382	1.0230	4.7448	77°50'
12°20'	.2136	.9769	.2186	4.5736	1.0236	4.6817	77°40'
12°30'	.2164	.9763	.2217	4.5107	1.0243	4.6202	77°30'
12°40'	.2193	.9757	.2247	4.4494	1.0249	4.5604	77°20'
12°50'	.2221	.9750	.2278	4.3897	1.0256	4.5022	77°10'
13° 0'	.2250	.9744	.2309	4.3315	1.0263	4.4454	77° 0'
13°10'	.2278	.9737	.2339	4.2747	1.0270	4.3901	76°50'
13°20'	.2306	.9730	.2370	4.2193	1.0277	4.3362	76°40'
13°30'	.2334	.9724	.2401	4.1653	1.0284	4.2837	76°30'
13°40'	.2363	.9717	.2432	4.1126	1.0291	4.2324	76°20'
13°50'	.2391	.9710	.2462	4.0611	1.0299	4.1824	76°10'
14° 0'	.2419	.9703	.2493	4.0108	1.0306	4.1336	76° 0'
14°10'	.2447	.9696	.2524	3.9617	1.0314	4.0859	75°50'
14°20'	.2476	.9689	.2555	3.9136	1.0321	4.0394	75°40'
14°30'	.2504	.9681	.2586	3.8667	1.0329	3.9939	75°30'
14°40'	.2532	.9674	.2617	3.8208	1.0337	3.9495	75°20'
14°50'	.2560	.9667	.2648	3.7760	1.0345	3.9061	75°10'
15° 0'	.2588	.9659	.2679	3.7321	1.0353	3.8637	75° 0'

(Bottom labels, reading complements: cos x | sin x | cot x | tan x | cosec x | sec x *)*

TABLE B-3 Four-Place Values of Functions (cont.)

x	cosec x	sec x	cot x	tan x	cos x	sin x	x
30'	2.6131	1.0824	2.4142	.4142	.9239	.3827	30'
40'	2.5949	1.0837	2.3945	.4176	.9228	.3854	20'
50'	2.5770	1.0850	2.3750	.4210	.9216	.3881	10'
23° 0'	2.5593	1.0864	2.3559	.4245	.9205	.3907	67° 0'
10'	2.5419	1.0877	2.3369	.4279	.9194	.3934	50'
20'	2.5247	1.0891	2.3183	.4314	.9182	.3961	40'
30'	2.5078	1.0904	2.2998	.4348	.9171	.3987	30'
40'	2.4912	1.0918	2.2817	.4383	.9159	.4014	20'
50'	2.4748	1.0932	2.2637	.4417	.9147	.4041	10'
24° 0'	2.4586	1.0946	2.2460	.4452	.9135	.4067	66° 0'
10'	2.4426	1.0961	2.2286	.4487	.9124	.4094	50'
20'	2.4269	1.0975	2.2113	.4522	.9112	.4120	40'
30'	2.4114	1.0990	2.1943	.4557	.9100	.4147	30'
40'	2.3961	1.1004	2.1775	.4592	.9088	.4173	20'
50'	2.3811	1.1019	2.1609	.4628	.9075	.4200	10'
25° 0'	2.3662	1.1034	2.1445	.4663	.9063	.4226	65° 0'
10'	2.3515	1.1049	2.1283	.4699	.9051	.4253	50'
20'	2.3371	1.1064	2.1123	.4734	.9038	.4279	40'
30'	2.3228	1.1079	2.0965	.4770	.9026	.4305	30'
40'	2.3088	1.1095	2.0809	.4806	.9013	.4331	20'
50'	2.2949	1.1110	2.0655	.4841	.9001	.4358	10'
26° 0'	2.2812	1.1126	2.0503	.4877	.8988	.4384	64° 0'
10'	2.2677	1.1142	2.0353	.4913	.8975	.4410	50'
20'	2.2543	1.1158	2.0204	.4950	.8962	.4436	40'
30'	2.2412	1.1174	2.0057	.4986	.8949	.4462	30'
40'	2.2282	1.1190	1.9912	.5022	.8936	.4488	20'
50'	2.2154	1.1207	1.9768	.5059	.8923	.4514	10'
27° 0'	2.2027	1.1223	1.9626	.5095	.8910	.4540	63° 0'
10'	2.1902	1.1240	1.9486	.5132	.8897	.4566	50'
20'	2.1779	1.1257	1.9347	.5169	.8884	.4592	40'
30'	2.1657	1.1274	1.9210	.5206	.8870	.4617	30'
40'	2.1537	1.1291	1.9074	.5243	.8857	.4643	20'
50'	2.1418	1.1308	1.8940	.5280	.8843	.4669	10'
28° 0'	2.1301	1.1326	1.8807	.5317	.8829	.4695	62° 0'
10'	2.1185	1.1343	1.8676	.5354	.8816	.4720	50'
20'	2.1070	1.1361	1.8546	.5392	.8802	.4746	40'
30'	2.0957	1.1379	1.8418	.5430	.8788	.4772	30'
40'	2.0846	1.1397	1.8291	.5467	.8774	.4797	20'
50'	2.0736	1.1415	1.8165	.5505	.8760	.4823	10'
29° 0'	2.0627	1.1434	1.8040	.5543	.8746	.4848	61° 0'
10'	2.0519	1.1452	1.7917	.5581	.8732	.4874	50'
20'	2.0413	1.1471	1.7796	.5619	.8718	.4899	40'
30'	2.0308	1.1490	1.7675	.5658	.8704	.4924	30'
40'	2.0204	1.1509	1.7556	.5696	.8689	.4950	20'
50'	2.0101	1.1528	1.7437	.5735	.8675	.4975	10'
30° 0'	2.0000	1.1547	1.7321	.5774	.8660	.5000	60° 0'
x	sec x	cosec x	tan x	cot x	sin x	cos x	x

x	sin x	cos x	tan x	cot x	sec x	cosec x	x
15° 0'	.2588	.9659	.2679	3.7321	1.0353	3.8637	75° 0'
10'	.2616	.9652	.2711	3.6891	1.0361	3.8222	50'
20'	.2644	.9644	.2742	3.6470	1.0369	3.7817	40'
30'	.2672	.9636	.2773	3.6059	1.0377	3.7420	30'
40'	.2700	.9628	.2805	3.5656	1.0386	3.7032	20'
50'	.2728	.9621	.2836	3.5261	1.0394	3.6652	10'
16° 0'	.2756	.9613	.2867	3.4874	1.0403	3.6280	74° 0'
10'	.2784	.9605	.2899	3.4495	1.0412	3.5915	50'
20'	.2812	.9596	.2931	3.4124	1.0421	3.5559	40'
30'	.2840	.9588	.2962	3.3759	1.0430	3.5209	30'
40'	.2868	.9580	.2994	3.3402	1.0439	3.4867	20'
50'	.2896	.9572	.3026	3.3052	1.0448	3.4532	10'
17° 0'	.2924	.9563	.3057	3.2709	1.0457	3.4203	73° 0'
10'	.2952	.9555	.3089	3.2371	1.0466	3.3881	50'
20'	.2979	.9546	.3121	3.2041	1.0476	3.3565	40'
30'	.3007	.9537	.3153	3.1716	1.0485	3.3255	30'
40'	.3035	.9528	.3185	3.1397	1.0495	3.2951	20'
50'	.3062	.9520	.3217	3.1084	1.0505	3.2653	10'
18° 0'	.3090	.9511	.3249	3.0777	1.0515	3.2361	72° 0'
10'	.3118	.9502	.3281	3.0475	1.0525	3.2074	50'
20'	.3145	.9492	.3314	3.0178	1.0535	3.1792	40'
30'	.3173	.9483	.3346	2.9887	1.0545	3.1516	30'
40'	.3201	.9474	.3378	2.9600	1.0555	3.1244	20'
50'	.3228	.9465	.3411	2.9319	1.0566	3.0977	10'
19° 0'	.3256	.9455	.3443	2.9042	1.0576	3.0716	71° 0'
10'	.3283	.9446	.3476	2.8770	1.0587	3.0458	50'
20'	.3311	.9436	.3508	2.8502	1.0598	3.0206	40'
30'	.3338	.9426	.3541	2.8239	1.0609	2.9957	30'
40'	.3365	.9417	.3574	2.7980	1.0620	2.9714	20'
50'	.3393	.9407	.3607	2.7725	1.0631	2.9474	10'
20° 0'	.3420	.9397	.3640	2.7475	1.0642	2.9238	70° 0'
10'	.3448	.9387	.3673	2.7228	1.0653	2.9006	50'
20'	.3475	.9377	.3706	2.6985	1.0665	2.8779	40'
30'	.3502	.9367	.3739	2.6746	1.0676	2.8555	30'
40'	.3529	.9356	.3772	2.6511	1.0688	2.8334	20'
50'	.3557	.9346	.3805	2.6279	1.0700	2.8118	10'
21° 0'	.3584	.9336	.3839	2.6051	1.0712	2.7904	69° 0'
10'	.3611	.9325	.3872	2.5826	1.0724	2.7695	50'
20'	.3638	.9315	.3906	2.5605	1.0736	2.7488	40'
30'	.3665	.9304	.3939	2.5386	1.0748	2.7285	30'
40'	.3692	.9293	.3973	2.5172	1.0760	2.7085	20'
50'	.3719	.9283	.4006	2.4960	1.0773	2.6888	10'
22° 0'	.3746	.9272	.4040	2.4751	1.0785	2.6695	68° 0'
10'	.3773	.9261	.4074	2.4545	1.0798	2.6504	50'
20'	.3800	.9250	.4108	2.4342	1.0811	2.6316	40'
30'	.3827	.9239	.4142	2.4142	1.0824	2.6131	30'
x	cos x	sin x	cot x	tan x	cosec x	sec x	x

TABLE B-3 Four-Place Values of Functions (cont.)

x	cosec x	sec x	cot x	tan x	cos x	sin x	x
30'	1.6427	1.2605	1.3032	.7673	.7934	.6088	30'
20'	1.6365	1.2633	1.2954	.7720	.7916	.6111	40'
10'	1.6304	1.2662	1.2876	.7766	.7898	.6134	50'
52° 0'	1.6243	1.2690	1.2799	.7813	.7880	.6157	38° 0'
50'	1.6183	1.2719	1.2723	.7860	.7862	.6180	10'
40'	1.6123	1.2748	1.2647	.7907	.7844	.6202	20'
30'	1.6064	1.2779	1.2572	.7954	.7826	.6225	30'
20'	1.6005	1.2808	1.2497	.8002	.7808	.6248	40'
10'	1.5948	1.2837	1.2423	.8050	.7790	.6271	50'
51° 0'	1.5890	1.2868	1.2349	.8098	.7771	.6293	39° 0'
50'	1.5833	1.2898	1.2276	.8146	.7753	.6316	10'
40'	1.5777	1.2929	1.2203	.8195	.7735	.6338	20'
30'	1.5721	1.2960	1.2131	.8243	.7716	.6361	30'
20'	1.5666	1.2991	1.2059	.8292	.7698	.6383	40'
10'	1.5611	1.3022	1.1988	.8342	.7679	.6406	50'
50° 0'	1.5557	1.3054	1.1918	.8391	.7660	.6428	40° 0'
50'	1.5504	1.3086	1.1847	.8441	.7642	.6450	10'
40'	1.5450	1.3118	1.1778	.8491	.7623	.6472	20'
30'	1.5398	1.3151	1.1708	.8541	.7604	.6494	30'
20'	1.5346	1.3184	1.1640	.8591	.7585	.6517	40'
10'	1.5294	1.3217	1.1571	.8642	.7566	.6539	50'
49° 0'	1.5243	1.3250	1.1504	.8693	.7547	.6561	41° 0'
50'	1.5192	1.3284	1.1436	.8744	.7528	.6583	10'
40'	1.5142	1.3318	1.1369	.8796	.7509	.6604	20'
30'	1.5092	1.3352	1.1303	.8847	.7490	.6626	30'
20'	1.5042	1.3386	1.1237	.8899	.7470	.6648	40'
10'	1.4993	1.3421	1.1171	.8952	.7451	.6670	50'
48° 0'	1.4945	1.3456	1.1106	.9004	.7431	.6691	42° 0'
50'	1.4897	1.3492	1.1041	.9057	.7412	.6713	10'
40'	1.4849	1.3527	1.0977	.9110	.7392	.6734	20'
30'	1.4802	1.3563	1.0913	.9163	.7373	.6756	30'
20'	1.4755	1.3600	1.0850	.9217	.7353	.6777	40'
10'	1.4709	1.3636	1.0786	.9271	.7333	.6799	50'
47° 0'	1.4663	1.3673	1.0724	.9325	.7314	.6820	43° 0'
50'	1.4617	1.3711	1.0661	.9380	.7294	.6841	10'
40'	1.4572	1.3748	1.0599	.9435	.7274	.6862	20'
30'	1.4527	1.3786	1.0538	.9490	.7254	.6884	30'
20'	1.4483	1.3824	1.0477	.9545	.7234	.6905	40'
10'	1.4439	1.3863	1.0416	.9601	.7214	.6926	50'
46° 0'	1.4396	1.3902	1.0355	.9657	.7193	.6947	44° 0'
50'	1.4352	1.3941	1.0295	.9713	.7173	.6967	10'
40'	1.4310	1.3980	1.0235	.9770	.7153	.6988	20'
30'	1.4267	1.4020	1.0176	.9827	.7133	.7009	30'
20'	1.4225	1.4061	1.0117	.9884	.7112	.7030	40'
10'	1.4184	1.4101	1.0058	.9942	.7092	.7050	50'
45° 0'	1.4142	1.4142	1.0000	1.0000	.7071	.7071	45° 0'
x	**sec x**	**cosec x**	**tan x**	**cot x**	**sin x**	**cos x**	

x	sin x	cos x	tan x	cot x	sec x	cosec x	x
30° 0'	.5000	.8660	.5774	1.7321	1.1547	2.0000	60° 0'
10'	.5025	.8646	.5812	1.7205	1.1567	1.9900	50'
20'	.5050	.8631	.5851	1.7090	1.1586	1.9801	40'
30'	.5075	.8616	.5890	1.6977	1.1606	1.9703	30'
40'	.5100	.8601	.5930	1.6864	1.1626	1.9606	20'
50'	.5125	.8587	.5969	1.6753	1.1646	1.9511	10'
31° 0'	.5150	.8572	.6009	1.6643	1.1666	1.9416	59° 0'
10'	.5175	.8557	.6048	1.6534	1.1687	1.9323	50'
20'	.5200	.8542	.6088	1.6426	1.1708	1.9230	40'
30'	.5225	.8526	.6128	1.6319	1.1728	1.9139	30'
40'	.5250	.8511	.6168	1.6212	1.1749	1.9049	20'
50'	.5275	.8496	.6208	1.6107	1.1770	1.8959	10'
32° 0'	.5299	.8480	.6249	1.6003	1.1792	1.8871	58° 0'
10'	.5324	.8465	.6289	1.5900	1.1813	1.8783	50'
20'	.5348	.8450	.6330	1.5798	1.1835	1.8699	40'
30'	.5373	.8434	.6371	1.5697	1.1857	1.8612	30'
40'	.5398	.8418	.6412	1.5597	1.1879	1.8527	20'
50'	.5422	.8403	.6453	1.5497	1.1901	1.8444	10'
33° 0'	.5446	.8387	.6494	1.5399	1.1924	1.8361	57° 0'
10'	.5471	.8371	.6536	1.5301	1.1946	1.8279	50'
20'	.5495	.8355	.6577	1.5204	1.1969	1.8198	40'
30'	.5519	.8339	.6619	1.5108	1.1992	1.8118	30'
40'	.5544	.8323	.6661	1.5013	1.2015	1.8039	20'
50'	.5568	.8307	.6703	1.4919	1.2039	1.7960	10'
34° 0'	.5592	.8290	.6745	1.4826	1.2062	1.7883	56° 0'
10'	.5616	.8274	.6787	1.4733	1.2086	1.7806	50'
20'	.5640	.8258	.6830	1.4641	1.2110	1.7730	40'
30'	.5664	.8241	.6873	1.4550	1.2134	1.7655	30'
40'	.5688	.8225	.6916	1.4460	1.2158	1.7581	20'
50'	.5712	.8208	.6959	1.4370	1.2183	1.7507	10'
35° 0'	.5736	.8192	.7002	1.4281	1.2208	1.7435	55° 0'
10'	.5760	.8175	.7046	1.4193	1.2233	1.7362	50'
20'	.5783	.8158	.7089	1.4106	1.2258	1.7291	40'
30'	.5807	.8141	.7133	1.4019	1.2283	1.7221	30'
40'	.5831	.8124	.7177	1.3934	1.2309	1.7151	20'
50'	.5854	.8107	.7221	1.3848	1.2335	1.7082	10'
36° 0'	.5878	.8090	.7265	1.3764	1.2361	1.7013	54° 0'
10'	.5901	.8073	.7310	1.3680	1.2387	1.6945	50'
20'	.5925	.8056	.7355	1.3597	1.2413	1.6878	40'
30'	.5948	.8039	.7400	1.3514	1.2440	1.6812	30'
40'	.5972	.8021	.7445	1.3432	1.2467	1.6746	20'
50'	.5995	.8004	.7490	1.3351	1.2494	1.6681	10'
37° 0'	.6018	.7986	.7536	1.3270	1.2521	1.6616	53° 0'
10'	.6041	.7969	.7581	1.3190	1.2549	1.6553	50'
20'	.6065	.7951	.7627	1.3111	1.2577	1.6489	40'
30'	.6088	.7934	.7673	1.3032	1.2605	1.6427	30'
x	**cos x**	**sin x**	**cot x**	**tan x**	**cosec x**	**sec x**	

579

TABLE B-4 American Wire Gage Data for Annealed
Copper at 20°C (68°F)

| Gage | Diameter, mils | Cross section | | Ohms per 1000 ft | Pounds per 1000 ft | Diameter, mm | Cross section, mm² | Ohms per kilometer | Kilograms per kilometer |
		Circular mils	Square inches						
0000	460.0	211,600	0.166 2	0.049 01	640.5	11.68	107.2	0.160 8	953.2
000	409.6	167,800	0.131 8	0.061 82	507.8	10.40	85.01	0.202 8	755.8
00	364.8	133,100	0.104 5	0.077 93	402.8	9.266	67.43	0.255 7	599.5
0	324.9	105,600	0.082 91	0.098 25	319.5	8.252	53.49	0.322 3	475.5
1	289.3	83,690	0.065 73	0.123 9	253.3	7.348	42.41	0.406 6	377.0
2	257.6	66,360	0.052 12	0.156 3	200.9	6.543	33.62	0.512 8	298.9
3	229.4	52,629	0.041 33	0.197 1	159.3	5.827	26.67	0.646 6	237.1
4	204.3	41,740	0.032 78	0.248 5	126.3	5.189	21.15	0.815 2	188.0
5	181.9	33,090	0.025 99	0.313 4	100.2	4.620	16.77	1.028	149.0
6	162.0	26,240	0.020 61	0.395 2	79.44	4.115	13.30	1.297	118.2
7	144.3	20,820	0.016 35	0.498 1	63.03	3.665	10.55	1.634	93.80
8	128.5	16,510	0.012 97	0.628 1	49.98	3.264	8.367	2.061	74.38
9	114.4	13,090	0.010 28	0.792 5	39.62	2.906	6.632	2.600	58.95
10	101.9	10,380	0.008 155	0.998 8	31.43	2.588	5.261	3.277	46.77
11	90.7	8,230	0.006 46	1.26	24.9	2.30	4.17	4.14	37.1
12	80.8	6,530	0.005 13	1.59	19.8	2.05	3.31	5.21	29.4
13	72.0	5,180	0.004 07	2.00	15.7	1.83	2.63	6.56	23.4
14	64.1	4,110	0.003 23	2.52	12.4	1.63	2.08	8.28	18.5
15	57.1	3,260	0.002 56	3.18	9.87	1.45	1.65	10.4	14.7
16	50.8	2,580	0.002 03	4.02	7.81	1.29	1.31	13.2	11.6
17	45.3	2,050	0.001 61	5.05	6.21	1.15	1.04	16.6	9.24
18	40.3	1,620	0.001 28	6.39	4.92	1.02	0.823	21.0	7.32
19	35.9	1,290	0.001 01	8.05	3.90	0.912	0.653	26.4	5.81
20	32.0	1,020	0.000 804	10.1	3.10	0.813	0.519	33.2	4.61

21	28.5	812	0.000 638	12.8	2.46	0.724	0.412	41.9	3.66
22	25.3	640	0.000 503	16.2	1.94	0.643	0.324	53.2	2.88
23	22.6	511	0.000 401	20.3	1.55	0.574	0.259	66.6	2.30
24	20.1	404	0.000 317	25.7	1.22	0.511	0.205	84.2	1.82
25	17.9	320	0.000 252	32.4	0.970	0.455	0.162	106	1.44
26	15.9	253	0.000 199	41.0	0.765	0.404	0.128	135	1.14
27	14.2	202	0.000 158	51.4	0.610	0.361	0.102	169	0.908
28	12.6	159	0.000 125	65.3	0.481	0.320	0.080 4	214	0.715
29	11.3	128	0.000 100	81.2	0.387	0.287	0.064 7	266	0.575
30	10.0	100	0.000 078 5	104	0.303	0.254	0.050 7	340	0.450
31	8.9	79.2	0.000 062 2	131	0.240	0.226	0.040 1	430	0.357
32	8.0	64.0	0.000 050 3	162	0.194	0.203	0.032 4	532	0.288
33	7.1	50.4	0.000 039 6	206	0.153	0.180	0.025 5	675	0.227
34	6.3	39.7	0.000 031 2	261	0.120	0.160	0.020 1	857	0.179
35	5.6	31.4	0.000 024 6	331	0.094 9	0.142	0.015 9	1,090	0.141
36	5.0	25.0	0.000 019 6	415	0.075 7	0.127	0.012 7	1,360	0.113
37	4.5	20.2	0.000 015 9	512	0.061 3	0.114	0.010 3	1,680	0.091 2
38	4.0	16.0	0.000 012 6	648	0.048 4	0.102	0.008 11	2,130	0.072 1
39	3.5	12.2	0.000 009 62	847	0.037 1	0.089	0.006 21	2,780	0.055 2
40	3.1	9.61	0.000 007 55	1,080	0.029 1	0.079	0.004 87	3,540	0.043 3
41	2.8	7.84	0.000 006 16	1,320	0.023 7	0.071	0.003 97	4,340	0.035 3
42	2.5	6.25	0.000 004 91	1,660	0.018 9	0.063	0.003 17	5,440	0.028 2
43	2.2	4.84	0.000 003 80	2,140	0.014 7	0.056	0.002 45	7,030	0.021 8
44	2.0	4.00	0.000 003 14	2,590	0.012 1	0.051	0.002 03	8,510	0.018 0
45	1.8	3.24	0.000 002 54	3,200	0.009 81	0.046	0.001 64	10,500	0.014 6
46	1.6	2.56	0.000 002 01	4,050	0.007 75	0.041	0.001 30	13,300	0.011 5
47	1.4	1.96	0.000 001 54	5,290	0.005 93	0.036	0.000 993	17,400	0.008 83
48	1.2	1.44	0.000 001 13	7,200	0.004 36	0.030	0.000 730	23,600	0.006 49
49	1.1	1.21	0.000 000 950	8,570	0.003 66	0.028	0.000 613	28,100	0.005 45
50	1.0	1.00	0.000 000 785	10,400	0.003 03	0.025	0.000 507	34,000	0.004 50

n	$\log_e n$	n	$\log_e n$	n	$\log_e n$
0.0	*	4.5	1.5041	9.0	2.1972
0.1	7.6974	4.6	1.5261	9.1	2.2083
0.2	8.3906	4.7	1.5476	9.2	2.2192
0.3	8.7960	4.8	1.5686	9.3	2.2300
0.4	9.0837	4.9	1.5892	9.4	2.2407
0.5	9.3069	5.0	1.6094	9.5	2.2513
0.6	9.4892	5.1	1.6292	9.6	2.2618
0.7	9.6433	5.2	1.6487	9.7	2.2721
0.8	9.7769	5.3	1.6677	9.8	2.2824
0.9	9.8946	5.4	1.6864	9.9	2.2925
1.0	0.0000	5.5	1.7047	10	2.3026
1.1	0.0953	5.6	1.7228	11	2.3979
1.2	0.1823	5.7	1.7405	12	2.4849
1.3	0.2624	5.8	1.7579	13	2.5649
1.4	0.3365	5.9	1.7750	14	2.6391
1.5	0.4055	6.0	1.7918	15	2.7081
1.6	0.4700	6.1	1.8083	16	2.7726
1.7	0.5306	6.2	1.8245	17	2.8332
1.8	0.5878	6.3	1.8405	18	2.8904
1.9	0.6419	6.4	1.8563	19	2.9444
2.0	0.6931	6.5	1.8718	20	2.9957
2.1	0.7419	6.6	1.8871	25	3.2189
2.2	0.7885	6.7	1.9021	30	3.4012
2.3	0.8329	6.8	1.9169	35	3.5553
2.4	0.8755	6.9	1.9315	40	3.6889
2.5	0.9163	7.0	1.9459	45	3.8067
2.6	0.9555	7.1	1.9601	50	3.9120
2.7	0.9933	7.2	1.9741	55	4.0073
2.8	1.0296	7.3	1.9879	60	4.0943
2.9	1.0647	7.4	2.0015	65	4.1744
3.0	1.0986	7.5	2.0149	70	4.2485
3.1	1.1314	7.6	2.0281	75	4.3175
3.2	1.1632	7.7	2.0412	80	4.3820
3.3	1.1939	7.8	2.0541	85	4.4427
3.4	1.2238	7.9	2.0669	90	4.4998
3.5	1.2528	8.0	2.0794	95	4.5539
3.6	1.2809	8.1	2.0919	100	4.6052
3.7	1.3083	8.2	2.1041		
3.8	1.3350	8.3	2.1163		
3.9	1.3610	8.4	2.1282		
4.0	1.3863	8.5	2.1401		
4.1	1.4110	8.6	2.1518		
4.2	1.4351	8.7	2.1633		
4.3	1.4586	8.8	2.1748		
4.4	1.4816	8.9	2.1861		

TABLE B-5   Natural Logarithms of Numbers

Chapter 1

Section 1-4, page 17

1 3.95×10^5 **3** 8.26×10^3 **5** 3.06×10^{-2} **7** 7.38×10^2
9 5.97×10^6 **11** 2.3×10^{-3} **13** 1.01×10^{-2} **15** 2.93×10^0
17 1.003×10^4 **19** 1.72×10^{-4}

Section 1-4, page 18

1 5×10^2 **3** 6.0×10^3 **5** 6.0×10^{-6} **7** 6×10^{-2}
9 4.05×10^{-4}

Section 1-4, page 19

1 6×10^{-4} **3** 6.91×10^5 **5** 1.08×10^1 **7** 1.01×10^{-9}
9 3×10^5

Section 1-4, page 20

1 10^1 **3** 10^{-1} **5** 2×10^1 **7** 2×10^{-1}
9 4.7×10^6

Section 1-4, page 22

1 2×10^3 **3** 2×10^2 **5** 1.69×10^{-4} **7** 2.43×10^{-2}
9 1.33×10^{-6}

Section 1-4, page 23

1 1×10^0 **3** 1×10^{-6} **5** 1.66×10^5

Section 1-4, page 24

1 6 protons and 6 neutrons   **3** 2.304 newtons   **5** 2.25×10^{39}

Chapter 2

Section 2-1, page 31

1 $E = 100$ V, $G = .01$ mho   **3** $I = 2$ A, $G = .5$ mho
5 $I = 3.8$ mA, $G = 213$ μmho   **7** $R = .15\,\Omega$, $G = 6.67$ mho
9 $E = 148$ V, $R = 23.8$ kΩ **11** $R = 320\,\Omega$

Section 2-2, page 36

1 $R = 10\,\Omega$, $G = 0.1\text{℧}$, $P = 10$ W   **3** $I = 200$ mA, $R = 1000\,\Omega$, $P = 40$ W
5 $E = 47$ V, $G = 213\,\mu\,\text{℧}$, $P = .47$ W   **7** $E = 50$ V, $R = 2.5$ kΩ, $G = 400\,\mu\,\text{℧}$
9 $E = 500$ V, $I = 500\,\mu$A, $R = 1$ MΩ

Section 2-3, page 42

1 $R = 46\,\Omega$ **3** $\alpha = .00051$ **5** $E = 9.4$ kV, $P = 18.8$ W
7 $I = 900$ mA, $P = 8.1$ W   **9** $I = 10$ mA, $E = 1$ kV

Section 2-4, page 47

1 $100\,\Omega$, 5%   **3** 2.2 kΩ, 2%   **5** $10\,\Omega$, 10%
7 Red-red-green-silver   **9** Green-blue-brown-red
11 Yellow-violet-gold-gold   **13** Brown-black-gold-gold

Section 2-7, page 57

1 $.25\,\Omega$ **3** $.19\,\Omega$ **5** 32.87 W   **7** 1.5 V   **9** .95 mW

Chapter 3

Section 3-1, page 69

1 4 V   **3** 1.25 A leaving the junction
5 $V_2 = 5$ V, $I_2 = 1$ A, $V_3 = 15$ V, $I_3 = 1.5$ A, $V_4 = 15$ V

Section 3-2, page 74

1 $R_{eq} = 15\,\Omega$, $I_t = .1$ A, $I_1 = .1$ A, $I_2 = .1$ A
3 $I_t = 1.28$ mA, $P_1 = 4.44$ mW, $P_2 = 16.44$ mW, $P_3 = 11.18$ mW
5 $V_1 = 1$ V, $V_2 = 2$ V, $V_3 = 4$ V
7 No, because the sum of the IR drops equals the difference in voltage between the two opposing sources.

Section 3-3, page 78

1 $R_{eq} = 200\,\Omega$, $V_1 = 10$ V, $V_2 = 10$ V, $I_t = 16.7$ mA, $I_2 = 33.3$ mA,
$P_1 = 167$ mW, $P_2 = 333$ mW
3 $G_1 = 1667\,\mu\text{℧}$, $G_2 = 3333\,\mu\text{℧}$, $G_t = 5000\,\mu\text{℧}$, $R_t = 200\,\Omega$, the same
5 The same, $R_t = 1\,\Omega$

Section 3-4, page 83

1 $V_1 = 3.33$ V   **3** $V_1 = 8$ V, $V_2 = 21.4$ V
5 $V_{out} = 10$ V, $V_{out} = 0$ V, $V_{out} = 1$ V, $V_{out} = 5$ V, no change, it depends on the way the resistances divide, not the amount of resistance.

Chapter 4

Section 4-1, page 95

1 $V_1 = 12.56$ V $V_2 = 12.44$ V $V_3 = 12.44$ V $I_1 = 12.56$ mA

$I_2 = 6.91\,\text{mA}$ $I_3 = 5.65\,\text{mA}$ $P_1 = 157.8\,\text{mW}$ $P_2 = 85.94\,\text{mW}$
$P_3 = 70.27\,\text{mW}$

3 $P_3 = 1.73\,\text{W}$

5 $V_1 = 3\,\text{V}$ $V_2 = 15\,\text{V}$ $V_3 = 18\,\text{V}$ $I_1 = 300\,\text{mA}$
$I_2 = 300\,\text{mA}$ $I_3 = 600\,\text{mA}$ $P_1 = 0.9\,\text{W}$ $P_2 = 4.5\,\text{W}$
$P_3 = 10.8\,\text{W}$ $P_t = 16.2\,\text{W}$ $I_t = 900\,\text{mA}$

Section 4-2, page 105

1 $R_4 = 37.2\,\text{k}\Omega$

3 $R_1 = 83.3\,\Omega$, $R_2 = 2000\,\Omega$, $P_1 = 0.3\,\text{W}$, $P_2 = 0.2\,\text{W}$

5 $R_1 = 2500\,\Omega$, $R_2 = 2500\,\Omega$, $P_1 = 2.25\,\text{W}$, $P_2 = 0.25\,\text{W}$

Section 4-3, page 112

1 Open between D and E

3 Normal $I_t = 10\,\text{mA}$, R_1 open $I_t = 5\,\text{mA}$—no effect on voltage
R_2 open $I_t = 6.67\,\text{mA}$, R_3 open $I_t = 8.88\,\text{mA}$—no change in voltage

5 $I_t = 6\,\text{mA}$, Yes—R_1 is open

7 Yes, R_1 has increased in value to $2\,\text{k}\Omega$

9 (a) 6 V,   (b) 0 V,   (c) 9 V,   (d) 7.2 V,   (e) 4 V,   (f) 7.2 V,   (g) 6.55 V

11 With R_1 open $V_A = 0\,\text{V}$, $V_B = 0\,\text{V}$, $V_C = 0\,\text{V}$
with R_2 open $V_A = 100\,\text{V}$, $V_B = 0\,\text{V}$, $V_C = 0\,\text{V}$
with R_3 open $V_A = 56.48\,\text{V}$, $V_B = 36.11\,\text{V}$, $V_C = 0\,\text{V}$
with R_4 open $V_A = 56.48\,\text{V}$, $V_B = 36.11\,\text{V}$, $V_C = 36.11\,\text{V}$
with R_5 open $V_A = 73.48\,\text{V}$, $V_B = 61.06\,\text{V}$, $V_C = 4.63\,\text{V}$

13 $V_A = 79.17\,\text{V}$, $V_B = 12.70\,\text{V}$, $V_C = 0.96\,\text{V}$

15 Only the connection between the negative source terminal block and the parallel bank

Chapter 5

Section 5-1, page 123

1 $R_{\text{int}} = 10\,\Omega$ **3** $V_L = 1.16\,\text{V}$

Section 5-2, page 128

1 $I_t = 244\,\text{mA}$, $V_L = 2.44\,\text{V}$

3 $I_t = 58\,\text{mA}$, $V_L = 2.90\,\text{V}$

5 $I_1 = 100\,\text{mA}$, $I_2 = 100\,\text{mA}$, $I_t = 200\,\text{mA}$, $V_L = 1.3\,\text{V}$

7 $I_1 = 50\,\text{mA}$, $I_2 = 50\,\text{mA}$, $I_t = 100\,\text{mA}$, $V_L = 1.4\,\text{V}$

Chapter 6

Section 6-1, page 157

1 $R_S = 1 \times 10^{-3}\,\Omega$ **3** $R_M = 20\,\Omega$

5 $R_S = 1.001\,\Omega$, $P_M = 10\,\mu\text{W}$, $P_S = 10.01\,\text{mW}$

Section 6-3, page 166

1 $R_S = 499,925\,\Omega$ ($500\,\text{k}\Omega$ introduces no significant error)

3 Current required for full scale deflection

5 49.08 V   **7** Assuming 100 V range, $10,000\,\Omega/\text{V}$

9 $5000\,\Omega$, $250,000\,\Omega$

Section 6-4, page 175

1 $R_S = 225\,\Omega$ **3** $500\,\mu\text{A}$

5 For 10%, $R_X = 5.56\,\Omega$, for 50%, $R_X = 50\,\Omega$, for 75%, $R_X = 150\,\Omega$

7 Shunt, $25\,\Omega$, $2.78\,\Omega$ **9** $75\,\text{k}\Omega$

Chapter 7

Section 7-1, page 187

1

	R (ohms)	I (amps)	V (volts)
R_1	3	0.4	1.2
R_2	6	1.47	8.8
R_3	3	1.07	3.2

3

	R (kohms)	I (mA)	V (volts)
R_1	20	0.6	12
R_2	10	0.2	2
R_3	10	0.8	8

5

	R (kohms)	I (mA)	V (volts)
R_1	1.5	69.41	104.12
R_2	2.7	55.59	150.09
R_3	0.560	125	70.0

Section 7-2, page 194

1 $V_3 = 6.10$ V, $I_3 = 1.22$ A **3** $V_5 = 1.96$ V, $I_5 = 0.39$ A
5 $V_l = 2.88$ V, $I_l = 61$ mA **7** $V_2 = 67$ V, $I_2 = 0.67$ mA
9 $V_3 = 21$ V, $V_4 = 59$ V

Section 7-3, page 198

1 $I_l = 42$ mA, $V_l = 8.3$ V **3** $I_5 = 0.525$ A, $V_5 = 6.30$ V
5 $I_3 = 91.91$ mA, $V_3 = 16.54$ V **7** $I_5 = 5$ mA, $V_5 = 0.5$ V
9 $I_1 = 2.5$ mA, $V_1 = 2.5$ V

Section 7-4, page 209

1

	R (ohms)	I (amps)	V (volts)
R_1	4	1.18	4.73
R_2	6	0.95	5.70
R_3	3	1.05	3.14
R_4	2	1.09	2.17
R_5	8	0.14	0.96
R_6	1	2.13	2.13

3

	R (ohms)	I (amps)	V (volts)
R_1	2	8.96	17.92
R_2	5	6.42	32.08
R_3	6	2.55	15.27
R_4	10	1.28	12.84
R_5	8	1.26	10.06
R_6	2	1.98	3.97
R_7	4	0.70	2.80
R_8	12	0.56	6.74

5 $R_a = 2\,\Omega$, $R_b = 1\,\Omega$, $R_c = 19.21\,\Omega$, $R_d = 4.43\,\Omega$, $R_e = 2.81\,\Omega$

Chapter 8

Section 8-1, page 226

1

	R (ohms)	I (amps)	V (volts)
R_1	2	2.08	4.17
R_2	1	1.67	1.67
R_3	4	0.42	1.67
R_4	2	2.08	4.17

3

	R (ohms)	I (amps)	V (volts)
R_1	1	1.73	1.73
R_2	2	1.09	2.18
R_3	4	0.64	2.56
R_4	6	1.02	6.12
R_5	8	0.71	5.68
R_6	5	0.08	0.40

5

	R (ohms)	I (amps)	V (volts)
R_1	2	2.93	5.86
R_2	5	1.94	9.70
R_3	4	0.99	3.96
R_4	6	0.81	4.88
R_5	2	2.23	4.45
R_6	3	0.28	0.85
R_7	1	0.18	0.18
R_8	10	0.53	5.30

Section 8-2, page 231

1

	R (ohms)	I (amps)	V (volts)
R_1	1	0.8	0.8
R_2	2	0.6	1.2
R_3	6	0.2	1.2

3

	R (ohms)	I (amps)	V (volts)
R_1	6	0.77	4.63
R_2	12	0.26	3.17
R_3	12	0.32	3.88
R_4	6	0.51	3.05
R_5	2	0.06	0.12
R_6	3	0.77	2.32

5

	R (ohms)	I (amps)	V (volts)
R_1	2	2.38	4.76
R_2	1	1.24	1.24
R_3	10	0.40	4.00
R_4	8	1.44	9.10
R_5	4	0.91	3.65
R_6	5	0.84	4.21
R_7	3	2.05	6.15
R_8	3	0.07	0.21

Section 8-3, page 240

1

	R (ohms)	I (amps)	V (volts)
R_1	2	0.37	0.74
R_2	4	0.22	0.89
R_3	6	0.15	0.89
R_4	1	0.37	0.37

3

	R (ohms)	I (amps)	V (volts)
R_1	1	2.00	2.00
R_2	5	1.64	8.18
R_3	2	1.91	3.82
R_4	4	1.55	6.18
R_5	12	0.36	4.36

5

	R (ohms)	I (amps)	V (volts)
R_1	2	1.79	3.57
R_2	4	0.21	0.86
R_3	1	1.00	1.00
R_4	3	1.21	3.64
R_5	10	0.09	0.93
R_6	2	1.69	3.39
R_7	8	0.31	2.46

7 $V_B/R_1 + V_C/r_c(1 + \beta) - \dfrac{V_E[(r_e + R_3)/R_3 r_c + 1/R_3]}{1 + \beta} = i_s$

$V_C(1/r_c(1 + \beta) - 1/R_2) - \dfrac{V_E(r_e + R_3 - \beta r_c)}{(1 + \beta)R_3 r_c} = 0$

$V_B/R_1 + V_C/R_2 + V_E/R_3 = i_s$

Chapter 9

Section 9-3, page 265

1 (a) 1200 Mx, 1200 lines,   (b) 42,000 Mx, 420 μWb,   (c) 3×10^4 G, 19.35×10^4 lines/in.^{2},
  (d) 3200 lines, 32 μWb,   (e) 75 T, 48.38×10^5 lines/in.^{2},   (f) 134.11 T, 134.11×10^4 G
3 $\phi = 19.63 \times 10^{-4}$ Wb   **5** $N = 300$ turns
7 $H = 94.5$ Oe   **9** CGS $\mu = 54,000$ MKS $\mu = 0.0682$
11 $\mu_r = 25,000$

Section 9-5, page 272

1 $\mathcal{R} = 1.94 \times 10^4$ Rels   **3** In MKS $\phi = 0.84$ Wb, in CGS $\phi = 8.4 \times 10^7$ Mx
5 $\mathcal{R}_e = 3527$ Rels, $\mathcal{R}_g = 13 \times 10^6$ Rels, $\mathcal{R}_t = 13 \times 10^6$ Rels, $\phi = 731$ μWb
7 $N = 16,688$ turns, circuit flux $= 253.53$ μWb

Section 9-6, page 283

1 $e = 62,500$ V

Chapter 10

Section 10-1, page 300

1

Position (deg)	0	15	30	45	60	75	90	105
Voltage	0	15.528	30	42.426	51.96	57.954	60	57.954

Position (deg)	120	135	150	165	180	195	210	225
Voltage	51.96	42.426	30	15.528	0	-15.528	-30	-42.426

Position (deg)	240	255	270	285	300	315	330
Voltage	-51.96	-57.954	-60	-57.954	-51.96	-42.426	-30

Position (deg)	345	360
Voltage	-15.528	0

Section 10-2, page 305

1 (a) $f = 1.6$ Hz, $T = .625$ sec   (b) $f = 20$ MHz, $T = 0.05$ μsec
(c) $f = 13.89$ Hz, $T = 0.072$ sec   (d) $f = 0.033$ Hz, $T = 30$ sec
(e) $f = 4$ Hz, $T = 0.25$ sec   (f) $f = 0.6$ Hz, $T = 1.667$ sec
(g) $f = 5.55 \times 10^2$ Hz, $T = 1.8$ msec   (h) $f = 43.33$ MHz, $T = 0.023$ μsec

Section 10-3, page 310

1 (a) 2 rad,   (b) 6 rad,   (c) 0.733 rad,   (d) 0.01 rad,   (e) 0.9549 rad,   (f) 0.01745 rad
3 (a) $\theta = 22.5$ deg,   (b) $\theta = 28.65$ deg,   (c) $\theta = 292.5$ deg,
(d) $\theta = 5.73$ deg,   (e) $\theta = 33.75$ deg,   (f) $\theta = 72$ deg
5 (a) $\theta = 270$ deg, $e = -90$ V,   (b) $\theta = 270$ deg, $e = -9$ V,
(c) $\theta = 86.4$ deg, $e = 29.94$ V,   (d) $\theta = 140$ deg, $e = 321.4$ V,
(e) $\theta = 180$ deg, $e = 0$ V,   (f) $\theta = 30$ deg, $e = 50$ V

Section 10-5, page 316

1

	peak V	p-p V	ave V	rms V
(a)	20	40	12.74	14.14
(b)	120	240	76.44	84.44
(c)	32	64	20.38	22.62
(d)	0.5	1	0.318	0.354
(e)	75	150	47.77	53.03
(f)	9	18	5.73	6.36

3	peak V	p-p V	rms V	Power
(a)	15	30	10.61	2.25
(b)	133	266	94.03	176.89
(c)	10	15	5.30	0.69
(d)	12	24	12	2.88
(e)	9	18	7.12	1.01

Chapter 11

Section 11-1, page 353

1 150 V   **3** 0.85 in.

5 (a) $T = 12$ msec, $f = 83.33$ Hz
(b) $T = 0.006\ \mu$sec, $f = 166.67$ Hz
(c) $T = 0.11$ sec, $f = 9.09$ Hz
(d) $T = 3\ \mu$sec, $f = 0.33$ MHz

7

9 (a) 90 deg. lag,   (b) 120 deg. lead,   (c) 150 deg. lag,   (d) 45 deg. lag,   (e) 75 deg. lead

Chapter 12

Section 12-1, page 366

1 $C = 250\ \mu$F   **3** $Q = 0.12$ C

Section 12-2, page 371

1 $C = 250$ pF, $BV = 240$ V   **3** $C = 0.0817\ \mu$F, $BV = 1500$ V
5 2.37×10^{-6} C   **7** 110×10^{-6} J
9 40,825 V

Section 12-3, page 375

1 $C_t = 25\ \mu$F, $Q_t = 0.00875$ J, $Q_1 = 0.0077$ J, $Q_2 = 0.0015$ J
3 $C_t = 0.0457\ \mu$F, $Q_t = 1.83 \times 10^{-6}$ C, $V_1 = 91.5$ V, $V_2 = 4.16$ V, $V_3 = 305$ V
5 $Q_1 = 2.84 \times 10^{-4}$ C, $Q_2 = 1.21 \times 10^{-4}$ C, $Q_3 = 1.21 \times 10^{-4}$ C
$Q_4 = 1.64 \times 10^{-4}$ C, $Q_5 = 2.84 \times 10^{-4}$ C
$V_1 = 71$ V, $V_2 = 10.1$ V, $V_3 = 4.8$ V, $V_4 = 14.9$ V, $V_5 = 14.2$ V

Section 12-4, page 398

1 $i_0 = 0.5\ \mu$A, $\tau = 8$ sec, $t = 40$ sec
3 $\tau = 2.8$ msec, $\tau = 4.2$ msec, 7.8 msec
5 32 sec, 88 sec, 140 sec
7 At the beginning of each pulse, $e_C = 0$ and $e_R = 90$;
at the end of each pulse, $e_C = 90$ and $e_R = 0$
9 At the beginning of each pulse, $e_C = 0$ and $e_R = 200$;
at the end of each pulse with $V_{in} = 200$, $e_C = 184$ and $e_R = 16$;
at the end of each pulse with $V_{in} = 0$, $e_C = 184$ and $e_R = -184$

11

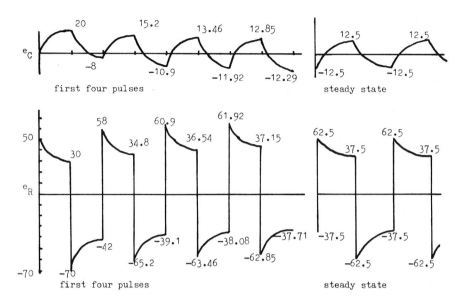

first four pulses   steady state

first four pulses   steady state

13 At 3 msec $e_C = 68.38$ V, $e_R = 331.62$ V, $i = 166$ mA;
at 20 msec $e_C = 19.59$ V, $e_R = -19.59$ V, $i = 9.8$ mA

Chapter 13

Section 13-1, page 418

1 $e_L = 1.25$ V   **3** $di/dt = 6200$ A/sec   **5** $L = 0.612$ mH
7 $N = 200$ turns

Section 13-2, page 423

1 $L_t = 60$ mH   **3** $L_t = 14\,\mu$H
5 $L_t = 0.465$ H   **7** $L_M = 1.49$ mH
9 $L_M = 0.002$ H, $k = 0.535$, first connection series opposing
11 $k = 0.754$, $L_t = 9.2$ H, with connections reversed $L_t = 34.8$ H

Section 13-3, page 433

1 2 msec,   **3** 0.4 sec   **5** $e_R = 30.6$ V   **7** $t = 31.75$ msec
9 $e_R = 44.04$ V, $e_L = 45.96$ V, $i = 11.01$ A
11 for 20%, $e_R = 36$ V, $e_L = 144$ V
for 50 %, $e_R = 90$ V, $e_L = 90$ V
for 85%, $e_R = 153$ V, $e_L = 27$ V

Chapter 14

Section 14-2, page 446

1 $\frac{1}{6}$ **3** $\frac{20}{3}$, 1467 V
5 $E_{S_1} = 300$ V, $E_{S_2} = 480$ V, $E_{S_3} = 30$ V
7 $I_P = 0.533$ A, $P_P = 128$ W
9 $I_P = 0.4253$ A

Section 14-3, page 452

1

R_L (ohms)	I (amps)	P_L (watts)
1	.478	.228
50	.400	8.000
100	.343	11.765
150	.300	13.500
200	.267	14.258
220	.255	14.306
240	.242	14.394
250	.240	14.400
260	.235	14.359
280	.226	14.301
300	.218	14.257
500	.160	12.800
1000	.096	9.216

$R_L = 250\,\Omega$ gives maximum P_L

$$\frac{N_S}{N_P} = \frac{1}{5}$$

3 $750\,\Omega$

5 $N_P/N_{S_1} = \frac{30}{1}$ $\qquad$ $N_P/N_{S_2} = \frac{10}{1}$ $\qquad$ $N_P/N_{S_3} = 2.12/1$
$I_P = 12.5\,\text{mA}$ $\qquad$ $I_1 = 125\,\text{mA}$ $\qquad$ $I_2 = 41.67\,\text{mA}$ $\qquad$ $I_3 = 8.8375\,\text{mA}$
$P_P = 375\,\text{mW}$ $\qquad$ $P_1 = 125\,\text{mW}$ $\qquad$ $P_2 = 125\,\text{mW}$ $\qquad$ $P_3 = 125\,\text{mW}$

Chapter 15

Section 15-1, page 470

1 $X_C = 0.00758\,\Omega$ $\qquad$ **3** $X_C = 13{,}262.75\,\Omega$ $\qquad$ **5** $C = 250\,\mu\text{F}$

Section 15-2, page 475

1 $X_L = 1508\,\Omega$ $\qquad$ **3** $L = 35\,\mu\text{H}$ $\qquad$ **5** $f = 1700\,\text{Hz}$

Section 15-3, page 485

1 $148.69\,\angle -55.13°\,\text{V}$ $\qquad$ **3** $(1.8 - 0.42j)\,V,\ 1.848\,\angle -13.13°$
5 $18.028\,\angle 56.31°$ $\qquad$ **7** $19.053\,\angle -30°,\ +60°$
9 $14.318\,\Omega$ $\qquad$ **11** $11.705\,\Omega$
13 $107.49\,\angle 12.36°$ $\qquad$ **15** $4365\,\angle 63.25°$

Section 15-4, page 493

1 $50\,\angle -36.87°$ $\qquad$ **3** $I_R = 25\,\angle 0°\,\text{mA},\ I_L = 25\,\angle -90°\,\text{mA},\ \theta = -45°$
5 $0.362\,\angle 27.98°\,\text{mA}$ $\qquad$ **7** $307.15\,\angle 68.55°\,\Omega$
9 $191 + 588j,\ 618\,\angle 72°$ $\qquad$ **11** $24.3\,\angle 71.07°$

Section 15-5, page 500

1 0.4472 $\qquad$ **3** 0.793 $\qquad$ **5** $P_t = 2.523\,\text{W}$
7 $P_t = 1.071\,\text{W}$, power factor is 0.4062
9 $Z_t = 56.4\,\angle -61.95°,\ P_t = 100.83\,\text{W}$
11 $Z_t = 152.174\,\angle -76.7°\,\Omega,\ X_C = 148.05\,\Omega,\ P_t = 12.24\,\text{W}$

Chapter 16

Section 16-1, page 511

1 $I_{L_1} = -5j\,\text{A}$ $\qquad$ $I_{C_1} = 1.838 + 1.103j\,\text{A}$ $\qquad$ $I_{R_1} = 1.138 + 1.103j\,\text{A}$
$E_{L_1} = 50\,\text{V}$ $\qquad$ $E_{C_1} = 13.23 - 22.06j\,\text{V}$ $\qquad$ $E_{R_1} = 36.76 + 22.06j\,\text{V}$

3 $I_{R_1} = 0.8123 - 0.0904j$ A ac $+ 0.6522$ A dc
$E_{R_1} = 6.4984 - 0.7232j$ V ac $+ 5.218$ V dc
$I_{R_2} = 0.6254 + 0.1808j$ A ac $- 1.6596$ A dc
$E_{R_2} = 2.5016 - 0.7232j$ V ac $- 6.7824$ V dc
$I_{R_3} = -.0421 - 0.2291j$ A ac $+ 1.0434$ A dc
$E_{R_3} = -.2105 - 1.1455j$ V ac $+ 5.218$ V dc
$I_{L_1} = 0.1859 - 0.2717j$ A ac $+ 1.0434$ A dc
$E_{L_2} = 2.712 + 1.869j$ V ac
$I_{C_1} = 0.2291 - 0.0412j$ A ac
$E_{C_1} = -.2105 - 1.1455j$ V ac $+ 5.218$ V dc

5 $I_{R_1} = -111.82 - 88.42j$ mA $E_{R_1} = -0.224 - 0.177j$ V
$I_{R_2} = 375.58 + 50.58j$ mA $E_{R_2} = 0.376 + 0.051j$ V
$I_{R_3} = 302.88 - 228.04j$ mA $E_{R_3} = 1.514 - 1.104j$ V
$I_{L_1} = 375.58 + 50.58j$ mA $E_{L_1} = -0.152 + 1.127j$ V
$I_{L_2} = -790.28 + 80.04j$ mA $E_{L_2} = -0.256 - 3.161j$ V
$I_{C_1} = -487.4 - 139.00j$ mA $E_{C_1} = -0.384 + 2.924j$ V
$I_{C_2} = 302.88 - 228.04j$ mA $E_{C_2} = -0.456 - 0.606j$ V

Section 16-2, page 516

1 $E_{Th} = 49.42 + 14.78j$ V, $Z_{Th} = 2.64 + 5.62j\,\Omega$
3 $I_L = 19.91 + 35.48j$ mA, $E_{R_L} = 0.4 + 0.71j$ V, $E_{C_L} = 0.53 - 0.3j$ V
5 $I_{AB} = 15.49 - 8.85j$ mA, $E_{AB} = -88.5 - 154.9j$ mV

Section 16-3, page 521

1 $I_N = 2.65 - 0.59j$ A, $Z_N = 16.85 - 11.81j\,\Omega$
3 $I_L = 5.81 - 3.67j$ A, $E_L = 55.05 + 87.15j$ V
5 $I_L = -0.45 + 2.61j$ mA, $E_L = 56.25 + 63.45j$ mV

Section 16-4, page 529

1 $Z_L = 0.8 - 3.6j\,\Omega$, $P_{ext} = 10.625$ kW, $P_{int} = 10.625$ kW
3 $Z_L = 25.24 - 15.26j\,\Omega$, $P_{ext} = 31.36$ W, $P_{int} = 31.36$ W
5 $Z_L = 38.73 + 9.68j\,\Omega$, $P_{ext} = 32.6$ mW, $P_{int} = 32.6$ mW

Section 16-5, page 533

1 $I_{L_1} = 1.75 - 1.18j$ A $E_{L_1} = 2.36 + 3.50j$ V
$I_{C_1} = 1.62 - 0.04j$ A $E_{C_1} = -0.08 - 3.24j$ V
$I_{R_2} = 1.62 - 0.04j$ A $E_{R_2} = 9.72 - 0.24j$ V
$I_{R_1} = 0.13 - 1.14j$ A $E_{R_1} = 0.52 - 4.56j$ V
$I_{L_2} = 0.13 - 1.14j$ A $E_{L_2} = 9.12 + 1.04j$ V
3 $I_{L_1} = 13.64 - 6.28j$ A $E_{L_1} = 81.84 + 163.68j$ V
$I_{L_2} = 8.31 - 0.17j$ A $E_{L_2} = 1.70 + 83.1j$ V
$I_{C_1} = 5.33 - 6.05j$ A $E_{C_1} = -72.6 - 63.96j$ V
$I_{R_1} = 5.33 - 6.05j$ A $E_{R_1} = 79.95 - 90.75j$ V
$I_{R_2} = 8.31 - 0.17j$ A $E_{R_2} = 66.48 - 1.36j$ V

Chapter 17

Section 17-1, page 538

1 $f_r = 530.5$ Hz   **3** $f_r = 142.4$ Hz   **5** $f_r = 530.7$ Hz, $L = 2.498$ mH

Section 17-2, page 544

1 $E_L = E_C = 2.0$ V

3 At resonance, $E_L = E_C = 625$ V
   10 Hz above f_r, $E_L = 625.015$ V, $E_C = 624.98$ V
   100 Hz above f_r, $E_L = 625.11$ V, $E_C = 624.79$ V
5 $f_r = 177$ Hz, $E_C = E_L = 900$ V

Section 17-3, page 553

1 $f_r = 26.5$ Hz
3 $Z_t = 500025\,\Omega$, $I_L = 2.39988$ mA, $I_C = 2.40000$ mA
5 For $R = 10\,\Omega$,   for $R = 100\,\Omega$,   for $R = 500\,\Omega$,   for $R = 1000\,\Omega$

$f_r = 3.1831 \times 10^3$ Hz	$f_r = 3.1829 \times 10^3$ Hz	$f_r = 3.1791 \times 10^3$ Hz	$f_r = 3.1671 \times 10^3$ Hz
$Z_t = 10$ MΩ	$Z_t = 1$ MΩ	$Z_t = 200{,}000$ ohms	$Z_t = 100{,}000$ ohms
$I_t = 5 \times 10^{-8}$ A	$I_t = 5 \times 10^{-7}$ A	$I_t = 2.5 \times 10^{-6}$ A	$I_t = 5 \times 10^{-6}$ A
$I_L = 50\,\mu$A	$I_L = 50\,\mu$A	$I_L = 50\,\mu$A	$I_L = 50\,\mu$A
$I_C = 50\,\mu$A	$I_C = 50\,\mu$A	$I_C = 49.9\,\mu$A	$I_C = 49.7\,\mu$A

Section 17-4, page 563

1 $Q = 250$, $R = 0.08\,\Omega$
3 $V_C = 7.5$ V, $R = 66{,}667\,\Omega$
5 $L = 4$ mH, $C = 10$ pF, $Z_t = 500\,\Omega$
7 $Q = 72$, $I_L = 127$ mA, $I_C = 127$ mA, $I_t = 1.76$ mA
9 $BW = 1.36$ kHz, $f_1 = 749.32$ kHz, $f_2 = 750.68$ kHz
11 $BW = 8.288 \times 10^4$ Hz, $f_2 = 6{,}672{,}897.1$ Hz, $Q = 80$
13 With C tuned to f_1 With C tuned to f_2 With C tuned to f_3

$C = 11.7\,\mu$F	$C = 0.0029\,\mu$F	$C = 0.0198\,\mu$F
$E_C(f_1) = 3.0$ mV	$E_C(f_1) = 99.9$ mV	$E_C(f_1) = 100$ mV
$E_C(f_2) = 0.1$ mV	$E_C(f_2) = 955$ mV	$E_C(f_2) = 73.8$ mV
$E_C(f_3) = 0.2$ mV	$E_C(f_3) = 285$ mV	$E_C(f_3) = 183.5$ mV